THE PHYSICS OF GLASSY POLYMERS

THE PHYSICS OF
GLASSY POLYMERS

Edited by

R. N. HAWARD

Professor of Industrial Chemistry
Department of Chemistry, University of Birmingham

A HALSTED PRESS BOOK

JOHN WILEY & SONS
New York—Toronto

PUBLISHED IN THE U.S.A. AND CANADA BY
HALSTED PRESS
A DIVISION OF JOHN WILEY & SONS, INC., NEW YORK

Library of Congress Cataloging in Publication Data
Main entry under title:

The Physics of glassy polymers.

"A Halsted Press book."
Includes bibliographical references.
1. Polymers and polymerization. 2. Amorphous substances.
I. Haward, Robert Nobbs, 1914–   ed.
TA455.P58P48   620.1'92   73–4469
ISBN 0–470–36214–6

WITH 28 TABLES AND 269 ILLUSTRATIONS

© APPLIED SCIENCE PUBLISHERS LTD 1973

Printed in Great Britain by Galliard Limited, Great Yarmouth, Norfolk, England

LIST OF CONTRIBUTORS

E. H. ANDREWS
  Department of Materials, Queen Mary College, University of London, Mile End Road, London E1 4NS, England

W. BORCHARD
  Physikalisch-Chemisches Institut Technischen Hochschule Clausthal, 3392 Clausthal-Zellerfeld, Adolf-Romer-Strasse 2A, West Germany

P. BOWDEN
  Department of Metallurgy and Materials Science, University of Cambridge, Pembroke Street, Cambridge CB2 3QZ, England

B. ELLIS
  Department of Glass Technology, University of Sheffield, Elmfield, Northumberland Road, Sheffield S10 2TZ, England

J. R. FITZPATRICK
  Research & Engineering Laboratories, Thorn Lighting Limited, Melton Road, Leicester LE4 7PD, England

M. J. FOLKES
  University of Bristol, H. H. Wills Physics Laboratory, Royal Fort, Tyndall Avenue, Bristol BS8 1TL, England

R. N. HAWARD
  Plastic Materials Laboratory, Centre for Materials Science, The University of Birmingham, PO Box 363, Birmingham B15 2TT, England

v

H. B. HOPFENBERG

Department of Chemical Engineering, North Carolina State University, Raleigh, North Carolina, USA

A. KELLER

University of Bristol, H. H. Wills Physics Laboratory, Royal Fort, Tyndall Avenue, Bristol BS8 1TL, England

J. MANN

Shell Research Limited, Carrington Plastics Laboratory, Urmston, Near Manchester, England

G. REHAGE

Physikalisch-Chemisches Institut Technischen Hochschule Clausthal, 3392 Clausthal-Zellerfeld, Adolf-Romer-Strasse 2A, West Germany

G. E. ROBERTS

Department of Polymer and Fibre Science, The University of Manchester Institute of Science and Technology, PO Box No. 88, Sackville Street, Manchester 1, England

V. STANNETT

Department of Chemical Engineering, North Carolina State University, Raleigh, North Carolina, USA

S. TURNER

ICI Limited, Plastics Division, PO Box No. 6, Bessemer Road, Welwyn Garden City, Hertfordshire, England

E. F. T. WHITE

Department of Polymer and Fibre Science, The University of Manchester Institute of Science and Technology, PO Box No. 88, Sackville Street, Manchester 1, England

G. R. WILLIAMSON

Shell Research Limited, Carrington Plastics Laboratory, Urmston, Near Manchester, England

PREFACE

This work sets out to provide an up-to-date account of the physical properties and structure of polymers in the glassy state. Properties measured above the glass transition temperature are therefore included only in so far as is necessary for the treatment of the glass transition process. This approach to the subject therefore excludes any detailed account of rubber elasticity or melt rheology or of the structure and conformation of the long chain molecule in solution, although knowledge derived from this field is assumed where required. Major emphasis is placed on structural and mechanical properties, although a number of other physical properties are included.

Naturally the different authors contributing to the book write mainly from their own particular points of view and where there are several widely accepted theoretical approaches to a subject, these are sometimes provided in different chapters which will necessarily overlap to a significant extent. For example, the main theoretical presentation on the subject of glass transition is given in Chapter 1. This is supplemented by accounts of the free volume theory in Chapter 3 and in the Introduction, and a short account of the work of Gibbs and DiMarzio, also in Chapter 3. Similarly, there is material on solvent cracking in Chapters 7 and 9, though the two workers approach the subject from opposite directions. Every effort has therefore been made to encourage cross-referencing between different chapters.

The work has been carried out in a period when most scientists are changing over to SI units of measurement and these have been generally employed in the text. Difficulties have, however, arisen where a large number of diagrams have been quoted from other workers and many results from the literature have had to be presented in CGS or Imperial units. To help the reader we have therefore included a conversion table as an Appendix.

Finally, I would like to thank the authors for their courtesy and co-operation and also my secretary, Miss C. A. Jones, for her sustained support without which it would not have been possible to meet the date of publication.

University of Birmingham   R. N. HAWARD

CONTENTS

Chapter 2
X-RAY DIFFRACTION STUDIES OF THE STRUCTURE OF AMORPHOUS POLYMERS
—J. R. FITZPATRICK and B. ELLIS

Chapter 3
RELAXATION PROCESSES IN AMORPHOUS POLYMERS
—G. E. ROBERTS and E. F. T. WHITE

Chapter 4
CREEP IN GLASSY POLYMERS—*S. TURNER*

Chapter 5
THE YIELD BEHAVIOUR OF GLASSY POLYMERS
—*P. B. BOWDEN*

Chapter 6

THE POST-YIELD BEHAVIOUR OF AMORPHOUS PLASTICS
—R. N. HAWARD

Chapter 7
CRACKING AND CRAZING IN POLYMERIC GLASSES
—E. H. ANDREWS

Chapter 8
RUBBER REINFORCED THERMOPLASTICS—J. MANN and
G. R. WILLIAMSON

Chapter 9

THE DIFFUSION AND SORPTION OF GASES AND
VAPOURS IN GLASSY POLYMERS—*H. B. HOPFENBERG
and V. STANNETT*

Chapter 10
THE MORPHOLOGY OF REGULAR BLOCK COPOLYMERS
—*M. J. FOLKES and A. KELLER*

INTRODUCTION

The Nature of Polymer Glasses, Their Packing Density and Mechanical Behaviour

R. N. HAWARD

The object of this introduction is two-fold. Firstly to supply the reader with some general information on the nature of polymeric glasses and of their structures and, secondly, to fill in certain areas which are not themselves dealt with in detail in the later chapters.

The introduction therefore contains a number of separate parts. The first part deals with some general concepts concerning the structure of organic glasses. The second part includes a discussion of the packing density of polymer glasses and includes a discussion of the various 'free volume' concepts which have been advanced to account for certain thermodynamic and flow properties. Finally there is a discussion of mechanical properties which includes a description of some recent theories which appear to account for the levels of short term moduli which are characteristic of both crystalline and glassy polymers.

THE NATURE OF POLYMERIC GLASSES

The common glassy polymers

The polymeric glasses comprise a class of plastic materials consisting essentially of long chain organic molecules having an amorphous structure. The polymer chains generally consist of single repeating monomer units which are joined together by covalent bonds. However, certain plastics are also used or marketed as copolymers, *i.e.* polymers containing more than one monomer unit, and these include styrene-acrylonitrile copolymers and copolymers of vinyl chloride and vinyl acetate.

Another feature which may cause differences between polymer samples of the same general type is that of molecular weight. With thermoplastics an increase in molecular weight leads to improved mechanical properties (*see* Chapters 3 and 6) but this is accompanied by increased melt viscosity and consequent greater difficulties in processing (*e.g.* injection moulding) the polymer. To meet this situation different grades of polymer having different molecular weights may be marketed (*e.g.* with polyethylene and PVC). However, since many important physical properties (*e.g.* glass transition temperature) reach a maximum limiting value at a certain level of molecular weight, the actual range of molecular weight covered by the major commercial materials is still fairly narrow when considered against the range of materials which can be made in the laboratory.

Even when a polymer is manufactured commercially as a homopolymer within a narrow average molecular weight range it may be formulated to contain small quantities of stabilisers, lubricants or of other co-monomers in order to obtain the most useful combination of properties. Thus not all the materials which are commonly used are actually pure polymers. However, under competitive pressures formulations of the main polymers from different manufacturers have generally tended to converge so that the properties measured on equivalent grades of the most widely used materials are often very similar. Thus general purpose standard polystyrene normally contains a small quantity of lubricant which reduces the glass transition temperature by about 10°C and improves the moulding properties. Differences between these polystyrenes from different sources would be small. On the other hand smaller quantities of relatively pure polymer are in this case also marketed as heat resistant grades. Rigid polyvinylchloride (PVC) though it may contain no plasticiser, does contain significant quantities of stabilisers which reduce its tendency to decompose on heating.

Thus differences between the formulations used will lead to minor differences between one supplier's material and another's. This makes life difficult for the polymer physicist who may be unacquainted with the technological factors which determine the polymer formulations actually marketed. Nevertheless, except where otherwise stated it should be assumed that most of the measurements described here relate to standard polymers as they are marketed.

Within these limitations the main chemical types of polymer glass may be simply represented as follows:

Polystyrene

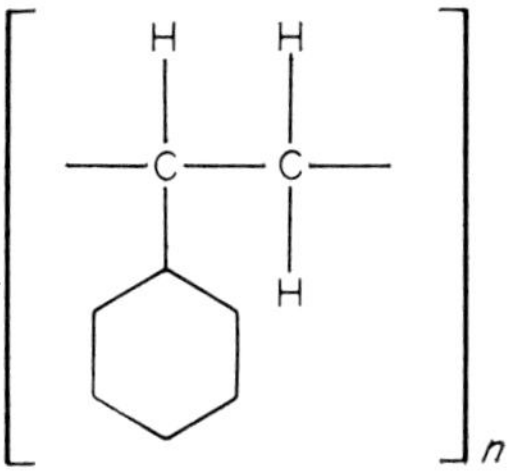

Polymethyl methacrylate

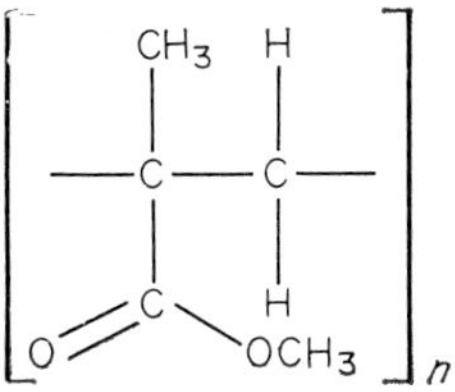

(other esters of methacrylic acid are also used and studied)

Polyvinylchloride

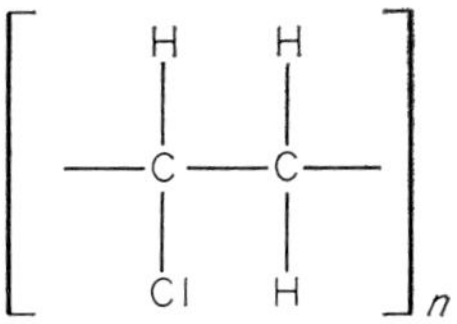

Polycarbonate

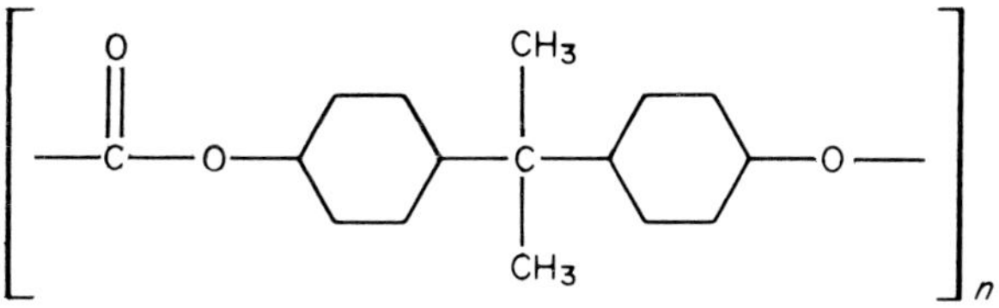

(polycarbonic ester of 2,2-bis-(4-hydroxyphenyl) propane)

Esters of cellulose

$$
\left[\begin{array}{c}
\text{CH}_2\text{OH} \\
| \\
\text{C} - \text{O} \\
\diagup \quad | \quad \diagdown \\
-\text{O} - \text{HC} \quad \overset{\text{H}}{\underset{\text{H}}{|}} \quad \text{H} \quad \text{CH} - \\
\diagdown \quad | \quad \diagup \\
\text{C} - \text{C} \\
| \qquad | \\
\text{HO} \qquad \text{OH}
\end{array}\right]_n
\quad \text{Cellulose}
$$

Generally acetic, butyric or nitric esters of cellulose are used, where the hydroxyl hydrogens in the cellulose unit are wholly or partly replaced by the acid group. For use as thermoplastics they are formulated to contain appreciable quantities of plasticisers.

Other glassy polymers include polyvinylacetate, the polysulphones, polyvinyl formals, polyvinyl carbazole and the cross-linked polyesters and epoxy resins used in fibre-glass laminates. Polyethylene terephthalate can also be obtained as a non-crystalline polymer glass. Many of the new high temperature heterochain polymers including the polyimides and poly-benzimidazoles may also be regarded as glassy polymers (*see* Appendix I).

The softening of polymer glasses
It will now be clear that most of the important polymer glasses consist of separate long chain polymer molecules. These soften and flow under the influence of heat, *i.e.* they are thermoplastic. This property enables them to be processed commercially at high speeds on a large scale to give moulded and formed products. Thus the thermoplastic glasses soften and flow reversibly. On the other hand some other glassy polymers contain a network of cross-links which allows them to soften at higher temperatures but not to flow (*see* p. 8).

Thus the important polymer glasses consist essentially of long chain molecules which have a random configuration and which are packed together to fill space. The precise properties, however, depend greatly on the temperature, the characteristic glassy properties being observed only below a particular temperature, generally called the glass transition temperature, below which the polymer hardens and becomes a glass. The nature of this transition will be discussed in detail in Chapter 1 and

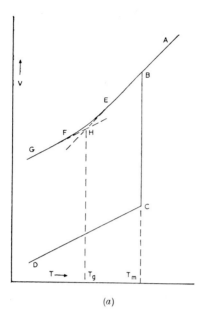

(a)

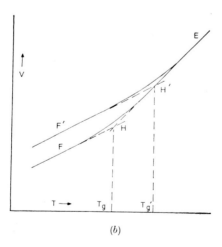

(b)

Fig. 1.   *Volume–temperature relations for crystalline and glassy substances.* (a) *Melting and glass transition of a low molecular weight substance.* (b) *Effect of rate of cooling on glass transition—curve EH'F' is for fast cooling and curve EHF for slow cooling. (Reproduced from reference 1 by permission of Taylor and Francis Ltd.)*

Chapter 3, but in order to assist the more general reader, a short description of some of the more significant changes which take place at the glass transition temperature are briefly described here.

As the temperature falls from a high level polymers contract in much the same way as a normal non-polymeric liquid, and at the same time the viscosity increases. If the polymer is capable of crystallisation a point will be reached where crystallisation sets in, giving a relatively hard and rigid product. On the other hand, if crystallisation does not occur then the viscosity will continue to increase until at a level of some 10^{15} poises (10^{14} Ns/m^2) the liquid becomes substantially immobile and the molecular rearrangements associated with the normal contraction of a liquid can no longer take place. At this point where the material becomes rigid the co-efficient of expansion falls to about half the previous figure. This behaviour is, however, not limited to polymers and may also be observed for certain low molecular weight materials as shown in Fig. 1(a).[1] Here, the behaviour of a glass is illustrated by the line ABG and of a crystalline compound by the line $ABCD$. For the glass there is a short temperature range FE over which the coefficient of expansion changes without any discontinuity of volume. However, by production of the two expansion lines it is possible to define a theoretical point H which may be regarded as the glass transition temperature (T_g), although, in fact, the material at no time passes through a condition defined precisely by this point. Further the position of the point H is itself variable in the sense that it depends on the rate of cooling of the system. If the material is cooled more quickly then the volume–temperature relations will follow the line $EH'F'$ as shown in Fig. 1(b).[1] Thus the precise value of T_g will depend on the rate of cooling and on other experimental conditions. In practice, however, the variation of T_g with rate of cooling is not so steep as to make it impossible to characterise polymers in this way over the range of cooling rates which it is convenient to employ in the laboratory. On the other hand, when several decades of frequency are concerned, variations in T_g of the order of 20–40°C may be observed. In all these properties the behaviour of a low molecular weight glassy compound is closely followed by that of a thermoplastic polymer glass.

There are many important polymers which show this type of behaviour. On the other hand, many other polymers do crystallise. In this case, however, they generally show two distinct differences as compared with low molecular weight compounds as is illustrated in Fig. 2,[1] where the line BD describes the behaviour of a polymer which crystallises completely. Unlike a low molecular weight compound the polymer does not show a sharp melting point but melts over a range of temperatures as shown by the line *BD*, so that the melting point (T_m) has to be defined as the point of discontinuity *B*. However, very few polymers do crystallise completely, particularly when they have a high molecular weight. Materials of this type follow a line of the term *A*, *B*, *E″ F″* which shows the melting behaviour of a normal

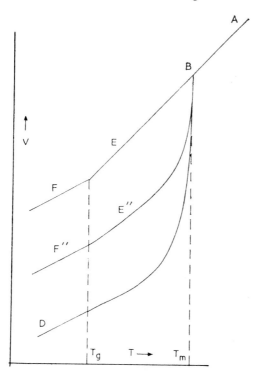

Fig. 2. Volume–temperature relations for polymers. Melting and glass transition in a polymer: EF no crystallisation; E″F″ partial crystallisation; BD complete crystallisation. (Reproduced from reference 1 by permission of Taylor and Francis Ltd.)

polymer, but in addition, the non-crystallised amorphous material present also shows a glass transition between *E″* and *F″*. However, if conditions can be found where the polymer does not crystallise then it will simply exhibit its glass transition as between *E* and *F* on the line *ABEF*. It appears therefore that the occurrence of a glass transition temperature is a characteristic of amorphous polymers in general, even when they constitute only a part of a largely crystalline material.

The theory of the glass transition and its relation to polymer structure constitutes a very important element in the understanding of the glassy state in polymers. These subjects are more rigorously examined in Chapters 1 and 3 of this book. Therefore to extend the present discussion here would serve no useful purpose. There are, however, a number of other subjects concerning the structure of glassy polymers and their packing volumes which will not be covered elsewhere and which will be discussed at this point, together with some other subjects which may help the more general reader to approach the problems associated with the properties of polymeric glasses.

Polymer melts and rubbers
Above the glass transition temperature there are marked differences between polymer melts which can flow into new forms under suitable conditions of temperature and shear stress, and rubbers which return to their original form completely after the stress field has been removed. This can be directly related to chemical structure in that rubbers are chemically cross-linked by covalent bonds, so that single polymer molecules do not exist and cannot migrate in the structure, while polymer melts consist of an assembly of polymer molecules which can move relatively to each other under shear. Typically the glassy plastics used commercially are formed by the cooling of a polymer melt. The reason for this is essentially commercial and technological. The materials derive a large part of their value from the fact that they can be processed as a thermoplastic under conditions of mass production. For this it is essential that they should be able to flow at elevated temperatures so that cross-linked materials cannot be used. On the other hand there are certain important areas of plastics technology where cross-linked glasses are directly prepared and employed. These generally comprise the epoxy and polyester resins which may be polymerised, together with a reinforcing filler such as glass fibre. This leads to quite a different type of technology from that associated with most glassy thermoplastics which are the main subject in this book. Nevertheless, it should be noted that below T_g the differences in physical behaviour between thermoplastics and thermosetting resins taken as groups may be relatively small, the differences within one group being greater than any generalised difference between the two groups. Generally, it is believed that the introduction of cross-links into polymer glass leads to increased brittleness, but the reasons for this behaviour are not well understood. For example, Boundy and Boyer[2] have reported an example where the polymerisation of increasing amounts of divinyl benzene with

styrene to give cross-linked products, leads first to a small increase in impact strength, and later, as the amount of cross-linking agent becomes large, to substantial embrittlement. In a more sophisticated way the effect of cross-links on crack propagation was investigated by Berry[3] in the case of methacrylate resins. He found that the energy of crack propagation was decreased by the introduction of a high level of cross-linking and the size of the 'inherent flaw' was reduced (*see* also Chapter 7).

The crystallisation of polymers

It will be clear from p. 6 that in order for a polymer to give a true polymer glass it must not crystallise. This condition follows from the fact that the crystalline melting point is always above the glass transition temperature, so that polymers have the opportunity of crystallising on cooling if they are able to do so, before the glass transition temperature is reached. Thus, the typical glassy plastics are those which do not crystallise and this in turn has implications in terms of molecular structure. In general most glassy polymers have a certain structural irregularity which prevents them forming a stable crystalline lattice, although there are some rather rare exceptions to this rule which will be discussed below.

Naturally structural irregularity can take many forms. For example most random copolymers, of the type formed in vinyl polymerisation, are non-crystalline, or have reduced crystallinity as compared with the homopolymers (*e.g.* ethylene and propylene can be copolymerised together to give a non-crystalline rubber). On the other hand, polymers with a symmetrical chain structure such as polyethylene or poly(oxymethylene) tend to crystallise whenever they are cooled below T_m. Between these two extreme groups there is a large group of polymers in which there is a pendent group on the polymer chain and in which, as shown by Natta,[4] the possibility of crystallisation depends on the stereochemistry of the pendent group, as typified by the case of polypropylene.

After studying the crystalline structure of different polypropylenes, Natta pointed to the existence of asymmetric carbon atoms in polymer chains of the type

$$\begin{bmatrix} -CH_2-CH- \\ | \\ R \end{bmatrix}_n$$

and concluded that three stereochemical types of chain structure were possible.

    I Isotactic structures where the same (dextro- or laevo-) configuration is maintained along the chain.

    II Syndiotatic structures where dextro and laevo carbon atoms alternate regularly.

    III Random structures where the asymmetric carbon atoms follow each other along the chain without any regular sequence.

These structures are illustrated in Fig. 3(*a*) and (*b*). In Fig. 3(*b*) Natta shows how an isotactic polypropylene is able to take up a helical structure whose existence can be demonstrated in the crystalline state. In later work

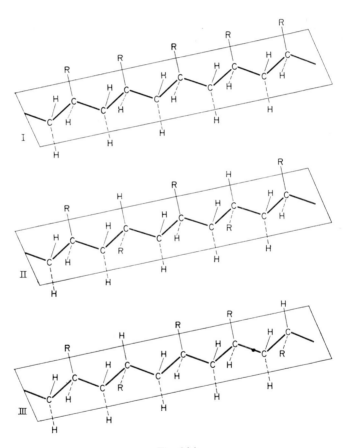

Fig. 3(a)

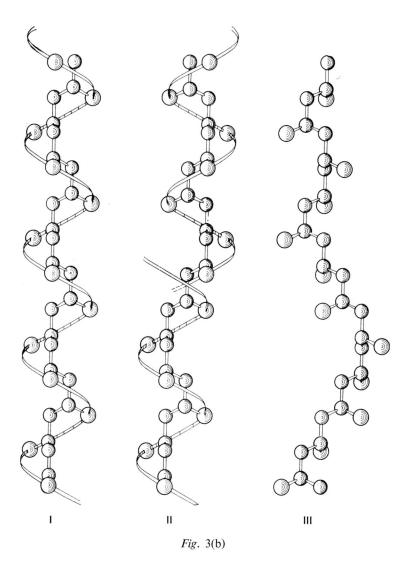

Fig. 3(b)

Fig. 3(a)   *Types of stereoisomeric chains.* (a) *Schematic drawing of the chains of poly-α-olefins stretched on a plane: I isotactic; II syndiotactic; III atactic.* (b) *Configurations of stereoisomeric chains: I isotactic chain helix; II chain with isotactic blocks; III atactic chain.* (*Reproduced from reference* 4 *by permission of Pergamon Press Ltd.*)

Natta[5] has elaborated a number of other types of regular chain structure based on the regular arrangement of molecules of the type

$$
\begin{bmatrix}
-CH-CH- \\
\ \ |\quad\ \ | \\
\ \ X\quad Y
\end{bmatrix}
$$

along a chain. Clearly, with a regular head to tail placement each of the asymmetric C atoms in this type of polymer can take up a dextro or laevo configuration and Natta shows that these possibilities lead to three further regular types of chain structure (Fig. 4), and each of these is, in principle,

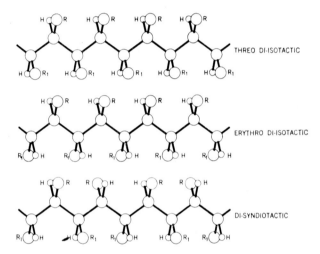

Fig. 4. *Stereoisomeric chains with two different substituent groups. Zig-zag planar projections of threo-di-isotactic, erythro-di-isotactic and di-syndiotactic polymer structures. (Reproduced from reference 5 by permission of the Society of Plastics Engineers, Inc.)*

capable of crystallisation. On the other hand, as the chain structure becomes more complex, especially in the absence of strong intermolecular forces, the tendency to crystallise may be reduced and in the limit chain regularity does not guarantee that the polymer will crystallise.

Amorphous isotactic polymers

Based on the study of a number of hydrocarbon polymers, Danusso et al.[6,7] have concluded that the state of the single macromolecule appears to be fairly independent of interactions with other macromolecules when considered from the point of view of its internal energy. Calculations based only on intramolecular interactions have shown that the most stable configuration for a stereoregular macromolecule corresponds to the conformation of that determined experimentally for the crystalline lattice. However, in order to attain real crystallinity, *i.e.* regular three-dimensional arrangement, a further condition is necessary; similar macromolecules in ordered configurations of the same type must pack together with a sufficient energy to obtain a stable crystalline lattice with a three-dimensional periodic structure, leading to a minimum value for the Free Energy of the system.

As an example of the way this principle works out Danusso[7] quotes the case of isotactic ortho and meta methyl styrene which crystallise, while similar *p*-ethyl and *p*-isopropyl styrenes do not. In many cases it can also be shown by means of infra-red spectra that the polymer molecule is present as an ordered helix, while the bulk polymer remains amorphous and glassy. A particularly striking case has been quoted by Natta[8] who prepared an isotactic poly *p*-chlorostyrene which, however, did not give a recognisable helix and did not crystallise. However, after hydrogenation of the benzene nucleus, which removed the chlorine atom, the resulting isotactic polyvinyl cyclohexane was crystalline. Thus, it is possible for a stereoregular polymer to be helical or non-helical in the chain configuration and to be crystalline or amorphous in bulk.

However, even if a stereo regular polymer can be made to crystallise it is by no means certain that it will always give a crystalline polymer. In this the crystalline transition shows a different behaviour to that of the glass transition. On cooling sufficiently below T_g a glass is always obtained. On the other hand, crystals are only formed if the conditions in the cooling melt and the time for which it remains under these conditions are such as to enable crystallisation to occur. This type of behaviour is illustrated by the case of isotactic polystyrene. Although this polymer has the requisite chain structure and is inherently capable of crystallisation, it does not do so when it is cooled quickly (quenched). Under these conditions a glass is obtained with the same density as that of the atactic material. Effective crystallisation is only achieved by a process of annealing at an elevated temperature. The reason for this has been demonstrated by Kenyon *et al.*[9] and by Hay[10] and is illustrated in Fig. 5. It will be seen that the rate of spherulite growth passes through a maximum at 175°C and falls to low values at each side of this temperature. If the melt is cooled quickly through this range only a very small proportion of crystals are formed and the material remains effectively a glass.

A rather similar situation arises in the case of the normally glassy polymer known as polycarbonate (the polycarbonic ester of 2,2-bis-(4-hydroxyphenyl) propane. When this polymer is cooled normally from the melt no doubly refracting spherulites can be observed. Only by slow cooling (<0·01°C min), or by heating for a period above 10 hours at a temperature of 190°C, is it possible to obtain spherulites visible under the optical microscope. Heating below a temperature of 181°C produced no spherulites in

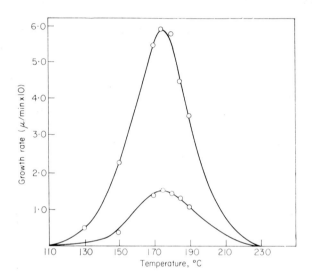

Fig. 5. The crystallisation of isotactic polystyrene. Rate of spherulite growth as a function of temperature. (Reproduced from reference 9 by permission of John Wiley and Sons Inc.)

24 hours.[11] On the other hand, McNulty[12] has shown that polycarbonates and polysulphones (in which the carbonate group is replaced by an SO_2 group) could also be crystallised by the use of suitable solvents which accelerated the formation of crystal spherulites. This process appeared to accelerate the phenomenon of solvent stress cracking (*see* Chapters 7 and 9) which occurs in many other cases in the absence of crystallisation. Thus these two polymers provide examples of rather regular substituted chains which are capable of crystallisation but generally do not do so, thus giving a polymer glass. Another group of rigid chain polymers which give amorphous products are provided by the cellulose esters and partial esters. Here of course the tendency to give amorphous materials will often

be increased by an uneven substitution of the polysaccharide units along the polymer chain, and by the presence of liquid plasticisers in technical formulations.

Thus we can conclude that the glassy plastics comprise not only random copolymers and atactic vinyl polymers but also certain polyesters with rather straight and apparently symmetrical chains. Also under suitable conditions stereospecific polymers may be obtained in the glassy state. Even the existence of ordered helices does not necessarily prevent the formation of amorphous products.

Now taking these considerations the other way round we must also observe that the fact that a polymer has the form of a disordered glass does not demonstrate that the chains themselves have a disordered structure. Following this line of argument proposals are now being put forward to suggest that the glass transition itself may be associated with the building up of relatively ordered chain arrangements which will of course be possible to some extent even in atactic polymer. This subject has been considered by Boyer for polystyrene[13] and by Reddish for PVC.[14] In the latter case there is significant evidence that the dipole interactions do provide a high degree of order below the glass transition temperature. However, the discussion of these topics is more appropriate to the relation of chemical structure and the glass transition and will be covered in detail in Chapter 3.

The morphology of amorphous polymers

So far we have been considering polymer glasses which have been formed by cooling of a melt or perhaps by casting from a good solvent. In such cases there is believed to be substantial interpenetration of the molecular coils, as in a rubber. Kargin,[15,16] however, has described some unusual globular polymer structures which can be observed in the electron microscope and which appear to differ from those normally obtained by cooling. It would appear that this work may conveniently be approached by considering, in the first place, electron micrography of isolated polymer molecules whose interpretation appears to be essentially unambiguous.

Among the early workers in this field Siegel et al.[17] deposited polystyrene dissolved in cyclo-hexane on a collodion support. Using a uranium shadowing technique it was then possible to obtain electron micrographs of molecularly dispersed polymer particles. This technique was further developed by Richardson[18] who employed very dilute solutions of polystyrene in mixtures of solvents and less volatile non-solvents. In this way by depositing very high molecular weight polystyrene on a mica-supported

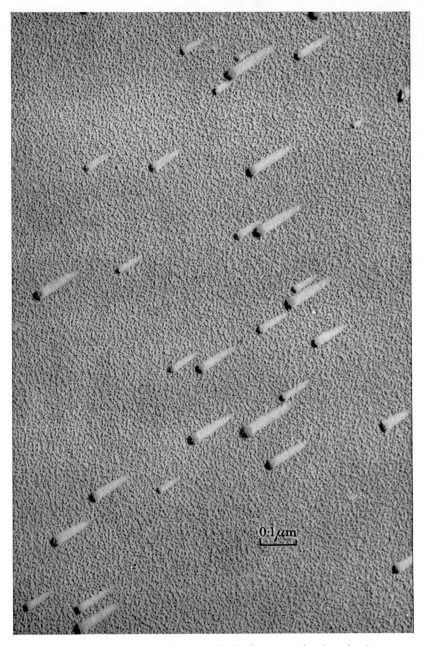

Fig. 6. Electron micrograph showing individual macromolecules of polystyrene. The polymer was sprayed from a $10^{-4}\%$ solution. (Reproduced from reference 18 by permission of The Royal Society, London.)

carbon film he was able to obtain individual molecules in spherical form as shown in Fig. 6. On the other hand, if the polymer solution was too concentrated, aggregates containing several polymer molecules were obtained. If, in addition, the substrate was not wetted, groups of aggregates were formed as shown in Fig. 7.

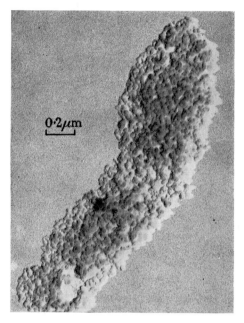

Fig. 7. Electron micrograph showing aggregates of polystyrene macromolecules. In this case the solution for spraying was more concentrated and did not wet the micro substrate. (Reproduced from reference 18 by permission of The Royal Society, London.)

Thus, Richardson demonstrated the possibility of preparing polymer molecules having different degrees of interpenetration and aggregation. Under the best conditions he obtained full separation of the polymer molecules and thus provided a new technique for measuring molecular weight. It may also be noted that Nasini et al.[19] have used this method to determine the molecular weight distribution of a polymethyl methacrylate and claimed agreement with other methods. Other measurements of molecular weight distribution have been obtained by Quayle[19a] who demonstrated that his results were independent of the concentration of the

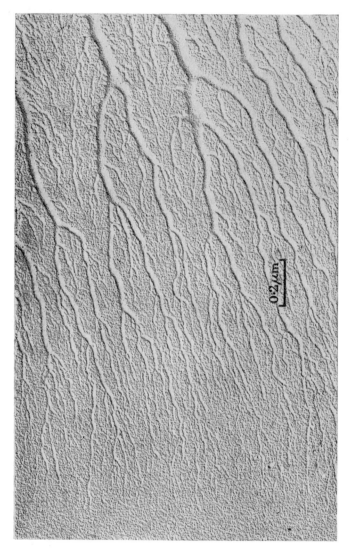

Fig. 8. Electron micrograph of polyacrylamide. Polyacrylamide sprayed from aqueous solution. It does not disperse as spherical molecules but as long fibrils, some of which are of molecular dimensions. (Reproduced by permission of The Royal Society, London.)

dilute solution used for spraying. Molecular weights could then be measured from shadow lengths. However, even when deposited from very dilute solutions, polymers do not always roll up into molecular or aggregated globules. Richardson also describes long fibrils, some of which are of molecular dimensions, which are deposited from aqueous solutions of polyacrylamide (Fig. 8).

These results may be supplemented by the work of Kargin and co-workers,[15,16] who showed that by the evaporation of dilute solutions below the glass transition temperature a great variety of polymers could be prepared in a 'globular form'. In these solutions, from which, as with Richardson, precipitation occurs during evaporation[16] the polymer molecules are assumed to be already rolled up into globules which do not blend together when the dispersant is removed and the consequent bulk polymer has different and generally inferior mechanical properties. A still more striking case of an apparently similar type is quoted by Slonimskii et al.[20] who studied the preparation and properties of the polyarylate obtained from phenolphthalein and isophthalic acid. This gave a stiff chain molecule which when prepared in the presence of a precipitant (di-tolyl-methane) had a super molecular structure consisting of spherical particles of about 1000 Å (see Fig. 9). When the polymerisation was carried out in a good solvent (α-chloronaphthalene) a product was obtained with a fibre-like super molecular structure (Fig. 10) and this was associated with much improved mechanical properties. Both polymers had similar molecular weights as measured by light scattering.

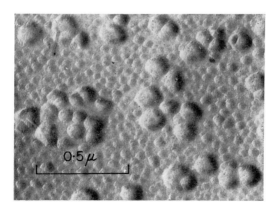

Fig. 9.   Electron micrograph of a polyarylate prepared in the presence of a poor solvent.[20] (Photograph supplied by Dr Slonimskii.)

Thus the results of these workers indicate that by means of certain specialised techniques, amorphous polymers can be prepared in the form of contracted, apparently globular molecules or groups of molecules, which according to the Russian workers have inferior mechanical properties. Although such formations clearly lack technical interest and are not normally generated during the cooling of a melt they obviously have significant implications for the structure of glassy polymers. Thus, Kargin's work throws light on the structure of amorphous polymers and especially of rubbers where a striped structure has been observed having some apparent analogies with the fibrillar structure observed by Richardson for polyacrylamide. An apparently similar sheaf-like, but crystalline structure has been observed by Keller for hexamethylene sebacamide.[21] On the other hand, rather different structures have been reported by Schoon[22] using several different electron microscopic techniques. He claims that a number of polymers, both rubbers and glasses, contain very small structural units, approximately spherical and having diameters independent of molecular weight at high molecular weights and being in the range of 30–60 Å. Thus, according to Schoon, polymer molecules have a 'pearl necklace' type of structure in the glassy state.

Naturally, many problems are raised in carrying out electron microscopy on polymer surfaces at high degrees of magnification, and difficulties inevitably arise as to the precise identity of the formation observed. To mitigate these problems Schoon has employed a number of different sample preparation techniques. In one of these a very thin film of polymer

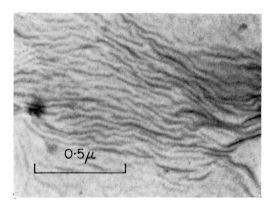

Fig. 10.   *Electron micrograph of a polyarylate prepared in the presence of a good solvent.*[20] (*Photograph supplied by Dr Slonimskii.*)

is deposited by solvent evaporation on to carbon and coated with silicon monoxide from all angles. After removal of the polymer and carbon the silicon monoxide provides a replica.[23] In another method a fragment of polymer is pulled off a fracture surface with gelatine and transferred to a formvar film after which the gelatine is dissolved completely. As a further alternative very thin polymer films could be deposited on collodion from solutions as dilute as 10^{-3} g/litre and contrasted with uranyl acetate or other heavy atoms.[24] By combining all these methods Schoon[22] claims to have demonstrated the existence of very small structural units whose size was only slightly dependent on molecular weight. He also showed that when polystyrene was broken down by ultra-sonic degradation the size of the fine structure was hardly affected.[25]

Fig. 11. Electron micrograph of polyethylene terephthalate. Surface replica of amorphous bulk polymer showing presence of ball-like structures. (Reproduced from reference 26.)

The work of Schoon and Kargin has raised many problems of technique and interpretation, and an increasing number of workers have sought to investigate the fine structure of glassy polymers. A particularly effective replica was obtained by Yeh and Geil[26] for polyethylene terephthalate in the glassy amorphous state, (Fig. 11) and this again showed a ball-like structure, and these were confirmed in transmission electron micrographs. On the other hand Frank *et al.*[27] found no detailed structure in the surface of untreated polycarbonate resin, but were able to observe striped formations, after ion-etching and annealing. Very small features of the size reported by Schoon and by Yeh and Geil were also observed by Magill on fracture surfaces of an aromatic siloxane polymer.[28] On the other hand, the information from fracture surfaces is by no means unambiguous. Many features can be seen which undoubtedly reflect the nature of the fracture process rather than the structure of the unperturbed polymer. For example, when polystyrene is fractured at $-196°C$ small rounded features are observed which are dependent on molecular weight and which lie in the range of 200–500 Å[29,30] *i.e.* much larger than those reported above. Here the explanation offered is related to the pulling out of thin fibrils of heat-softened polymer during the fracture process, and such features are clearly to be regarded as artefacts not relating directly to the structure of the amorphous polymer[30] (Fig. 12).

Further, the work of Schoon has been criticised by Zingsheim and Bachman on technical grounds.[30a] These workers were unable to confirm Schoon's work when correctly focused electron micrographs were taken. Only defocused pictures showed spherical structures of the type reported.[22]

Evidence favouring the conventional statistical picture of the glassy state
Thus the contribution of electron micrography to determining the fine structure of polymeric glasses is still at a very early stage and it is difficult to be sure how far the various features observed may be presumed to relate to the structure of the bulk polymer and how far they should be regarded as artefacts or purely surface effects. Another very serious problem which would arise if the polymer molecule could be shown to have the 'pearl necklace' type of structure as envisaged by Schoon, concerns the relationship of such structures to the statistical structures assumed to exist in rubbers according to the theory of rubber elasticity.[31] As is well known, this theory provides an elaborate picture of the long chain molecule having a random configuration of chain links and this model is generally considered to apply to amorphous polymers also in the glassy state. For example,

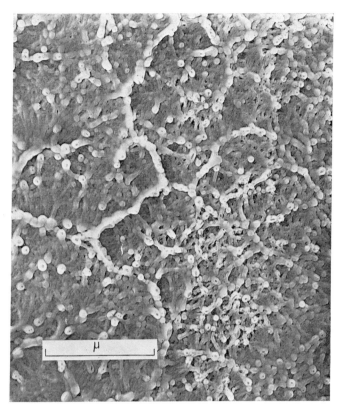

Fig. 12.   *Fracture surface of polystyrene. Carbon replica of polystyrene fractured at liquid air temperatures. Shows knob-like structures believed to be due to pulling out of polymer softened during fracture. The knobs have a diameter about equal to the statistical end-to-end distance of the polymer chains. (Reproduced from reference* 30 *by permission of Iliffe Science and Technology Publications Ltd.)*

Flory[31a] considered that the molecules of a bulk amorphous polymer would have a configuration equivalent to that in a theta solvent, and it is probable that most workers in the field of glassy polymers have assumed a structure of this type. On the other hand, it is a matter of considerable difficulty to prove that a polymer glass does actually consist of an assembly of polymer molecules with any particular configuration.

Recently, however, some efforts have been made to measure the molecular configurations occurring in an organic glass. For example, Graessley[31b] has analysed the relationship between the average dimensions of a chain in a polymer solid and the subsequent frequency of intramolecular cross-linking when the chains are joined at random. Clearly, chains which are tightly coiled, or have a 'pearl necklace' structure, would give a relatively large amount of internal cross-linkage compared with chains having a more extended configuration. In later work Graessley and Alberino[31c] measured the cross-linking of bulk and dissolved polystyrene by high energy radiation and observed no trends which could be related to tighter coils in the bulk systems. As a result they concluded that chain dimensions in bulk were at least as large as in a theta solvent.

Another approach to this problem was used by Krigbaum and Godwin[31d] who prepared the di-silver salts of polystyrenes terminated at each end by carboxyl groups. When these polymers were mixed at 5% concentration with normal polystyrene it was possible to determine their configuration by means of low angle X-ray scattering (*see* Chapter 2). The results again indicated that the configuration of chains in the bulk polymer was only slightly more extended than in a theta solvent.

Further support for Flory's ideas about the structure of bulk polymers is provided by studies with block polymers (*see* Chapter 10). These systems were also studied by Hoffman[31e] in a series of measurements aimed at elucidating the structure of amorphous rubbers. In this work he showed that the polystyrene domain size in styrene–butadiene blocks followed the expected relationship to M (diameter proportional to $M^{0.58}$) and this was in accordance with the concept of the statistical polymer coil in the glassy state. In his studies with different rubbers he supported this conclusion by measurements on the light scattering of 0·6–1·2% polybutadiene in trans polypentenes and by the study of diffusion of soluble polymer mixtures. In particular he showed that the diffusion of polymers in high molecular weight solvents obeyed the same laws as in low molecular weight ones. This strongly supports a model in which the high molecular weight polymer has the same configuration in each system. This conclusion was further supported by investigations on the flow and relaxation of polydimethyl siloxanes in silicon oils.

Thus there is now a considerable body of evidence to suggest that the molecular configuration of polymer molecules in the bulk amorphous phase is not substantially different from that in solution. Results from electron microscopy have therefore also to be considered from this point of view, but, for reasons which have already been given, it is not clear how the two types of evidence are to be related to each other. Meanwhile, most polymer scientists will probably continue to follow Flory and to regard glassy amorphous polymers as consisting essentially of inter-penetrating statistical coils having dimensions not very different from those measured in a theta solvent.

PACKING VOLUME IN THE GLASSY STATE

As previously indicated, when a polymer melt is cooled below T_g a change is observed in the coefficient of volume expansion α, so that the value α_L above $T_g > \alpha_g$ the value below T_g. The fundamental reasons for this change will be presented in Chapter 1. More generally volume changes play a significant part in many theories concerned with the properties of polymer glasses so that it is appropriate at this stage to consider some of the different concepts which have been put forward. Thus it is possible to consider a polymer glass as having a certain minimum packing volume under specified conditions (*e.g.* 0°K *see* below) and to treat the subsequent expansion at higher temperatures as leading to the formation of 'free' or unoccupied volume. Again in principle the unoccupied volume in the glassy state, for example at T_g, could be derived by extrapolating the volume at T_g down to absolute zero under conditions in which the polymer reaches its equilibrium volume. If this hypothetical α could be assumed to be constant over the required temperature range then the unoccupied volume at T_g would simply be $\alpha_L T_g$. This value has in fact been proposed by Boyer and Simha[32] and for different polymers, values of $(V_g - V_0)/V_g$ between 0·12–0·23 have been derived. These figures provide a rough estimate of the expansion volume (*see* below) for different polymer glasses, but they are also probably on the high side, as indeed recognised by Boyer and Simha who suggested that a more significant estimate of 'free volume' would be given by

$$(\alpha_L - \alpha_g)T_g$$

In this way smaller figures of about 0·11 are obtained. However, this procedure runs immediately into several difficulties, the most obvious of which is that neither α_L nor α_g can properly be considered to be independent of temperature. Thus, the coefficient of volume expansion of most liquids is not constant, but is known to fall with the temperature.[33] The same absence of linearity applies to polymers both as a glass[34] and above T_g.[35] Thus, this approach to the concept of unoccupied volume in a glass is not particularly convincing. However, in order to develop a more thorough approach it is necessary to provide a more complete definition of the quantities concerned.

Definitions of free volume

Here it is convenient to follow the definitions of the different possible concepts of free volume given by Bondi and Hildebrand.[36] These are summarised below. They may be quoted in terms of cubic centimetres per mole, density at $0°K$, or specific volume at $0°K$, as well as in fractional volumes. In practice a number of different terms have been used but in this discussion we shall express all volumes in $cm^3/mole$ and certain fractional volumes as separately defined. The following three measures of unoccupied volume may now be defined.

Empty volume (V_E)

$$V_E = V_T - V_W$$

where V_T is the observed volume ($cm^3/mole$) at temperature T and V_W = volume per mole of the substance as calculated from the van der Waals' dimensions obtained by an X-ray diffraction method or from gas kinetic collision cross-sections. Thus, according to this definition the argon atom would be regarded as a sphere and V_E is the total volume outside the van der Waals' radius of the spheres.

Expansion volume (V_F)

$$V_F = V_T - V_0$$

where V_0 is the volume occupied by the molecules at $0°K$ in a close-packed crystalline state. Thus, expansion volume is extra free space generated by thermal motion. It must always be smaller than the empty volume.

Fluctuation volume (V_f)

$$V_f = N_A V_Q$$

where V_Q is the volume swept out by the centre of gravity of one molecule as the result of its thermal vibration, and N_A is the Avogadro number.

These three concepts have the advantage of being clearly defined in relation to a given molecular assembly. It should, however, be realised that the above distinctions have not always been clearly recognised. Some workers use the term 'free volume' without further definition as though its meaning were evident. Often the meaning is, of course, quite clear from the context.

Values of these different volumes for the case of certain simple liquids have been calculated by Bondi and some of these are presented in Table 1. Clearly, the determination of the volumes occupied by molecules in contact

TABLE 1

VOLUME PROPERTIES OF SEVERAL SIMPLE SUBSTANCES
(ALL IN CM^3/MOLE)

Sub-stance	$T°K$	V_T	$V_0{}^a$	V_W From crystal data	From collision diameters	V_f Calculated	From sound velocity^b
A	84	28·1	23·4	17·4	12·5	0·80	(87°K) 0·85
N$_2$	63·3	31·9	27·4	15·8^c	12·65	(87°K) 0·97	0·405
CH$_4$	90·5	35·0	30·65	17·1^c	17·2	0·59	0·53
CCl$_4$	293	96·5	74·6	51·4^c	57	0·42	0·24

^{a} From Biltz. W., et al. (1930). Z. Physik Chem., 151, 13.
　　Biltz. W., and Sapper A. (1932). S. Anorg. allgem. Chem., 203, 277.
^{b} From $V_f = V_T(U_g/U_L)3$ where U_g, U_L are sound velocity of vapour and liquid states.
^{c} See Bondi.[36]

and of the radii which separated their centres under these conditions is of great importance. This subject has recently been reviewed by Bondi[37] who has provided an extensive compilation of van der Waals' volumes and radii. From the concept of a van der Waals' volume it is possible to derive an expression for the fluctuation volume V_f, assuming that the free path is small compared with the molecular diameter. Thus Bondi shows that:

$$V_f = \frac{4}{3} \frac{V_E{}^3}{A} \times N_A$$

where N_A is the Avogadro number and A is the area per mole of molecules. In the case of atoms this equation becomes:

$$V_f = \frac{V_E{}^3}{27V_W{}^2}$$

Values of V_f in Table 1 are derived from this relation and compare satisfactorily with values of V_f derived from the velocity of sound. Bondi also cites further data from paraffin hydrocarbons in support of this point of view. This treatment assumes that all the empty volume is accessible to the thermal motions of the molecules in the liquid state.

In the case of a polymer chain it certainly seems unlikely that the entire 'empty volume' can be accessible to thermal motion and it seems more reasonable to consider the expansion volume as the prime candidate for treating the interrelation of volume and physical properties. This concept is discussed here in conjunction with certain theories in which volume and physical properties are related and which have been considered by other workers in the polymer and liquid field. It should be appreciated that the application of the concepts of fluctuation and empty volume (as defined above) to the treatment of polymer properties has not seriously been undertaken so far, and their possible significance in future work is therefore not clear.

The expansion volume of amorphous polymers

As previously stated the expansion volume of a polymer is given by $(V_T - V_0)$ or in a fractional form as $[(V_T - V_0)/V_T)]$, where V_0 is the volume at $0°K$ under conditions of closest packing and V_T is the readily determined volume at the particular temperature. Thus the determination of the expansion volume simply involves an estimate of V_0. Three methods are available to do this. The first consists essentially of deriving V_0 based on an analogy with a liquid. The other two methods are capable of being applied directly to the polymer.

V_0 by analogy with liquids

In this case the estimation of V_0 depends on the use of one or more additive systems which it has been possible to apply to liquids. In principle, there is no certainty that they should apply to polymeric materials, but comparison with the limited results obtained directly with polymers, suggests that they may, in fact, give quite reasonable results.

Sugden's system

The first such additive system was proposed by Sugden[39] who obtained his experimental data from Goldhamer's Rule.[40] This is simply a convenient technique for extrapolating a value for ρ_0, the density of a liquid at $0°K$ from measurement of density at higher temperatures. From this, of course, the molar volume V_0 may be readily obtained.

Goldhamer proposed that

$$\rho_L - \rho_V = M\rho_c\left(1 - \frac{T}{T_c}\right)^{\frac{1}{3}}$$

where ρ_L, ρ_V are the densities of the liquid and vapour phase respectively, and the subscript, c, refers to critical conditions. Here M is a constant (generally equal to about 3·8). Once M has been determined, the equation allows for a precise extrapolation of ρ_0. Its accuracy depends on the true linearity of the $(\rho_L - \rho_V)$ vs. $[1 - (T/T_c)]^{\frac{1}{3}}$ plot. However, judging from the results of Matthews,[41] these plots are surprisingly good, so that the application of Goldhamer's rule does, in fact, give a quite definite estimate of ρ_0 for different liquids.

Sugden assembled a large number of these values and showed that they could be calculated from chemical structure by using a simple series of structural constants. The constants he obtained are given in Table 2

TABLE 2

EXAMPLES OF CALCULATED AND MEASURED VALUES OF V_0
(CM³/MOLE FROM SUGDEN AND BILTZ)

Compound	Sugden		Biltz	
	Observed[a]	Calculated	Observed[b]	Calculated[c]
Ethane	41·4	42·4	40·0	40·3
Benzene	71·2	71·4	69·3	69·3
Mesitylene	115·0	114·9	111·3	110·3
Methanol	32·3	30·9	30·5	30·6
Acetic acid	46·7	45·9	44·7	44·1
Dodecyl alcohol	186·4	190·4	180·8	181·0
Acetone	56·0	56·5	55·2	53·1
Benzyl alcohol	88·3	88·9	88·1	87·1
Diethyl ether	77·1	77·3	75·8	78·2

[a] From Goldhamer's Rule.[40]
[b] From Crystal Densities.[43]
[c] From additive system.

together with those derived by another method described below. We may also note here that Doolittle[42] compared various methods of extrapolating V_0 directly for the n-paraffins and obtained values in good agreement with those given by Goldhamer's Rule.

Estimations from the density of crystals

While Sugden was approaching the estimation of V_0 by extrapolating liquid densities, Biltz estimated V_0 from the crystalline state. After an extensive series of researches in this field he summarised his conclusions in a textbook.[43] Basically, the determination of V_0 for a solid is simpler than for a liquid as the volume at the melting point (V_m) is within 10% of that at 0°K. For example, Gruneisen[44] pointed out that $(V_m/V_0) \sim 1.075$. Biltz examined a number of methods of extrapolating V_0, including direct measurements down to $-196°C$ and extrapolation over what was, in many cases, only the small volume change expected below this temperature and, as a result, he suggested that the best value of $(V_0/V_m) = 0.91$. It will be seen that here we are talking about differences of the order of 1%

between Biltz and Gruneisen. Thus, the values of V_0 extrapolated from crystal densities can hardly be in any considerable doubt, and like Sugden, Biltz went on to develop another additive system for deriving values of V_0 from chemical constitution. On the other hand, questions can arise as to the applicability of his values to the liquid state and the extent to which they agree with the figures obtained from the Goldhamer Rule. It is therefore of interest to compare the two additive systems and the experimental and 'calculated' results obtained by the two workers for a number of organic compounds. These results are summarised in Table 2. It will be seen that the volumes obtained by Sugden are generally some 2–3% above those given by Biltz, and this no doubt reflects the differences in the two methods of measuring V_0.

Additive systems for estimating the occupied volume (V_0) of a liquid in cm³/mole

Atomic constants in cm³/mole according to Sugden[31]

H = 6·7	I = 28·3	Triple bond 13·9
C = 1·1	P = 12·7	Double bond 8·0
N = 3·6	S = 14·3	Three membered ring 4·5
O = 5·9	O = (in alcohol) 3·0	Four membered ring 3·2
F = 10·3	N = (in ammonia) 0·9	Five membered ring 1·8
Cl = 19·3		Six membered ring 0·6
Br = 22·1		

Atomic constants in cm³/mole according to Biltz[43]
C (aliphatic) 0·77, (aromatic) 5·1; H 6·45, double bond 8·6, triple bond 16; C = 0 (ketonic) 12·1, O (alcoholic) 10·5; O.O (carboxyl) 23·2; Cl 16·3; Br 19·2; I 24·5.

The application of crystal density measurements directly to polymers
Clearly, a method such as that applied by Biltz[43] which involves the measurement of crystal densities can be applied to polymers, and this approach has been explored by Bondi.[45]

He employed the available data on crystal densities together with their coefficients of expansion, or that of the glass, to provide extrapolated values of V_0. The results are given in Table 3.[45] Bondi calculates all three of the volumes which hc has previously defined and quotes with it a value

TABLE 3

FRACTIONAL FREE VOLUMES (BY DIFFERENT MODELS) IN
VARIOUS AMORPHOUS POLYMERS AT T_g DERIVED FROM
ESTIMATED 0°C CRYSTAL DENSITIES (AFTER BONDI[45])

Polymer	Van der Waals' empty volume (V_E)	Expansion volume	'WLF' free volume	Fluctuation volume
Polyisobutylene	0·320	0·125	0·026	0·0017
Polystyrene	0·375	0·127	0·025	0·0035
Poly(vinyl acetate)	0·348	0·14	0·028	0·0023
Poly(methyl methacrylate)	0·335	0·13	0·025	0·0015
Poly(n-butyl methacrylate)	0·335	0·13	0·026	0·0010

of the 'WLF' free volume which will be discussed again later. It is, however, clear that the 'WLF' figure is not the same as that of any of the quantities defined by Bondi.[36]

The application of the Hildebrand condition to polymers
The concept of internal pressure (P_i) in the liquid state was introduced by Hildebrand who defined it as follows:

$$P_i = \left(\frac{dU}{dV}\right)_T = T\left(\frac{dP}{dT}\right)_V - P = \frac{T\alpha}{\beta_T} - P$$

where U is the internal energy, P the pressure and β_T the isothermal compressibility of the liquid.

He then went on to point out that when $P_i = 0$, U should be at a minimum from which it followed that the molecules should be in the same positions which they would occupy at 0°K. Although this method has not been extensively applied to liquids some reasonable results have been obtained which have been reviewed elsewhere.[38] However, the method is intrinsically applicable to polymers and has been used to estimate the value of V_0 for polystyrene.

In order to use this concept it is necessary to make PVT measurements above the glass transition temperature at high pressures. Measurements of this type became available through the work of Rehage and Breuer[35,46] and their results were used to derive the Hildebrand conditions, in co-operation with Haward.[47] The graph of P_i against volume, which was obtained, gave a good indication of the expected value of V_0 (Fig. 13), although there is a possible error of $+3\%$ (-0%) due to the experimental

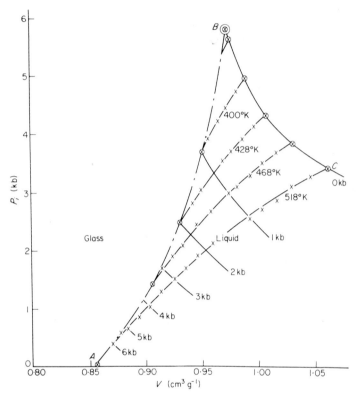

Fig. 13. Application of the Hildebrand condition to polystyrene. The internal pressure $(\partial U/\partial V)_T$ of polystyrene in relation to specific volume. AB is the liquid–glass transition line; BC is the isobar at zero pressure. The point A corresponds to V_0. (Reproduced from reference 47 by permission of John Wiley and Sons Inc.)

difficulty of measuring α_L at high pressures. In Table 4 we provide the figures for V_0 obtained by this method and compare them with the results obtained by Bondi[14] and that given by the additive systems of Biltz[43] and Sugden.[39] Generally, it seems reasonable to conclude that V_0 for polystyrene at T_g is between 0·82–0·85 cm³/g (85–88 cm³/base mole) with a fractional expansion volume (at atmospheric pressure) of 13–16%.

All these treatments attempt to provide a value for the expansion volume of a polymeric glass and may also be regarded as a more exact approach to the question of measuring the value of free volume as understood by Simha and Boyer and which they first estimated by using the quantity $\alpha_L T_g$.

TABLE 4

TABLE 4

THE VOLUME OF CLOSEST PACKING AND EXPANSION
VOLUME AT $T_g{}^a$ OF POLYSTYRENE

	Volume of closest packing, V_0		Fractional expansion volume at T_g $= \dfrac{V_G - V_0}{V_G}$
	cm^3/g	$cm^3/base\ mole$	
Bondi[45]	0·849	88·4	0·127
Haward, Rehage and Breuer[47]	0·85	88	0·13
Biltz[43]	0·82	84	0·17
Sugden[39]	0·83	86	0·15

^{a} V_G at atmospheric pressure = 0·973 cm^3/g.

Free volume concepts derived from viscosity theories

There is no doubt that volume (or density) is a major factor in determining the viscosity of a liquid. Indeed in some cases it is apparent that volume is the sole relevant factor, independent of the levels of temperature and pressure.[48] It is not surprising therefore to find that many attempts have been made to base theoretical or semi-empirical theories of viscosity on changes in volume. Such treatments have achieved a high degree of application and acceptance in recent years and can undoubtedly provide a valuable representation of experimental measurements. We should, however, note that many other treatments are possible both for liquids and polymers. In particular Bondi[49] has explored the relation between the viscosity of liquids and their structure. For this purpose he treats viscosity as the sum of three components, *viz*: a gas kinetic component, a contribution due to rigid core encounters and an intermolecular force component. Bondi proceeds from these concepts to apply Prigogine's ideas[50] of external degrees of freedom to derive a range of liquid properties including viscosity in terms of reduced dimensionless parameters depending on temperature pressure and volume.

Theories of the type proposed by Bondi, although more thorough, are also more complicated than treatments which may be based on volume only. Thus, there is also scope, within defined limits, for the development of semi-empirical proposals which provide a workable account of viscosity changes in liquids and polymers. Here an initial approach was made by Doolittle and co-workers[42,51] who treated the case of liquid *n*-paraffins. Doolittle defined a 'free volume' V_F' for a liquid in terms of the expansion volume ($V_T - V_0$) where $V_T - V_0 = V_F$ and proposed the relation, viscosity $= \eta = A \exp(BV_0/V_F)$. Here, neither V_0 nor V_F were disposable constants, since V_0 was obtained by his previously mentioned method of extrapolating density data. He particularly selected the case of heptadecane for evaluating his theory because of the large liquid temperature range between the freezing point (22°C) and the boiling point (302°C) and demonstrated that the proposed free volume equation fitted the results between 100 and 300°C better than the conventional Arrhenius equation $\eta = A \exp(B/T)$. However, below 100°C the free volume equation shows significant deviations from experimental results and these reached a level of 16·6% at the melting point. In terms of volume this means that a good fit was given in the range $(V_0/V_F) = 1\cdot4$–3 but that deviations occurred at lower values of V_F where $(V_0/V_F) \geq 3\cdot0$ $[(V_F/V) = 0\cdot25]$ for organic liquids.

A theoretical basis for the Doolittle free volume equation
An equation similar to Doolittle's free volume viscosity equation has been derived by Cohen and Turnbull[52] who argued on the following lines: Molecular transport processes occur by the movement of molecules into voids formed by redistribution of the free volume and which have a size greater than a critical value.

Starting from the concept that the contribution of a molecule to diffusion $D(V)$ is given by:

$$D(V) = ga(V)U$$

where g is a geometric factor, U the molecular viscosity and $a(V)$ is roughly the diameter of the cage, they proposed that $D(V)$ will be zero unless V exceeds a critical value V^* just large enough to permit another molecule to jump in. Therefore, the average diffusion coefficient is:

$$D = \int_{V^*}^{\infty} D(V)P(V)\,dV$$

where $P(V)$ is the probability of finding a free volume between (V) and $(V + dV)$. Maximising the number of ways of distributing free volume then leads to the equation: $P(V^*)$, the probability of finding a hole of volume exceeding V^*

$$= \int_{V^*}^{\infty} P(V)dV = \exp\left(\frac{-\gamma V^*}{V_F}\right)$$

where γ is a constant, later shown to be near to unity, and where V^* is near to the molecular volume. Finally the equation for D becomes

$$D = ga^*U \exp(-\gamma V^*/V_F)$$

and this is close to the equation of Doolittle with the exception that U contains the relatively slowly changing (but not always negligible) term $(T)^{\frac{1}{2}}$. Although Cohen and Turnbull discuss V^* in terms of the van der Waals' volume, as defined by Bondi,[36] they make it clear in their eqn. (16) that the critical quantity V_F is actually to be defined as the expansion volume, since it falls to zero at $0°K$, which does not happen with the van der Waals' volume as understood by Bondi, and in this they agree with Doolittle. Further, when we put $V^* = V_0$ this definition of free volume becomes the same as Doolittle.

The viscosity of liquids at lower temperatures and volumes
As pointed out by Doolittle[42] the free volume equation, as he developed it, does not work so well at low volumes and temperatures. On the other hand, this general form of the equation has still been found useful by a number of workers, provided a further modification is introduced. According to these proposals the volume V_F where $V_F = (V - V_0)$ is now treated as a disposable constant. Alternatively, a temperature may be defined, other than $0°K$, at which the free volume is considered to be zero. There have been a number of approaches to this type of treatment, but, following Cohen and Turnbull[52] we may select T_0 as the temperature where $V_F = 0$ and so write:

$$V_F = \alpha \bar{V}_m(T - T_0)$$

where α and $\bar{V}_m$ are mean values over the relevant temperature range. Similarly, if β is the compressibility,

$$V_F = \alpha \bar{V}_m(T - T_0) - \beta \bar{V}_p \Delta P$$

where $\bar{V}_p$ is a similar mean molecular volume for the pressure increment ΔP. This then leads to the equation:

$$D = ga^*U \exp\left(\frac{\gamma V^*}{[\bar{V}_m\alpha(T - T_0) - \bar{V}_p\beta\Delta P]}\right)$$

Finally, Cohen and Turnbull show that this can describe the viscosity of several liquids (including carbon tetrachloride in the range 20–140°C) in terms of temperature and also at pressures up to a few hundred bars.

In the absence of pressure the Cohen and Turnbull equation can be used to express the viscosity temperature relation for liquids. In this way, disregarding the minor temperature variation involved in U, $(T^{\frac{1}{2}})$, one arrives at an equation of the type:

$$\ln \eta = A + \frac{B}{T - T_0}$$

As might be expected, a simple equation of this type has already been suggested[53,54,55] and recently it has been applied to the Newtonian viscosities of liquids at low and moderate temperatures, by Miller,[56] Barlow et al.[57] and by Davies and Matheson.[58] In some cases, e.g. with di-isobutylphthalate, or s-butylbenzene, Barlow et al. distinguish two regions of behaviour characterised by two different values of T_0.

There is little doubt that the introduction of the new disposable constant T_0 can very usefully improve the performance of the free volume type of viscosity temperature relation in terms of representing a wider range of data, and makes it possible to represent viscosity data at lower volumes and temperatures, i.e. under the conditions in which Doolittle found that his own treatment was no longer adequate. Miller,[56] for example, has shown that such a modification can improve the representation of n-paraffin viscosities as compared with the equation used by Doolittle. Difficulties arise, however, concerning the interpretation T_0 in terms of a free volume concept. In order to overcome these difficulties Miller proposed that the occupied volume could vary with temperature, a concept which takes the theory a further considerable step beyond the original concepts of Doolittle and of Cohen and Turnbull. He also reported that the introduction of the $T^{\frac{1}{2}}$ term according to the Cohen and Turnbull treatment improved the performance of the Doolittle equation.

Viscosity and free volume in polymers
The Williams, Landel, Ferry ('WLF') equation

We have seen how, in the case of many liquids, the viscosity at high volumes and temperatures is largely dependent on the volume, and the relation between viscosity and temperature can be expressed through the Doolittle free-volume equation. At lower temperatures many liquids depart from this equation, though their behaviour can still be treated by equations of a similar type by making the free volume a disposable constant.

In the case of polymers it is not possible to measure viscosities at high volumes, since degradation invariably occurs before the expansion volume as previously defined (see p. 26) reaches values appreciably above a level of 0·25. Measurements of the viscosity of polymers are, therefore, concerned with conditions under which $(V - V_0)/V \sim 0·13$ (or the value at

T_g if different) to $(V - V_0)/V \sim 0.25$. This situation and the basic similarity in structure of different long-chain polymers leads to distinct analogies in their viscosity temperature behaviour. These similarities were first clearly pointed out by Williams et al.[59] ('WLF'). They defined a quantity, α_T, to represent the temperature variation of the segmental friction coefficient for any mechanical relaxation and showed that it could be represented by an equation of the type:

$$\ln \alpha_T = \frac{-C_1(T - T_g)}{C_2 + T - T_g}$$

This equation, which with some variations,[60] generally gives a good representation of a wide range of experimental results,[61–6] can be shown to be equivalent to those of Doolittle[42] and of Cohen and Turnbull.[52] Based on this analogy, as shown in Chapter 3, p. 176 it is found that a value of about 0.025 is required for the fractional free volume of most polymers at T_g (Table 3). This concept of free volume has been represented by Ferry in a diagram (Fig. 14(a)) where it will be seen that he employs the concept of a temperature-dependent occupied volume which therefore differs from the expansion volume used by Bondi and Hildebrand.[36] Taken by themselves the viscosity arguments for a particular value (e.g. 0.025) of free volume at T_g do not seem to be conclusive for the following reasons.

(1) The analogy with the Doolittle equation is based on volumes and densities where Doolittle reported that his equation did not apply.

(2) Cohen and Turnbull's derivation of the distribution of free volume is based on maximising the number of ways of redistributing the free volume among a large number of molecules. This is not the only possible treatment. For example Bueche[67] and Arakawa[68] have used an error function to describe the distribution of free volume and when this is done a relation is obtained which is claimed by Bueche to be a satisfactory equivalent of the 'WLF' equation, and which can be treated to give volumes more in line with the unoccupied volumes obtained for other sources.[38]

(3) As shown in Chapter 3, p. 179, an equation similar to the 'WLF' equation has been derived from completely different concepts by Adam and Gibbs.[70] These workers started from the theory of glass transition provided by Gibbs and DiMarzio,[69] based on consideration of entropy and not of free volume.

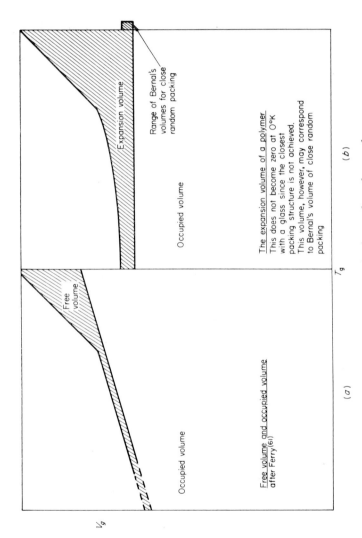

Fig. 14. *The free and occupied volume of a polymer glass.*

Geometrical factors affecting the possible value of the free volume at T_g
In his discussion of free volume in relation to temperature and viscosity,
Ferry[61] makes use of a simplified volume diagram (Fig. 14). In this he
assumes that there is an occupied volume less than the measured volume
by an amount equal to that of the previously discussed 'WLF' free volume.
This again implies the existence of a (temperature dependent) occupied
volume given by 97·5% of that of the glass itself at T_g, *i.e.* substantially
greater than V_0 and this leads us directly to the consideration of Bernal's
concept of a random close packing.

Bernal's random close packed volume
A more basic approach to the disordered packing of spheres has been made
by Bernal[71] and Scott.[72] Bernal took the concept of dense random packing, previously considered by Rice,[73] and set out to define this condition
more closely. He started by computing a Monte Carlo assembly of points
in space which was restricted so that no two points were less than a defined
distance apart. According to this procedure, space was filled at random until
no further points could be inserted. He then devised a further procedure
whereby, without altering the basic random structure, he shortened all
the possible nearest-neighbour distances to the minimum level. This

Fig. 15a.

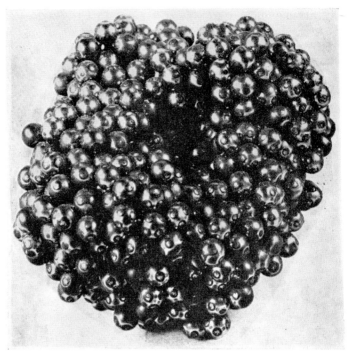

Fig. 15b.

Fig. 15. *Two methods of packing spheres:* (a) *a regular pile of spheres;* (b) *a random close packed heap of spheres.* (*Reproduced from reference* 74 *by permission of Elsevier, Amsterdam.*)

structure he defined as that of dense random packing and showed that it had a relative density of 0·63. An illustration of this concept is given in Fig. 15.[74] He also demonstrated that the distribution round a particular sphere was similar to that which could be derived for dense monatomic liquids from X-ray and neutron interaction data. Striking confirmation of Bernal's treatment was then supplied by Scott[72] who investigated the random packing of steel balls. He showed that by a process of filling cylinders with gentle tapping he arrived at a relative volume which, after extrapolating to cylinders of infinite volume had a value of 0·63.[72] This compared with 0·74 for regular close packed spheres and indicated a relative density:

$$\frac{\text{Dense random packing}}{\text{Regular close packing}} = 0·86$$

a figure which was reassuringly close both to Bernal's calculations and to the earlier result of 0·85 estimated by Rice.[73]

Naturally, some doubt may be expressed as to how far the precise figure of 0·86, calculated by Bernal for spheres, should be applied to a linear polymer, where in two directions the packing is effected by covalent bonds. It may be that here a value of $(0.95)^2 \sim 0.90^{71}$ would be more appropriate. However, within the range of possible values it is clear that Bernal's concepts do allow the possibility of obtaining a volume of the magnitude of the 'WLF' free volume, or a temperature T_0 associated with it, where excess entropy and volume are zero, *i.e.* 'WLF' free volume ~ 0.025 (at T_g) = V_g − Bernal close packed volume.

Alternatively, it would be logical to relate the Bernal volume to the actual volume of the glass at 0°K (*see* Fig. 14).

Cohen and Turnbull[75] have further indicated that the Bernal concept of a random close packing is in harmony with their general concepts and those of Stillinger *et al.*[76] on the nature of the glassy state, *i.e.* a condition in which, although a large number of different structures exist, their entropy is still zero because they are mutually inaccessible (*see* Chapter 1).

Bernal's concepts, and those of Cohen and Turnbull, have something in common with the more simplified picture of Simha and Boyer[32] and Boyer[63] who regard the glassy state as iso-free volume state with a free volume of about 0·13, $(V − V_0)/V$. If one wishes to justify a free volume figure of 0·025 at T_g it might be better to take Bernal's concept, as the starting point as compared with the rather involved analogies inherent in the 'WLF' concepts. For many purposes, however, it seems better to employ the concept of expansion volume $(V − V_0)$, and it is possible to make some use of this concept in treating the relation between elastic modulus of glassy polymers and volume changes (*see* p. 47).

THE RIGIDITY OF POLYMER GLASSES

The rigidity of a solid is measured by its short-time modulus. However, with plastics, including polymer glasses at low temperatures, the different moduli are not completely independent of the time scale of the experiment, as described in Chapter 3. On the other hand, there is generally a tendency for the magnitude of the change in modulus, plotted against log time, to diminish at low temperatures, small strains, and high frequencies. An example of this type of behaviour is given in Fig. 16[77] where the observed modulus of polymethyl methacrylate is plotted against log time at a series of temperatures. At the lowest temperature of 40°C the change in modulus

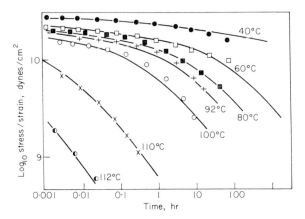

Fig. 16. *Modulus curves for polymethyl methacrylate at different times and temperatures. At short times and low temperatures the modulus tends to become relatively independent of time.* (Reproduced by permission of Academic Press Inc.)

is about 5% for a decade in time. In these circumstances it is possible to speak of a short-time modulus with an accuracy of $\pm 10\%$ over a frequency range of some four decades. Sometimes this constancy of modulus applies over much longer times of measurement. For example, Murray and Hull report a modulus for polystyrene at $293°K$ which is independent of strain rate in a range of $4 \times 10^{-4} - 10^{-7}$ sec^{-1}.[78] Similarly, by measuring real and imaginary moduli at high frequencies, Lamberson et al.[79] found that the imaginary part of the modulus was only 1% of the storage modulus for polymethyl methacrylate and only 0.2% for polystyrene at 6 MHz. In this respect the glassy polymers are generally closer to ideal Hookean behaviour than are partly crystalline polymers, especially when, as in the case of polypropylene, a non-crystalline fraction is present above its glass transition temperature.[80]

Under conditions when the modulus is independent of time a polymer glass will obey the conventional equations for an elastic solid, *viz.*:

$$E = 2G(1 + v) = 3B(1 - 2v)$$

where:

 E is the Young's modulus

 v Poisson's ratio

 B the bulk modulus, and

 G the modulus of rigidity (or shear modulus).

Further, since v is found to be about 0.33 for most polymer glasses (*see* Table 5)[81,82] it follows that $E \sim 2.7 G$ and the Young's modulus and the bulk modulus are numerically equal. The question therefore arises as to the way in which the level of these moduli are related to polymer structure.

At one time it was thought that the value of these moduli was determined by the bending of carbon–carbon and other molecular bonds in the polymer molecules[83] but for a number of reasons this now seems unlikely. For example Muller[84] showed that when a paraffin crystal was compressed there was negligible contraction along the paraffin chain, virtually all the change in volume being attributable to a contraction in a direction perpendicular to the chains. Also it turns out that the compressibilities of

TABLE 5

COMPARISON OF ELASTIC MODULI OF VARIOUS MATERIALS

Material	Young's Modulus MN/m^2	Poisson's Ratio
Steel (mild)	$2 \cdot 2 \times 10^5$	0·28
Glass	6×10^4	0·23
Vitreous silica	7×10^4	0·14
Granite	3×10^4	0·3
Polystyrene[a]	$3 \cdot 4 \times 10^3$	0·33
Polymethyl methacrylate[a]	$3 \cdot 7 \times 10^3$	0·33
Nylon 6–6	2×10^3	
Polyethylene (low density)	$2 \cdot 4 \times 10^2$	0·38
Rubber	2×10	0·49

[a] Glassy polymers.

polymer glasses are much closer to the values obtained for organic liquids (10^3 MN/m^2) than they are to diamond (10^6 MN/m^2). Further it has now become possible to calculate the modulus for an oriented chain assembly (polyethylene) from the force constants of covalent bonds as obtained from infra-red spectra. In this way Treloar[85] obtained a value of $1 \cdot 8 \times 10^5$ MN/m^2 which was later confirmed experimentally by Sakurada et al.[86] who measured the change in the lattice constants of oriented polyethylene crystals under stress and obtained a modulus of $2 \cdot 4 \times 10^5$ MN/m^2 along the chains. More recently all the elastic constants for a polyethylene crystal have been calculated by Odajima and Maeda.[87] For the modulus along the oriented chains they obtained a value of $2 \cdot 57 \times 10^5$ MN/m^2, similar to that found by Treloar and by Sakurada (ibid.). This appears to be the level associated with the direct stretching of close packed carbon–carbon zig-zags. However, when the bond concentration in the plane perpendicular to the applied stress is lower than with polyethylene, or when a polymer helix is extended, bond stretching moduli may be considerably lower, as shown by Sakurada for the cases of isotactic polypropylene $(4\cdot2 \times 10^4$ MN/m$^2)$ or isotactic polystyrene $(1\cdot2 \times 10^4$ MN/m$^2)$.[86]

Based on their calculations of modulus for the polyethylene crystal, in different directions, Odajima and Maeda[87] were able to go on to calculate the modulus of a polycrystalline aggregate. For this purpose they used two different combinations of their own equations (Set I and Set II) and applied them in conjunction with two different elastic models, namely

Reuss' Model which assumes a uniform state of stress in the polycrystal, with non-uniform strain, and

Voigt's Model which assumes a strain which is uniform throughout the assembly, while stress is not (*see* Table 6).

The results were compared with the measurements of Davidse *et al.*[88] for Young's Modulus (E) and to those of Hellwege *et al.*[89] for compressibility. Both sets of results could be extrapolated to 100% crystallinity.

The results strongly support the Reuss' model, which also agrees with the early observations of Muller[84] who observed that the strains in a compressed paraffin crystal were indeed non-uniform. Clearly the levels of the moduli in the crystal aggregate are largely determined by the intermolecular forces. Further confirmation of this point is provided by the experimental extrapolated compressibility for solid argon at $0°K$[90] which falls between the value for polyethylene polycrystal (Table 6) and for polystyrene glass (Fig. 17).

On the other hand, the modulus associated with a concentrated system of self-supporting covalent bonds should lie in the range of 10^5–10^6 MN/m^2. Further support for this concept is provided by carbon fibres which also have high moduli in the range 2–4×10^5 MN/m^2 [91] together with a mutually supporting covalent structure.[92,93] The difference between these levels and those actually observed with polymer glasses is illustrated in Fig. 17.[94] These are clearly determined by the level of intermolecular

TABLE 6

ELASTIC MODULI OF POLYCRYSTAL POLYETHYLENE[87]

	Reuss' Average		Voigt's Average		Experimental
	Set I	*Set II*	*Set I*	*Set II*	
E, 10^3 MN/m^2	4·90	5·82	15·6	15·8	5·05
G, 10^3 MN/m^2	1·92	2·23	18·5	18·8	2·0
$1/B = \beta_T$,					
10^{-4} m^2/MN	2·72	1·99	0·32	0·33	1·95

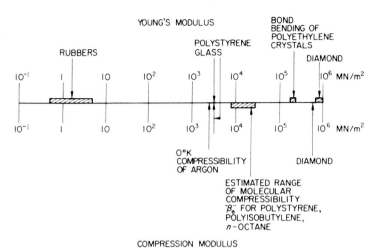

Fig. 17. *Line diagram showing the moduli for different compounds. (Reproduced by permission of John Wiley and Sons Inc.)*

forces, as with a polyethylene polycrystal, but in a glassy polymer they clearly cannot be calculated in the same way.

A more promising approach to the level of moduli actually found in organic glasses would appear to lie through an understanding of the compressibility of liquids. These may be considered as involving two changes which occur under the influence of the applied pressure, namely

(1) A reduction in unoccupied volume.
(2) A contraction in occupied volume related to the intermolecular forces between the molecules themselves.

Clearly the level of intermolecular forces provides an upper limit to the modulus obtainable with an organic glass having no segmental mobility. Various attempts have been made to extrapolate liquid or other moduli to a condition of zero unoccupied volume with a view to estimating this quantity. The application of a modified van der Waals' equation[95] in which the compressibility of polystyrene above T_g is plotted against $\alpha(V - V_0)$, where α is the coefficient of expansion (*see* Fig. 18), gives a value of around 10^{-4} m²/MN for the compressibility "β_0" at V_0. A similar result *i.e.* $B = 10^4$ MN/m² $(= 1/\beta_0)$ is given by the use of a modification of a relation proposed by Miller.[96] Other methods have been applied to liquids and given results of the same order.[97] Since the normally measured modulus of a polystyrene glass is around 3–4×10^3 MN/m² there is

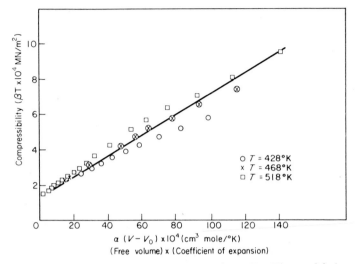

Fig. 18. *The compressibility of polystyrene above* T_g. *The modified van der Waals' plot allows an estimate of the modulus at* $V = V_0$ *to be made* $[\alpha(V - V_0) = 0]$. *Experimental measurements Rehage, G. and Breuer, H.* (1967). *Koll. Zeit.,* **159** 216–17. (*Reproduced from reference* 94 *by permission of John Wiley and Sons Inc.*)

clearly some contribution to compressibility due to a contraction of free space, also depending on inter-molecular forces but often involving as well (especially at long times) some minor molecular rearrangements with a dependency on time (*see* Chapter 3, Fig. 16). Following these lines, it is possible to treat the volume dependence of the modulus of a polymer glass, especially if it is measured under high frequency adiabatic conditions to minimise the effect of time-dependent rearrangements, in terms of a conventional model for the intermolecular force field.[98] For example, taking the Lennard–Jones potential expression we may write

$$U = \frac{A}{V^{n/3}} - \frac{B}{V^{m/3}} \tag{1}$$

in which U is the intermolecular potential for the system of molar volume V, and A, B, n and m are constants. (n and m usually have values of 9 and 6, or 12 and 6 respectively). Equation (1) can be rewritten thus:

$$U = K\left\{ \left(\frac{V_0}{V}\right)^{n/3} - \frac{n}{m}\left(\frac{V_0}{V}\right)^{m/3} \right\} \tag{2}$$

in which K is a constant and V_0 is the molar volume of the system for the condition that $(\mathrm{d}U/\mathrm{d}V)(V = V_0) = 0$, *i.e.* when the expansion volume is zero.

Since the adiabatic bulk modulus, B, equals $-V(\mathrm{d}^2U/\mathrm{d}V^2)_s$, eqn. (2) can be used to derive the following relationship between B and V:

$$B = \frac{B_0}{(n-m)}\left\{(n+3)\left(\frac{V_0}{V}\right)^{(n+3)/3} - (m+3)\left(\frac{V_0}{V}\right)^{(m+3)/3}\right\} \quad (3)$$

B_0 is the modulus corresponding to the volume V_0. This gives for $n = 12$,

$$m = 6, \qquad B = \frac{B_0}{6}\left\{15\left(\frac{V_0}{V}\right)^5 - 9\left(\frac{V_0}{V}\right)^3\right\}$$

This equation can be tested by using the results of Asay *et al.*[99] who measured the high frequency elastic modulus of polymethyl methacrylate under a wide range of temperatures and pressures. For this purpose it is necessary to know a value of V_0 (75·5 cm^3/mol) which can be derived from the estimates of Bondi.[45] These results are plotted on Fig. 19[98] which may be regarded as providing support for the validity of the above equations.

Generally, therefore, it may be concluded that the moduli of organic glasses are largely dominated by the intermolecular forces, with some

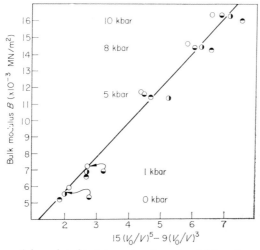

Fig. 19. Bulk modulus related to intermolecular potential function. A plot of B, the adiabatic bulk modulus, versus $15(V_0/V)^5 - 9(V_0/V)^3$ *for data on polymethyl methacrylate.[99] The values were obtained at different temperatures. (○, 25°C; ●, 40°C; ◐, 55°C; ◖, 75°C) and at the pressures indicated beside the points. (Reproduced from reference 98 by permission of Iliffe Science and Technology Publications Ltd.)*

molecular rearrangements taking place, especially at longer times, and at temperatures approaching the glass transition temperatures.

LARGE DEFORMATIONS AND FRACTURE

The subject of large deformations in glassy polymers and their relation with the fracture process is one which has developed rapidly in recent years. As it will be fully covered in the ensuing Chapters (5–7) there is no requirement for any extensive technical discussion at this point. However, the subject has had an interesting and uneven history and illustrates in an intriguing manner the interaction between academic science and industry. During the 1930s the dominant thermoplastics were the plasticised cellulose derivatives, with PVC also gradually emerging as an important plastic. All these polymers are essentially tough. In a tensile test they undergo large deformations and absorb appreciable energy before fracture takes place. On the other hand, when, towards the end of the thirties and beginning of the forties polystyrene came on the scene[100] it was found to be a brittle material, which had low impact strength and which showed no observable elongation in a tensile test. From the first it was clear that this brittleness presented serious problems for the application of the polymer, and several large manufacturers are said to have hesitated or decided not to develop the polymer on this account. Clearly there were doubts as to how it could compete with tougher materials. However, in the end it turned out that polystyrene did have an irresistable combination of four favourable properties, namely: low price, rigidity, good appearance and excellent processing properties. With these advantages numerous large applications were found where its strength was adequate. Finally during the 1950s technologists learnt how to control the spread of cracks in polystyrene by the dispersion of rubber particles in the resin (see Chapter 8), and the high impact polystyrenes were developed. These represented a major advance in eliminating the brittleness of polystyrene and promoted its further commercial success until it became by far the most important glassy polymer.

However, polystyrene was not only a commercial success, it was also an academic success. For this purpose it has several very attractive properties. It was easy to prepare and to control in a reproducible way. It was also easily soluble in convenient organic solvents. Its molecular weight was also relatively easy to measure as compared with other polymers, and it could be readily fractionated to determine its molecular weight distribution. For this reason, polystyrene became in the 1950s the plastic most familiar to academic polymer scientists, and its mechanical properties, which had provided serious problems for research directors in the early 1940s, became increasingly to be regarded as typical of an organic glass. Thus the previously accepted concept that 'polymers' continued to show bulk yielding at temperatures well below their glass transition temperatures, was forgotten, and instead, the reverse hypothesis was considered to constitute normal behaviour. Numerous examples could be quoted from the literature to show how this concept was widely accepted but we will content ourselves with one.

At temperatures below the glass transition temperature all but the extremely long time response of the plastic will be the result of movements between segments. Long range motion between chains will take such a long time that most practical measurements will not be influenced by it.[101]

It will of course be appreciated that this concept was never generally true, even in tension, because of the exceptions quoted, but with the development of several new and tough polymer glasses, e.g. polysulphones, polycarbonate, and polyphenylene oxide, the idea became generally untenable. Also, investigations with other types of stress field, and especially under compression, by Hoff[102] and by Binder and Muller[103] showed that virtually all the polymer glasses, whether tough or brittle, were capable of showing very large deformations. These are not reversible below T_g but on heating above T_g the test piece resumes its undistorted shape.[104,105]

More recently it has been demonstrated that, even when brittle polymers fracture with low overall deformation, the process of fracture itself does involve large deformations.

An example of very large extensions during the fracture process, leading to the formation of long thin filaments is shown in Fig. 20.[30] These observations, together with the important studies of crack propagation initiated by Berry[106] and of the structure of crazes by Hsiao and Sauer,[107] Bessonov,[108] Kambour[109] and others[110,111] have lead to a new and interesting approach to the problem of strength, although it is still too early to say how far it will be successful in dealing with a wide range of fracture problems. According to this approach the strength and toughness of a polymer is determined by the nature of the large deformation process which takes place at the crack tip. These processes may also determine whether or not a crack or craze can be formed at all. Obviously such concepts represent a complete reversal of the idea that large deformations do not take place in rigid materials, and much interest attaches to their

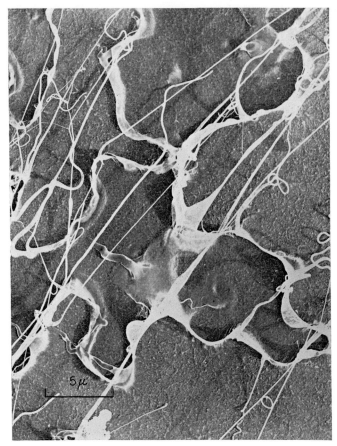

Fig. 20.   *Long fibrils formed during the fracture of polystyrene at room tempera-*
ture. Carbon replica of a fracture surface. Such long filaments had previously
been seen only with high density polyethylene.[105a] (*Reproduced from reference* 30,
by permission of Iliffe Science and Technology Publications Ltd.)

development. At the present time it is not clear how they can be used to
explain the type of failure which occurs after a substantial bulk extension
of the polymer has taken place. Under these conditions the fracture of
thermoplastics may prove to have something in common with the fracture
fibres. A full account of the fracture process must also provide for the other
significant phenomena which are observed, including such features as
microcracks[112] and the formation of free radicals.[113] All these matters
will be discussed in detail in Chapters 5–7.

REFERENCES

1. Gee, G. (1970). *Contemp. Phys.*, **11**, 313.
2. Boundy, R. H. and Boyer, R. F. (1952). *Styrene*, Chapter 16, Reinhold, New York, p. 725.
3. Berry, J. (1964). *Fracture Processes in Polymeric Solids*, Chapter IIB, Interscience, New York, p. 224.
4. Natta, G. (1955). *JACS*, **77**, 1708; (1956). *Angew. Chemie*, **68**, 373; (1957). *Materie Plastiche*, **23**, 541; Natta G. and Danusso, F., *Stereo regular polymers and stereo specific polymerisation*, vol. I, Pergamon Press, Oxford (1967), pp. 149–77.
5. Natta, G., *SPE Trans.*, April 1963, p. 100.
6. Danusso, F. (1962). *Polymer*, **3**, 423.
7. Natta, G., Danusso, F. and Sianesi, D. (1958). *Makromol. Chem.*, **28**, 253.
8. Natta, G. (1960). *Makromol. Chem.*, **35**, 93.
9. Kenyon, A. S., Gross, R. C. and Wurstner, A. L. (1959). *J. Pol. Sci.*, **40**, 159.
10. Hay, J. N. (1965). *J. Pol. Sci.*, **A3**, 433.
11. Falkai, Von B. and Rellensman, W. (1964). *Makromol. Chem.*, **75**, 112.
12. McNulty, B. J. (1969). *J. Pol. Sci.*, A1 **7**, 3038. (1968). *Polymer*, **9**, 41.
13. Boyer, R. F., ACS Organic Coatings and Plastics Division, 160th meeting, Chicago, September 1970, vol. 30, Paper 2, p. 1.
14. Reddish, W. (1966). *J. Pol. Sci.*, **14**, 123.
15. Kargin, V. A. (1966). *Pure and Applied Chem.*, **12**, 35.
16. Kargin, V. A. (1968). *Pure and Applied Chem.*, **16**, 303.
17. Siegel, B. M., Johnson, D. H. and Marek, H. (1950). *J. Pol. Sci.*, **5**, 111.
18. Richardson, M. J. (1964). *PRSA*, **279**, 50.
19. Nasini, A. G., Ostacoli, G., Saini, G., Maldifassi, G. and Trosarelli, L. (1955). *Suppl. Recerca. Scient. Ricista. Memorie.*, **25**, 452.
19a. Quayle, D. V. (1969). *Br. Pol. J.*, **1**, 15.
20. Slonimskii, G. L., Korshak, V. V., Vinogradova, S. V., Kataigoeodskii, A. I., Akadskii, A. A., Salazkin, S. N. and Biecauceva, E. M. (1964). *Dok. Akad. Nauk. USSR*, **156**, 924.
21. Keller, A. and Waring, J. R. S. (1955). *J. Pol. Sci.*, **17**, 447.
22. Schoon, T. G. F. (1970). *Brit. Polymer Journal*, **2**, 86.
23. Schoon, T. G. F. and Teichman, O. (1964). *Koll. Zeit.*, **197**, 35.
24. Schoon, T. G. F. and Kretschmer, R. (1964). *Koll. Zeit.*, **197**, 45, 51.
25. Schoon, T. G. F. and Kretschmer, R. (1966). *Koll. Zeit.*, **211**, 53.
26. Yeh, G. S. Y. and Geil, P. H. (1967). *J. Macromol. Chem.* (Phys), **B1(2)**, 235.
27. Frank, W., Goddard, H. and Stuart, H. A. (1967). *Polymer Letters*, **5**, 711.
28. Magill, J. H. (1969). *J. Pol. Sci.*, A2 **7**, 743.
29. Mann, J., Bird, R. J., Pogany, G. and Rooney, G. (1966). *Polymer, London*, **7**, 307.
30. Haward, R. N. and Brough, I. (1969). *Polymer*, **10**, 724.
30a. Zingsheim, H. P. and Bachman, L. (1971). *Koll. Zeit.*, **246**, 561.
31. Treloar, L. R. G. (1958). *The Physics of Rubber Elasticity*, 2nd ed., Oxford Univ. Press.
31a. Flory, P. J. (1949). *J. Chem. Phys.*, **17**, 303.
31b. Graessley, W. W. (1964). *J. Chem. Phys.*, **41**, 3604.
31c. Alberino, L. M. and Graessley, W. W. (1968). *J. Phys. Chem.*, **72**, 4229.
31d. Krigbaum, W. R. and Godwin, R. W. (1965). *J. Chem. Phys.*, **43**, 4523.
31e. Hoffman, M. (1971). *Makromol. Chem.*, **144**, 309.
32. Simha, R. and Boyer, R. F. (1962). *J. Chem. Phys.*, **37**, 1003.
33. Rowlinson, J. S. (1969). *Liquids and Liquid Mixtures*, Butterworth, London.
34. Martin, G., Rogers, S. S. and Mandelkern, D. (1959). *J. Pol. Sci.*, **20**, 579.

35. Breuer, H., Dissertation 'Untersuchungen uber die glasige Erstarrung von Hochpolymeren unter hohen Drucken'. Tech. Hochsch., Aachen, 1965. (See also refs. 38, 46.)
36. Bondi, A. (1954). *J. Phys. Chem.*, **58**, 929.
37. Bondi, A. (1964). *J. Phys. Chem.*, **68**, 441.
38. Haward, R. N. (1970). *J. Macromolecular Sci. Reviews. Macromol. Chem.* **C4(2)**, 191.
39. Sugden, S. (1927). *JCS*, 1780, 1786.
40. Goldhamer, D. A. (1910). *J. Physik Chem.*, **71**, 577.
41. Matthews, A. P. (1916). *J. Phys. Chem.*, **20** (5542). (See also ref. 38.)
42. Doolittle, A. K. (1951). *J. App. Phys.*, **22**, 471.
43. Biltz, W. (1934). *Raumchemie der Festen Stoffe*, B. Voss, Leipzig.
44. Gruneisen (see Biltz (43), p. 12).
45. Bondi, A. (1964). *J. Pol. Sci.*, **A2**, 3159.
46. Breuer, H. and Rehage, G. (1967). *Koll. Zeit.*, 216–7, 159.
47. Haward, R. N., Bueuer, H. and Rehage, G. (1966). *Polymer Letters*, **4**, 375.
48. Lee, A. L. and Ellington, R. T. (April 1965). *J. Chem. Eng. Data*, **10**, 101.
49. Bondi, A. (1967). *Rheology, Theory and Application*, vol. IV, ed. R. H. Eirich, Academic Press, New York. See also: (1968). *Phys. Props. of mol. liquids, crystals and glasses*, John Wiley and Sons Inc., New York, p. 337. (1963). *I and EC Fundamentals*, **2**, 95.
50. Prigogine, I. (1957). *The molecular theory of solutions*, Interscience, New York. See also: Prigogine, I., Trappeniers, N. and Mathot, V. (1953). *Disc. Farad. Soc.*, **15**, 93; (1953). *J. Chem. Phys.*, **21**, 559. Prigogine, I., Billemans A. and Naar-Cohen, C. (1957). *J. Chem. Phys.*, **26**, 751.
51. Doolittle, A. K. and Doolittle, D. B. (1957). *J. App. Phys.*, **26**, 901.
52. Cohen, H. H. and Turnbull, D. (1959). *J. Chem. Phys.*, **31**, 1164.
53. Vogel, H. (1921). *Physik. Zeit.*, **22**, 645.
54. Fulcher, G. S. (1925). *JACS*, **8**, 339.
55. Tamman, G. and Hesse, W. (1926). *Z. Anorg. Allgem Chem.*, **156**, 245.
56. Miller, A. A. (1963). *J. Phys. Chem.*, **67**, 1031.
57. Barlow, A. J., Lamb, J. and Matheson, A. J. (1966). *Proc. Roy. Soc.*, **A292**, 322.
58. Davies, D. B. and Matheson, A. J. (1967). *Trans. Farad. Soc.*, **63**, 596.
59. Williams, M. I., Landel, R. F. and Ferry, J. D. (1955). *JACS*, **77**, 3701.
60. Simpson, W., Bridge, L. and Holt, I. (1965). *J. App. Chem.*, **15**, 208.
61. Ferry, J. D. (1965). *Viscoelastic Properties of Polymers*, John Wiley and Sons Inc., New York pp. 201–7.
62. Bueche, F. (1956). *J. Chem. Phys.*, **29**, 418.
63. Boyer, R. F. (1963). *Rubber Reviews*, XXXVI, 1303.
64. Kovacs, A. J. (1966). *Rheol. Acta.*, **5**, 262. (1968). *Rubber Chem. & Tech.*, **41**, 555.
65. Bueche, F. (1962). *The Physical Chemistry of Polymers*, Interscience, New York.
66. West, G., Wright, B. and Haward, R. N. (1967). *Adv. Pol. Science & Tech.* SCI Monograph No. 26, London, p. 348.
67. Bueche, F. (1962). *J. Chem. Phys.*, **36**, 2940.
68. Arakawa, K. (1965). *Zairo*, **14**, 243.
69. Gibbs, J. H. and DiMarzio, E. A. (1958). *J. Chem. Phys.*, **28**, 373.
70. Adam, G. and Gibbs, J. H. (1965). *J. Chem. Phys.*, **43**, 139.
71. Bernal, J. D. (1959). *Nature*, **183**, 141; (1960). **185**, 68.
72. Scott, G. D. (1960). *Nature*, **188**, 908.
73. Rice, O. K. (1944). *J. Chem. Phys.*, **12**, 1.
74. Bernal, J. D. (1965). *Liquids: Structure, Properties Solid Interactions*, ed. T. J. Hughel, Elsevier, Amsterdam, p. 22.
75. Cohen, H. H. and Turnbull, D. (1964). *Nature*, **203**, 964.

76. Stillinger, S., DiMarzio, E. A., Kornegay, E. A. and R. L. (1964). *J. Chem. Phys.*, **40**, 1564.
77. McLoughlin, J. R. and Tobolsky, A. V. (1952). *J. Coll. Sci.*, **7**, 555.
78. Murray, J. and Hull, D. (1970). *J. Pol. Sci.*, A2 **8**, 1521.
79. Lamberson, D. L., Asay, J. R. and Guenther, H. H. (1972). *J. Appl. Phys.*, **43**, 976.
80. Ogorkievicz, R. M. (Sept. 1969). *Brit. Plast.*, 125.
81. Turner, S. (Dec. 1969). *Plastics and Polymers*, 517.
82. Nielson, E. (1962). *Mechanical Properties of Polymers*, Rheinhold, New York, p. 7.
83. Tuckett, R. F. (1943). *Chem. and Ind.*, **62**, 430.
84. Muller, A. (1941). *Proc. Roy. Soc.*, **158A**, 227.
85. Treloar, L. R. G. (1960). *Polymer*, **1**, 95.
86. Sakurada, L., Ito, T. and Nakamae, K. (1966). *Makromol. Chem.*, **75**, 1.
87. Odajima, A. and Maeda, J. (1966). *J. Pol. Sci.*, **C15**, 55.
88. Davidse, P. D., Waterman, H. I. and Wasterdijk, J. B. (1962). *J. Pol. Sci.*, **59**, 389.
89. Hellwege, K. W., Knappe, W. and Lehman, P. (1962). *Koll. Zeit.*, **183**, 110.
90. Jones, G. O. and Sparkes, A. R. (1966). *Phil. Mag.*, **10**, 1053.
91. Moreton, R., Watt, W. and Johnson, W. (1967). *Nature*, **213**, 690.
92. Bailey, J. E. and Clarke, A. J. (1970). *Chemistry in Britain*, **6**, 484.
93. Watt, W. (1969). *Proc. Roy. Soc. (London)*, **A.319**, 5.
94. Haward, R. N. (1969). *J. Pol. Sci.*, A2 **7**, 219.
95. Haward, R. N. (1966). *Trans. Farad. Soc.*, **62**, 828.
96. Miller, A. A. (1966). *J. Pol. Sci.*, A2 **4**, 415.
97. Kudryavtsev, B. B. and Samgina, G. A. (1965). *Russ. J. Phys. Chem.*, **39**, 476.
98. Haward, R. N. and McCallum, J. R. (1971). *Polymer*, **12**, 189.
99. Asay, J. R., Lamberson, D. L. and Gunther, A. G. (1969). *J. App. Phys.*, **40**, 1768.
100. Ohlinger, H. (1955). *Polystyrol*, Springer-Verlag, Berlin, p. 68.
101. Bueche, F. (Ref. 65.) p. 247.
102. Hoff, E. A. W. (1952). *J. App. Chem.*, **2**, 441.
103. Binder, G. and Muller, P. H. (1961). *Koll. Zeit.*, **177**, 129.
104. Gurevich and Kobeko (1940). *Rubber, Chem. & Tech.*, **13**, 904.
105. Haward, R. N. (1942). *Trans. Farad. Soc.*, **42**, 267.
105a. Preuss, H. H. W. (1963). *Plaste u. Kautschuk*, **10**, No. 6, 330.
106. Berry, J. P. (1961). *J. Pol. Sci.*, **50**, 107, 313.
107. Hsiao, C. C. and Sauer, J. A. (1950). *J. App. Phys.*, **21**, 1071.
108. Bessonov, M. I. and Kuvshinskii, E. V. (1959). *Soviet Physics—Solid State*, **1**, 1441; (1961). **3**, 607 (English ed. **3**, No. 2, p. 445).
109. Kambour, R. P. (1964). *Polymer*, **5**, 143; (1964). *J. Pol. Sci.*, **A2**, 4159.
110. Spurr, O. K. and Niegisch, W. D. (1962). *J. App. Pol. Sci.*, **6**, 585.
111. Murphy, B. M., Haward, R. N. and White, E. F. T. (1971). *J. Pol. Sci.* A2, **9**, 801.
112. Zhurkov, S. N., Kuksenko, V. S. and Slutsker, A. J. Second Int. Conf. on Fracture. Brighton, April 1969, Paper 46/1.
113. Schmeling, H. H. K.-B. von (1970). *Rev. of Macromol. Chem.*, **5**, Part 2, 97.

CHAPTER 1

THE THERMODYNAMICS OF THE GLASSY STATE

G. REHAGE AND W. BORCHARD

1.1 INTRODUCTORY THERMODYNAMIC CONSIDERATIONS

Ever since the fundamental investigations by Tamman it has been known that liquids can be transformed into the glassy state if crystallisation can be suppressed.[1] The glassy state is therefore a state of matter which in many substances can be observed in addition to the classical states, *i.e.* gaseous, liquid and crystalline. In particular, in high molecular weight substances a glassy solidification takes place frequently in combination with partial crystallisation. The rapid development of this technologically important class of materials has therefore called attention to the glassy state.

Phenomenologically the glassy state is characterised by certain experimental results which occur on the isobaric cooling of a liquid or a melt. Normally a melt crystallises at a definite temperature, the melting temperature T_m, if nuclei of the new phase are present and the rate of cooling is less than the rate of crystallisation.[2] If these conditions are not fulfilled, the crystallisation can be suppressed by cooling, and a metastable phase which is called 'a supercooled liquid or melt' is obtained below the melting point. On further cooling the shear viscosity η increases further, the temperature dependence of η being well represented by an exponential function in the first approximation. At even lower temperatures, when the supercooled melt has already become highly viscous, the viscosity increases very much more strongly with decreasing temperature than would correspond to an exponential function.[3] When the melt reaches a viscosity of *ca.* 10^{11}–10^{13} P we say that in the corresponding temperature range the melt solidifies to a glass.

In this temperature range many physical properties of the supercooled

54

melt change in a characteristic manner, *e.g.* coefficient of expansion, specific heat, modulus of elasticity, dielectric constant, coefficient of diffusion, etc. The temperature dependence of these quantities is used to describe the glassy solidification.

With the aid of an isobaric volume–temperature diagram the process of the glassy solidification can be readily examined (Fig. 1). Frequently one

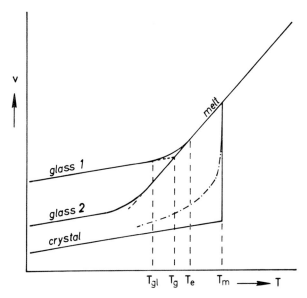

Fig. 1. *Volume–temperature relation between glassy, liquid and crystalline states. Glass* 1 *fast cooling, glass* 2 *slow cooling* ($T_m = $ *melting point,* T_e *and* T_{gl} *temperatures at the beginning and the end of the vitrification process,* $T_g = $ *glass temperature,* $T_e = $ *freezing-in temperature*).

uses, instead of the volume, other extensive thermodynamic functions, *e.g.* the enthalpy; one should also recognise that, because of the temperature dependence of the specific heat, the enthalpy–temperature curve is not linear. In the schematic representation in Fig. 1 it is assumed that the substance can crystallise or solidify into a glass, depending on the experimental conditions. If the substance crystallises, it is found that at the melting temperature T_m a jump occurs in the volume, usually a volume decrease; in some cases, however, there is a volume increase, *e.g.* in water. The coefficients of expansion of the melt and of the crystal are assumed to be constant in the vicinity of the melting temperature.

When the melt is cooled, and the crystallisation prevented from taking place, there begins at the temperature T_e the transition from the highly viscous supercooled melt to the rigid glass. The volume–temperature curve deviates at this point from the curve for the melt and joins the curve for the glass at T_{gl}. Below T_{gl} the dependence is again linear. T_e is the temperature of the start of the solidification, at which the first deviations from the curve for the metastable equilibrium of the supercooled melt are observed. T_{gl} is the temperature at which the solidification is terminated; here the viscosity is so high that below this temperature changes of volume with time can hardly be observed within reasonable periods. The temperature at the intersection of the extrapolated curves for the melt and the glass is normally called the glass temperature T_g. The measurements show that the coefficient of expansion of a particular substance in the glassy state differs only very little from that in the crystalline state. Simon concluded that the molecules in the glassy state as well as in the crystalline state essentially oscillate about their equilibrium positions and that interchange of places (in the sense of self-diffusion), which takes place very frequently in the liquid state, either does not occur at all or only very rarely in the glassy state.[4] X-ray diagrams show that a short-range order exists in glasses as is well known from liquids; however, the long-range order as observed in crystals does not occur (see Chapter 2).[5] One may say that a glass represents the state of order of a liquid which is frozen-in in the range between T_{gl} and T_e and which is essentially preserved at lower temperatures.

For the supercooled liquid in the range between T_m and T_e at a given rate of cooling the equilibrium distribution corresponding to each temperature is reached within the duration of the measurement. This is formulated as follows: 'The substance is in an internal thermodynamic equilibrium with reference to the arrangement and the distribution of the molecules'.[4] The equilibrium is recognised from the fact that the volume of the phase of this single component system is a distinct function of temperature and pressure. In this case homogeneity and isotropy are assumed and surface phenomena as well as electrification and magnetisation are excluded. Below T_{gl}, after a temperature change, the equilibrium order appropriate to the new temperature is not reached within the duration of the measurement. Thus a glass is a frozen-in supercooled liquid. Here the concept frozen-in means that we deal with an inhibited non-equilibrium state. This relationship was clearly expressed for the first time by Simon in the course of investigations into Nernst's theorem.[4]

In essence the glassy solidification is the inhibition of a kinetic process.

This is seen from the fact that below T_e one can still observe relaxation phenomena which are the slower the lower the temperature of the experiment.

The temperatures T_e, T_g and T_{gl} depend on the duration of the measurement, *i.e.* on the frequency (*see* Chapter 3). As shown in Fig. 1, the volume–temperature curve of glass 1 is displaced towards that of glass 2 if the rate

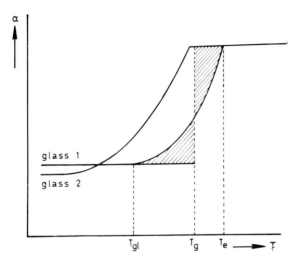

Fig. 2.   *Expansion coefficient at slow cooling (glass 2) and fast cooling (glass 1).*

of cooling is lower. At a lower rate of cooling the curve of the internal equilibrium is left at a lower temperature. In general it is observed that in the vicinity of the glass temperature the extension of the curve for the melt to lower temperatures is the equilibrium curve (supercooled melt).

The isobaric coefficient of expansion α as a function of temperature is schematically plotted in Fig. 2. This temperature curve in an idealised form is characterised by a step. At a lower rate of cooling (glass 2) the step is displaced towards lower temperatures compared with the curve for glass 1, the two curves intersecting. This small difference in the coefficient of expansion cannot, generally, be established, but is observed in measurements of the pressure dependence. The normally measured volume–temperature curve deviates from the idealised curve represented by linear branches. Since, however, the volumes obtained in both ways are the same at the temperatures T_e and T_{gl} respectively, the areas shown hatched in Fig. 2, which are adjacent to the step value of α at T_g, must be of the same size.[6]

Besides the shift of the transition process with the time of measurement (heating or cooling rate) we also have in general hysteresis phenomena, even at equal cooling and heating rates. These were found experimentally in measurements of the refractive index of polystyrene (PST).[7] They were predicted by Volkenstein and Ptitsyn.[8] The volume hysteresis is shown schematically in Fig. 3.

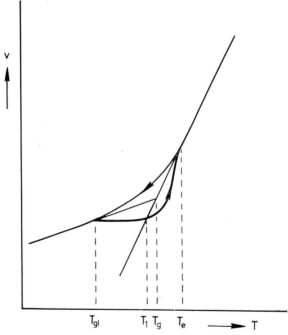

Fig. 3.   Volume hysteresis.

On cooling from the melt $(T > T_e)$ the curve marked by the arrow downwards is observed, relaxations of the volume already occurring in the freeze-in interval with respect to the equilibrium curve which is drawn as a straight line. These processes become slower with decreasing temperature. On heating at the same rate, relaxations can again occur in the range $T_1 > T > T_{gl}$. The volume decreases because the equilibrium curve lies below the glass curve. The relaxations due to the change in order decrease as T_1 is approached and for $T_e > T > T_1$ may reverse their sign as shown in Fig. 3. Near T_e the volume for the heating experiment reaches the melt curve again. This behaviour can be interpreted such that the volume corresponding to the temperature T_1 is characterised unambiguously by the pressure P_1 and, for example, a further internal parameter ξ which represents the molecular order. Along the curve for the melt and the supercooled melt all ordering variables are characterised by equilibrium

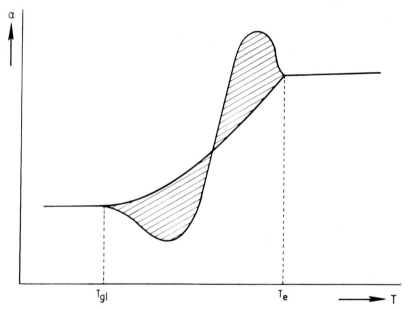

Fig. 4. *Expansion coefficient on relaxation* (see *text*).[9]

values. Thus the volume at constant pressure is a definite function of the variables T and ξ. If now a temperature $T_1 + dT$ is reached with a finite heating rate, at which the order corresponding to the temperature T_1 has not yet changed to the order corresponding to the temperature $T_1 + dT$, after-effects occur above T_1 which result in a volume increase, since in this case the equilibrium curve lies above the non-equilibrium curve shown. If there is more than one order variable the situation becomes more complicated and will not be discussed here.

In Fig. 4 the coefficient of expansion is plotted against temperature. For the reasons mentioned above the hatched areas in the diagram between the cooling curve and the heating curve which show two extremes must have the same value. As was already shown by Jones, a distinctive minimum appears when the rate of cooling is greater than the rate of heating. The maximum (Fig. 4) is very marked when the rate of cooling is smaller than the rate of heating.[9] In particular, in measurements of the specific heat such maxima or minima and even 'apparent' negative values have been reported.[10,11] At very high rates of cooling the freeze-in interval can become so small that it is no longer possible to distinguish experimentally between the temperatures T_e, T_g and T_{gl}. Since T_e has a physical significance we shall call this temperature the 'freeze-in' temperature.

It is seen that the glass curves in the freeze-in interval cannot be traversed reversibly since the volume and other extensive quantities no longer represent a definite function of temperature and pressure because of the influence of the kinetic processes. We therefore introduce internal parameters conjugated to the so-called affinity† so as to be able to describe the thermodynamic behaviour in analogy to homogeneous chemical reactions.[12-15]

When we describe the internal order of a phase by a single ordering parameter, for the sake of simplicity we have, for a phase in internal equilibrium,

$$V = V[P, T, \bar{\xi}(T, P)] \tag{1}$$

The bar means that we deal with an equilibrium order, its characteristics being that the affinity $A(T, P, \xi)$ vanishes at equilibrium

$$A(T, P, \bar{\xi}) = 0 \tag{2}$$

Here $\bar{\xi}$ is a single-valued function of T and P. At a given pressure eqn. (1) shows that the volume in a one-component system depends only on the temperature. This holds for the liquid and crystalline states as well as for the supercooled liquid state. In the glassy state we have, however,

$$V = V(T, P, \xi) \tag{3}$$

since the state of order is frozen-in. For $T < T_{gl}$ the value of ξ is assumed to be constant, but it depends on the experimental conditions as we have seen above. This relationship is important for the thermodynamic treatment given in the next section.

Before this, however, we have to make some remarks which concern the shape of the equilibrium curve below the glass temperature.

† The notation affinity was introduced by De Donder and is given by the expression $A \equiv -\sum_i \nu_i \mu_i$, where ν_i and μ_i are the stoichiometric coefficients and chemical potentials respectively of species i in a chemical reaction.

The crystallisation of high molecular weight substances is generally more complicated than is the case with low molecular weight material. In most cases the crystallisation is not complete, as can be seen from Fig. 1. The volume–temperature curve follows the dashed–dotted curve if the substance crystallises only partially. In this case the step value which would be expected with complete crystallisation is only partially reached. In addition we find that crystallisation or melting takes place over a more or less extended temperature interval.[16-21] In the case of partial crystallinity a portion of the macromolecular substance is present in the amorphous state which manifests itself in the X-ray scattering experiment in the shape of a broad 'peak'. Superposed on this are the crystal interferences which correspond to the crystalline regions. It is possible to attempt to describe the physical behaviour of a partially crystalline substance by the so-called 'two-phase model', in which the total volume is obtained by the addition of the volumes of the amorphous and crystalline phases. The degree of crystallinity, and with this the volume–temperature curve, depends on the experimental conditions, whereby the rate of nucleated growth is of importance compared with the rate of cooling.[22,23] The amorphous parts of partially crystalline substances which are crystallised over a temperature range also solidify into a glass below the crystallisation interval.

For the considerations which are to follow let us assume that a substance can solidify in three ways: glassy, completely crystalline and partially crystalline. In the literature there are known multiple transitions of polymers, and especially of copolymers, which can be treated by the same considerations used here.[123]

At absolute zero the crystal shows the highest possible state of order, characterised by zero entropy. At higher temperatures, due to the thermal energy, the order is no longer perfect because defects of some kind are formed. To each temperature corresponds a defect equilibrium. In the liquid state we have, in general, no random disorder, but a state of order which we call 'short-range order'.[4]

The order in a melt improves as the melting temperature is approached. At the melting point the degree of defect order of the liquid decreases to the very much smaller degree of defect order of the crystal corresponding to this temperature. In a supercooled liquid the increase in order takes place continuously, and in the case of helium reaches the highest possible order at the absolute zero, just as in the crystal.[4] In the case of the glassy solidification, however, the order reached for the supercooled liquid at the freeze-in temperature is essentially preserved on further cooling.

If we now consider the transformation from the glass to the crystal at a temperature, *e.g.* $T < T_{g1}$ (Fig. 1), then if this process is possible the order should increase. The degree of order also increases if the transformation from the glass into the metastable liquid state can take place. It is possible, depending on the experimental conditions, in particular by different cooling or heating rates or by producing isothermal after-effects, to produce many states between the limiting curves of an infinitely, *i.e.* very fast, cooled glass and that of a crystal, which is cooled so slowly that the defect equilibria are always reached (*see* Fig. 1). Here it will be possible, in the range $T_e < T < T_m$ at partial crystallisation, not only to produce different degrees of crystallinity, crystallite sizes and defect concentrations, but also different types of crystals depending on the circumstances. It is known that in high polymers not only can crystals be formed in which the molecules are folded, but also crystals in which the molecules are stretched or alternately folded and stretched (shishkebab structures).[24] The multiplicity of the morphological phenomena which are affected by stereospecific configurations, sequence length distributions and endgroup effects makes the conditions difficult to disentangle.[25] In most cases we are dealing with non-equilibrium states. With the aid of the entropy and thus the degree of order the different states of the material, melt, supercooled melt, crystal and glass can be readily distinguished.

Since, however, each macromolecule comprises a unique combination of chemical constitution, configuration, conformation and molecular weight, the concept of degree of order can only be visualised by model calculations. For simple polymers, in some cases quantitative relations have recently been established by Pechhold, Blasenbrey and others using kink and meander models.[26]

The behaviour of the specific heat, c_p, of glassy solidifying substances is similar to that for the coefficient of expansion. It has been measured in a number of polymers by many authors over an extended temperature range and shows at T_g a step similar to α in the idealised representation.[27–29,64,124]

Figure 5 shows the specific heat c_p of glycerine according to measurements by Simon, because this substance can either crystallise or solidify as a glass, depending on the experimental conditions.

The melting point lies at 291°K and the glass temperature at 180°K. The melting point shows a discontinuity in the specific heat and the melting entropy ΔS_m is approximately 15 entropy units. In the freeze-in range one finds a step-shaped decrease. It is seen that the c_p values in the glassy range below T_{g1} differ only little from those of the crystal. As in the case of the coefficient of expansion it follows that the oscillatory motion is essentially responsible for the specific heat in the glassy state. The dashed curve would be reached, according to Simon, on infinitely slow cooling, it corresponding to the curve of the internal thermodynamic equilibrium of the melt. It is seen that the liquid, because of its high c_p value compared to that of the crystal in the temperature range $T_g < T < T_m$, experiences

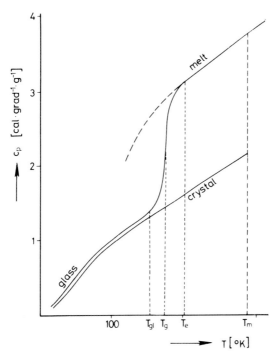

Fig. 5.   Specific heat of glycerol in the fluid, crystalline and glassy state.[4]

a large change in entropy which is due to a continuous change of the degree of order. The entropy differences, calculated from the specific heats, between the liquid and the crystal for $T > T_e$ and between the glass and the crystal for $T < T_e$ are shown in Fig. 6 as a function of the temperature at constant pressure. The figure shows that the entropy difference between glass and crystal below T_e down to the absolute zero decreases only little. From this it can be concluded that a glass maintains essentially the order of the supercooled melt below T_e. The entropy difference ΔS

does not vanish at absolute zero, it has a positive value. The dashed curve which can be followed experimentally only a few degrees below the freeze-in temperature reproduces the entropy difference, as suggested by Simon, between the supercooled liquid in internal equilibrium and the crystal. It follows from this that the entropy of the infinitely slowly cooled liquid would vanish at absolute zero.[4] It is clear that for any ΔS curve other than that sketched by Simon the extrapolation of the curve for the liquid

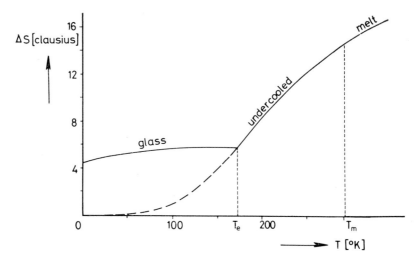

Fig. 6. *Entropy differences between fluid resp. glassy and crystalline glycerol.* *Clausius = entropy unit = cal/deg K. Dashed curve, undercooled liquid (internal* *equilibrium).*[4]

without change of direction would lead to negative ΔS values which is, however, not possible.[30] Similar considerations, on account of stability criteria, show that the linear extrapolation of the volume–temperature curve from values in the melt range into the temperature range below the glass temperature is not allowed in a large temperature interval.[31]

The finite value of the zero point entropy of the glass does not contradict Nernst's heat theorem since this only holds for phases which are in internal thermodynamic equilibrium down to the absolute zero as regards the order and distribution of the molecules.[4] This condition is obviously not fulfilled for glassy phases. In a series of papers Gutzow calculated the zero entropy of glasses following a model of the hole theory. With this model, vapour pressures of glasses and solubilities of glasses were calculated.[130]

1.2 GLASSY SOLIDIFICATION AND TRANSITION PHENOMENA

1.2.1 General considerations and transitions of different order

The question whether the glassy solidification is a purely kinetic process or can be considered to be a thermodynamic transition has been frequently discussed.[1,4,7,32] In the literature the glassy solidification has been treated as a transition of either first, second or third order;[33-41] therefore a few fundamental considerations will be discussed.

If, for the description of a transition, temperature and pressure are chosen as independent variables, a first-order transition, such as melting or vaporisation, is so defined that at the transition point the first derivatives of the free enthalpy G with respect to the intensity parameters T and P show discontinuities. This holds for the volume V, the enthalpy H and the entropy S.[42] The second derivatives of G with respect to T and P, i.e. α, c_p and κ (κ = isothermal compressibility) become infinite. Accordingly, an nth order transition is so defined that the nth derivatives of G with respect to T and P show a discontinuity and the $(n + 1)$-th derivatives become infinite. In a first-order transition we have a two-phase equilibrium, the upper and lower limits of the value at the discontinuity corresponding to the co-existing phases. In Fig. 7 the temperature dependence is shown for the specific quantities g, v, h, s and the derivatives α, c_p and κ for first- and second-order transitions and for the glassy solidification.

Since a third-order transition, because of the temperature dependence of α, c_p and κ, shows no resemblance with the glassy solidification,[40] the only question remaining to be discussed is whether, because of the formal similarity with a second-order transition, the glassy solidification can be interpreted as a second-order transition or not. The known second-order transitions are single-phase transitions. Examples of the order–disorder transitions are the rotational transitions, the disappearance of the ferromagnetism at the Curie point and the transition of liquid helium at 2·2°K. In transitions of this type one finds a kink at the values T_{tr} and P_{tr} (the subscript 'tr' meaning transition) at the transition point for the functions v, h, s and a discontinuity for the derivatives α, c_p and κ, as is seen from Fig. 7. The figure also shows that in contrast to a second-order transition in the glassy solidification the values of the quantities α, c_p and κ are smaller below the glass temperature than above it. A further difference is found in the behaviour at different rates of cooling. In Section 1.1 it was shown that the glass temperature shifts to higher temperatures as the cooling rate increases. In phases which experience a second-order transition,

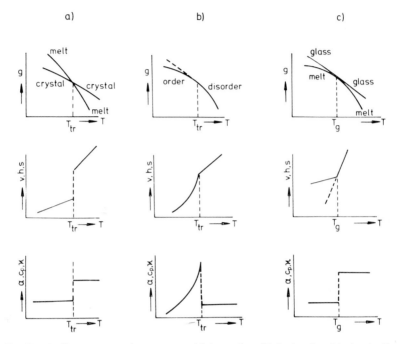

Fig. 7.   *Different types of transitions: (a) 1st order; (b) 2nd order; (c) the vitrifica-*
tion process.[32]

temperatures below the transition temperature are often reached on fast
cooling; the transition temperature is, however, never shifted to higher
temperatures. If, due to supercooling, the second-order transition does not
occur, the temperature dependence for v, h, s which is found above T_{tr}
is preserved at lower temperatures. At very low rates of cooling the kink
in the temperature curve for the quantities v, h and s occurs at the transition
temperature T_{tr}. In the case of a single-phase system this temperature is an
equilibrium temperature which, at a given pressure, has a definite value.
In the P–T diagram this distinctive point corresponds to a fixed point on
the transition curve. Since, however, this transition occurs in a single phase,
the conditions here are different from those for a heterogeneous equilibrium.

In the glassy solidification the freeze-in temperature is lowered by slow
cooling.† These reasons and the considerations outlined in Section 1.1
indicate that the glassy solidification is caused by an inhibition of kinetic

---

† When freeze-in and glass temperatures are not differentiated they are intended to
represent the same concept. This is sufficient for most considerations.

processes. The solidification to a glass cannot be described as a transition in the thermodynamic sense, because there does not exist an internal thermodynamic equilibrium on *both* sides of the glass temperature, as is the case, for example, for a second-order transition.

The question whether the transition process can be considered as a second-order transition is asked time and time again because the relationships, derived from the formalism of the second-order transition, for the pressure dependence of the transition temperature are in partial agreement with experimental results.[43-50,82,125-127] This question will be discussed in greater detail below.

As shown in Fig. 7, in a first-order transition the first derivatives of the free enthalpy g with respect to the intensity parameters T and P, *i.e.* the quantities s, v and h, show a discontinuity. From the Gibbs equilibrium condition one obtains for the pressure dependence of the transition temperature the well-known Clausius–Clapeyron relation:[40]

$$\left(\frac{dP}{dT}\right)_{tr} = \frac{s' - s''}{v' - v''} = \frac{\Delta s}{\Delta v} = \frac{\Delta h}{T \Delta v} \tag{4}$$

The index 'tr' refers to the transition curve. The primed and double primed quantities refer to the two phases in equilibrium.

In a second-order transition one obtains from the continuity of the functions $v(T, P)$ and $s(T, P)$ at the transition point for the total differentials along the transition curve

$$dv'(T, P) = dv''(T, P) \tag{5}$$

and

$$ds'(T, P) = ds''(T, P) \tag{5a}$$

The indices $'$ and $''$ refer to the same phase immediately above and below the transition temperature.

From eqns. (5) and (5a) one obtains, because v and s are state functions,

$$-\kappa' \, dP + \alpha' \, dT = -\kappa'' \, dP + \alpha'' \, dT \tag{6}$$

$$-\alpha' \, dP + \frac{c'_p}{T} \, dT = -\alpha'' \, dP + \frac{c''_p}{T} \, dT \tag{6a}$$

Here κ, α and c_p are specific quantities which are defined as follows:

$$\kappa \equiv -\left(\frac{\partial v}{\partial P}\right)_T ; \qquad v \equiv \frac{V}{m} \tag{7}$$

$$\alpha \equiv \left(\frac{\partial v}{\partial T}\right)_P; \tag{7a}$$

$$c_p \equiv T\left(\frac{\partial s}{\partial T}\right)_P; \qquad s \equiv \frac{S}{m} \tag{7b}$$

m is the mass, V and S are the total values of the volume and the enthalpy respectively, whereas v and s are the specific quantities.

From eqns. (6) and (6a) we obtain two equations for the pressure dependence of the transition temperature as was first shown by Ehrenfest:[42]

$$\left(\frac{dP}{dT}\right)_I = \frac{\Delta\alpha}{\Delta\kappa} \tag{8}$$

$$\left(\frac{dP}{dT}\right)_{II} = \frac{\Delta c_p}{T\Delta\alpha} \tag{8a}$$

By equating (8) and (8a) one obtains:

$$\frac{T(\Delta\alpha)^2}{\Delta\kappa\Delta c_p} = 1 \tag{8b}$$

Here Δ means the step value at the discontinuity of the corresponding quantity at the transition temperature. In a second-order transition both Ehrenfest relationships, eqns. (8) and (8a), must be fulfilled as must eqn. (8b).

It is possible to test whether eqns. (8) and (8a) *formally* describe the glassy solidification at a given rate of cooling by determining the temperatures of the start of the freeze-in at different pressures from the $v(T, P)$ data in the melt and glassy ranges. The curve drawn through these points is the so-called 'freeze-in curve'.[6,32] Its slope $(dP/dT)_e$ is compared with the slopes $(dP/dT)_I$ and $(dP/dT)_{II}$ calculated from $\Delta\alpha$, $\Delta\kappa$ and Δc_p. Here it is important that the dilatometric and calorimetric measurements are carried out on the same substance and at the same rate of cooling.

Equation (6) is shown in Fig. 8 in a schematic volume–temperature diagram. The full curves are volume isobars at pressures P and $P + dP$ with the transition temperatures T_{tr} and $T_{tr} + dT_{tr}$. The dashed–dotted line $\overline{AB}$ represents the transition curve in the volume–temperature diagram along which the volume changes by dv_{tr}. The differential dv_{tr} on the right-hand side of the transition curve $\overline{AB}$ consists of the portions

$$\overline{DB} = -\kappa'\,dP$$

and

$$\overline{DF} = \alpha'\, dT$$

and that to the left-hand side of the transition curve of the portions

$$\overline{AC} = -\kappa''\, dP$$

and

$$\overline{EC} = \alpha''\, dT$$

It is seen that the Ehrenfest equations only hold when we have equilibrium on both sides of the transition, *i.e.* when the thermodynamic quantities of the substance can be described by two and only two variables, *e.g.* T and P (a phase with two degrees of freedom).

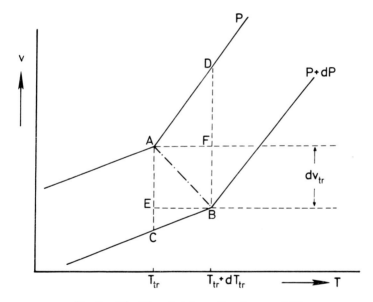

Fig. 8. The Ehrenfest formalism (see text).[72]

1.2.2 Glassy solidification with one or several internal parameters

As we have seen in the previous sections the Ehrenfest relationships cannot describe the existing non-equilibria. It can, however, be shown that under certain conditions the description of the glassy solidification with an additional internal variable ξ_i results in relationships which are formally similar to the Ehrenfest equations.

Firstly we consider the case where only one additional ordering parameter is necessary for the complete description of the volume and entropy of the glass. Then one obtains along the freeze-in curve (also called the freeze-in boundary)

$$dv_g(T, P, \xi) = dv_m[T, P, \bar{\xi}(T, P)] \tag{9}$$

and

$$ds_g(T, P, \xi) = dv_m[T, P, \bar{\xi}(T, P)] \tag{9a}$$

The index 'g' refers to the glassy state ($\xi \neq \bar{\xi}$), 'm' to the liquid state or the melt ($\xi = \bar{\xi}$). For the liquid state we have for the concept of affinity according to eqn. (2) $A = 0$ (as index A). For the glassy range $A(T, P, \xi) \neq 0$.

From eqns. (9) and (9a) one obtains (index ξ meaning ξ is constant)

$$-\kappa_\xi \, dP + \alpha_\xi \, dT + \left(\frac{\partial v}{\partial \xi}\right)_{T,P} d\xi = -\kappa_A dP + \alpha_A dT \tag{10}$$

$$-\alpha_\xi \, dP + \frac{c_{p,\xi}}{T} \, dT + \left(\frac{\partial s}{\partial \xi}\right)_{T,P} d\xi = -\alpha_A dP + \frac{c_{p,A}}{T} \, dT \tag{10a}$$

Thus

$$\kappa_\xi \equiv -\left(\frac{\partial v_g}{\partial P}\right)_{T,\xi}; \qquad \kappa_A \equiv -\left(\frac{\partial v_m}{\partial P}\right)_{T,A} \tag{11}$$

$$\alpha_\xi \equiv \left(\frac{\partial v_g}{\partial T}\right)_{P,\xi}; \qquad \alpha_A \equiv \left(\frac{\partial v_m}{\partial T}\right)_{P,A} \tag{11a}$$

$$c_{p,\xi} \equiv T\left(\frac{\partial s_g}{\partial T}\right)_{P,\xi}; \qquad c_{p,A} \equiv T\left(\frac{\partial s_m}{\partial T}\right)_{P,A} \tag{11b}$$

From eqns. (10) and (10a) follow the relationships corresponding to the Ehrenfest equations:

$$\left(\frac{dP}{dT}\right)_e = \frac{\Delta\alpha^*}{\Delta\kappa^*} - \frac{1}{\Delta\kappa^*}\left(\frac{\partial v}{\partial \xi}\right)_{T,P}\left(\frac{d\xi}{dT}\right)_e \tag{12}$$

and

$$\left(\frac{dP}{dT}\right)_e = \frac{\Delta c^*_p}{T\Delta\alpha^*} - \frac{1}{\Delta\alpha^*}\left(\frac{\partial s}{\partial \xi}\right)_{T,P}\left(\frac{d\xi}{dT}\right)_e \tag{12a}$$

The index 'e' refers to the freeze-in curve which represents the locus for all freeze-in temperatures at the different corresponding pressures.

In the above formulae the following abbreviations were used:

$$\Delta\alpha^* \equiv \alpha_A - \alpha_\xi \tag{13}$$

$$\Delta\kappa^* \equiv \kappa_A - \kappa_\xi \tag{13a}$$

$$\Delta c^*_p \equiv c_{p,A} - c_{p,\xi} \tag{13b}$$

The values at the discontinuities in eqns. (13) to (13b) give the differences between the values in the equilibrium state and those at a fixed internal order. In the Ehrenfest equations the co-ordinates of the discontinuities hold for internal equilibrium above and below the transition point.

It is further seen that eqns. (12) and (12a) formally correspond to the Ehrenfest relationships (8) and (8a) if $(d\xi/dT)_e$ vanishes, i.e. if the internal equilibrium order is constant along the freeze-in line. This connection was already indicated by Prigogine and Defay,[52] Meixner[53] as well as Davies and Jones[54,55] and Staverman.[56]

We then have

$$\left(\frac{\partial P}{\partial T}\right)_\xi = \frac{\Delta\alpha^*}{\Delta\kappa^*} \tag{14}$$

$$\left(\frac{\partial P}{\partial T}\right)_\xi = \frac{\Delta c^*_p}{T\Delta\alpha^*} \tag{14a}$$

From these equations one obtains (14b), which is formally identical with the summarised Ehrenfest equation (8b).

$$\frac{\Delta\alpha^*}{\Delta\kappa^*} = \frac{\Delta c^*_p}{T\Delta\alpha^*} \tag{14b}$$

For the case where the internal ordering variable ξ is held constant along the freeze-in boundary no distinction can be made between a second-order transition and a freeze-in process.

In eqns. (12) and (12a) we have

$$\frac{1}{\Delta\kappa^*}\left(\frac{\partial v}{\partial \xi}\right)_{T,P} = \frac{1}{\Delta\alpha^*}\left(\frac{\partial s}{\partial \xi}\right)_{T,P} \tag{15}$$

This can be seen as follows: from eqns. (10) and (10a) one obtains with the abbreviations (13) and (13a)

$$\Delta\kappa^* = -\left(\frac{\partial v}{\partial \xi}\right)_{T,P}\left(\frac{\partial \xi}{\partial P}\right)_T \tag{16}$$

$$\Delta\alpha^* = -\left(\frac{\partial s}{\partial \xi}\right)_{T,P}\left(\frac{\partial \xi}{\partial P}\right)_T \tag{16a}$$

From these relations eqn. (15) follows immediately.

Equations (12) and (12a) can now be written in the following form:

$$\left(\frac{dP}{dT}\right)_e = \frac{\Delta\alpha^*}{\Delta\kappa^*} - a\left(\frac{d\xi}{dT}\right)_e \tag{17}$$

$$\left(\frac{dP}{dT}\right)_e = \frac{\Delta c^*_p}{T\Delta\alpha^*} - a\left(\frac{d\xi}{dT}\right)_e \tag{17a}$$

Here a is given by the left-hand and right-hand sides in eqn. (15).

The relationships (17) and (17a) lead to an expression like the summarised Ehrenfest equation, namely (14b). With eqn. (14b) it is not possible to differentiate between a genuine thermodynamic second-order transition and a freeze-in process which requires only one independent ξ parameter. The Ehrenfest equations (8) and (8a), however, differ from eqns. (12) and (12a) and (17) and (17a) respectively.

Figure 9 shows eqn. (10) (*cf.* also Fig. 8). The full curves represent two volume isobars at the pressures P and $P + dP$ as obtained in a cooling

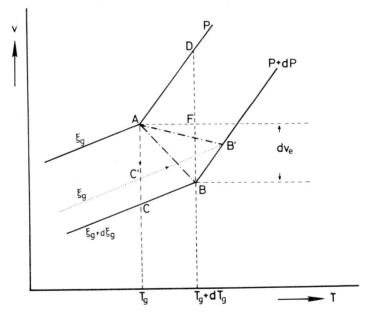

Fig. 9. *Vitrification process described by one internal parameter (see text).*[72]

experiment. The corresponding freeze-in intervals are extrapolated to kink points at the respective glass temperatures T_g and $T_g + dT_g$. At pressure P at point A the internal equilibrium order described by ξ_g freezes in and remains constant during further cooling. At pressure $P + dP$ this holds also for the equilibrium order described by $\xi_g + d\xi_g$ at point B. The dashed–dotted line $\overline{AB}$ is therefore the freeze-in curve along which the internal variable changes by $d\xi_g$ from A to B. The total differential of the volume dv_e along the freeze-in curve $\overline{AB}$ consists, on the side of the melt, of the portions $\overline{DB} = -\kappa_A \, dP$ and $\overline{DF} = \alpha_A \, dT$. The volume curves in the glassy range correspond to the different, but constant, internal order values ξ_g and $\xi_g + d\xi_g$. From point A it is therefore not possible to get to point C by an increase in pressure dP, since during a compression in the glassy range the internal order does not change. One gets to the point C′ at which exists the same internal order as at A. For the same reason the volume curves measured as isotherms and plotted as isobars, as shown in Fig. 12 below, have an irregular course in the freeze-in and glassy range. The line $\overline{AC}$ is composed of the portions $\overline{AC'} = -\kappa_\xi dP$ and $\overline{C'C} = (dv/d\xi)_{T,P} \, d\xi_g$.

Through the point C′ one can construct the volume isobar which belongs to the pressure $P + dP$ and the constant internal ordering parameter ξ_g (dotted). This intersects the equilibrium isobar of the pressure $P + dP$ at B′. At B′ we now have as equilibrium value the same internal order as at C′ in the glassy state, since at the point of intersection B′ the pressures, temperatures and volumes of the curves $\overline{C'B'}$ and $\overline{BB'}$ are the same.

The line $\overline{AB'}$, therefore, represents a line in the equilibrium range along which the internal order is constant and at which the pressure and temperature influences compensate each other to form a constant equilibrium order.

Equations (12), (12a) and (14b) can be easily generalised for the case where more than one ξ parameter is required for the description of the glassy state. In eqns. (12) and (12a) we then have, instead of the single ξ term, additional terms, sums of these expressions. Meixner[53] and Davies and Jones[55] showed that on introducing more than one independent internal ordering variable instead of the 'summarised Ehrenfest' equation (14b) the following inequality is obtained:

$$\frac{T(\Delta\alpha^*)^2}{\Delta\kappa^* \Delta c^*_p} \leq 1 \tag{17b}$$

It cannot, however, be stated *a priori* how far the value deviates from unity; in any case it is difficult to determine $\Delta\alpha^*$, $\Delta\kappa^*$ and Δc^*_p with sufficient accuracy. This holds particularly for $\Delta\kappa^*$. In general it is to be expected that more than one ξ value will be necessary for the description of the frozen-in state, but eqn. (17b) is not very well suited to test whether we have a thermodynamic transition or a freeze-in process. The most suitable manner would be to investigate the path dependence as will be shown later.

The description of the glassy solidification with one or several order parameters does not yet provide a criterion for the physical significance of those parameters. For a more accurate description, one therefore needs a relation between the quantities which characterise the freeze-in temperature, such as the viscosity or the different relaxation times, and the thermodynamic functions. A few simple cases were discussed by Goldstein and Staverman.[46,56] The assumption that along the freeze-in boundary a volume fraction of the liquid reaches a constant critical value leads to the relation (14) which holds formally, as was shown above, for freeze-in processes only if $(d\xi/dT)_e = 0$. The assumption that either an entropy fraction or an enthalpy fraction of the liquid has a critical value on freezing-in then leads correspondingly to eqn. (14a) with $(d\xi/dT)_e = 0$. From the experimental values Goldstein concluded that the 'concept of the free volume' cannot be correct.[46] The theory of the isofree volume state according to Fox and Flory[57] says that the fraction of the free volume in the form of holes, in the sense of the hole theory, below the freeze-in temperature is constant. According to Bondi[57,58] there exist several definitions of the free volume which are, however, related to each other (see Introduction, pp. 25–27). O'Reilly,[43a,] Maurer[59] and Bueche[82] have already pointed out that, if this theory is valid, the density of a glass made under high pressures would at lower temperatures be independent of the pressure at which the glass was made. This is in contrast to the observed path dependence.[2,6,32] In a free volume approach Chompff formulated the dependence of the glass temperature of polymers or polymer networks on structural entities analytically.[51]

1.2.3   Experimental results

In order to test the thermodynamic relationships, the discontinuities in the expansion coefficient, the specific heat and the isothermal compressibility must be determined. The quantities α, c_p and κ are determined directly, for reasons of accuracy, and not by differentiation of the 'integral functions' $V(T)$, $V(P)$ and $H(T)$. For the determination of $(dP/dT)_e$ the measurements must extend over a larger pressure range. This is also necessary because the freeze-in interval, e.g. for $\Delta\kappa$, can extend over several kb (kilobar) at higher temperatures (cf. Fig. 10). It is almost superfluous to remark that,

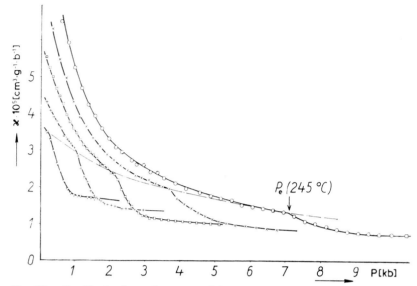

Fig. 10. Specific isothermal compressibility κ in cm³ g⁻¹ (bar)⁻¹ of atactic polystyrene versus P in kilobars. ∇ 107°C, + 126°C, □ 155·1°C, × 194·9°C *and* ○ 245°C. *Dashed–dotted curve, boundary of the beginning of vitrification.*[32]

if possible, the measurements should be carried out on one and the same substance.

In the experimental results which follow, these points have been taken into consideration. Figure 10 shows the specific isothermal compressibility of an atactic polystyrene† in the temperature range between 100–250°C and up to pressures of 10 kb.[6,32] In the liquid range, above the dashed–dotted curve the compressibility at constant temperature decreases as a hyperbola. The kinks show the start of the freeze-in range; for example, on the isotherm with $T = 245°C$ the pressure is $P_e = 7$ kb. The adjoining freeze-in region also shows a continuous curve. Only in an idealised presentation is it possible to talk of a compressibility 'step' $\Delta\kappa$, which decreases with increasing temperature, but this 'step' cannot be determined with any degree of accuracy from this graph. Measurements by other authors on polystyrene cover pressure ranges up to a maximum of 3·5 kb.[62,63,126] It is seen from the figure that these pressures are too small to study the behaviour of polystyrene up to the decomposition temperature; in any case the freeze-in intervals alone cover 1–2 kb. At pressure ranges as small as this it is not possible to cover the total freeze-in range.

† Modified polystyrene VI of BASF.

Particularly at lower temperatures the curves in the glassy range show overlaps which indicate that the compressibility in the glassy range depends on the prevailing freeze-in conditions as well as on temperature and pressure.

In order to determine more accurately the 'jump' values $\Delta\kappa$ and the width of the freeze-in range it is more useful to plot the reciprocal of the compressibility because of the hyperbolic shape of the curves $\kappa(P)$ in the liquid range.

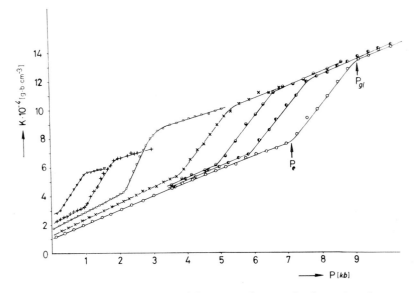

Fig. 11.   *Specific compression modulus K in g bar cm^{-3} of atactic polystyrene versus pressure P in kilobars.* ∇ 107°C, + 126°C, □ 155·1°C, × 194·9°C, ◖ 217°C, ◑ 230°C and ○ 245°C. P_e and P_{gl} are the pressures at the beginning and end of the vitrification process at 245°C.[32]

In Fig. 11 is plotted the isothermal specific modulus of compression, $K = (1/\kappa)$, against pressure.

Linear relationships are found in liquid as well as glassy regions. From the kink points of the isothermal modulus of compression–pressure curves one can determine the pressure at the start of the freeze-in P_e, the pressure at the end of the freeze-in P_{gl} and thus the 'jump' value $\Delta\kappa$ via ΔK with reasonable accuracy. The difficulties in determining $\Delta\kappa$ are thus not encountered.

Additional dilatometric measurements at normal pressure now enable us to plot the state diagram of the polymer. Figure 12 shows such a state diagram for polystyrene. In the liquid range, above the dashed–dotted curve all isobars are straight lines whose slope α decreases with increasing pressure. The dashed–dotted sloping straight line shows the boundary of the start of the freeze-in. Along the freeze-in boundary in the

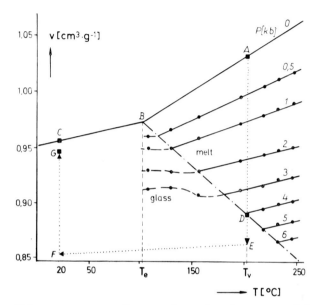

Fig. 12. *Volume–temperature diagram of atactic polystyrene and densification cycle* (see *text*).[72]

temperature range between 100–250°C the volume decreases by about 12%. In the glassy range the isobars follow an irregular course. This again indicates that the volume in the glass and freeze-in ranges is path dependent. The arrow in Fig. 12 indicates that the compressibility measurements from which the diagram was constructed were carried out under isothermal conditions. For the liquid state this is of no importance because the measurements are path independent.

With the aid of the calorimetrically determined value for Δc_p[64] one obtains for $T_e = 102°C$ and $P = 1\,b$

$$\frac{\Delta\alpha^*}{\Delta\kappa^*} = 20\ b\ °K^{-1}; \qquad \frac{\Delta c^*_p}{T\Delta\alpha^*} = 21\ b\ °K^{-1}$$

The two expressions are identical within the limits of accuracy, as they should be according to the assumptions leading to eqns. (17) and (17a). For the pressure dependence of the freeze-in temperature it was found:

$$\left(\frac{dP}{dT}\right)_e = 40 \text{ b } °K^{-1}$$

The differences lie far outside the limits of accuracy, and according to the experimental results the Ehrenfest equations are thus not applicable. The glassy solidification, therefore, is not a second-order transition and cannot be described by its formalism. It is also not possible that one of the two Ehrenfest equations would apply to the glassy solidification and the other not. According to the above values eqns. (12) and (12a) together with eqn. (15) hold. We thus have for this special case

$$\frac{1}{\Delta\kappa^*}\left(\frac{\partial V}{\partial \xi}\right)_{T,P}\left(\frac{\partial \xi}{\partial T}\right)_e \equiv \frac{1}{\Delta\alpha^*}\left(\frac{\partial S}{\partial \xi}\right)_{T,P}\left(\frac{\partial \xi}{\partial T}\right)_e = -20 \text{ b } °K^{-1}$$

From the above experimental values it follows that

$$\frac{T(\Delta\alpha^*)^2}{\Delta\kappa^*\Delta c_p^*} \approx 1$$

Equation (14b) appears to be applicable. In Section 1.3 it is shown that for glassy polystyrene a set of ξ parameters must be assumed. Equation (17b) therefore holds. It is also shown experimentally that eqn. (14b) is insensitive and therefore not suitable for differentiating between glassy solidification as a kinetic process and a thermodynamic transition.

A more evident criterion than the applicability of the Ehrenfest equations is the test for the already mentioned path dependence of physical quantities in the vicinity of a transition point and a transition curve respectively. Path dependence means that in the range studied T and P no longer suffice to characterise the state of a phase. It can occur at the different transition and freeze-in processes and is not bound to the appearance of a second-order transition.

The path dependence of the volume–pressure–temperature cycles has been known since Tamman, and has been investigated on glasses by several authors.[2,63,124–127] Breuer and Rehage showed that the specific volumes of a glass along the path ABC (Fig. 12) were larger than those along the path ADEFG.[72] The path ABC represents an isobaric cooling of the sample at normal pressure from the temperature T_v to T_e and down to

20°C. Here the internal equilibrium order freezes-in at B. The path ADE corresponds to the compression of the sample at a compression temperature T_v to the freeze-in boundary, the state of order belonging to D freezing-in. Cooling to 20°C and subsequent pressure decrease occurs along the path EFG. At the points C and G the pressures and temperatures are equal, but the specific volumes are different. The volume difference thus

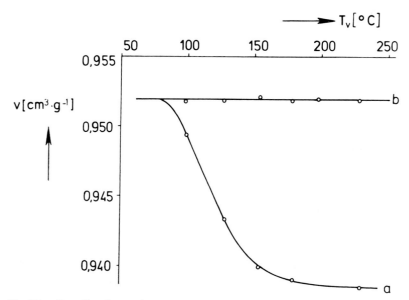

Fig. 13. *Specific volume of atactic polystyrene at 20°C and 1 bar versus densification temperature* T_V *(curve a); values after annealing at 140°C measured at 1 bar and 20°C (curve b).*[72]

reflects the difference between the internal equilibrium orders at the points B and D. As can be seen from Fig. 13, this difference in specific volume increases very strongly initially with increasing temperature T_v and only very little above 170°C. Curve 'a' represents the specific volumes of polystyrene at 20°C after a compression cycle (ADEFG in Fig. 12). The horizontal straight line 'b' reproduces the volume values which the compressed sample showed after short annealing at 140°C and subsequent cooling at a pressure $P = 1$ b at 20°C. The volume change at a compression temperature of 250°C is about 1·4% relative to the volume at 20°C. From this it is seen that along the freeze-in boundary the internal order of the material must have changed. The path dependence leads to the conclusion that in the glassy state volume, entropy, enthalpy and other quantities are not uniquely determined by pressure and temperature alone but depend on the internal order present at the freeze-in boundary.

1.2.4 Position of the equilibrium curve below the glass temperature

Kauzmann[30] was the first to pose the problem of the course of the equilibrium curve below the glass curve. He showed that the liquid curves of the thermodynamic functions of glass-forming materials should show a different course below the glass temperature, at least at lower temperatures than above the glass temperature. This already becomes clear from the entropy measurements by Simon reproduced in Fig. 6. On linear extrapolation the entropy–temperature curve of the supercooled liquid would intersect that of the crystal, thus making the zero point entropy negative under certain conditions. This, of course, is not possible. If, however, it is assumed that the slope of the entropy–temperature function of the supercooled liquid decreases steadily as the temperature decreases and vanishes at absolute zero, as indicated in Fig. 6, these difficulties do not occur.

In the last few years this complex of problems has been treated again by Gibbs and DiMarzio[66] and Adam and Gibbs.[67] This will be discussed in more detail in Chapter 3. From their model calculations the authors postulate a second-order transition T_2 about 50–60°C below the normal glass temperature. The usually observed transition to the glassy state is treated as a kinetic process by these authors, but at infinitely slow cooling the transition temperature should be lowered to such an extent that it coincides with the transition temperature T_2. This would then make the glassy solidification a genuine second-order transition. This model is certainly very useful for the qualitative description of some phenomena, but this transition, purely for experimental reasons, cannot be proved. This follows from measurements of the isothermal volume after-effects at which only a few degrees below the transition temperature the equilibrium curve cannot be reached within reasonable time.[68-71,32] This can also be seen from Table 1 in which the time $t_{1/e}$ of the refractive index relaxation is given for a polystyrene whose glass temperature was 89°C.[32] Here $t_{1/e}$ is the time in which the isothermal–isobaric refractive index relaxation has reached the eth fraction of the initial deviation from the equilibrium curve. The time $t_{1/e}$, which serves as a substitute for the relaxation time spectrum given, would, for the hypothetical transition temperature T_2, be 10^{14} years for this relatively low molecular weight polystyrene.

It is therefore not possible to reach the equilibrium curve at lower temperatures. An attempt has been made, under certain assumptions, to construct the equilibrium curve.[70,71] The underlying idea is as follows: If a polystyrene–solvent system can be found in which the volumes of mixing over an extended concentration range are composed additively from the volumes of the pure components, then the volume of the pure polymer can be obtained by extrapolation on zero solvent concentration.

TABLE 1

T in °C	$t_{1/e}$
100	10^{-2} sec
95	1 sec
91	40 sec
90	2 min
$T_E = 89$	5 min
88	18 min
86·5	1 h
85	5 h
82	50 h
79	60 d
77	1 a
50	10^{12} a
20	10^{34} a

This may hold in a certain temperature range. It is required in this case that the mixed phases be in internal equilibrium and not frozen-in. The extrapolation, however, only provides reliable values if the conformations in the highly concentrated solutions correspond to those of the melt. A system that is strictly additive in the values from the pure components was not found. It was found, however, that in the system polystyrene–malonic ester the coefficient of expansion of the mixtures at temperatures between 20 and 60°C is a linear function of the concentration.[71] The measurements were carried out up to a polystyrene content of about 90%. Only then did the solutions set to a glass. The expansion coefficients of the polystyrene ($M_n = 2\cdot10^4$ g mol^{-1}) between 20 and 60°C could be obtained by extrapolation with great certainty. From this the volume–temperature curve for the polystyrene was constructed over this range. In Fig. 14 the $V(T)$ curve between 20 and 60°C, as obtained by extrapolation, is shown as a dashed line. It was slightly curved and followed a quadratic function, as is usually found for liquids over a larger temperature range. This function also

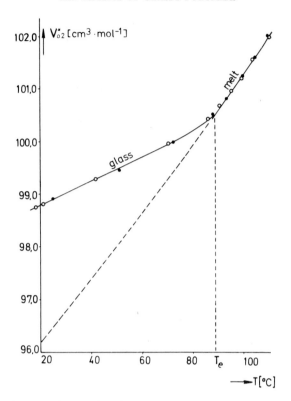

Fig. 14.   Volume per base mole, V^*_{o2}, *of atactic polystyrene with* $M_n = 20\ 000\ g$
mol^{-1} *versus temperature in the glassy and liquid state for two different samples.*
Dashed line, extrapolated volume from solutions. [32, 71]

represents the directly measured values above T_e quite accurately. Up
to 70°C below the transition temperature there was no indication of a
transition.

The state diagram makes it possible to estimate the shape of the equilibrium curve at normal pressure below T_g. [72] This isobar corresponds to the
imagined experiment of the infinitely slow cooling. The volume–temperature diagram presented in Fig. 15 shows in the upper part the fully drawn
liquid isobar at $P = 1$ b (~ 0 kb) which would, in a normal cooling
experiment, at the glass transition temperature pass into the dashed glass
curve with the internal variable ξ_1. Along the dashed–dotted freeze-in
boundary the internal order changes which is characterised by the parameter ξ_2 at point B. It is shown in Fig. 12 and discussed in the adjoining

text that point D in Fig. 15 represents the specific volume of the sample with the internal order described by ξ_2 at 20°C and 1 b (~0 kb). In order to obtain this point one must follow the path ABCD. From point D one can draw the thin dashed glass isobar with the slope $\alpha_{\xi_2, P=0} = (\partial v/\partial T)_{\xi_2, P=0}$. The ordering parameter ξ_2 is maintained along the straight line. Starting

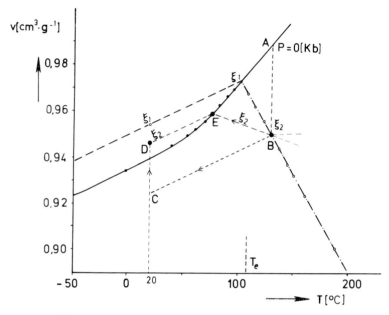

Fig. 15.   Volume–temperature plot of polystyrene for the construction of the equilibrium curve of infinitely slow cooling (full curve). P = 0 kb corresponds to P = 1 bar.

from point B it is possible to calculate the line of constant internal equilibrium order with the slope $(\partial v/\partial T)_\xi$. For the calculation of the slope $(\partial v/\partial T)_\xi$ one starts from the total differential of the volume at constant order[32,72]

$$dv = \alpha_\xi \, dT - \kappa_\xi \, dP \tag{18}$$

Dividing by dT one obtains from this the 'thermal coefficient of expansion at fixed equilibrium order'

$$\left(\frac{\partial v}{\partial T}\right)_\xi = \alpha_\xi - \kappa_\xi \left(\frac{\partial P}{\partial T}\right)_\xi \tag{19}$$

From this one obtains with eqn. (14), with $(\mathrm{d}P/\mathrm{d}T)_\xi = (\Delta\alpha^*/\Delta\kappa^*)$, the relation

$$\left(\frac{\partial v}{\partial T}\right)_\xi = \alpha_\xi - \kappa_\xi \frac{\Delta\alpha^*}{\Delta\kappa^*} \tag{20}$$

The dashed straight line passing through B with this coefficient of expansion can therefore be easily calculated. P and T change along this line. The two straight lines starting from B and D intersect at point E, at which the values for the internal ordering parameter (ξ_2), the temperature and the volume of both lines are the same. Therefore, the pressures must also be equal. The internal ordering parameter ξ_2, which along the line $\overline{\mathrm{DE}}$ does not represent the equilibrium value, is, however, the equilibrium value along the line $\overline{\mathrm{BE}}$ which equals $\overline{\xi}_2$.

Therefore, point E belongs to the equilibrium isobar with $P = 0$. In this manner one obtains from the various volume values of curve 'a' in Fig. 13 and the corresponding glass temperatures $T_g = T_v$ the fully drawn equilibrium isobar below the glass temperature at $P = 0$ (Fig. 15). This curve shows a wide curved course on which one cannot very well distinguish a kink point.

In this discussion it is assumed that the slope $(\partial v/\partial T)_\xi$ along the freeze-in curve does not change. This means that the slope of line BE is the same as that of line AB' in Fig. 9. It could only be determined at $P = 0$, i.e. at $\xi_i = \xi_1$. It can, however, be assumed that this coefficient of expansion decreases as temperature and pressure increase. Then the curvature of the equilibrium curve below T_e decreases and it resembles even more the curve which was obtained by extrapolation from the solution.

We thus have a second method for determining the course of an equilibrium curve far below T_e. Up to about 100°C below the freeze-in temperature $T_e = 102°C$ there is no indication of a transition in this polystyrene either. A linear extrapolation from the range of the supercooled liquid is, however, not possible for a larger temperature interval below T_e.[31] At lower temperatures the equilibrium curve shows a definite curvature.

1.2.5   Zero point volume of a polymer

From the PVT data the intrinsic volume of a liquid can be estimated if it is assumed with Hildebrand that this is characterised by the vanishing of the internal pressure $P_i = (\partial u/\partial v)_T$.[73] We thus have

$$P_i = T\frac{\alpha}{\kappa} - P = 0 \tag{21}$$

(u = specific internal energy). The intrinsic volume is put equal to the volume at $0°K$. In Fig. 13 of the Introduction (p. 32) the internal pressure is plotted as a function of the specific volume for atactic polystyrene. It is seen that the isotherms between 100 and 250°C are easily extrapolated to the intrinsic volume $v_0 = 0·852$ cm^3 g^{-1} ($P_i = 0$).[72,74,75,126a,c] This method is useful because it is generally difficult to determine the zero point volume of polymers in the liquid state. The value found is also very plausible. As we have seen in Section 1.2.4 a linear extrapolation of the volume of the melt above T_g to absolute zero is not possible.

The zero point volume allows us to estimate the free volume of a polymer, or more accurately the expansion volume.[74,75] (see Introduction, pp. 28–33).

1.3 RESULTS OF THE THERMODYNAMIC THEORY OF LINEAR RELAXATION PHENOMENA

In the previous sections we have dealt qualitatively with the observed time-dependent changes of thermodynamic functions on the basis of a non-equilibrium condition in the glassy state. These after-effects which, in the case of time-dependent changes of an intensive parameter (e.g. a change in temperature or pressure) are called relaxation and which in the case of time-dependent changes of extensive parameters (e.g. volume or enthalpy) are called retardation, can be divided into linear and non-linear regions. In the linear region the Boltzmann superposition principle is valid. This means that two separate effects may be superimposed without distortion according to their causes.

In the field of irreversible thermodynamic processes Meixner[13–15] has developed a general theory of linear after-effect phenomena. This theory assumes an approach to equilibrium for all internal processes in a closed homogeneous system so that the general phenomenological relations are valid. Meixner deduced an expression for volume retardation which is valid for any after-effect function. In this context it did not matter whether the retardation behaviour was described by a single time constant or a distribution of time constants.

The theories of Hirai and Eyring,[76] Ptitsyn,[77] Adam,[78,79] Kubat[81] and Tobolsky and Eyring[80] describe the non-linear phenomena and provide a single time constant for the linear region.[94–98] The theory of Bueche[82] deals with linear behaviour with a special form of after-effect function.

The non-linear phenomena shall not be considered further here as they normally do not fall within the field of the thermodynamics of irreversible processes.

Meixner's linear thermodynamic treatment gives the following equation for isothermal or isobaric volume retardation after stepwise changes in temperature or pressure:

$$\frac{v - v_\infty}{v_0 - v_\infty} = a(t) \qquad (22)$$

where v_∞, v_0 and v refer to specific volumes at time $t = \infty$, $t = 0$ and t. The function $a(t)$ is called the after-effect function. In the case of a single retardation time τ the well-known relation applies

$$a(t) = \exp\left(-\frac{t}{\tau}\right) \qquad (23)$$

According to eqn. (22) there is linearity between $(v - v_\infty)$ and the after-effect function $a(t)$. The expression $[(v - v_\infty)/(v_0 - v_\infty)]$ depends only on the time and is independent of the initial difference or amplitude $(v_0 - v_\infty)$. This behaviour is called linearity of time-dependent properties.[83] When $a(t)$ depends on amplitude the behaviour is non-linear.

Measurements of non-linear phenomena, which are, of course, of considerable technical interest, have been carried out by several authors.[84-93] The linear region is of great interest for the theoretical treatment of after-effect phenomena. Here investigations originate from the work of Goldbach and Rehage.[94-98] These authors made measurements by the method of stepwise changes in temperature and pressure and showed that atactic polystyrene had a measurable linear region of iso-thermal–isobaric volume retardation. The relations became non-linear when the temperature steps exceeded about 1·8°C and the pressure jumps exceeded 40 atm. In the linear region the initial differences of the specific volume from equilibrium reached a magnitude of 10^{-4} cm^3 g^{-1} and below.

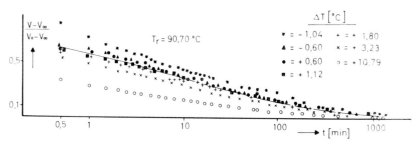

Fig. 16.　Volume–retardation curves after jumps of temperatures ΔT at 1 bar. T_r = retardation temperature.[96]

Figure 16 shows that at a retardation temperature $T_r = 90\cdot7°C$ and a retardation pressure of 1 atm the quantity $(v - v_\infty)/(v_0 - v_\infty)$ can be represented by a master curve only for small temperature jumps. The ΔT values represent the magnitude of the initial temperature jumps so that for $\Delta T > 0$ volume contraction occurs and for $\Delta T < 0$ volume dilatation occurs. With larger temperature changes non-linear behaviour is clearly observed. With the expansion (as opposed to the contraction) curves the boundary for linearity is less than $1\cdot8°C$.

For volume retardation resulting from stepwise changes in pressure a linear region has also been found as shown in Fig. 17.[94,96]

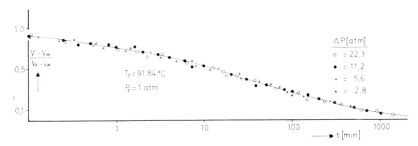

Fig. 17.   Volume–retardation curves after jumps of pressure ΔP. T_r = retardation temperature, P_r = retardation pressure.[96]

The value of this method is based on an almost instantaneous recording of the after-effect phenomena and on ignoring the minor changes in temperature which are caused by the work of compression. The master curve drawn in Fig. 17 shows the volume retardation curve for expansion at a retardation temperature $T_r = 91\cdot84°C$ and a retardation pressure $P_r = 1$ atm.

Rehage and Goldbach further demonstrated that the retardation function $a(t)$ could not be described by an exponential function as in eqn. (23). This type of behaviour is illustrated in Fig. 18 in which the function $\ln[(v - v_\infty)/(v_0 - v_\infty)]$ is plotted against a linear time axis. If eqn. (22) together with eqn. (23) is obeyed the curves in Fig. 18 would follow a straight line. The relations for volume retardation with stepwise changes in (a) pressure and (b) temperature are, even after long retardation times, slightly curved. This means that the linear retardation properties of poly-styrene cannot be described by means of a single retardation time. Instead a distribution of retardation times must be assumed. If we neglect the prob-lem of non-instanteous achievement of a uniform temperature distribution

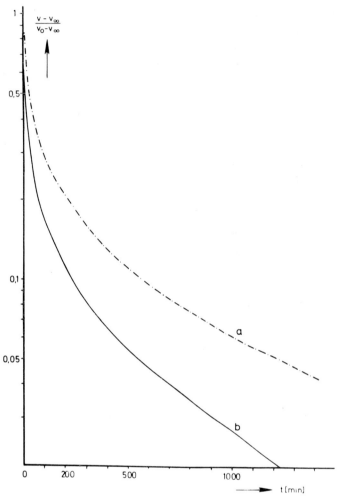

Fig. 18.   *Function* $(v - v_\infty)/(v_0 - v_\infty)$ *on a logarithmic scale versus time. Curve a: pressure jumps at* $T_r = 91\cdot84°C$, $P_r = 1$ *bar; curve b: temperature jumps at* $T_r = 90\cdot70°C$, $P_r = 1$ *bar,* $T_r = $ *retardation temperature,* $P_r = $ *retardation pressure.*[96]

arising from the temperature jump procedure, we can see from Fig. 18 that the retardation functions are not identical for both temperature and pressure jumps. Although the temperature ($T_r = 90\cdot7°C$) applying to the temperature jump measurements is somewhat lower than with the pressure jump measurements ($T_r = 91\cdot84°C$) curve (b) is steeper than curve (a).

This shows that in the region of linear volume changes for polystyrene a pressure change has a different effect from a temperature change.

The observation that volume retardation following a pressure change can be different from that following a temperature change, may be accounted for by Meixner's thermodynamic theory of linear retardation. The integral form of the dynamic equation of state which contains an explicit description of after-effect phenomena leads to an isothermal–isobaric volume retardation given by

$$\left(\frac{v - v_\infty}{v_0 - v_\infty}\right)_{\Delta P} = \left[\sum_{i=1}^{n}\left(\frac{\tau_{i,TP}}{\tau_{i,TV}} - 1\right)\right]^{-1} \sum_{i=1}^{n}\left(\frac{\tau_{i,TP}}{\tau_{i,TV}} - 1\right)\exp\left(-\frac{t}{\tau_{i,TP}}\right) \qquad (24)$$

and

$$\left(\frac{v - v_\infty}{v_0 - v_\infty}\right)_{\Delta T} = \left[\sum_{i=1}^{n}\left(\frac{\tau_{i,TP}}{\tau_{i,PV}} - 1\right)\right]^{-1} \sum_{i=1}^{n}\left(\frac{\tau_{i,TP}}{\tau_{i,PV}} - 1\right)\exp\left(-\frac{t}{\tau_{i,TP}}\right) \qquad (24a)$$

These two equations have the same form as eqn. (22) whereby the right-hand side of eqns. (24) and (24a) represent the after-effect function $a(t)$, provided a discontinuous distribution of retardation times may be assumed. Equations (24) and (24a) describe the time-dependent volume changes following a pressure or temperature jump; this is expressed through the index ΔP or ΔT in the expression related to the initial amplitude on the left-hand side of the equations. The retardation time $\tau_{i,TP}$ of the internal change i refers to isothermal isobaric conditions. The times $\tau_{i,TV}$ and $\tau_{i,VP}$ signify relaxation times under isothermal–isochoric and isochoric–isobaric conditions.

Equations (24) and (24a) show that the volume effects resulting from the pressure and temperature jump method are identical when the following condition applies:

$$\tau_{i,TV} = \tau_{i,PV} \qquad (25)$$

or when the weighting factors of the exponential expressions of eqns. (24) and (24a) have a constant ratio C

$$\frac{\tau_{i,TP}}{\tau_{i,TV}} - 1 = C\left(\frac{\tau_{i,TP}}{\tau_{i,PV}} - 1\right) \qquad (26)$$

When conditions (25) or (26) are not fulfilled, there is a difference in the after-effect functions depending on whether the pressure-jump or tempera-ture-jump method is chosen.

The theories quoted above,[76-81] which describe non-linear after-effect phenomena, provide formulas with only one retardation time in the linear region by means of a Taylor-series expansion. These theories cannot therefore be used in the case of polystyrene in the linear region. The theory developed by Bueche[82] which describes linear behaviour contains a particular retardation spectrum which does not describe the retardation properties of the polystyrene used.[94] The theory of linear volume retardation phenomena published by Kästner is based on the thermodynamic phenomenological theory of Meixner and includes both a continuous and a discontinuous distribution of retardation times.[99] With this theory, assuming a box-type function for retardation times, the measurements obtained with polystyrene in a medium range of times can be successfully described.[96] Under very complicated retardation conditions anomalous isotherms with a maximum in the volume–time curve are reported by Hozumi.[60] He used a modified theory of Bueche to describe these phenomena which are reminiscent of a wide distribution of retardation times.

In summary it can be said that the investigation of after-effect phenomena leads to the result that the glassy solidification must be regarded as the hindrance of a kinetic process. Unfortunately, by these methods, the equilibrium curve can only be reached down to about 10°C below the normal glass temperature, in reasonable times. At still lower temperatures the course of the curve of internal thermodynamic equilibrium can at present only be estimated by the methods described in Section 1.2.4.

1.4 GLASSY MIXED PHASES

1.4.1 The glassy solidification of polymer solutions

The non-equilibrium phenomena described in the previous sections are not limited to one-component systems. Thus binary mixed phases, as, for example, solutions or gels, can solidify to a glass so that the overall phase may be treated from the thermodynamic point of view as a frozen state. The freezing of mixed phases has been calorimetrically investigated by Jenckel and Gorke[101,102] by dissolving glasses in low molecular solvents. Similar experiments based on volume measurements were carried out by Rehage.[71]

If a glassy substance is dissolved in sufficient liquid so that the resulting solution is in internal equilibrium, an exothermic heat change and a volume contraction occur due to the fact that the glassy component attains equilibrium during the solution process.

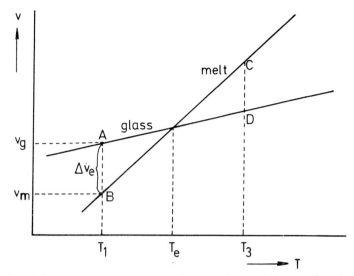

Fig. 19. Schematic representation for the dependence of the specific volume on temperature at constant pressure in the liquid and glassy states on dissolution of a glass (see text).[71]

The volume change during the solution of a glass is shown schematically in Fig. 19. A glass which is dissolved at a temperature T_1 below the temperature T_e changes its volume by the amount

$$\Delta v_e = v_m - v_g$$

assuming for simplicity the volume additivity on mixing. In the process the glass changes from a volume v_g into a state of internal equilibrium which is represented by the volume v_m on the extension of the liquid curve.

The volume difference Δv_e may be called the 'freeze-in volume' by analogy with the term 'freeze-in heat' formed by Jenckel and Gorke for the isothermal enthalpy change during the solution of a glass. The 'freeze-in heat' and the 'freeze-in volume' effects are superimposed on the real heat of solution and volume of mixing, based on molecular interactions. According to Jenckel and Gorke this is the reason why high molecular solution processes are often exothermic due to the liberation of the 'freeze-in heat'.

If the amount of liquid dissolved in the glassy polymeric substance is small enough for the mixed phase to remain frozen-in, it is assumed that the solvent, which is in a state of internal equilibrium by itself, changes into the glassy state. In Fig. 19 this corresponds to a transition of the solvent

from C to D at the temperature T_3 which is above the glass temperature†
of the solvent. The resulting volume decrease leads to a contraction caused
by the freezing-in of the solvent. Thus the 'freeze-in heat' and the 'freeze-in
volume' of the solvent in the glassy mixed phase superimpose themselves
on the real heats and volumes of solution. The representation of the concentration dependence of the functions free enthalpy, enthalpy and
volume in binary mixed phases has been extensively studied.[71]
[101,102,104-8]

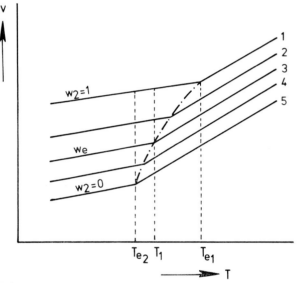

Fig. 20.   *Schematic volume–temperature diagram of two pure components and
their mixtures in the glassy and liquid states. Dashed–dotted curve = freeze-in
temperatures (see text).*[71]

In Fig. 20 the volume–temperature relations of a glassy polymeric
material and of a solvent also assumed to solidify to a glass at a sufficiently
low temperature are represented schematically, together with that of the
corresponding solutions; w_2 is the weight fraction of the polymer, w_1
that of the solvent. In this representation it has been assumed for simplicity
that the expansion coefficients of the polymer with a freeze-in temperature
T_{e1} and of the solvent with a freeze-in temperature T_{e2} are equal. It is
further assumed that the volumes of the mixtures may be derived from the
sum of the volumes of the pure components. Consequently, curves 1–5,

† From here on no difference is made between freeze-in and glass temperature.

for which the weight fractions w_2 decrease regularly by 0·25 in the same series for $w_2 = 1$ to $w_2 = 0$, are equidistant within the liquid region. Along the dashed–dotted line the glass temperature decreases as the solvent is added. The concentration at the glass formation $w_2 = w_e$ is related to the temperature T_1. At a temperature T_{e1}, the phases represented by curves 2–5 are in internal equilibrium, at a temperature T_{e2} all phases are solidified. At T_1 all phases with $w_2 > w_e$ are in a glassy state and those with $w_2 < w_e$ are in internal equilibrium.

If one presents the freeze-in temperatures as a function of concentration, one obtains, depending on the solvent, more or less bent curves, which are steepest near the freeze-in temperature of the pure polymer. In general the freeze-in temperature of a glassy polymer is lowered by the addition of a solvent as shown in Fig. 20. In some cases it is possible to follow the concentration dependence of the freeze-in temperature right down to that of the pure solvent.[100]

All solvents considerably decrease the viscosity of polymer melts with the result that place exchange processes are frozen-in at progressively lower temperatures. Basically this is the effect of the so-called plasticisers which play such a large part in the application of plastics.

1.4.2 The glassy solidification of cross-linked systems. The coexistence of glassy phases with phases in internal equilibrium

Cross-linked systems, such as swollen gels, can solidify to a glass in the same way as normal polymer solutions. At a given temperature gels can only absorb a limited amount of solvent until the saturation concentration is reached. At equilibrium the mixed gel phase coexists with the pure solvent. If the gel solidifies to a glass the heterogeneous equilibrium between the cross-linked glassy phase and the pure solvent can be established. The time to reach equilibrium increases with lower and lower temperatures. In this case the coexistence of glassy phases with phases in internal thermo-dynamic equilibrium can be examined. It has been shown that a glassy phase can only coexist with another, non-glassy phase when the hetero-geneous equilibrium between the phases is reached more quickly than the internal equilibrium within the glassy phase.[103,107,108] A frozen-in phase may be compared to a non-equilibrium state, namely a hindered chemical reaction; for example, that between oxygen and hydrogen gas. Although the chemical equilibrium is not reached at sufficiently low temperatures, the heterogeneous solubility equilibrium with a liquid phase can be reached for such a mixture of gases. The heterogeneous equilibrium between the two phases can be independently reached, whether or not the chemical equilibrium is attained. The same is true of a glassy solidified mixture which is in equilibrium with the vapour, although the internal equilibrium in the glass has not been reached. If the non-equilibrium state of the glass changes, however, the vapour pressure above the glass changes too.

Following this line of thought on the treatment of swelling equilibrium we assume, when referring to the glassy state, that the relaxation processes take place only very slowly towards the state of internal equilibrium. Under these conditions the swelling equilibrium can set in although the internal equilibrium has not been reached. These considerations have a general character and are, in principle, valid for all conceivable heterogeneous equilibria between glassy, or glassy mixed phases and other phases. The curve which at constant pressure represents the dependence of temperature on the saturation concentration in the gel is called the swelling curve. Its slope is described by eqn. (27)[109,110]

$$\left(\frac{\partial T}{\partial x^*_1}\right)_{P,s} = \frac{T(\partial \mu_1/\partial x^*_1)_{T,P}}{\Delta H_{1s}} \quad (27)$$

Here x^*_1 is the concentration of solvent expressed as base mole fraction:

$$x^*_1 = \frac{n_1}{n_1 + v^*z}$$

where n_1 is the number of moles of solvent, v^*z is the number of basic moles of the polymer (v^* = number of network chains in moles and z = number average of basic units per chains). μ_1 is the chemical potential of the solvent and ΔH_{1s} the differential heat of dilution at the swelling maximum, also called the 'final heat of dilution'. The index s refers to the saturation concentration.

It follows by definition that

$$\Delta H_{1s} \equiv \left(\frac{\partial \Delta H}{\partial n_1}\right)_{T,P,s} \quad (28)$$

where ΔH is the total heat of swelling at saturation (index s). Since in stable phases $(\partial \mu_1/\partial x^*_1)_{T,P}$ must remain positive, the trend of the swelling curve is determined by the sign of the 'final heat of dilution'.[105,110] In the athermal case $\Delta H_{1s} = 0$, i.e. $(\partial T/\partial x^*_1)_{P,s} = \infty$. This means that the saturation concentration is independent of the temperature. If ΔH_{1s} is negative (exotherm) then $(\partial T/\partial x^*_1)_{P,s}$ is also negative, i.e. with increasing temperature deswelling occurs. If ΔH_{1s} is positive (endotherm) then

$(\partial T/\partial x^*_1)_{P,s}$ is likewise positive, *i.e.* with increasing temperature the material swells further. If at the temperature T_1 the gel changes into a glassy state, the swelling curve shows a bend. This is most easily seen in the athermal case as shown in Fig. 21. Above T_1 the swelling curve is parallel with the ordinate since $\Delta H_{1s} = 0$. At the temperature T_1 the swelling

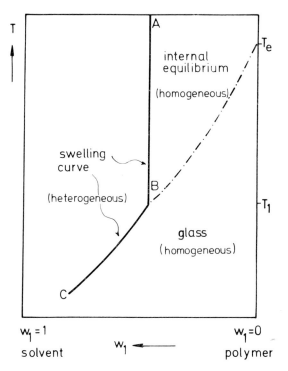

Fig. 21. Schematic representation of the swelling curve ABC *of a chemically cross-linked polymer:* w_1 = *weight fraction of the solvent;* T_e = *freeze-in temperature of the pure polymer;* T_eB = *freeze-in temperature–concentration curve of the gels.*[108]

curve BC bends down in the direction of the pure solvent. Its course indicates that the gel phase has become frozen, the freeze-in heat of the pure solvent being liberated and thus determining the trend of the swelling curve. As the gel represents a glassy mixed phase, the solvent must also be frozen inside the gel, as thermodynamics recognises macroscopically for one phase only one state of matter (crystalline, liquid, gaseous or glassy, etc.). If one assumes also athermal behaviour for different glassy concentrations, ΔH_{1s}

(in Fig. 21 below T_1) is identical with the freeze-in heat of the pure solvent
at the corresponding temperature and is therefore negative (*cf.* transition
from C to D in Fig. 19). According to eqn. (27) the frozen cross-linked
phase swells further at the swelling equilibrium as the temperature is
decreased. The downward bend at the glass temperature always occurs in
such a way that in the glassy state more solvent can be absorbed at saturation than would be the case in a state of internal equilibrium at the same
temperature. This also applies to the non-additive behaviour of enthalpy
in the gel and glassy states, because, in general, the real heats of solution
are small compared with the freeze-in heat of the solvent. This result,
which is based on pure thermodynamic reasoning, is understandable
because a glass, as compared with the equilibrium state of a melt, retains

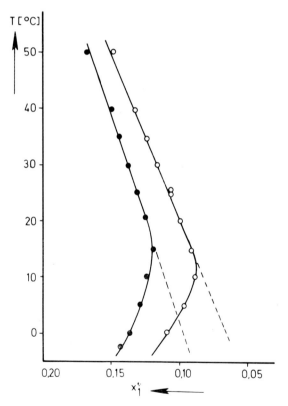

Fig. 22.   Swelling curves of polystyrene in heptane (●) and octane (○).
$x^*_1 = $ *base mole fraction of the solvent.*[107]

a structure which requires more space and can therefore absorb more solvent.

Although from a thermodynamic point of view the solvent is in a frozen state, it still retains sufficient mobility so that the heterogeneous equilibrium between the pure solvent and the glassy cross-linked mixed phase can still take place in a reasonable time at temperatures which are not too far below the glass temperature of the gel at saturation (B in Fig. 21).

In Fig. 22 the experimentally determined swelling curves for polystyrene in heptane and octane are shown.[107] It can clearly be seen that the slope of the swelling curve $(\partial T/\partial x^*_1)_{P,s}$ is positive above c. 15°C. This means that with increasing temperatures further swelling takes place. At $T < 15°C$ the trend of the swelling curve changes. As explained above, this is based on the liberation of the freeze-in heat of the solvent. If the equilibrium gels were also at internal equilibrium below the glass transition point, the swelling curves in Fig. 22 would be represented by the dashed sections of the curves which are obtained by extrapolating the swelling curves measured above the glass temperature to lower temperatures.

These examples show that mixed phases can also solidify to a glass. In the case of the swelling equilibrium it can be shown that a coexistence of glassy phases with phases in internal equilibrium is possible.

1.5   THE MOBILITY AND STRUCTURE OF GLASSY PHASES

Up to now the thermodynamic macroscopic method of interpretation has only dealt with glassy phases as such in order to emphasise the differences between them and the non-frozen phases. In the previous sections it has been shown that the glassy state, even of a single substance, can vary significantly according to its past history. In recent years great efforts have also been made to understand the fine structure of a glassy phase and to interpret it on a molecular basis. At this point it is necessary to go outside the field provided by phenomenological thermodynamics and here, with the help of a few examples, some concluding considerations are presented on the way in which problems of the fine structure of glasses can be approached. In this connection we are here particularly concerned with two questions:

1. What type of mobility can take place in glassy polymers?
2. What can be said about the microstructure?

Point 1 is dealt with in detail in Chapter 3. Here only one example will be discussed and this is based on thermodynamic measurements. It has already been mentioned that the freeze-in temperature occurs at higher temperatures at higher rates of cooling. This is shown in Fig. 23 in which the specific expansion coefficient α of a high molecular weight polystyrene $(M_n = 5 \times 10^5 \text{ g mol}^{-1})$ is represented at three different cooling rates.

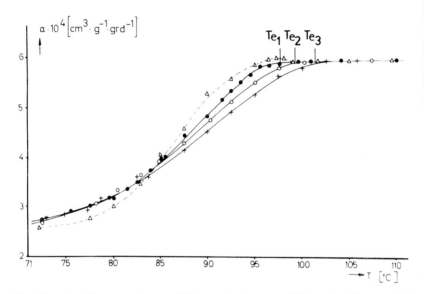

Fig. 23.   Specific expansion coefficient of polystyrene $(M_n = 5 \cdot 10^5 \text{ g mol}^{-1})$ versus temperature at three different cooling rates. $\dot{T}(^{\circ}C \ min^{-1})$: $+ = -0.33$; $\bigcirc = -0.05$; $\bullet = -0.012$; dashed line on heating $= +0.012$. T_{e3}, T_{e2}, $T_{e1} = $ corresponding freeze-in temperatures.[32]

It is known from measurements of torsional oscillation that at temperatures below the freeze-in temperature polystyrene exhibits a further transition (β-process).[112–117] Measurements of the expansion coefficient of this high molecular weight polystyrene show a small step about 50°C below T_e which relates to the β-process (Fig. 24).[111] A similar pressure-dependent step of the specific isothermal compressibility has been reported by Quach and Simha.[126a,c] Curiously the step moves to lower temperatures with increased cooling rates, thus behaving in the opposite way to the glass temperature. As this result contradicted earlier expectations it was checked by means of torsional oscillations.

The real part G' of the complex shear modulus was measured at constant frequency as a function of the temperature in the range reaching beyond T_e. The storage modulus G' is a measure of the elastically stored work of deformation. During vitrification G' increased stepwise at lower temperatures.[111] This confirms the results of the measurements of expansion coefficient. Besides the step relating to the glass formation a further step relating to the β-process was found at temperatures 30–50°C below T_e, which with an increased rate of cooling moved downwards to lower temperatures.

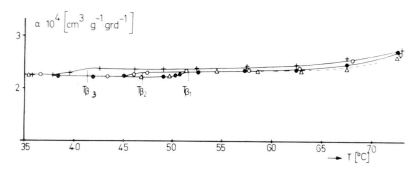

Fig. 24. Specific expansion coefficient of polystyrene versus temperature in the temperature region of the β-process. Cooling rates $\dot{T}(°C\ min^{-1})$: $+ = -0.33$; $\bigcirc = -0.05$; $\bullet = -0.012$; dashed curve on heating $= +0.012$. T_{β_3}, T_{β_2}, $T_{\beta_1} = $ corresponding freeze-in temperatures.[32]

In attempting a molecular interpretation of this result it is worthy of note that each step of G' on cooling corresponds to the freezing-in of one mechanism of molecular mobility. According to Adam the freezing-in of polystyrene can be ascribed to interaction forces between the phenyl groups of different molecules.[113] Such interaction is said to give some alignment of the phenyl groups of different molecules. Thus, some kind of 'bond' is formed between parts of molecules and these 'bonds' can be regarded as 'physical cross-linking points'.

Above the freeze-in temperature the frequency of change of position is very large, so that, on average, only a small number of physical crosslinkage points can be formed. The polymer chains can glide past each other and reach their equilibrium positions within the predetermined measuring period. As the temperature is lowered, the frequency with which the phenyl groups change their positions decreases, and a growing number of cross-linking points are formed. At the glass temperature, the density of cross-linking is so large that any regrouping of parts of the main chains is predominantly prevented. The polymer solidifies to a glass.

The β-relaxation range can also be attributed to a freezing-in of phenyl groups. Adam assumes that not all phenyl groups are frozen-in at T_e. There are probably positions in the material which do not allow of an alignment of the phenyl groups owing to steric hindrance. Some of the phenyl groups can then go on to change position even below T_e, and they will only be frozen-in at still lower temperatures.

The decrease of T_β with increasing cooling rate can now be interpreted. For equal values of T and P the volume below T_e is the larger the more rapidly the specimen is cooled. On average more space is available for the voluminous phenyl groups in a rapidly cooled specimen than if it is cooled slowly. The number of phenyl groups which can still change positions below the vitrification temperature is therefore the larger the larger is the specific volume. This is reflected in the steps of the modulus and of the expansion coefficient, which are the larger the larger is the specific volume of the specimen in the glassy state for given values of T and P. The larger the volume is the lower is the temperature T_β, for which changes of position of phenyl groups are still just possible below T_e. With rapid cooling the phenyl groups are therefore frozen at lower temperatures. With very slow cooling, on the other hand, the frequency of change of position of the phenyl groups decreases so much, even at higher temperatures, that a β-relaxation range can no longer be observed.

With this molecular interpretation the temperature dependence of G' and α can be explained. The β-relaxation range is therefore strongly dependent on the pretreatment of the material. Measurements of the torsion modulus alone are not sufficient for this interpretation; they must be supplemented by thermodynamic data, e.g. volume measurements.

The time dependence of the β-process of polystyrene could also be of significance with respect to the physical ageing of synthetic materials. It has often been proposed[117a,b,123a] that brittleness, hardening, notch hardness, etc. of amorphous polymers are closely related to the β-relaxation range. Above the β-process stresses can be relaxed by molecular rearrangement. Below the β-process molecular changes of position are hindered. In this way, mechanical work done on a specimen cannot be dissipated; the material is hard and brittle. This will be dealt with in detail in other chapters.

We have seen that with glassy polymers certain molecular mobilities can be preserved and will freeze-in only at lower temperatures. Solvent molecules can also retain their mobility to a certain degree in the glassy state of the polymerised material as was shown by Kosfeld and Jenckel[118a] from nuclear magnetic resonance measurements. If a system consists of a solid and a liquid part, the nuclear resonance spectrum shows a broad and a narrow line which are superimposed on each other. In Fig. 25 the line

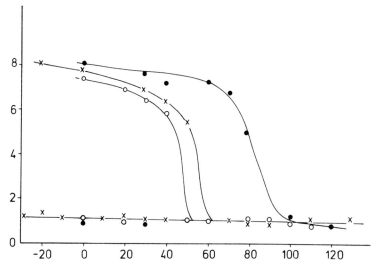

Fig. 25. *Half-width of NMR-absorption versus temperature in the system polystyrene–cyclohexane:*[118] $\bullet = 5\cdot2\%\ C_6H_{12};\ \times = 10\cdot8\%\ C_6H_{12};\ \bigcirc = 14\cdot8\%\ C_6H_{12}$. *Ordinate, half-width of NMR-absorption; Abscissa, temperature (°C).*

width of the nuclear resonance signal is represented as a function of temperature in the system polystyrene–cyclohexane with various concentrations of the plasticiser. In addition to the broad line, which must be ascribed to the freezing-in of the polystyrene, a narrow line of constant half-width is clearly observed whose intensity decreases with falling temperature. This means that in the solidified glassy polystyrene some of the plasticiser molecules are nearly as mobile as they were in the liquid state. Quantitative relations of the proportion of mobile plasticiser molecules have been given on the basis of nuclear magnetic resonance experiments by Kosfeld.[118b] With decreasing temperature more and more of the plasticiser molecules become immobile. Only if the temperature falls to 100°C below T_e is the intensity of the narrow line no longer clearly noticeable, so that then a mobility of the solvent molecules can no longer be detected.

With carbon tetrachloride as solvent, which does not contain protons, no narrow nuclear resonance line was found but only the absorption signal of the polystyrene. This shows that the narrow absorption band must be ascribed to the mobility of the plasticiser (Fig. 26).

As regards the microstructure of a glassy phase, it has already been pointed out in Section 1.1 that intermediate states are possible between the

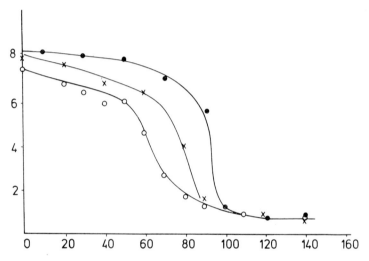

Fig. 26.   Half-width of NMR-absorption versus temperature in the system poly-styrene–carbon   tetrachloride:[118]   ● = 10·6% CCl_4;   × = 15·2% CCl_4;   ○ = 21·5% CCl_4. Ordinate, half-width of NMR-absorption; Abscissa, temperature (°C).

truly amorphous and the truly crystalline states and that these states can be obtained depending on the past history of the specimen and the way in which the experiment was conducted. An example of this is polyvinyl-chloride, which has been known for a long time to form a gel in suitable solvents. Now, gel formation is an indication of cross-linking. As gelation is also observed if there is no chemical cross-linking, some kind of physical cross-linking must exist. X-ray radiation analysis showed that there were domains of cross-linking of a higher degree of order than that of the surrounding amorphous matrix.[119] These domains can be described as 'crystal nuclei' areas or as very minute crystallites of appreciable random-ness of orientation. They are in a sense the first stages of the ordered crystals, the latter having an appreciably higher degree of order than the

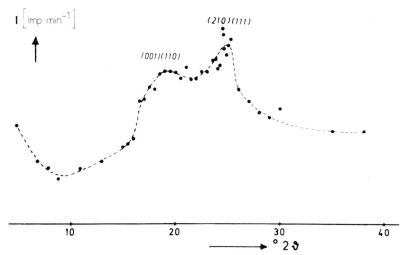

Fig. 27.   X-ray diagram of atactic PVC: I = intensity; 2ϑ = scattering angle
(see text).[119]

areas of crystal nuclei. This indicates that the borders between amorphous
and minute crystalline regions are not rigidly determined and that there
are intermediate states between the truly 'amorphous', *i.e.* completely
random orientation, and truly 'crystalline', *i.e.* the highest order of
orientation.[128,129] To prove this point, X-ray diffraction patterns of
atactic and syndiotactic polyvinylchloride were measured (Figs. 27 and
28). Atactic polyvinylchloride clearly showed two broad diffraction
maxima.

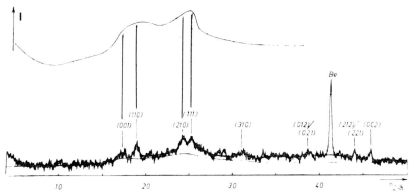

Fig. 28.   X-ray diagrams: upper curve, atactic PVC; lower curve, syndiotactic
PVC. The diagrams were taken with Cu $K_{\alpha 1}$-radiation at 25°C (see text).[119]

The syndiotactic material gave eight interferences which were interpreted in accordance with Rosen et al.[120] The degree of crystallisation was about 25%. On comparing the diagrams of atactic and syndiotactic polyvinylchloride it appears that the two maxima of scattered radiation of the atactic material indicate scattering angles at which the relatively strongest interferences of syndiotactic polyvinylchloride occur. They are the (001)- and (110)-interferences at $2\vartheta = 17°$ and 19° and the (210)- and (111)-interferences at $2\vartheta = 24·5°$ and 25·5°. This might be regarded as proof that small ordered (crystalline) regions also exist in so-called amorphous polyvinylchloride, giving rise to a three-dimensional linking of macromolecules and hence gel formation in solvents. We estimate that the degree of crystallisation is about 5%. It can be concluded from the width of the reflections that the crystal nuclei are very small and greatly disoriented. Hermann and Gerngross' model of fringe micelles[121,122] might be applicable to this case.

ACKNOWLEDGEMENTS

We wish to thank Dr Dietrich Steinkopff Verlag, Darmstadt, for permission to reproduce Figs. 8, 9, 12, 13, 15, 16, 22, 23 and the Verlag Chemie, GmbH, Weinheim/Bergstrasse, for permission to reproduce Figs. 5, 6, 7, 10, 11, 17, 18, 19, 24, 25, 26, 27, 28, 29 and Table 1.

REFERENCES

1. Tammann, G. (1922). Aggregatzustände, Leipzig.
2. Tammann, G. (1933). Der Glaszustand, Leipzig.
3. Jenckel, E. (1939). Z. phys. Chem., A **184**, 309.
4. Simon, F. (1930). Ergebn. exakt. Naturwiss., **9**, 222; (1931). Z. anorg. allg. Chem., **203**, 219.
5. Kast, W. and Prietzschk, A. (1941). Z. Elektrochemie, **47**, 112.
6. Breuer, H. (1965). Thesis, Aachen.
7. Jenckel, E. (1956). In Stuart, H. A. (ed.), Die Physik der Hochpolymeren, Vol. III, 608 f., Berlin–Göttingen–Heidelberg.
8. Volkenstein, M. V. and Ptitsyn, O. B. (1957). Soviet Phys.-Tech. Phys., **1**, 2138.
9. Jones, G. O. (1956). Glass, Methuen.
10. Illers, K.-H. (1969). Makromol. Chem., **127**, 1.
11. Wunderlich, B. and Bodily, D. M. (1963). J. Polymer Sci., Part C, **6**, 137.
12. De Donder, T. (1936). Affinity, Stanford University Press.
13. Meixner, J. (1953). Kolloid-Z., Z. Polymere, **134**, 3.
14. Meixner, J. (1954). Z. Physik, **139**, 30.
15. Haase, R. (1963). Thermodynamik der irreversiblen Prozesse, Darmstadt.

16. Jenckel, E. and Stuart, H. A. (1955). *Die Physik der Hochpolymeren*, Vol. III, 535, Berlin–Göttingen–Heidelberg.
17. Flory, P. J. (1953). *Principles of Polymer Chemistry*, New York.
18. Mandelkern, L. (1963). *Crystallization of Polymers*, McGraw-Hill Series in Advanced Chemistry.
19. Kilian, H.-G. (1967). *Kolloid-Z., Z. Polymere*, **231**, 534.
20. Zachmann, H. G. (1967). *Kolloid-Z., Z. Polymere*, **216**, 180.
21. Matsuoka, S. (1960). *J. Polymer Sci.*, **42**, 511.
22. Avrami, M. (1939). *J. Chem. Phys.*, **7**, 1103; (1940). **8**, 212; (1941). **9**, 177.
23. Evans, R. U. (1945). *Trans. Faraday Soc.*, **41**, 365.
24. Pennings, A. J. and Kiel, A. M. (1965). *Kolloid-Z., Z. Polymere*, **205**, 160.
25. Geil, Ph.-H. (1963). 'Polymer single crystals,' in *Polymer Reviews*, Interscience, New York.
26. Pechhold, W. and Blasenbrey, S. (1967). *Kolloid-Z., Z. Polymere*, **216/217**, 235; Pechhold, W. (1968). *Kolloid-Z., Z. Polymere*, **228**, 1; Baumgärtner, A., Blasenbrey, S., Dollkopf, W. and Pechhold, W. (1972). Presented at Freiburger Kolloquium.
27. Wilski, H. (1966). *Kolloid-Z., Z. Polymere*, **210**, 37; (1966). *Kunststoff-Rundschau*, **13**, 1.
28. Wunderlich, B. and Jones, L. D. (1969). *J. Macromol Sci.-Phys.*, **B 3**, 67; Wunderlich, B., Bodily, D. M. and Kaplan, M. H. (1964). *J. Appl. Phys.*, **35**, 95,
29. Wunderlich, B. and Baur, H. (1970). *Adv. Polymer Sci.*, **7**, 151.
30. Kauzmann, W. (1948). *Chem. Rev.*, **43**, 219.
31. Borchard, W. Symposium of Physics in Nauheim, 1972, presented for publication.
32. Rehage, G. (1970). *Ber. Bunsenges*, **74**, 796.
33. Boyer, R. F. (1952). *Changements de Phases*, Comptes Rendues IIième Réunion, 383, Paris.
34. Boyer, R. F. and Spencer, R. S. (1946). *Adv. in Colloid Sci.*, Vol. II, Interscience, New York.
35. Boyer, R. F. and Spencer, R. S. (1945). *J. Appl. Phys.*, **16**, 594.
36. Gee, G. (1947). *Quarterly Reviews*, **1**, 272.
37. Buchdahl, R. and Nielsen, L. E. (1950). *J. Appl. Phys.*, **21**, 482.
38. Witte, R. S. and Anthony, R. L. (1951). *J. Appl. Phys.*, **22**, 689.
39. Bauer, E. (1952). *Changements de Phases*, Comptes Rendues IIième Réunion, 3, Paris.
40. Münster, A. and Staverman, A. J. (1955). *In* Stuart, H. A. (ed.), *Die Physik der Hochpolymeren*, Vol. III, 414, Berlin–Heidelberg–Göttingen.
41. Ueberreiter, K. and Bruns, W. (1966). *Ber. Bunsenges*, **70**, 17.
42. Ehrenfest, P. (1933). *Proc. Kon. Akad. Wetensch. Amsterdam*, **36**, 153.
43a. O'Reilly, J. M. (1962). *J. Polymer Sci.*, **57**, 429.
43b. Gee, G. (1966). *Polymer*, **7**, 177.
44. McKinney, J. E., Belcher, H. V. and Marvin, R. S. (1960). *Trans. Rheol.*, **4**, 347.
45. Ferry, J. D. and Stratton, R. A. (1960). *Kolloid-Z., Z. Polymere*, **171**, 107.
46. Goldstein, M. (1963). *J. Chem. Phys.*, **39**, 3369.
47. Gibbs, J. H. (1960). 'Nature of the glass transition and the vitreous state', *in* J. D. Mackenzie (ed.), *Modern Aspects of the Vitreous State*, Butterworths, London.
48. Bianchi, U. (1965). *J. Phys. Chem.*, **69**, 1497.
49. O'Reilly, J. M. (1964). *In* J. D. Mackenzie (ed.), *Modern Aspects of the Vitreous State*, Vol. III, 59, Butterworths, London.
50. Goldstein, M. (1964). *In* J. D. Mackenzie (ed.), *Modern Aspects of the Vitreous State*, Vol. III, 90, Butterworths, London.
51. Chompff, A. J. (1971). *In* Chompff, A. J. and Newman, S. (ed.), *Polymer Networks*, p. 145, Plenum Press, New York–London.

52. Prigogine, I. and Defay, R. (1950). *Thermodynamique chimique*, Chap. 19, 308.
53. Meixner, J. (1952). Changements de Phases, 432, Paris.
54. Davies, R. O. (1952). Changements de Phases, 425, Paris; (1953). *Adv. in Phys.*, 2, 370.
55. Davies, R. O. and Jones, G. O. (1953). *Proc. Roy. Soc.*, 217 A, 26.
56. Staverman, A. J. (1966). *Rheol. Acta*, 5, 283.
57. Fox, T. G. and Flory, P. J. (1950). *J. Appl. Phys.*, 21, 581; Bondi, A. (1954). *J. Phys. Chem.*, 58, 929; (1964). *J. Polymer Sci.*, A2, 3159.
58. Kanig, G. (1969). *Kolloid-Z.*, Z. Polymere, 233, 829.
59. Maurer, R. D. (1957). *J. Am. Ceram. Soc.*, 40, 211.
60. Hozumi, S. (1971). *Polymer J.*, 2, 756.
61. Shihkin, N. J. (1960). *Soviet Phys. Solid State*, 2, 358.
62. Hellwege, K.-H., Knappe, W. and Lehmann, P. (1961). *Kolloid-Z.*, Z. Polymere, 183, 110.
63. Heydemann, P. and Guicking, H. D. (1963). *Kolloid-Z.*, Z. Polymere, 193, 16.
64. Koplin, H. (1962). Thesis, Aachen.
65. Rehage, G. and Breuer, H. (1967). *J. Polymer Sci.*, C 16, 2299.
66. Gibbs, J. H. and DiMarzio, E. A. (1958). *J. Chem. Phys.*, 28, 373.
67. Adam, G. and Gibbs, J. H. (1965). *J. Chem. Phys.*, 43, 139.
68. Boyer, R. F. and Spencer, R. S. (1944). *J. Appl. Phys.*, 15, 398.
69. Goldbach, G. (1966). Thesis, Aachen.
70. Kovacs, A. J. (1952). Changements de Phases, 428, Paris.
71. Rehage, G. (1955). Thesis, Aachen.
72. Breuer, H. and Rehage, G. (1967). *Kolloid-Z.*, Z. Polymere, 216, 159.
73. Hildebrand, J. H. (1929). *Phys. Rev.*, 34, 984.
74. Haward, R. N., Breuer, H. and Rehage, G. (1966). *Polymer Letters*, 4, 375.
75. Haward, R. N. (1970). *J. Macromol. Sci.-Revs. Macromol. Chem.*, C4, 191.
76. Hirai, N. and Eyring, H. (1959). *J. Polymer Sci.*, 37, 51.
77. Ptitsyn, O. B. (1955). *Rep. Acad. Soc. USSR*, 103, 1045.
78. Adam, G. (1962). *Kolloid-Z.*, Z. Polymere, 180, 11.
79. Adam, G. (1964). *Kolloid-Z.*, Z. Polymere, 195, 1.
80. Tobolsky, A. and Eyring, H. (1943). *J. Chem. Phys.*, 11, 129.
81. Kubat, J. (1953). *Kolloid-Z.*, Z. Polymere, 134, 205.
82. Bueche, F. (1962). *J. Chem. Phys.*, 36, 2940.
83. Staverman, A. J. and Schwarzl, F. (1956). *In* Stuart, H. A. (ed.), *Physik der Hochpolymeren*, Vol. IV, 1, Berlin–Göttingen–Heidelberg.
84. Jenckel, E. (1937). *Z. Elektrochem. angew. physik. Chem.*, 43, 796.
85. Rehage, G. and Jenckel, E., unpublished results (see Jenckel, E., ref. 16).
86. Spencer, R. S. and Boyer, R. F. (1946). *J. Appl. Phys.*, 17, 398.
87. Kovacs, A. J. (1954). Thesis, Fac. Sci., Paris.
88. Kovacs, A. J. (1961). *Phénomènes de Relaxation et de Fluage en Rhéologie non-linéaire*, Edité par le CNRS, Paris.
89. Kovacs, A. J. (1958). *J. Polymer Sci.*, 30, 131.
90. Kovacs, A. J. (1961). *Trans. Soc. Rheol.*, 5, 285.
91. Kovacs, A. J. (1963). *Fortschr. Hochpolym.-Forschg.*, 3, 394.
92. Hozumi, S., Wakabayashi, T. and Sugihara, K. (1964). *Rep. Progr. Polymer Physics Japan*, 7, 105.
93. Hozumi, S., Wakabayashi, T. and Watanabe, H. (1964). *Rep. Progr. Polymer Physics Japan*, 7, 101.
94. Goldbach, G. and Rehage, G. (1967). *Rheol. Acta*, 6, 30.
95. Goldbach, G. and Rehage, G. (1967). *J. Polymer Sci.*, C 16, 2289.
96. Rehage, G. and Goldbach, G. (1966). *Ber. Bunsenges*, 70, 1144.
97. Goldbach, G. and Rehage, G. (1966). *Rheol. Acta*, 5, 302.

98. Rehage, G. and Goldbach, G. (1966). *Kolloid-Z., Z. Polymere*, **206**, 166.
99. Kästner, S. (1965). *Kolloid-Z., Z. Polymere*, **206**, 143.
100. Jenckel, E. and Heusch, R. (1953). *Kolloid-Z., Z. Polymere*, **130**, 89.
101. Jenckel, E. and Gorke, K. (1954). *Z. Naturforschg.*, **7a**, 440.
102. Jenckel, E. and Gorke, K. (1956). *Z. Elektrochem.*, **60**, 579.
103. Rehage, G. (1959). *Z. Elektrochem.*, **63**, 987.
104. Jenckel, E. (1955). *Z. Kunststoffe*, **45**, 3.
105. Rehage, G. (1964). *Kolloid-Z., Z. Polymere*, **194**, 16.
106. Rehage, G. (1964). *Kolloid-Z., Z. Polymere*, **196**, 97.
107. Rehage, G. (1964). *Kolloid-Z., Z. Polymere*, **199**, 1.
108. Jenckel, E., Adam, G., Illers, K.-H., Kosfeld, R. and Rehage, G. (1962). *In* Wolf (ed.), *Kunststoffe*, Vol 1, 160, Berlin–Göttingen–Heidelberg.
109. Breitenbach, J. W. and Frank, H. F. (1948). *Mh. Chemie*, **79**, 531.
110. Rehage, G. (1958). *Verhandlgsber. d. Kolloid-Ges.*, **18**, 47.
111. Goldbach, G. and Rehage, G. (1967). *Kolloid-Z., Z. Polymere*, **216/217**, 56.
112. Illers, K.-H. and Breuer, H. (1961). *Kolloid-Z., Z. Polymere*, **176**, 110.
113. Adam, G. (1958). Diplomarbeit, Aachen.
114. Illers, K.-H., (1958). Thesis, Aachen.
115. Hemmer, E. A. (1954). Diplomarbeit, Aachen.
116. Kosfeld, R. (1960). *Kolloid-Z., Z. Polymere*, **172**, 182.
117. Schmieder, K. and Wolf, K. (1953). *Kolloid-Z., Z. Polymere*, **134**, 149.
117a. Heijboer, J. (1969). *Brit. Pol. J.*, **1**, 1.
117b. Boyer, R. F. (1968). *Polymer Eng. & Sci.*, **8**, 161.
118a. Kosfeld, R. and Jenckel, E. (1959). *Kolloid-Z., Z. Polymere*, **165**, 136.
118b. Kosfeld, R. (1965). Advances in Chem. Ser. 48, Am. Chem. Soc. 49.
119. Rehage, G. and Halboth, H. (1968). *Makromol. Chem.*, **119**, 235.
120. Rosen, J., Burleigh, P. H. and Gillespie, J. F. (1961). *J. Polymer Sci.*, **54**, 31.
121. Gerngross, O., Hermann, K. and Abitz, W. (1930). *Z. physik. Chem.* (B), **10,**3 71; (1930). *Biochem. Z.*, **228**, 409.
122. Gerngross, O., Hermann, K. and Lindemann, R. (1932). *Kolloid-Z., Z. Polymere*, **60**, 276.
123a. Boyer, R. F. (1963). *Rubber Chem. Technol.*, **36**, 1303.
123b. Halden, R. A. and Simha, R. (1968). *J. Appl. Phys.*, **39**, 1890.
124. Dale, W. C. and Rogers, C. E. (1972). *J. Appl. Pol. Sci.*, **16**, 21.
125a. Ichihara, S., Komatsu, A., Tsujita, Y., Nose, T. and Hata, T. (1971). *Polymer J.*, **2**, 530.
125b. Ichihara, S., Komatsu, A. and Hata, T. (1971). *Polymer J.*, **2**, 642.
125c. Ichihara, S., Komatsu, A. and Hata, T. (1971). *Polymer J.*, **2**, 650.
126a. Quach, A. (1971). Thesis, Case Western Research University.
126b. Quach, A. and Simha, R. (1972). *J. Phys. Chem.*, **76**, 416.
126c. Quach, A. and Simha, R. (1971). *J. Appl. Phys.*, **42**, 4606.
127. Manabe, S. and Kobayashi, N. *et al.* (1970). *J. Chem. Soc. Japan, Ind. Chem. Sect.*, **73**, 1557.
128. Kargin, V. A. (1958). *J. Polym. Sci.*, Part C, **30**, 247.
129. Kashmiri, M. I. and Sheldon, R. P. (1969). *Polymer Letters*, **7**, 51.
130. Gutzow, I. (1972). *Z. Physik., Chem.*, (B), **81**, 195.

CHAPTER 2

X-RAY DIFFRACTION STUDIES OF THE STRUCTURE OF AMORPHOUS POLYMERS

J. R. FITZPATRICK AND BRYAN ELLIS

2.1 INTRODUCTION

The purpose of the present chapter is to review the contribution of X-ray diffraction studies to the elucidation of the structure of glassy amorphous polymers. The general theory of X-ray diffraction by matter has been treated in many texts and an up-to-date account is that of Warren[1] which has sections dealing with the application of X-ray methods to amorphous materials. A very thorough treatment was given by Hosemann and Bagchi[2] with a preface which contains an interesting short critical review of the historical development of X-ray diffraction studies. The application of X-ray diffraction methods to polymers has been the subject of a textbook[3] which deals with both theoretical interpretations and experimental methods and contains a listing of the crystallographic data available for about 270 polymers (up to 1968 in an Appendix compiled by R. L. Miller); however, crystalline polymers are beyond the scope of this review. Here we will be concerned with amorphous polymers in which the X-ray scattering is observed in Laue photographs as a diffuse amorphous halo similar in general features to that obtained from other amorphous structures, such as gases, liquids and inorganic glasses.

A typical diffractogram for an amorphous polymer, natural rubber, is given in Fig. 1(a), and in 1(b) the experimental method of making such measurements is illustrated. Laue photographs are given in Fig. 1(c). Although the general principles for the analysis of the X-ray scattering from amorphous materials were developed many years ago[1] (Debye,[4] 1915, and Zernicke and Prins,[5] 1927) there have been far fewer studies of amorphous materials than of crystalline solids.

The X-ray scattering curve for partially crystalline polymers has 'sharp

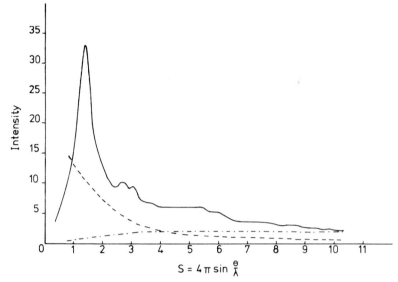

Fig. 1(a). *X-ray diffraction curve* $I(S)$ vs. (S) *for natural rubber.*[119] ——— *total diffracted intensity;* $-----$ f^2—*the atomic scattering;* $-\cdot-\cdot-\cdot$ *Compton (incoherent) scattering* (see *Sections 2.2.3, 2.2.4 and 2.6*).

peaks' due to scattering from the crystalline regions together with a broad diffuse scattering from the amorphous phase. For quantitative measurements it is necessary to separate these two forms of scattering in order to estimate crystalline:amorphous ratios,[6] and also for accurate intensity measurements for crystal structure determinations. Interpretation along these lines implies that a two phase (crystalline-amorphous) model is satisfactory for polycrystalline partially amorphous polymers. This is, of

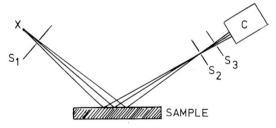

Fig. 1(b). *Geometrical arrangement of the specimen for diffractometry with symmetrical reflection. X is the X-ray source;* S_1, S_2 *and* S_3 *are slits; C is a counter. In the experimental arrangement used for the measurements in Fig.* 1(a), *a bent crystal monochromator was inserted between the sample and* S_2.

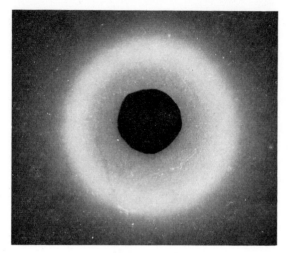

(i) unstrained.

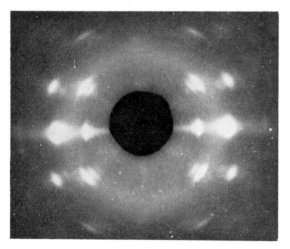

(ii) stretched to about 650% *extension. Natural rubber crystallises on extension but with an oriented amorphous polymer the diffuse halo has an azimuthal variation of intensity* (see *Section* 2.4).

Fig. 1(c).   *X-ray Laue photographs of vulcanised rubber.*

X-ray Laue photograph is by Dr I. H. Hall, reproduced with permission from Introduction to Polymer Science, *L. R. G. Treloar, Wykeham Publications* (*London*) *Ltd.,* 1970.

course, an approximation since there may be more than one crystal form, crystal imperfections of many different types[7] and the boundary of the crystallites may be diffuse. Refined methods have been developed by Ruland[8] and others to determine structural parameters in non-crystalline and partially crystalline solids such as polymers.[9]

It is convenient to discuss X-ray measurements at large and small scattering angles separately. In all X-ray measurements there is a reciprocal relationship between scattering angle and real space dimensions. Thus, in normal and wide-angle X-ray scattering experiments the measurable structural features have dimensions of 1 to 10 Å; which is the distance between the first and perhaps up to the fifth nearest atomic neighbours. In small-angle X-ray scattering (SAXS) the measurable structures have dimensions of 50 to 1000 Å, which is of the order of size found in colloidal dispersions, such as the separation of crystallites in polycrystalline polymers, para-crystalline structures and dispersed phases in bulk polymers.[10]

In general the interpretation of X-ray scattering measurements of amorphous materials would be aided by the determination of structural parameters using other methods, such as birefringence, or infra-red dichroism, which would, for example, reveal any preferred orientation in the sample (see Section 2.3.2). An alternative technique is neutron scattering when both the elastic and inelastic scattering can be measured to obtain information about the structure and the vibrational spectrum of amorphous solids. Leadbetter et al.[11] have reviewed the application of neutron scattering to amorphous solids and the inelastic scattering has been used to determine the low frequency vibrational motions of polymers.[12,13] However, these other techniques are beyond the scope of this chapter; here the application of X-ray methods to amorphous polymers will be reviewed.

2.2 THE INTERACTION OF X-RAYS WITH MATTER

The interaction of electromagnetic radiation with matter has been discussed at length in standard texts[14,15] and in particular the scattering of X-rays has been dealt with in detail in manuals on their application to structure determination.[16,17] Thus it would be inappropriate to give full derivations here, but the main effects are recalled by short descriptions which will serve as definitions. An outline of the interactions of X-rays with matter is given because an appreciation of these effects is essential for an understanding of the treatment of experimental X-ray scattering measurements.

2.2.1 Scattering by a free electron[18]

Electromagnetic waves such as X-rays are accompanied by a periodically changing electric field as they proceed outward from their source. An electron in the path of such a wave is excited to periodic vibrations by the changing electric field and thus now becomes a source of electromagnetic waves of the same frequency and wavelength and there is a new spherical wave front with the electron at its centre. This process is known as scattering and it occurs in all directions, but the intensity has an angular dependence. This angular dependence is given by the Thomson eqn. (1). (After J. J. Thomson, 1898)

$$I_r = \frac{I_0}{r^2} \cdot \frac{e^4}{m^2 c^4} \cdot \frac{1}{2}(1 + \cos^2 2\theta) \tag{1}$$

where 2θ is defined in Fig. 2, I_0 is the incident intensity and I_r that scattered at distance r from a single electron of charge e and mass m.

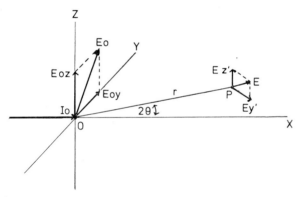

Fig. 2.   *Classical scattering of an unpolarised primary beam of X-rays by a single free electron at* 0. *Scattered intensity at P is* $I = (c/8\pi)\langle E^2 \rangle$ *and the orienta-tional dependence by eqn. (1). c is the velocity of light and* **E** *is the electric vector which is resolved into components at O and P.*

The term $\frac{1}{2}(1 + \cos^2 2\theta)$ is called the polarisation factor although it enters the equation because the incident beam is unpolarised. The second term is equal to $7\cdot940\ 30 \times 10^{-26}$ cm^2 and is called the Thomson factor. From this factor it is readily seen that scattering of X-rays is produced predominantly by electrons; scattering by protons is negligible since they have a rest mass about 1800 times greater than that of the electron, and the Thomson factor is inversely proportional to the square of the mass of the scattering particle.

It is convenient to consider the scattering power of a sample to be equivalent to the number of free and independent electrons with scattering according to eqn. (1) that would be required to give the same scattered intensity as would be observed from the sample.

2.2.2 Interference among scattered waves[19]

For an object which contained only two electrons, Fig. 3, the phase shift between the scattered waves is:

$$\alpha = \frac{2\pi}{\lambda} \cdot (\text{Difference in path length})$$

$$\alpha = 2\pi s \cdot x \tag{2}$$

It will be seen that the scattering vector $s = (2 \sin \theta)/\lambda$ or $k = 2\pi s$ is of paramount importance in the discussion of X-ray scattering. For an object

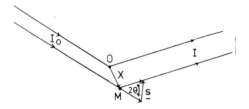

Fig. 3.   Phase shift with scattering from two points.

with n electrons in positions $x_1, x_2, \ldots, x_n$ the scattered amplitude is given by:

$$A(s) = A_0 \sum_{j=1}^{n} \exp - (2\pi is \cdot x_j) \equiv A_0 \sum_{j=1}^{n} \exp - (i k \cdot x_j) \tag{3}$$

The observed scattered intensity is obtained from the square of the amplitude and replacement of summation by integration over volume element dx^3

$$I(s) = |A(s)|^2 = \int P(x) \cdot \exp - (2\pi is \cdot x) \, dx^3 \tag{4}$$

where $P(x) = \int \rho(u)\rho(u - x) \, du^3$ is the Patterson distribution which is the product of the electronic densities at two points separated by the vector x.[20]

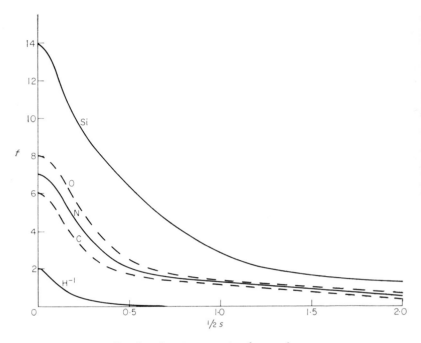

Fig. 4.   *Atomic scattering factors f* vs. s.

2.2.3   Atomic scattering factor†[21]

For an isolated atom with atomic number Z the scattered X-rays will be the resultant of scattering by all the Z electrons. Thus, using eqn. (3) and introducing an electron density $\rho(\mathbf{x})$ and replacing the summation by an integration over the volume element dx^3 eqn. (5) is obtained.

$$f(\mathbf{s}) = \int \rho(\mathbf{x}) \exp - (2\pi i \mathbf{s} \cdot \mathbf{x}) \, dx^3 \qquad (5)$$

which defines the atomic structure factor $f(\mathbf{s})$. It is in fact possible for $\rho(\mathbf{x})$ to be calculated and tables of atomic scattering factors are readily available.[22] Factors for typical atoms with lower atomic numbers are given in Fig. 4. This graph shows that the scattering decreases as the scattering vector $\mathbf{s}$ increases. Also, the scattering from hydrogen is very small and there is little difference between carbon and nitrogen. Thus to recapitulate it is directly related to the number of scattering electrons per atom, the atomic number, as given by eqn. (5), via $\rho(\mathbf{x})$. Measured scattered

† This is also called the 'atomic structure factor'.

intensities have to be corrected for atomic scattering before it is possible to obtain structural information on the spacial arrangements of the atoms in non-crystalline solids.

2.2.4 Compton scattering[23]

Only part of the scattered radiation has the same wavelength as the incident X-rays, the rest has a slightly longer wavelength which depends on the angle of scattering. The effect was discovered by Compton (1926) and is

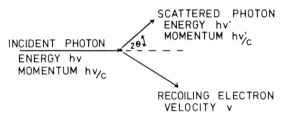

Fig. 5.   Compton scattering.

interpreted on a corpuscular model, that is, the impact of a photon with an electron, Fig. 5. In the absence of relativistic effects for a free electron the following relations are obeyed:

Conservation of energy

$$h\nu = h\nu' + \tfrac{1}{2}m\upsilon^2 \tag{6}$$

Conservation of momentum

$$\frac{h\nu}{c} \cdot I_0 = \frac{h\nu'}{c} \cdot I + m\upsilon \tag{7}$$

Since there is only a small change in frequency

$$\lambda' = \lambda + d\lambda$$

$$d\lambda = \frac{2h}{mc} \sin^2 \theta = 0.048 \sin^2 \theta$$

$$= 0.024(1 - \cos 2\theta)$$

The Compton scattering is independent of wavelength and increases with scattering angle. It is very important to have a correct estimate of the Compton scattering at large values of the scattering vector **s**, especially for the determination of radial distribution functions (r.d.f.—*see* Section 2.6) and is more troublesome in studies of materials consisting of mainly light atoms such as carbon.

In the case of a bound electron, eqns. (6) and (7) are not obeyed exactly, but the Compton scattering covers a band of frequencies with average values given by eqns. (6) and (7), due to motion of the bound electrons. Because Compton scattered light has a different wavelength from the incident light it is not possible for phase coherence to exist, and so Compton scattering is usually referred to as incoherent scattering. In normal X-ray scattering it is found that there is both coherent and incoherent (Compton) scattering. The total intensity scattered per electron ($I_{coh} + I_{incoh}$) is given by the classical formula of Thomson, eqn. (1). Thus I_{incoh} is given by

$$I_{incoh} = I_e - I_{coh}$$
$$= I_e(1 - f^2)$$

where f^2 is given by an equation of similar form to (5).

For an atom with Z electrons the coherent scattering amplitude is the sum of the scattering from each electron

$$I_{coh} = f^2 I_e = \left(\sum_1^z f_j\right)^2 \cdot I_e$$

where f_j is the scattering factor for the jth electron given by an equation of similar form to (5). Also, for an atom with Z electrons

$$I_{incoh} = \sum_1^z (1 - f_j^2) \cdot I_e$$

In studies of amorphous materials the observed intensities have to be corrected for the Compton, incoherent, scattering because it is independent of the spatial arrangement of the atoms.

As well as correcting for the atomic scattering factor (Section 2.2.3) and the Compton scattering it may be necessary to correct for absorption in the material and for other factors.[24]

2.3   ORDER AND ORIENTATION IN POLYMERS

2.3.1   Order

The problem of order in polymers has been reviewed[25] and Robinson[26] has posed the essential problem in the form of two limiting postulates; the first is a quasi-crystalline model for the amorphous state, in which polymer chains collect into 'bundles' (after Kargin[27]). The other is that in an amorphous polymer there is no ordering of polymer chains in the bulk, and that the random coil prediction of the mean-end-to-end distance, the chain displacement length, is the only parameter required to specify the 'order', or rather lack of it, in an amorphous polymer. Robinson has attempted to develop a method for the computation of the density of an amorphous polymer and from his calculations concludes that these two models are not mutually exclusive, but it would appear that this cannot be so, because the random coil model precludes the occurrence of locally ordered regions. Kurata and Stockmayer[28] take a different point of view and cite the work of Tchen[29] in support of their position.

In the specification of a polymer it is necessary to define molecular factors which may affect packing in the amorphous state. Molecular geometry has been discussed from this point of view by both Vainshstein[30] and Alexander[31] as well as in polymer textbooks.[32] It is well known that lack of a high degree of tacticity will prevent a polymer from crystallising, but there has been much less work reported on the effect of structural variables on molecular packing in the amorphous state (see pp. 9–25 and Ch. 3).

In two dimensions it is possible to use a diagram,[33] Fig. 6, to illustrate the type of order that may be present in a polymer, which obviously could be generalised to three dimensions with a solid model. A diagram, such as Fig. 6, can also be used as a model for a polycrystalline polymer with crystallites in an amorphous matrix, but it is necessary to specify the minimum dimensions of a unit of matter which will be regarded as crystalline. Ruland has developed methods for determination of the crystallinity and disorder parameters of polymers and applied these methods to nylons[34] and more recently to the small-angle scattering from carbon fibres produced by controlled thermal treatment of polymeric precursors.[35] These methods have been applied to determine the degree of disorder in cellulose fibres and cellophane[36] and Ruland[8] has given a general review of the problems of the determination of the structure of amorphous materials from X-ray diffraction measurements.

Other methods such as light scattering may be used to determine the structure of amorphous materials[37] and this has been applied to polymers[38] such as amylose films[39] where the problems are similar to those in cellulose.

Intermediate degrees of order may be characterised as 'para-crystals'.[40] A single para-crystal is defined as a structure consisting of an individual lattice, but the lattice vectors change both their magnitude and direction from cell to cell. Interpretation of para-crystallinity in amorphous silica,[41] polyvinylchloride and polyacrylonitrile has been attempted.[42]

Gutman[43] has considered the specification of order in amorphous

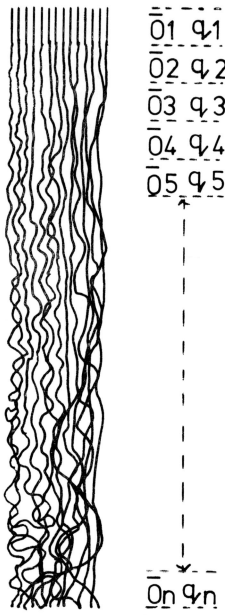

Fig. 6. Schematic mass-order distribution. $\overline{O}_1 \to \overline{O}_n$ *specified order;* $q_1 \to q_n$, q_i *represents the quantity of the sample with order* O_i.

polymers in terms of small random disturbances of the lattice spacing considering one dimension only. Fleming[44] has disputed this analysis and Gutman has replied.[45] The more general problem of mathematical models for one- and two-dimensional amorphous structures has been discussed by Cooper and Auborg.[46] A model[47] for glassy silica has been constructed with distributions of both Si–O– bond lengths and Si–O–Si bond angles. Use of this model has allowed calculation of some of the properties of vitreous silica, such as the vibration spectra.[48,49]

The problem of order and structure in amorphous polymers is an active area of research.[50] The controversy referred to at the beginning of this section has been discussed in detail by Tonelli[51] who summarises the evidence in favour of the formation of local ordered aggregates, 'bundles'. However, he concludes from calculations based on the rotational isomeric state model for polyethylene and comparison with experimental measurements that there is little segmental order in bulk polymers. Also he presents arguments[52] against the existence of local order in amorphous polymers below their glass transition temperatures deduced from thermal effects. Despite the claims of the protagonists these questions have not yet been resolved. Whilst it should be possible to define experimentally verifiable criteria for order it will not be possible to draw generalised conclusions from the study of only a few amorphous polymers. In fact the degree of order in a specific polymer may well depend on the thermal and strain history of the test specimen.

2.3.2 Orientation

Orientation has been discussed generally, both of crystallites and of the polymeric chains in an amorphous or a partially crystalline sample.[53,54] It is possible to define an orientation vector[55] which for instance for polyethylene is perpendicular to the plane defined by the two hydrogen and the carbon atoms of the methylene group. For an unoriented polymer there is a uniform distribution of these vectors. Stein and others have followed Hermans in defining for three axes α, β and ε an orientational function:

$$f_\alpha = \tfrac{1}{2} (3 \langle \cos^2 \alpha \rangle - 1) \qquad (8)$$

The average value $\langle \cos^2 \alpha \rangle = \tfrac{1}{3}$ for a uniform spherical distribution, i.e. $f_\alpha = 0$ when there is no preferred orientation. There are three functions similar to eqn. (8), one for each axis and they are mutually related by:

$$f_\alpha + f_\beta + f_\varepsilon = 0 \qquad (9)$$

Orientation factors can be expressed in terms of a series of spherical harmonics and Legendre functions.[56,57]

It is also possible to discuss the types of orientation in terms of operations on an ideal crystal. Distribution functions can be defined for such operations as shifts, turns and net distortions. By a combination of these operations on a perfect crystal it is possible to obtain a random orientation.[58]

Stein and Read[56] have written a very useful critical assessment of the methods for the determination of orientation in amorphous polymers. These methods include birefringence,[59] infra-red dichroism,[60] visible dichroism of dyed polymers, polarised fluorescence and the effect of orientation on thermal conductivity and expansion and diamagnetic anisotropy.[61] Recently[62] molecular orientation in drawn atactic (non-crystalline)-polymethyl methacrylate has been measured by broadline nuclear magnetic resonance. The method is a development of that previously used for semi-crystalline polymers and demands high accuracy in the determination of the second moments of the n.m.r. absorption signal.[63]

2.4   DIFFRACTION OF X-RAYS BY AMORPHOUS MATERIALS

The diffraction of X-rays by amorphous materials, that is, disordered substances is characterised by a distribution function $g(r)$ which is determined by the effective atomic packing density. There is no distinct difference between the functions corresponding to compressed gases, liquids or vitreous solids and early work in this field has been reviewed and discussed in standard texts.[64,65,66] The experimentally observed scattered intensity is shown in Fig. 1 and in all cases there is a large maximum which may be followed at larger values of s (or $\sin 2\theta$) by several less pronounced maxima. In some cases, such as amorphous atactic polystyrene, there is a subsidiary maximum at smaller values of s which must be related to longer range order.

Early X-ray studies of natural rubber have been reviewed[67] and the glass transition in polystyrene and polymethyl methacrylate has been investigated using X-ray methods.[68] X-ray diffraction patterns for polymers have been compiled, using a standard experimental procedure, and includes both crystalline and amorphous polymers.[69] Ruland[70] determined the structural parameters of small aromatic systems in non-crystalline solids using a least squares analysis for diffuse scattering developed by Diamond.[71] Vainshstein[72] has defined a density distribution, $D(\alpha)$, which specifies the probability that the molecular axis will deviate from the principal axis by an angle α. The operations of shifts, turns and net distortions (Section 2.3.2) can be related to $D(\alpha)$ which can be determined from X-ray diffraction measurements.

For atactic polystyrene the relative intensities of the subsidiary and main maxima (for Cu $K_\alpha - 2\theta \sim 10°$ and $19°$ respectively[68]) are dependent on the orientation of the sample, Fig. 7, which has been correlated with

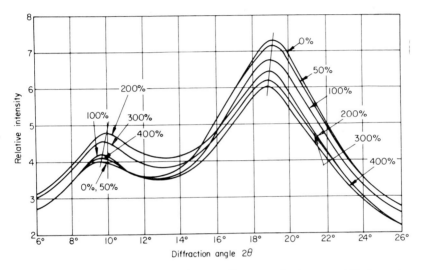

Fig. 7. X-ray spectrometer curves of uniaxially oriented polystyrene; % elongation is indicated on the curves. (Reproduced from Hsiao, C. C. (1960). J. Poly. Sci., 47, 251, by permission of John Wiley and Sons Inc.)

strength measurements.[73] The suggestion that the positions of these maxima shift with increased draw ratio requires confirmation, and from preliminary experiments it would seem that the accuracy of these measurements is not sufficient to be certain that such a shift occurs but the change in relative intensity with orientation has been confirmed[74] and previously it was reported that a separation of the inner arc (Laue photograph) occurs for oriented polystyrene.[75] From general considerations it would be expected that increased longer range order introduced by drawing would cause the subsidiary maximum to shift to smaller values of **s** and that the main maximum would remain unchanged, since the main contribution to the main maximum is from first, second and third neighbours which would be unaffected by increased orientation and order. However, further experimental work is required on the effect of orientation on the angular dependence of the scattered intensity.

The results of X-ray diffraction measurements on amorphous polymers have often been treated by insertion of the value of θ_m (i.e. the value of θ corresponding to the main intensities maximum, Fig. 1) into the Bragg equation and calculating the first-order reflection (i.e. $n = 1$) which is then called a 'd' spacing. This procedure is not valid; even for diatomic molecules the Bragg equation requires modification.[76] The 'modified' Bragg equation may be put into this form[76]

$$K\lambda = 2x_m \sin \theta_m \qquad (10)$$

where x_m corresponds to the separation of a large number of pairs of atoms, and K is a constant somewhat larger than unity (usually 1·1 or 1·2). However, it is not possible to give a general expression for K because it depends on the arrangement of all the atoms and hence would have to be calculated from the complete diffraction curve, i.e. the whole of the scattered intensity curve. Also, it is incorrect to attribute maxima in the intensity curve to particular dimensions of the molecules.[76] An application of eqn. (10) is to interpret the changes in structure of an amorphous poly-carbonate due to a compressive stress.[77] Thus, for the amorphous poly-carbonate in compression with only small deformations the equivalent equation is:

$$K\lambda = 2x'_m \sin \theta'_m \qquad (10a)$$

The modulus of elasticity may be defined by:

$$E = \frac{\sigma}{\varepsilon} = \sigma \cdot \frac{\sin \theta'_m}{\sin \theta_m - \sin \theta'_m} \qquad (10b)$$

in which K does not appear. Thus, small changes in intermolecular distances due to an applied stress may be represented by $\lambda/(2 \sin \theta_m)$. The diffraction curves for an amorphous and a partially crystalline polycarbonate are given in Fig. 8. Figure 9 shows the dependence of $\lambda/(2 \sin \theta_m)$ on the compressive stress for both partially crystalline and amorphous polymers. The amorphous maximum moves to larger angles with compressive stress corresponding to a closer packing of the molecules and $\lambda/(2 \sin \theta_m)$ decreases linearly with applied stress up to a stress of ca. 49 MN/m². Elastic moduli were calculated for both the amorphous and crystalline diffraction maxima, and it is clear that the amorphous material has the lower modulus. This has been interpreted on the basis of the heterogeneous structure of the amorphous material with lower 'cohesion' than in the crystalline phase.

This opinion contradicts the assumption that amorphous polycarbonate contains very small crystalline regions, so small that they give only a diffuse X-ray diffraction maximum.[77a] This conclusion would appear reasonable, but the problem is rather subtle. Further work in this area is obviously warranted and application of the radial distribution analysis (*see* Section 2.6) to glassy polymers under stress and SAXS (*see* Section 2.5) may well help to solve these problems.

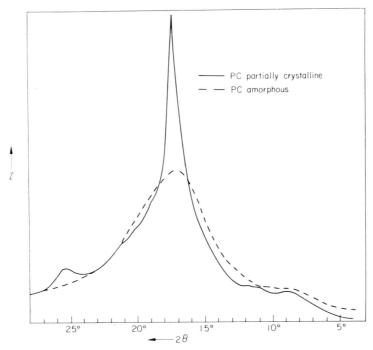

*Fig. 8.   The superimposed X-ray diffraction curves of two specimens of polycarbonate partially crystalline and amorphous. (Reproduced with permission from Boukal, I. (1970). European Polym. J., **6**, 17.)*

An approximate analysis of the X-ray diffraction curve for disordered materials such as polymers is given by Klug and Alexander[78] who define a scattering function (the bracketed term r.h.s. of eqn. (11)) in terms of interatomic vectors with some particular frequently occurring magnitude R.

$$I_R(\mathbf{k}) = N_R f^2(\mathbf{k}) \left(1 + \frac{\sin \mathbf{k} \cdot R}{\mathbf{k} \cdot R} \right) \qquad (11)$$

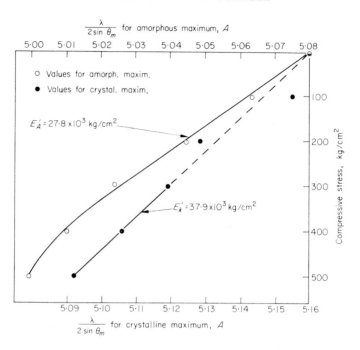

Fig. 9.   *The dependence of $\lambda/(2 \sin \theta_m)$ on the compressive stress for amorphous and crystalline X-ray diffraction maxima of polycarbonate; E'_A and E'_K are the respective moduli of elasticity. (Reprinted with permission from Boukal, I. (197 0). European Polym. J., **6**, 17.)*

Maxima occur at $k \cdot R = (1 + 4n)\pi/2$, and the strongest when $n = 1$. Thus, the relationship between R and a Bragg 'd' spacing is given by

$$R = \frac{5}{4} \cdot \frac{\lambda}{2 \sin \theta} = 1 \cdot 25 \cdot d_{\text{Bragg}} \qquad (12)$$

Klug and Alexander[78] stressed that eqn. (12) involves approximations and should only be used with caution. Inspection of Table 1 will show the magnitude of the error involved in the calculation of a 'd' spacing by insertion of θ_m into the Bragg equation. Also, it is important to realise that in an amorphous material there is not a reproducible layer spacing, such as the 'd' spacing in a crystalline solid and the application of eqn. (12) is wrong conceptually as well as numerically.

Two different experimental approaches to X-ray diffraction from amorphous polymers are discussed in the next sections. For longer range features

TABLE 1[a]

Polymer	$d = \dfrac{\lambda}{2 \sin \theta}$	$R = \dfrac{5}{8} \cdot \dfrac{\lambda}{\sin \theta}$
Polytrifluorochlorethylene	5·5	6·8
Cellulose	5·0	6·2
Polyisobutylene	6·3	7·8
Natural rubber	4·8	5·9
Polymethylmethacrylate	6·6	8·1
Polyacrylonitrite[b]	5·24	6·55
Polyacrylonitrite-styrene copolymer[b] (0·816 mole % AN)	5·38	6·72

[a] Klug H. P. and Alexander L. E. (1954). *X-ray Diffraction Procedures*, John Wiley and Sons Inc., New York p. 633.
[b] From Beevers R. B. and White E. F. T. *Polymer Letters* **2**, 793 (1964); *Trans. Far. Soc.* **56**, 1535 (1960).

(ordered structures) small-angle X-ray scattering (SAXS) is used (Section 2.5), whilst for local order it is possible to determine a radial distribution function (r.d.f.) (Section 2.6) similar to that for gases, liquids and inorganic glasses. This involves a Fourier inversion of the total scattered intensity curve after certain corrections to the experimentally determined intensities distribution have been made.

2.5   SMALL ANGLE X-RAY SCATTERING

2.5.1   Introduction

During recent years there have been considerable developments in the application of small-angle X-ray scattering techniques (SAXS) and in this section only an introduction to this topic can be given.[79] SAXS is concerned with scattering at small angles and hence there are considerable experimental difficulties of which some of the more important are discussed in Section 5.2.

Many substances produce a 'continuous' small angle scattering which in the domain of small angles decreases monotomically with increasing scattering angle. The analysis of this continuous scattering by Guinier is based on the concept that the intensity function is practically due to 'particle' scattering, the exact meaning of the 'particle' remaining to be defined. Kratky holds the view that in the case of densely packed systems the continuous small angle scattering is due to interference effects 'between the particles'.[81] It would seem that ancillary experimental methods such as electron microscopy would aid identification of the scattering moiety.

For discontinuous small angle scattering there are interference maxima or diffuse reflections which are caused by interference effects between the particles. Vainshstein[82] has discussed the typical appearance of such diffuse reflections for collagen, polyethylene, polyamides and polyesters and has suggested suitable models for the arrangement of the polymer chains to account for the characteristic diffuse bands.

Small angle scattering normally means coherently scattered X-ray intensity whose domain extends up to scattering angles 2θ of only a few degrees, in contrast to the domain of large angle scattering by crystals, liquids and gases which extends from *ca.* $2\theta \sim 5°$ (depending on λ) up to

TABLE 2

RELATIONSHIP BETWEEN LONG SPACINGS
AND SMALL ANGLE SCATTERING ANGLE
FOR Cu K RADIATION

Spacing or periodicity in Å	$\sin \theta$	2θ
25	0·030 84	3° 32′
50	0·015 42	1° 46′
400	0·001 927	13·25′
1000	0·000 770 9	5·3′

as large an angle as it is possible to make meaningful measurements. Because of the reciprocal relationship between scattering vector and the distance between scattering centres the presence of small angle scattering shows that some sort of statistical inhomogeneity must be present, such as clusters, micelles, paracrystallites, crystalline domains or may be inclusions of another polymer. The relationship between periodicity and scattering angle for Cu K_α radiation is given in Table 2.

Here we discuss briefly the experimental (Section 5.2) problems involved in SAXS together with an outline of the theoretical interpretation of such results (Section 5.3) and some applications (Section 5.4).

2.5.2   Experimental requirements for SAXS

The experimental requirements for small-angle scattering measurements are extreme[83] but there are, nowadays, a number of commercial instruments which can meet these demands. Those requirements which are divorced from the X-ray unit itself include the provision of air-conditioning for the laboratory, anti-vibration mounting for the instrument and constant temperature control of the cooling water. The general arrangements for making small-angle measurements are shown in Fig. 10. Diffractometric measurements of high accuracy take a long time to perform and hence suitable automation of these measurements must be provided. One of the most important practical problems in small angle scattering is the production of a primary X-ray beam which has a uniform distribution of intensity in the direction of its length within a sufficiently long zone in the plane of registration (*i.e.* at the position of the photographic plate or proportional

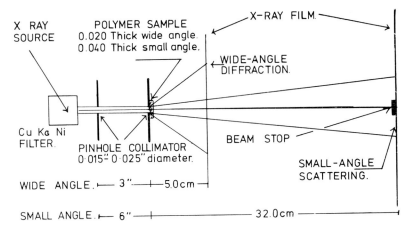

Fig. 10. *The experimental arrangement for making small-angle X-ray scattering measurements.*

counter) and it has been discussed at length in a number of publications notably those of Kratky and his co-workers.[84] The requirement can be met by using what is termed 'short focus', that is an X-ray tube whose focus is somewhat shorter than the diameter of the X-ray window. This method has the additional advantage that the energy yield is some two or three times that of the normal long focus tube since further narrowing of the beam is not necessary.

In diffractometry, for accurate measurements monochromatisation is absolutely necessary. For the highest degree of monochromatisation a crystal monochromator is used in either the incident or diffracted beam. There are a number of different methods of monochromatisation such as the pulse height discriminator and the Ross balanced filter and these have been reviewed by Alexander.[85]

Absolute intensity measurements, that is, quantitative comparison of the scattered intensity to the intensity of the primary beam, are necessary to obtain parameters such as the molecular weight and the electron density distribution of the material. Parameters such as the length, area and volume of a system can be obtained from relative intensity measurements. The experimental difficulty in obtaining absolute intensities lies in the fact that the incident and scattered intensities may differ by several orders of magnitude. The most generally used method of overcoming the difficulty consists of weakening the primary beam in a defined way. Luzzati[86] has measured the primary beam intensity after attenuation by absorbing nickel filters. This method is acceptable only if the primary beam is strictly monochromatic because of the strong dependence of X-ray absorption on wavelength. Also exact calibration of the filters is required. Kratky[87] and his co-workers have developed a method which attenuates the primary beam by means of a perforated rotor.

In order to obtain a higher initial intensity in the X-ray beam for more sensitive measurements of the scattered intensity it is necessary to use slit collimators. The general theory of small angle scattering was originally developed for primary X-ray beams of point-like cross section, that is, beams collimated using pin holes. Thus the experimental data obtained using slit collimators requires modified mathematical treatment and corrections. A general review of the problem of collimation error corrections giving the important references has been made by Alexander.[88]

2.5.3   Outline of the theory of SAXS[79−81]
The overall characterisation of any polymer system is given from the volume fraction of the phases which make up the system and their electron densities or rather the mean square fluctuation of electron density $\langle (\rho - \bar{\rho})^2 \rangle$ which may be called the scattering power of the system. From the theories of Porod[89] and Debye[90] integral scattering intensities are of the form

$$Q = \int s^2 I(s) \, ds$$

or

$$\tilde{Q} = \int s \tilde{I}(s) \, ds \qquad (13)$$

with Q or $\tilde{Q}$ as invariant quantities for pinhole and slit collimation respectively. Here I is the relative intensity measured with idealised point collimation and $\tilde{I}$ is that measured with collimation by infinitely long and narrow slits. With the intensity I_n or $\tilde{I}_n$ measured in absolute units the mean-square fluctuation of the electron density $\langle(\rho - \bar{\rho})^2\rangle = \langle(\Delta\rho)^2\rangle$ may be calculated from the equation

$$\frac{\langle(\Delta\rho)^2\rangle}{\bar{\rho}} = \frac{2\pi\mathcal{K}}{\eta} \int_0^\infty s\tilde{I}_n(s)\,ds \qquad (14)$$

for slit collimation where η is the thickness of the sample expressed in electrons per square centimetre of surface and $\mathcal{K} = (\lambda^2 I_e)^{-1}$ where $I_e = 7.9 \times 10^{-26}$ is the Thomson factor for the free electron (*see* Section 2.2.1) and λ is the wavelength of the X-rays in angstroms. For the important case of a two-phase system the following relation holds for the scattering power $\langle(\Delta\rho)^2\rangle$

$$\langle(\rho - \bar{\rho})^2\rangle = (\rho_1 - \rho_2)^2\, w_1 \cdot w_2 = (\Delta\rho)^2\, w_1 w_2 \qquad (\text{with } w_1 + w_2 = 1)$$
$$(15)$$

where ρ_1 and ρ_2 are the electron densities of the two phases, and w_1 and w_2 are the volume fractions of each phase. Thus from eqn. (15) it can be seen that w_1 and w_2 can be obtained from a knowledge of $\Delta\rho$ and the scattering power $\langle(\rho - \bar{\rho})^2\rangle$. Alternatively the scattering power can be calculated from ρ_1, ρ_2, w_1 and w_2.

There are practical difficulties in determining the very low angle portion of the invariant Q or $\tilde{Q}$. It is clear that the scattering curve cannot be measured at zero angle and extrapolations have to be made, and such extrapolations may not always be possible. For example, with strongly polydispersic systems (*e.g.* fibrous materials) the scattering intensity rises very steeply with decreasing angle. At larger angles undue weight is given to the small value of I or $\tilde{I}$ by multiplication by the large value of s. The accuracy of this portion of the curve can be improved by making use of the theory of Porod[89] which shows that at high angles the scattering should correspond to a limiting value of $m^4 I(m)$ or $m^3 I(m)$ depending on whether the scattering curve is corrected for collimation error or not. Here m corresponds effectively to s and is the distance between the incident and scattered rays in the plane of registration, since

$$s = \frac{m}{a\lambda}$$

where a is the distance between the sample and the recording plane. For the two-phase system if the experimental results confirm this theoretical model then an important structural parameter can be defined;[91] this is the specific inner surface O_s which is given by the ratio of the area of the phase interface O to the volume occupied by the disperse phase V_2. For collimation by infinitely long and narrow slits

$$O_s = \frac{O}{V_2} = \frac{8\pi w_1}{a\lambda} \cdot \frac{\lim [m^3 I^2(m)]}{Q_m} \tag{16}$$

It should be noted that absolute intensities are not necessary for the determination of O_s.

Another important concept in the study of dense two-phase systems is that of the correlation function[92] defined by

$$\Psi(r) = \frac{\langle (\Delta\rho)_1 (\Delta\rho)_2 \rangle}{(\Delta\rho)^2} \tag{17}$$

where $(\Delta\rho)_1$ and $(\Delta\rho)_2$ are the local deviations of the electron density from the average value $\bar{\rho}$ at points 1 and 2 separated by a distance r. Physically the meaning of the correlation function is that it is an average distribution of scattering matter in the vicinity of an origin which may be anywhere in the system. It is therefore a model with continuously varying electron density that is scattering equivalent to the particular inhomogeneous system under consideration. For a random distribution of two phases, each of uniform density (ρ_1 and ρ_2) such as holes in a solid or particles interspersed with voids then[92]

$$\Psi(r) = \exp\left(\frac{-r}{\bar{l}_c}\right) \tag{18}$$

and

$$\frac{O}{V} = \frac{4w_1 \cdot w_2}{\bar{l}_c} \tag{19}$$

$\bar{l}_c$ is the correlation length, a measure of the size of the inhomogeneities.

2.5.4 Some applications of SAXS

Many of the applications of SAXS have been to study the morphology of partially crystalline polymers and hence are outside the scope of the present chapter. However, any inhomogeneity with dimensions and repeatability in the range of 50 Å–1000 Å could in principle be measured using SAXS.

There are several methods of analysing SAXS measurements[79–82,93] and recently Buchanan[94] has examined Tsvankin's[95] method by application to melt-crystallised polyethylene, Kratky[96] has reviewed the general applicability of SAXS to polymers, and Fischer[97] has discussed its application to phase transitions in partially crystalline polymers, in particular, investigation of the glass transition that occurs in the amorphous phase.

Flory has related his analysis of the rotational isometric state model to scattering behaviour, including SAXS.[98] Essentially, it is necessary to obtain information on the unperturbed dimensions of polymer chains represented by the average $\langle r_0{}^2 \rangle$ the statistical mechanical average of r^2 over all configurations where $r = \mathbf{r}$ the chain vector connecting the ends of the chain in a given configuration ($\mathbf{r}$ is also called the chain displacement length). Such measurements have to be made with the polymer in solution at the theta, Φ, point, determined by the chemical nature of the polymer solvent pair and the temperature.[99] More recently Fujiwara and Flory[100] have presented a theory and numerically calculated the intensity of radiation scattered by chain molecules on the basis of realistic rotational-isometric-state models for polymethylene and also for isotactic and vinyl chains. The results of these calculations were discussed in terms of the applicability of SAXS for the determination of the configurational characteristics of chain molecules.

From solution studies the radius of gyration of the dissolved 'particles' may be obtained from[80,93,96]

$$I = I_0 \exp\left(-\kappa R^2 \theta^2\right) \qquad (20)$$

where κ is a universal constant ($= 16\pi^2/3\lambda^2$), θ is half the scattering angle and R is the radius of gyration, i.e. the square root of the average square distance of all scattering particles, from the centre of gravity.[101] The data are evaluated by a Guinier plot of $\log I$ vs. θ^2. Precautions are necessary for valid results to be obtained; thus to obtain linear Guinier plots experimental data must be obtained at very small scattering angles.[96] Other parameters of the molecules in solution which may be determined are the molecular weight, the persistence length, a measure of the 'tendency' for a randomly linked chain to maintain its direction.[102]

The behaviour of low molecular weight cellulose nitrates in acetone has been studied[84] and the Guinier plots of $\log I$ vs. θ^2 are given in Fig. 11. In Fig. 12 are given $I\theta^2$ vs. θ plots[96] for the same cellulose nitrates in acetone and also in a poor solvent. The persistence lengths, a, Table 3, are consistently shorter in the poor solvent, but there is good agreement between the experimental radius of gyration R_{exp} and that calculated, R_{calc}, for a Gaussian coil, since the 10–15% difference between these two values can be attributed to the effect of polydispersity.

A very interesting development has been the 'labelling' of chains with

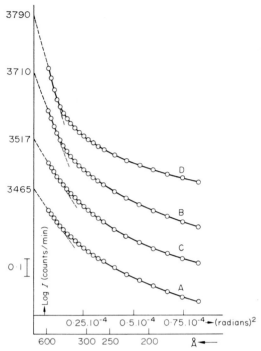

*Fig. 11.   Guinier plots for low molecular weight cellulose nitrates in acetone. Curves
are displaced vertically and the ordinate scale is indicated by the bar. See
Table 3a. (Reproduced by permission from O. Kratky in* Small-Angle X-ray
Scattering, *ed. by H. Brumberger (1967). Gordon & Breach, London.)*

atoms which have large scattering cross-sections for X-rays.[93,103]
Alkanes with bromine or iodine atoms at their ends have been studied
and the end-to-end distance of the molecules in solution determined.
Clustering of the molecules with one iodine end group was found and to
account for this effect a model was proposed in which there is the formation

TABLE 3a
LOW MOLECULAR WEIGHT CELLULOSE NITRATES IN
SOLUTION (O. Kratky[84])

Acetone

Sample	%N	P	L (Å)	a (Å)	x = L/a	R_{calc} (Å)	R_{exp} (Å)
A	11·08	78	403	54·3	7·4	72·2	83·5
B	11·19	145	750	49·4	15·2	101·5	115·5
C	11·96	90	464	56·6	8·2	81·0	89
D	12·09	157	810	59·4	13·6	113·0	133

TABLE 3b

LOW MOLECULAR WEIGHT CELLULOSE NITRATES IN A POOR
SOLVENT (O. Kratky[84])

Poor solvent

Sample	%N	P	L (Å)	a (Å)	x = L/a	R_{calc} (Å)	R_{exp} (Å)
A	11·08	78	403	36·8	10·9	62·7	71
B	11·19	145	750	44·2	17·0	97·1	110·5
C	11·96	90	464	49·6	9·3	77·0	83

%N = the percentage nitrogen in the cellulose nitrate
 P = the degree of polymerisation
 L = the hydrodynamic or contour length
 a = persistence length
R_{calc} = radius of gyration calculated for a Gaussian coil
R_{exp} = experiment radius of gyration.

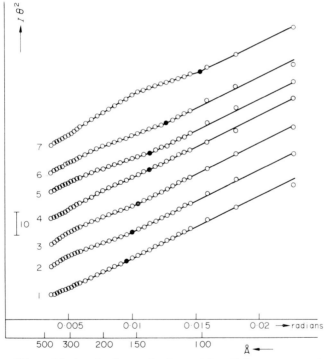

Fig. 12. $I\theta^2$ vs. 2θ plots for low molecular weight cellulose nitrates. The curves
are displaced vertically. Curves 1, 2, 5 and 3 are samples D, C, B and A in acetone. Curves 4, 6 and 7 are samples C, B and A in a poor solvent. See Tables 3a
and 3b. The degree of polymerisation, P, is proportional to $(I\theta)_0$ obtained from
the linear branch of these $I\theta^2$ plots. (Reproduced by permission from O. Kratky in
Small-Angle X-ray Scattering, Ed. by H. Brumberger (Gordon & Breach 1967).)

of quasi-liquid-crystal regions with the alkane chains lying parallel to each other and the iodine atoms in contact. Labelling has also been used with polymers such as *p*-iodo-polystyrene where results similar to those for an analogous monomeric species (*p*-iodo-toluene) were obtained which shows that there was no periodicity of the iodine atoms and that a random coil conformation with very short segment length specifies the structure. Kratky and co-workers[104] have recently published a very detailed study

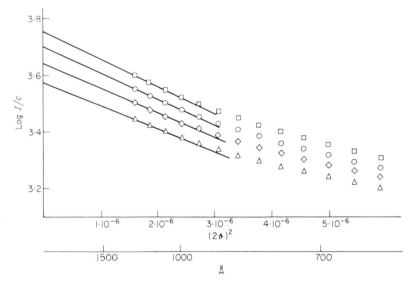

Fig. 13. *Guinier plot of desmeared scattering curves of poly-o-bromostyrene. (Reproduced from Durchschlag, H., Puchwein, G., Kratky, O., Breitenbach, J. W. and Olaj, O. F., J. Polym. Sci., (1970) C, No. 31, 311 with permission of John Wiley and Sons Inc.)*

of poly-*m*-bromostyrene in benzene solution, with estimation of the molecular weight, radius of gyration, persistence length, radius of gyration of the cross-section, mass per unit length and hydrodynamic length. For poly-*o*-bromostyrene it was established that helical and coil arrangements co-exist in the solution but the helical zones were not long. The Guinier plots for poly-*o*-bromostyrene[104] are shown in Fig. 13 and the calculated parameters in Table 4.

Application of SAXS to solid polymers has also been reviewed.[79,96] Polyurethane elastomers containing either polyester or polyether 'flexible blocks' have been studied[105] using SAXS and typical densitometer traces

TABLE 4

PARAMETERS OF POLY-*O*-BROMOSTYRENE IN BENZENE AND ON
EXTRAPOLATION TO ZERO CONCENTRATION (H. Durchschlag *et al.*[104])

M	Molecular weight	$5 \cdot 51 \times 10^5$
P	Degree of polymerisation	3010
R, Å	Radius of gyration	$206 \cdot 0$
a, Å	Persistence length	$16 \cdot 5$
L, Å	Hydrodynamic or contour length	6085
L/a		369

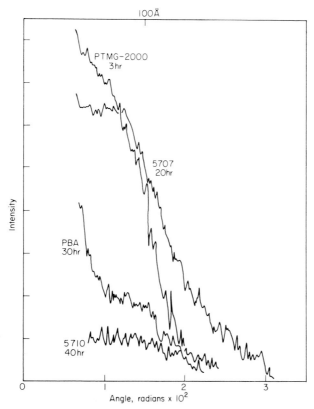

Fig. 14. *Densitometer scans from SAXS photographic films; intensity versus scattering angle 2θ. Exposure times for each specimen are indicated. The upper curve is for a polyurethane with a polytetramethylene glycol (PTMG) flexible component and the lower three curves are for polyurethanes containing poly-1,4-butylene adipate (PBA) flexible segments of different molecular weights.* (*Reproduced with permission from Clough, S. B., Schneider, N. S. and King, A. O. (1968). J. Macromol. Sci. Phys.,* **B2** (4), 641.)

are shown in Fig. 14. Not shown in Fig. 14 is an azimuthal dependence of scattered intensity although the polyurethane film had no overall orientation. The SAXS evidence of the presence of local oriented structures is consistent with local birefringence extending over distances of millimetres. This local orientation is probably the result of the processing history of the sample. Since there is no evidence for crystallinity in this sample the SAXS has been attributed to heterogeneity due to partial segregation of the 'hard blocks' of the polyurethane into domain structures, which have dimensions too small to scatter visible light. The X-ray scattering persists above T_2, the transition near 80°C which has been interpreted as due to dissociation of hydrogen bonds between urethane $>$N–H groups and oxygen atoms in the flexible segments. That the X-ray scattering persists above T_2 is regarded as supporting evidence for attributing the T_3 transition at about 150°C to dissociation of the domain structure. The SAXS results confirm and extend the conclusions drawn from mechanical and thermal methods. It was shown that in the polyether urethanes there was a higher degree of structural ordering than in the equivalent polyesters. A more refined analysis of the SAXS measurements should yield further

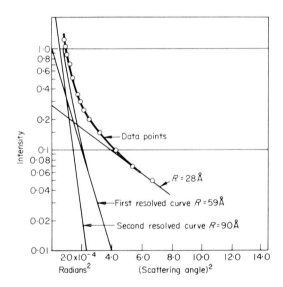

Fig. 15. *Analysis of meridional diffuse scattering of as-spun amorphous polyethylene terephthalate. R denotes the radius of the inhomogeneity. (Reproduced from Statton, W. O. (1962). J. Polym. Sci., 58, 205 by permission of John Wiley and Sons Inc.)*

information on the structure of these polymers, and this is clearly a field for further work. The morphology of styrene–butadiene block copolymers has also been studied using SAXS together with electron microscopy[106] (*see* Chapter 10).

The determination of void content, void sizes and the elongation of voids with drawing of films and fibres is also possible using SAXS.[80] Void sizes may be obtained from plots of log I vs. θ^2. For an as-spun

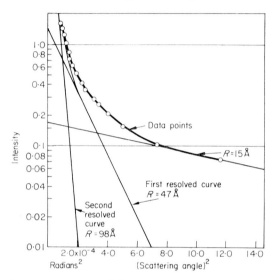

Fig. 16. *Analysis of equatorial diffuse scattering of as-spun amorphous poly-ethylene terephthalate. Note that R is smaller than in Fig.* 15 *because of the ellipsoidal shape of the inhomogeneities.* (*Reproduced from Statton, W. O.* (1962). J. Polym. Sci., **58**, 205, *by permission of John Wiley and Sons Inc.*)

amorphous polyethylene terephthalate fibre[80a] the void lengths are obtained from the meridional diffuse scattering (Fig. 15) and the void widths from the equatorial trace (Fig. 16). The data was analysed in a similar way to that used for rayons[80b] and a silica glass powder.[80c] The method of analysis is simpler than a Fourier transformation to obtain a continuous distribution and was initially employed in the analysis of small angle scattering from γ-alumina and carbon black.[80d] The graphical method involves drawing a tangent to the log I vs. θ^2 curve at the largest angle studied. From the slope and intercept and reference to tabulated data an estimate is obtained of the size and relative number of the smallest inhomogeneity or void. The procedure is repeated for other portions of the log I vs. θ^2 curve, after subtraction of the tangent(s). For the amorphous polyethylene terephthalate studied it can be concluded from Figs. 15 and 16 that the void lengths, l, are longer than the void widths, r, and quantitative estimates of the ratio l/r can be made. Such information agrees with the qualitative assessments that can be made from a description of the characteristic diamond shape of the diffuse small angle scattering photographs.

An interesting new application[106a] of low angle X-ray scattering is for the study of sub-microscopic cracks that are formed in polymers under load.

It is now well established that craze formation is an important feature of the fracture of glassy polymers. The factors that may be responsible for the formation of voids and crazes have been assessed[106b] and an experimental study[106c] shows that the crazes in polystyrene have a fibrillar structure with the fibrils having a diameter of 200–400 Å. Recently there has been a very careful study[106d] of the low angle X-ray scattering from crazes and fracture surfaces formed in polystyrene. It was found that there was anisotropic scattering for an incident beam perpendicular to the 'draw' direction in the craze (so-called 'edge' impingement). For an incident beam in the 'draw' direction (normal impingement) there was isotropic scattering. The scattering was interpreted by use of Guinier plots and the radius of gyration of the scattering particles were estimated to be about 60 Å. Since the density of the craze voids is approximately half that of the bulk material it is estimated that 120 Å is probably an average of the 'gyrational diameter' of the hole and the material between the holes. Extension of this work should provide further insight into the structure of crazes which can be studied directly by low angle X-ray scattering which is not possible by electron microscopy. A recent application of SAXS has been the determination of the surface areas of silica fillers dispersed in a silicone rubber.[127]

2.6   THE RADIAL DISTRIBUTION FUNCTION FOR AMORPHOUS POLYMERS

In general the distribution of atoms in an amorphous or disordered structure varies from atom to atom and the relative arrangement is determined only statistically. Thus in gases and liquids it is obvious that the local structure near a particular atom will change rapidly during a physical measurement due to thermal motion. This is also true for elastomers at temperature above T_g and thermoplastic melts.

There is no distinct difference between X-ray diffraction from gases, liquids, inorganic vitreous solids and amorphous polymers. In all cases a diffuse 'halo' is observed similar to that shown in Fig. 1, whilst for gases and liquids consisting of small molecules there will be a simple statistical distribution of the particles of matter; for polymers the 'structure' is determined by the bond lengths and bond angles of the main chain atoms. The disorder in a polymer is due to a random sequence of *trans-gauche* rotations about the bonds in the main backbone skeleton. The configurational statistics of such molecules has been discussed elegantly by Flory in his recent book[98] on the rotational isomeric state model for polymer molecules. For elastomers and other polymers at temperatures above T_g there is frequent rotation from one rotational isomeric state to another. For a crystallisable polymer there will be a regular sequence of rotational isomeric states, but for some polymers a regular lattice is not available because of steric irregularity; for example, atactic placements of vinyl monomer units containing an asymmetric carbon atom, such as commercial polystyrene or polymethylmethycrylate. Even for crystallisable polymers there will exist disordered regions where a regular sequence of rotational states has not been attained.

The distribution of atoms in disordered matter is specified by a radial distribution function (r.d.f.). This is used for the discussion of all forms of disordered matter and has been discussed in detail in standard texts.[107,108] The theory of liquids has an extensive literature[109] and it is possible to relate the properties of simple liquids to a r.d.f.

For a simple liquid the radial distribution function g(r) specifies the 'structure' of the liquid and is defined by

$$g(r) = \left(\frac{V}{N}\right)\left[\frac{N(r)}{4\pi r^2 \Delta r}\right] \tag{21}$$

where $N(r)$ is the number of particles within the radial distance r to $(r + \Delta r)$ of an arbitrary reference particle. For a spherically symmetrical intermolecular potential which is pair-wise additive it is possible in principle to calculate from g(r) as a function of density and temperature the internal energy, pressure and other thermodynamic properties.[110] In general such an approach is invalid except for the simplest liquids because of the restrictions on the form of the intermolecular potential and has at present little applicability to polymers.

The basic relations between X-ray scattering and the atomic distribution function of a monatomic substance can be written in the form[111]

$$g(r) = 4\pi r^2 \left[\rho(r) - \rho_0\right] = \frac{2r}{\pi} \int_0^\infty S\left[\frac{I(S) - Nf^2}{Nf^2}\right] \sin \mathbf{r} \cdot \mathbf{S} \cdot d\mathbf{S} \quad (22)$$

Here $\rho(r)$ is the number of atoms per unit volume at a distance r from a reference atom and $4\pi r^2 \rho(r)\,dr$ is the number of atoms contained in a spherical shell of radius r and thickness dr. ρ_0 is the average density of atoms in the sample and $\mathbf{S} = 4\pi \sin \theta/\lambda$.

It has been emphasised by Finbak[112] that when atomic radial distribution functions are used the presence in the function of the factor $1/Nf^2$ which increases rapidly with scattering angle adds undue weight to the experimental intensities at higher angles. Small errors in the intensities at high angles have a large influence on the integration and the experimental difficulties of measurement are greatest in this angular region. Finbak[112] thus defines an electronic radial distribution $\varphi(r)$ in terms of the probability $\varphi(r)\,dr$ of an electron in any system being found at a distance r and $r + dr$ from another electron. The equation for the electronic radial distribution $4\pi r^2 \varphi(r)$ is

$$\varphi(r) = \frac{2r}{\pi} \int_0^\infty S[I(S) - Nf^2] \sin \mathbf{r} \cdot \mathbf{S} \cdot d\mathbf{S} \quad (23)$$

This equation differs from eqn. (22) since f^2 is not in the denominator and consequently the electronic function is not unduly sensitive to small intensity errors at large S values.

The formulae discussed apply to the unmodified coherent scattering by a specimen. This type of scattering must be separated from other types of scatter adding to the observed intensity, in particular, the Compton scattering (Section 2.2.4). The incoherent scattering must be subtracted from the total intensity curve either experimentally or by approximate theoretical calculation. When S becomes large, the experimental coherent intensity becomes equal to the intra-atomic contribution, the structure independent coherent scattering equal to Nf^2. The intensity curves must also be corrected for the effects of polarisation and absorption. In fact for organic substances and incident radiation such as Mo K_α the absorption correction shows little variation with scattering angle and can be readily ignored. The scattering curves for a sample of natural rubber are shown in Fig. 1.

Erroneous detail in the radial distribution curves are nearly always caused by insufficient accuracy in the intensity, particularly at larger S values. These errors in the intensities manifest themselves as secondary maxima in the radial distribution curve which are in general sharper than the 'true' maxima. They also frequently produce peaks at values of r lower than the sum of the smallest pair of atomic radii involved in the material under study and these peaks can have no physical significance. By and large these errors, when recognised, can be eliminated or greatly reduced by careful experimental technique and suitable computational procedures. Detailed discussions of the sources of error and their treatment have been given.[108]

The manner in which false detail in the radial distribution function may affect the interpretation of that r.d.f. and an indication of the care with which these interpretations must be made can be seen from the conflicting conclusions deduced from a number of diffraction measurements on amorphous selenium, an inorganic polymer. Early measurements[113] suggested a structural model of amorphous selenium by analogy with monoclinic selenium which consisted of irregularly puckered rings containing eight or even more atoms or conversely a random arrangement of spiral chains.[114,115] Kaplow et al.[116] carried out very careful measurements and obtained thoroughly mathematically corrected r.d.f.'s. Distribution functions for all the molecular arrangements in the possible crystal structures were also obtained and thus direct comparison could be made with the amorphous data. These authors conclude that the structure of amorphous selenium consists mainly of slightly distorted Se_8 rings along with a small number of rings open sufficiently to develop a weak localised trigonal symmetry or a few greatly deformed chains. Optical and Raman spectra[117] provide strong supporting evidence for this conclusion.

There have been only relatively few computations of radial distribution functions for amorphous polymers, although Simand and Warren,[118] in 1936, did calculate an r.d.f. for natural rubber. Klug and Alexander[108] carried out a similar analysis for 'synthetic natural', a synthetic cis-1,4-polyisoprene, finding some detailed differences from natural rubber which they attributed to the structures of the polymer samples. The detailed differences are due to technique and not to a difference in structure, because in more recent work on natural rubber a r.d.f. was obtained which agreed essentially with that obtained for the synthetic cis-1,4-polyiso-prene.[119] Also, the maxima in the r.d.f. at ca. 5 Å which Simand and Warren attributed to an interchain spacing is not found in the later work and should not be regarded as an interchain spacing, since there are intrachain carbon–carbon spacings within this radial distance. Klug and Alexander[108] give a detailed account of the method of calculating the

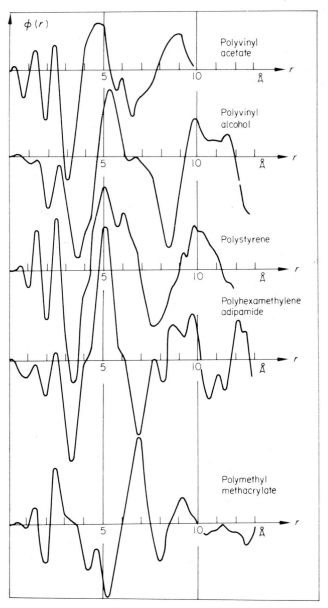

Fig. 17.   *Radial distribution $\varphi(r)$ distribution curves. (Reproduced from Bjørnhaug, A., Ellefsen, Ø. and Tønnesen, B. A. (1954). J. Polym. Sci., **12,** 621, by permission of John Wiley and Sons Inc.)*

r.d.f. and the method of interpretation in terms of an averaged interatomic distance (carbon–carbon).

Other polymers which were studied by Bjørnhaug et al.[120] include polyvinylacetate, polyvinylalcohol, polystyrene, polymethylmethacrylate, and typical r.d.f.'s are given in Fig. 17. An examination of Fig. 17 shows common features among the five curves. The first two maxima occur at distances of 1·5 Å and 2·5 Å. These maxima are considered to be C_1–C_2 and C_1–C_3 distances. The authors concluded that the positions of the main maxima are determined chiefly by the chain-to-chain distances. As an example, for the polyvinyl derivatives shown in Fig. 17 there are similarities in the region around 5 Å where the maxima correspond to the average distance between neighbouring chains. To determine the intramolecular

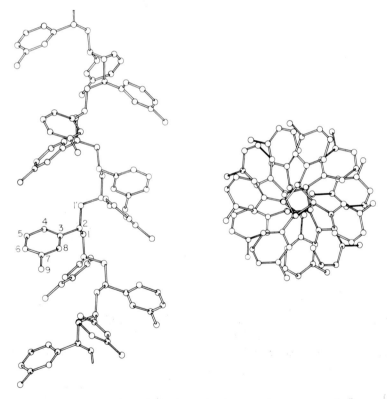

Fig. 18.   Side and end views of the chain of poly-m-methystyrene used as a model by Kilian and Boueke. (Reproduced from Corradini, P. and Ganis, P. (1960). J. Polym. Sci., **43**, 311, by permission of John Wiley and Sons Inc.)

contributions to the experimental curve, molecular models were built and distances could then be calculated to the nearest 0·1 Å. This method, however, has its drawbacks. In the case of polyvinyl alcohol two different structures fitted the experimental curve, one with a repetition period of 2·5 Å and one with a repetition unit of 5 Å.

Theoretical distribution curves were calculated for two-atomic systems and calculations for polyhexamethylene adipamide show that randomly oriented semi-crystallised polyhexamethylene adipamide consists principally of rather fully extended planar zig-zag chains with a periodicity of 17·4 Å as in the crystalline state. Whilst it is still possible that another arrangement of atoms may give a similar distribution curve the structural model proposed is probably correct. These investigations represent one of the first and most detailed X-ray studies of polymeric substances.

A very detailed study of polystyrene has been carried out by Kilian and Boueke.[121] X-ray photographs of amorphous 'polystyrene VI' were taken in the range 20 → 160°C which includes the glass transition temperature. An 'effective permanent group' or repetition unit was calculated from the diffraction pattern originating from the intramolecular contributions. This is seen as a measure of the mean statistical range where a correlation between neighbouring atoms in a macromolecule determines their position. The length of the permanent group is 11 Å. The helix formed from the structure of the isotatic crystal (Fig. 18 from Corradini and Ganis[121a]) has a similar distance. The experimental radial distribution curve for polystyrene at 160°C is shown in Fig. 19. Also shown is the distribution curve calculated from the model of two spirals similar to the structure of Fig. 18. The intermolecular contributions to the distribution curve and ultimately to the structure are determined by phenyl groups. Diffraction patterns obtained at the different temperatures were used to assess the importance of the phenyl groups in determining the structure. Amorphous phenolphthalein was investigated in the same manner as an indirect examination of the method and as a check on the results for polystyrene.

Arndt and Riley[122] have performed radial distribution studies on a number of proteins, particularly α-proteins, to obtain information on the types of helices present. The interpretation of the structure models was made by a comparison of experimental and calculated intensity curves. Whilst their detailed comparisons between proteins lead to a definite conclusion regarding the configurational model it is stressed once again that the structural model to be tested must be expressed in mathematical form, however complex. After this some chemical knowledge must be used and rational guesses made concerning the molecular conformations.

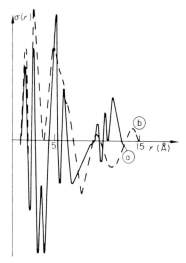

Fig. 19.   Radial distribution function: (a) *Experimental for 'polystyrene VI' at 160°C;* (b) *calculated for the model with a two fold helix, similar to that shown in Fig.* 18. (*Reproduced from Kilian, H. G. and Boueke, K.* (1962). *J. Polym. Sci.,* **58,** 311, *by permission of John Wiley and Sons Inc.*)

The structures of materials possessing cylindrical symmetry, such as oriented high polymer fibres must be studied by means of a cylindrical distribution function. This has not been used a great deal because of the considerable labour involved in obtaining the function and difficulties with its interpretation. A simplified cylindrical distribution may be appropriate for some systems.[123] This distribution is the difference between the cylindrical and radial distribution functions on an arbitrary scale, measured from an unknown baseline. Although these features limit the information obtained, that which is obtained may be of considerable use in elucidating fibre structures.

To obtain high resolution in the r.d.f. it is necessary to have accurate intensity measurements at large values of s. For materials of low atomic number the Compton modified intensity at large values of s may be several times the intensity of the unmodified scattering. Thus, there may be considerable error in the computed values of I_{coh} which are computed by subtracting calculated values of the Compton scattering from the experimentally measured intensities. Ruland[124] has discussed the possibility of separating the coherent and incoherent Compton scattering by monochromatisation of the scattered radiation. Warren and Mavel[125] have developed an experimental method which eliminates the Compton scattering by use of fluorescent excitation, Fig. 20.

The scattered radiation enters a receiving slit and falls upon a sheet of molybdenum at 45° to the beam. The molybdenum fluorescence K radiation is excited and is received by a counter at 90° to the diffracted beam and close to the molybdenum foil. Because of the short wavelength of the

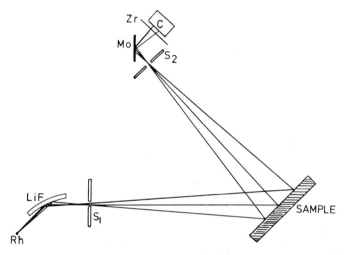

Fig. 20. Elimination of Compton scattering by fluorescent excitation. (Rh) *line focus rhodium target tube;* (LiF) *bent crystal;* (S_1, S_2) *slits;* (Mo) *thin sheet of molybdenum which fluoresces;* (Zr) *zirconium filter;* (C) *counter.*

rhodium $K\alpha$ and of the molybdenum most of the Compton scattering is of too long a wavelength to be able to excite fluorescence radiation and hence the unmodified scattering can be measured.

Until recently X-ray studies of materials with more than one kind of atom were interpreted on the assumption that the different atomic scattering factors could be considered as proportional to one another. In general this is an approximation and Warren[126] has described a method of interpretation based upon the use of pair functions.

For example, by application of the pair distribution function Warren has been able to determine Si–Si, Si–O and O–O distances in vitreous silica. With the possibility of determining pair distributions X-ray diffraction at wide angles should find more application to amorphous polymers in the future.

ACKNOWLEDGEMENT

We are very grateful to Dr C. Maghrabi, Department of Glass Technology, University of Sheffield, for many helpful discussions on X-ray diffraction by amorphous materials.

REFERENCES

1. Warren, B. E. (1969). *X-ray Diffraction*, Addison–Wesley.
2. Hosemann, R. and Bagchi, S. N. (1962). *Direct Analysis of Diffraction by Matter*, North Holland.
3. Alexander, L. E. (1969). *X-ray Diffraction Methods in Polymer Science*, Interscience–John Wiley, New York.
4. Debye, P. (1915). *Ann. Physik.*, **46**, 809.
5. Zernike, F. and Prins, J. (1927). *Z. Physik*, **41**, 184.
6. Miller, R. L. (1966). 'Crystallinity', *Encyclopaedia of Polymer Science and Technology*, ed. H. F. Mark, N. G. Gaylord and N. M. Bikales, Interscience–John Wiley, New York, vol. 4, p. 449. See also: Gupta, V. D. and Beevers, R. B. (1963). *Encyclopaedia of Gamma Rays and X-rays*, ed. G. L. Clark, Reinhold, New York, p. 783.
7. Hosemann, R. (a) (1963). *J. Appl. Phys.*, **34**, 25; (b) (1962). *Polymer*, **3**, 349.
8. Ruland, W. (1969). *Pure and Applied Chemistry*, **18**, 489.
9. Alexander, L. E. (1969). *X-ray Diffraction Methods in Polymer Science*, Interscience–John Wiley, New York, p. 143 ff.
10. Hosemann, R. and Bagchi, S. N. (1962). *Direct Analysis of Diffraction by Matter*, North Holland, Ch. XVIII, p. 587 ff.
11. Leadbetter, A. J., Wright, A. C. and Apling, A. J. (1972). *Amorphous Materials*, ed. R. W. Douglas and B. Ellis, John Wiley and Sons Inc., Ch. 42, p. 423.
12. Stafford, G. S. and Naumann, A. W. (1967). *Adv. Polym. Sci.*, **5**, 1.
13. Holiday, L. and White, J. W. (1971). *Pure and Applied Chemistry*, **26**, 545.
14. Vainshstein, B. K. (1966). *Diffraction of X-rays by Chain Molecules*, Elsevier.
15. Warren, B. E. (1969). *X-ray Diffraction*, Addison–Wesley, Ch. 1, p. 1. Hosemann, R. and Bagchi, S. N. (1962). *Direct Analysis of Diffraction by Matter*, North Holland, Ch. 1, p. 1.
16. Compton, A. H. and Allison, S. K. (1935). *X-rays in Theory and Experiment*, D. van Nostrand, p. 117 ff.
17. Bacon, G. E. (1966). *X-ray and Neutron Diffraction*, Pergamon Press. (A general introduction with reprints of some of the most important original papers.)
18. Guinier, A. (1963). *X-ray Diffraction*, W. H. Freeman and Co., p. 9, and Vainshstein, B. K. (1966). *Diffraction of X-rays by Chain Molecules*, Elsevier, p. 14.
19. Guinier, A. and Dexter, D. L. (1963). *X-ray Studies of Materials*, Interscience–John Wiley, New York, p. 24.
20. Alexander, L. E. (1969). *X-ray Diffraction Methods in Polymer Science*, Interscience–John Wiley, New York, p. 459.
21. Warren, B. E. (1969). *X-ray Diffraction*, Addison–Wesley, p. 7 ff. See also: Hosemann, R. and Bagchi, S. N. (1962). *Direct Analysis of Diffraction by Matter*, North Holland, pp. 17, 238. Vainshstein, B. K. (1966). *Diffraction of X-rays by Chain Molecules*, Elsevier, p. 21. Guinier, A. (1963). *X-ray Diffraction*, W. H. Freeman and Co., p. 15. Guinier, A. and Dexter, D. L. (1963). *X-ray Studies of Materials*, Interscience–John Wiley, New York, p. 26.

James, R. W. (1967). *The Optical Principles of the Diffraction of X-rays*, G. Bell & Sons Ltd., Ch. III, pp. 93–134; has an extensive discussion of atomic scattering factors.

22. Cromer, D. and Waber, J. (1965). *J. Acta. Cryst.*, **18**, 104.
23. Guinier, A. (1963). *X-ray Diffraction*, W. H. Freeman and Co., p. 11.
    Compton, A. H. and Allison, S. K. (1935). *X-rays in Theory and Experiment*, D. van Nostrand, p. 199 ff.
    Hosemann, R. and Bagchi, S. N. (1962). *Direct Analysis of Diffraction by Matter*, North Holland, Ch. X, pp. 354–86.
24. Alexander, L. E. (1969). *X-ray Diffraction Methods in Polymer Science*, Interscience–John Wiley, New York, p. 39 ff. Kaplow, R., Rowe, T. and Averbach, B. L. (1968). *Phys. Rev.*, **168**, 1068. Bienenstock, A. (1959). *J. Chem. Phys.*, **31**, 570.
25. Gupta, V. D. and Beevers, R. B. (1962). *Chem. Rev.*, **62**, 665.
26. Robinson, R. E. (1965). *J. Phys. Chem.*, **69**, 1575.
27. Kargin, V. A. (1958). *J. Polym. Sci.*, **30**, 247.
28. Kurata, M. and Stockmayer, W. H. (1963). *Adv. in Polymer Sci.*, **3**, 196.
29. Tchen, C. M. (1952). *J. Chem. Phys.*, **20**, 214.
30. Vainshstein, B. K. (1966). *Diffraction of X-rays by Chain Molecules*, Elsevier, Ch. II, p. 35.
31. Alexander, L. E. (1969). *X-ray Diffraction Methods in Polymer Science*, Interscience–John Wiley, New York, pp. 12 ff, 357 ff.
32. See for example: (a) Meares, P. (1965). *Polymers, Structure and Bulk Properties*, D. van Nostrand, Ch. 2, pp. 17–50; or (b) Miller, R. L. (1966). *The Structure of Polymers*, Reinhold Publish. Corp., New York, Ch. 8, p. 339.
33. Marchessault, R. H. and Howsmon, J. A. (1957). *Textile Res. J.*, **27**, 30.
34. Ruland, W. (1964). *Polymer*, **5**, 89.
35. Perret, R. and Ruland, W. (1968). *J. Appl. Cryst.*, **1**, 308; (1969). *Ibid.*, **2**, 209. Ruland, W. (1969). *J. Polym. Sci.*, **C.28**, 143.
36. Viswanathan, A. and Venkatakrishnan, V. (1969). *J. Appl. Polym. Sci.*, **13**, 785. Viswanathan, A. (1969). *Ibid.*, **13**, 2459.
37. Ross, G. (1972). *Amorphous Materials*, ed. R. W. Douglas and B. Ellis, John Wiley and Sons Inc., New York, Ch. 36, p. 347.
38. Stein, R. S. and Picot, C. (1970). *J. Polym. Sci.*, A2, **8**, 1955.
39. Borch, J., Muggli, R., Sarko, A. and Marchessault, R. H. (1971). *J. Appl. Phys.*, **42**, 4571.
40. Hosemann, R. and Bagchi, S. N. (1962). *Direct Analysis of Diffraction by Matter*, North Holland, Ch. IX, p. 302.
    Hosemann, R. (1962). *Polymer*, **3**, 349.
41. Seward, T. P. and Uhlmann, D. R. (1972). *Amorphous Materials*, ed. R. W. Douglas and B. Ellis, John Wiley and Sons Inc., Ch. 34, p. 327.
42. Miller, R. L. (1966). *The Structure of Polymers*, Reinhold Publish. Corp., New York, p. 503. See also: Gupta, V. D. and Beevers, R. B. (1962). *Chem. Rev.*, **62**, 665.
43. Gutman, F. (1967). *Electrical Conduction Properties of Polymers*, ed. A. Rembaum and R. F. Landel, Interscience, New York, and (1967). *J. Polym. Sci.*, **C17**, 41.
44. Fleming, R. J. (1971). *Polymer Let.*, **9**, 573.
45. Gutman, F. (1970). *J. Polym. Sci.*, **8**, 1731.
46. Cooper, A. R. and Auborg, P. F. (1972). *Amorphous Materials*, ed. R. W. Douglas and B. Ellis, John Wiley and Sons Inc., New York, Ch. 31, p. 301.
47. Dean, P. and Bell, R. J. (a) (1970). *New Scientist*, p. 104; (b) December 1967, National Physical Laboratory, Report: *The Structure and Spectra of Glasses: The Construction and Properties of a Model of Vitreous Silica*.

48. Bell, R. J. and Dean, P. (1972). *Amorphous Materials*, ed. R. W. Douglas and B. Ellis, John Wiley and Sons Inc., New York, Ch. 43, p. 443.
49. Bell, R. J. and Dean, P. (1970). *Disc. Farad. Soc.*, **50**, 55.
50. Yeh, G. S. Y. (1972). *Pure and Applied Chemistry*, **31**, 65.
51. Tonelli, A. E. (1970). *J. Chem. Phys.*, **53**, 4339.
52. Tonelli, A. E. (1971). *Macromolecules*, **4**, 653.
53. Wilkes, G. L. (1971). *Adv. in Polymer Sci.*, **8**, 91–136.
54. Wilchinsky, Z. W. (1962). *Adv. in X-ray Analysis*, **6**, 231. (1968). 'Orientation' *Encyclopaedia of Polymer Science and Technology*, ed. H. Mark, N. G. Gaylord and N. Bikales, Interscience, vol. 9, p. 624. See also: Miller, R. L. (1966). *The Structure of Polymers*, Reinhold Publish. Corp., New York, p. 566 ff. Alexander, L. E. (1969). *X-ray Diffraction Methods in Polymer Science*, Interscience–John Wiley, New York, Ch. 4, p. 200.
55. Stein, R. S. (1964). *Newer Methods of Polymer Characterisation*, ed. B. Ke, Interscience, Ch. IV, p. 155.
56. Stein, R. S. and Read, B. E. (1969). *Applied Polymer Symposia*, **8**, 255. See also: Vainshstein, B. K. (1966). *Diffraction of X-rays by Chain Molecules*, Elsevier, p. 347.
57. Nomura, S., Kawai, H., Kimura, I. and Kagiyama, M. (1970). *J. Polym. Sci.*, **8**, 383.
Nomura, S., Nakamura, N. and Kawai, H. (1971). *J. Polym. Sci.*, **9**, 407.
58. Vainshstein, B. K. (1966). *Diffraction of X-rays by Chain Molecules*, Elsevier, p. 92 ff.
59. Le Grand, D. G. (1970). *Macromolecules*, **3**, 764.
60. Zbinden, R. (1966). *Infra-red Spectroscopy of High Polymers*, Academic Press, Ch. V, p. 166.
61. Miller, R. L. (1966). *The Structure of Polymers*, Reinhold Publish. Corp., New York, Ch. 11, p. 557 ff.
62. Kashiwazi, M., Folkes, M. J. and Ward, I. M. (1971). *Polymer*, **12**, 697.
63. McBrierty, V. J. and Ward, I. M. (1968). *Brit. J. Appl. Phys.*, **1**, 1529.
64. James, R. W. (1967). *The Optical Principles of the Diffraction of X-rays*, G. Bell and Sons Limited, Ch. IX, pp. 458–512.
Compton, A. H. and Allison, S. K. (1935). *X-rays in Theory and Experiment*, D. van Nostrand, p. 168.
65. Randall, J. T. (1934). *The Diffraction of X-rays and Electrons by Amorphous Solids, Liquids and Gases*, Chapman & Hall, London.
66. Debye, P. (1960). *Non-crystalline Solids*, ed. V. D. Fréchette, John Wiley and Sons Inc., New York, Ch. I, p. 1.
67. Gehman, S. D. (1940). *Chem. Revs.*, **26**, 203.
68. Krimm, S. and Tobolsky, A. V. (1951). *Textile Res. J.*, **21**, 805.
69. Turley, J. W. (1965). *X-ray Diffraction Patterns of Polymers*, Chemical Physics Research Laboratory, The Dow Chemical Company, Midland, Michigan, USA.
70. Ruland, W. (1959). *Acta Cryst.*, **12**, 679.
71. Diamond, R. (1958). *Acta Cryst.*, **11**, 129.
72. Vainshstein, B. K. (1966). *Diffraction of X-rays by Chain Molecules*, Elsevier, p. 92 ff and Ch. 7.3, p. 345 ff.
73. Hsiao, C. C. (1960). *J. Polym. Sci.*, **47**, 251.
74. Wright, P. V., Maghrabi, C. and Ellis, B. (Unpublished results.)
75. Williams, J. L., Cleerman, K. J., Karam, H. J. and Rinn, H. W. (1952). *J. Polym. Sci.*, **8**, 345.
76. Guinier, A. (1963). *X-ray Diffraction*, W. H. Freeman and Co., pp. 72–4.
Guinier, A. and Dexter, D. L. (1963). *X-ray Studies of Materials*, Interscience–John Wiley, New York, p. 77.

77. Boukal, I. (1970). *Eur. Polymer J.*, **6**, 17.
77a. Prietzchk, A. (1958). *Kolloid Z.*, **156**, 8.
    Mercier, J. P., Aklonis, J. J., Litt, M. and Tobolsky, A. V. (1965). *J. Poly Sci.*, **9**, 447.
78. Klug, H. P. and Alexander, L. E. (1954). *X-ray Diffraction Procedures*, John Wiley and Sons Inc., p. 631 ff.
79. Guinier, A. and Fournet, G. (1955). *Small Angle Scattering of X-rays*, J. Wiley and Sons Inc., New York. See also: Alexander, L. E. (1969). *X-ray Diffraction Methods in Polymer Science*, Interscience–John Wiley, Sect. 1.5 p. 62 and Ch. 5, p. 280. Klug, H. P. and Alexander, L. E. (1954). *X-ray Diffraction Procedures*, John Wiley and Sons Inc., Ch. 12, p. 634.
80. Statton, W. O. (1964). *Newer Methods of Polymer Characterisation*, ed. B. Ke, Interscience, Ch. IV, p. 232.
80a. Statton, W. O. (1962). *J. Poly. Sci.*, **58**, 205.
80b. Statton, W. O. (1956). *J. Poly Sci.*, **22**, 385.
80c. Hoffman, L. C. and Statton, W. O. (1955). *Nature*, **176**, 561.
80d. Jellinek, M. H., Solomon, E. and Fankuchen, I. (1946). *Ind. Eng. Chem. Anal. Ed.*, **18**, 172.
    Jellinek, M. H. and Fankuchen, I. (1945). *Ind. Eng. Chem.*, **37**, 158.
81. Hosemann, R. and Bagchi, S. N. (1962). *Direct Analysis of Diffraction by Matter*, North Holland, Ch. XVII, p. 587.
82. Vainshstein, B. K. (1966). *Diffraction of X-rays by Chain Molecules*, Elsevier, Sect. VII 6, pp. 378–92.
83. Alexander, L. E. (1969). *X-ray Diffraction Methods in Polymer Science*, Interscience–John Wiley, New York, p. 102 ff.
    Guinier, A. and Fournet, G. (1955). *Small Angle Scattering of X-rays*, John Wiley and Sons Inc., New York, Ch. 3, pp. 83–115.
    Klug, H. P. and Alexander, L. E. (1954). *X-ray Diffraction Procedures*, John Wiley and Sons Inc., New York, p. 636.
    Statton, W. O. (1964). *Newer Methods of Polymer Characterisation*, ed. B. Ke, Interscience, New York, Ch. IV, p. 232.
84. Kratky, O. (1967). *Proc. Conf. on Small Angle X-ray Scattering* (Syracuse University, June 1965), ed. H. Brumberger, Gordon and Breach.
85. Alexander, L. E. (1969). *X-ray Diffraction Methods in Polymer Science*, Interscience–John Wiley, New York, p. 119 ff.
86. Luzzati, V. (1963). *X-ray Optics and X-ray Microanalysis*, ed. H. H. Pattee, V. E. Cosslett and A. Engström, Academic Press.
87. Kratky, O. (1960). *Makromol. Chem.*, **35A**, 12.
    Stivala, S. S., Herbst, M., Kratky, O. and Pilz, I. (1968). *Archives Biochem. and Biophys.*, **127**, 795.
88. Alexander, L. E. (1969). *X-ray Diffraction Methods in Polymer Science*, Interscience–John Wiley, New York, p. 286.
89. Porod, G. (1951). *Kolloid-Z.*, **124**, 83.
90. Debye, P. and Bueche, A. M. (1949). *J. Appl. Phys.*, **20**, 518.
91. Guinier, A. and Fournet, G. (1955). *Small Angle Scattering of X-rays*, John Wiley and Sons Inc., New York, p. 156.
    Alexander, L. E. (1969). *X-ray Diffraction Methods in Polymer Science*, Interscience–John Wiley, New York, p. 294.
92. Debye, P., Anderson, H. R. and Brumberger, H. (1957). *J. Appl. Phys.*, **28**, 679.
93. Brady, G. W. (1971). *Accounts of Chemical Research*, **4**, 367.
94. Buchanan, D. R. (1971). *J. Polym. Sci.*, **A2, 9**, 645.
95. Tsvankin, D. Ya. (1964). *Polym. Sci.*, USSR, **6**, 2304.

96. Kratky, O. (1966). *Pure and Applied Chemistry*, **12**, 483. For a recent review *see* Kratky, O. and Pilz, I. (1972). *Quart. Rev. Biophysics*, **5**, 481.
97. Fischer, E. W. (1971). *Pure and Applied Chemistry*, **26**, 385.
98. Flory, P. J. (1969). *Statistical Mechanics of Chain Molecules*, Interscience, New York, Ch. IX, p. 340.
99. Dondos, A. and Benoit, H. (1971). *Macromolecules*, **4**, 279. See Flory, P. J. (1969). *Statistical Mechanics of Chain Molecules*, Interscience, New York; p. 34 for definition and discussion of the Θ point.
100. Fujiwara, O. Y. and Flory, P. J. (1970). *Macromolecules*, **3**, 288.
101. Flory, P. J. (1969). *Statistical Mechanics of Chain Molecules*, Interscience, New York, p. 4 and Appendix A, p. 383.
102. Peterlin, A. (1960). *J. Polym. Sci.*, **47**, 403.
103. Brady, G. W., Wasserman, E. and Wallendorf, J. (1967). *J. Chem. Phys.*, **47**, 855. Brady, G. W., Cohen-Addad, C. and Lyden, E. F. X. (1969). *J. Chem. Phys.*, **51**, 4309.
104. Durchschlag, H., Puchwein, G., Kratky, O., Breitenbach, J. W. and Olaj, O. F. (1970). *J. Polym. Sci.*, **C31**, 311.
105. Clough, S. B., Schneider, S. N. and King, A. O. (1968). *J. Macromol. Sci. Phys.*, **B2**, 641.
106. Lewis, P. R. and Price, C. (1971). *Polymer*, **12**, 258.
106a. Zhurkov, S. N. *et al.* (1969). *Soviet Physics*—Solid State Eng. Edition, **11**(2), 238.
106b. Haward, R. N. (1972). *Amorphous Materials*, ed. R. W. Douglas and B. Ellis, John Wiley and Sons Inc., New York, Ch. 49, p. 513.
106c. Beahan, P., Bevis, M. and Hull, D. (1971). *Phil. Mag.*, **24**, 1267.
106d. Le Grand, D. G., Kambour, R. P. and Haaf, W. R. (1972). 'Low-angle X-ray scattering from crazes and fracture surfaces in glassy polymers. I. Polystyrene.' General Electric Report No. 72 CRD019, Jan. See also: Kambour, R. P. (1964). *J. Polym. Sci.*, **A2**, 4165.
107. Hosemann, R. and Bagchi, S. N. (1962). *Direct Analysis of Diffraction by Matter*, North Holland, Ch. XVI, p. 553. See also: James, R. W. (1967). *The Optical Principles of the Diffraction of X-rays*, G. Bell and Sons Ltd, Ch. IX, p. 458 ff.
108. Klug, H. P. and Alexander, L. E. (1954). *X-ray Diffraction Procedures*, John Wiley and Sons Inc., New York, Ch. 11, p. 586 ff.
109. Pryde, J. A. (1966). *The Liquid State*, Hutchinson. Egelstaff, P. A. (1967). *An Introduction to the Liquid State*, Academic Press.
110. McDonald, I. R. and Singer, K. (1970). *Quart. Revs. Chem. Soc.*, **24**, 238.
111. Booth, A. D. (1955). *The Vitreous State*, The Glass Delegacy of the University of Sheffield, p. 1. See also: Warren, B. E. (1969). *X-ray Diffraction*, Addison–Wesley, Ch. 10, p. 116. Alexander, L. E. (1969). *X-ray Diffraction Methods in Polymer Science*, Interscience–John Wiley, New York, p. 370.
112. Finbak, C. (1949). *Acta. Chem. Scand.*, **3**, 1279. See also: Alexander, L. E. (1969). *X-ray Diffraction Methods in Polymer Science*, Interscience–John Wiley, New York, p. 370.
113. Krebs, H. and Schultze-Gebhardt, F. (1956). *Z. Angem. Chem.*, **282**, 177.
114. Richter, H. and Breitling (1966). *Z. Naturforsch*, **21A**, 1710.
115. Henninger, E. H., Buschert, R. C. and Heaton, L. (1967). *J. Chem. Phys.*, **46**, 586.
116. Kaplow, R., Rowe, T. A. and Averbach, B. L. (1968). *Phys. Rev.*, **168**, 1068.
117. Lucovsky, G., Mooradian, A., Taylor, W., Wright, G. B. and Keezer, R. C. (1967). *Solid State Commun.*, **5**, 113.
118. Simand, G. L. and Warren, B. E. (1936). *J. Amer. Chem. Soc.*, **58**, 507.
119. Ellis, B., Fitzpatrick, J. R., Maghrabi, C. and Wright, P. V. Unpublished work.
120. Bjørnhaug, A., Ellefsen, Ø. and Tønnesen, B. A. (1954). *J. Polym. Sci.*, **12**, 621.
121. Kilian, H-G. and Boueke, K. (1962). *J. Polym. Sci.*, **58**, 311.

152   THE PHYSICS OF GLASSY POLYMERS

121a. Corradini, P. and Ganis, P. (1960). *J. Polym. Sci.*, **43**, 311.
122. Arndt, U. W. and Riley, D. P. (1955). *Trans. Roy. Soc.*, **A247**, 409.
    Riley, D. P. (1958). *Non-crystalline Solids*, ed. V. D. Fréchette, Ch. 2, p. 26.
123. Millberg, M. E. (1962). *J. Appl. Phys.*, **58**, 311. See also: Alexander, L. E. (1969).
    X-ray Diffraction Methods in Polymer Science, Interscience–John Wiley, New
    York, p. 376 ff.
124. Ruland, W. (1964). *Brit. J. Appl. Phys.*, **15**, 1301.
125. Warren, B. E. and Mavel, G. (1965). *Rev. Scient. Inst.*, **36**, 196.
126. Warren, B. E. (1972). *Amorphous Materials*, ed. R. W. Douglas and B. Ellis, John
    Wiley and Sons Inc., New York, Ch. 28, p. 263. See also: Warren, B. E. (1969).
    X-ray Diffraction, Addison–Wesley, p. 135 ff.
127. Brown, D. S., Warner, F. P. and Welton, R. E. (1972). *Polymer*, **13**, 575.

CHAPTER 3

RELAXATION PROCESSES IN AMORPHOUS POLYMERS

G. E. ROBERTS AND E. F. T. WHITE

3.1 INTRODUCTION

It is of everyday experience that the major physical and mechanical properties of articles made from polymers are affected by changes in temperature. These effects are particularly observed when the article is used close to its glass–rubber transition region. The occurrence of this transition temperature region, above which a linear polymer exhibits properties characteristic of a rubber and below which it has the properties of a rigid brittle glass, is now universally recognised. However, the origins of the glass–rubber transition remain obscure, and the molecular explanations that have been advanced do not have similar universal approval.

A transition from glass-like to rubber-like behaviour at some temperature is the rule for the majority of linear amorphous polymers, the few exceptions being those materials which are unstable below their anticipated transition region. Of course, among the wide range of available polymeric substances the transition temperatures vary enormously: the lowest temperature being observed for the highly flexible siloxane rubbers; the highest glass-transitions for organic materials being over 300°C for some of the polar, highly substituted and sterically hindered materials that are now becoming available for high temperature use. Useful compilations of glass-transition data are available[1,2] and the general relationship between chemical structure and composition have been extensively reviewed by Boyer.[3]

Much attention has naturally been directed towards establishing the basic nature and effects of the glass-transition process because of its obvious importance in determining the major physical properties of polymers, and a number of reviews of these subjects have appeared[4,5,6,7] as well as the

153

important contributions by Boyer.[1,8,9] Even so there are still serious difficulties in interpreting all the features of the glass-transition phenomenon, and in particular explaining the relationship with the other relaxational processes that occur in both the liquid and solidified states of polymers.

This chapter will attempt to discuss in a general fashion the origin and mechanism of the various relaxational processes that occur in addition to the glass transition T_g, and will further attempt to assess the impact of these various relaxations on the general physical and mechanical behaviour of the glassy state. A thermodynamic treatment of glass transition phenomena has already been given in Chapter 1 and a summary of glass transition measurements is provided in Appendix I.

3.2 MOLECULAR MOTION IN POLYMERIC MELTS AND GLASSES

3.2.1 General description of relaxational processes

In the melt, at temperatures well removed from the temperature at which flow first becomes possible, it is normally accepted that the individual polymer molecules are in a state of continuous random chaotic motion without semblance of order. Every type of molecular, segmental and sub-molecular motion is possible and the structure is continually changing. In view of the extremely high viscosity of the liquid melt, perhaps $> 10^6$ poise, some types of motion such as co-ordinated translational movements of the whole molecules are restricted, but there are nevertheless ample opportunities for each part of a molecule to engage in otherwise free and unrestricted motion, the available thermal energy being generally in excess of the energy barriers which would otherwise restrict molecular motion.

On cooling from the melt some polymeric materials will solidify, freezing in the apparently random structure similar to that which existed in the melt. It has been generally assumed that during the cooling process there are no structural changes relating to an alteration in the molecular packing but solely a reduction in the mobility of the molecular and segmental species. Recent evidence, originating with the X-ray observations of Krimm and Tobolsky[10] in which an increasingly dense packing at temperatures below 160°C for polystyrene was observed, require the simple view of randomness in the solidifying melt to be modified. There is little evidence of energy changes resulting from any closer intermolcular packing, the change from liquid melt into solid is a usually smooth continuous one, the viscosity changing rapidly but evenly, without major discontinuity. Spencer and Dillon[11] do, however, show that polystyrene exhibits some

changes in the slope of the zero shear melt viscosity–temperature curve in
the melt, evidence that is supported by the data of Fox and Flory[12] as
reported by Boyer.[13] At this point—still above the glass-transition region—
the molecular structure of the material is not very different from that
which existed in the melt, but co-operative translational movement of
molecules has become severely restricted. Flow can be observed, but only
under the influence of stress or after prolonged observational times.

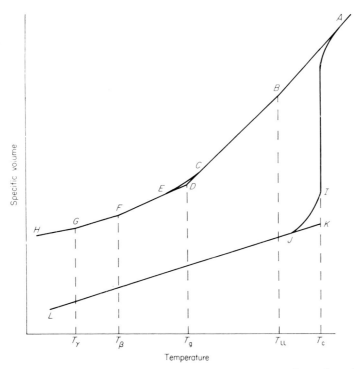

Fig. 1.   A schematic diagram of the volume–temperature relationships for an
amorphous and a crystallisable polymer.

The material at this stage is in a pliant elastomeric state exhibiting the
normal highly-extensible properties characteristic of a rubber. For non-
crystallising polymers, usually, but not exclusively those materials of low
symmetry or lacking tactic order in the chain, further cooling will lead to
vitrification at the glass temperature.

Up to this point the volume changes associated with the fall in temperature may be represented by the line ABC in Fig. 1 which represents the

hypothetical behaviour of an idealised melt which shows some slight rearrangements above T_g. However, on further cooling below C, the point at which the vitrification process commences, a change of slope of the volume–temperature plot is seen, and over a fairly narrow range of temperature ($\sim 5°C$), shown as a curved line CE, the material changes its properties to those of a glass. From E to F in the diagram there is again a linear dependence of volume on temperature, the intersection D of the two linear portions BC, FE locating the glass-transition temperature T_g. As we shall see, the glass-transition temperature is not uniquely determined by the thermodynamic parameters of the system but depends on the previous thermal and mechanical history of the sample and is also affected by the kinetics of the cooling process.

Well above the glass-transition temperature, the volume is determined by the P–V–T relationships for the material and is largely independent of the rate of cooling, provided that the time scale is not inordinately short and that crystallisation phenomena do not intervene. As the glass-transition region is approached the system becomes increasingly time dependent and the physical properties, including volume, are now no longer solely determined by the temperature but are to some extent governed by the previous treatment of the sample. Given time, however, an equilibrium of sorts will be set up and again thermodynamic reversibility will obtain.

On passing through the glass-transition region CE the molecular structure and physical properties consequent upon that structure will be effectively 'frozen-in' to a quasi-equilibrium state with a structure depending on the conditions pertinent at that time. An irreversible unique structure will result, with properties that differ with the prevailing conditions.

Kovacs[14] in a series of studies of the effect of rate of cooling on the V–T relationships at constant pressure has demonstrated the apparent increase in T_g which occurs as the heating or cooling rate increases. These effects are illustrated in Fig. 2 in which the isobaric specific volume of polyvinylacetate is shown as a function of temperature for two different cooling rates. The lower of the two transitions is observed at the slower cooling rate. Similar results to those obtained by Kovacs have since been observed for many other polymers and by other observational processes. Barton,[15] for example, has measured the variation of T_g with heating rate for a number of high molecular weight polystyrenes and shown a similar rate dependence of T_g.

The particular structure that is frozen-in to the glass below T_g is dependent not only on the cooling rate prior to the glass-transition region but also on the hydrostatic pressure during the cooling procedure. It is clear

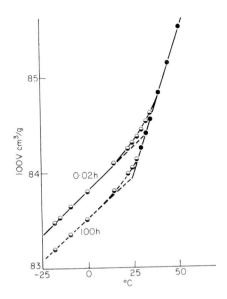

Fig. 2.   Isobaric volume–temperature relationships for polyvinylacetate. The two lower temperature lines represent measurements made after 0·02 h and 100 h. (Kovacs.[14])

from the review of Gee[16] that a spectrum of materials with a range of physical properties may be prepared from glass forming polymers by suitable processing techniques. Allen et al.[17] have shown that by compressing polystyrene at temperatures of 135°C and a pressure of 1260 atmospheres and maintaining the pressure whilst the sample cools through its transition region densified polystyrene with a density of 1·055 g/cm³ may be prepared—an increase of some 0·6% above polystyrene cooled from the melt at atmospheric pressure. These materials will retain their increased density indefinitely unless they are heated to temperatures close to their glass-transition region. It is interesting to note that the normal and densified polystyrene samples prepared by Allen did *not* differ significantly in energy from ordinary polystyrene, a result at variance with that observed by Bianchi et al.[18] who had suggested that there was a conformational contribution to the specific heat in such materials (*see* p. 74 *et seq.*).

Above the T_g it is clear that many modes of molecular motion are possible and that the molecules have time and the necessary volume in which to reorganise—not into any particularly ordered structure but one to which the maximum disorder is prevalent. Clearly at the sharp changes in the expansivities of polymeric materials in the transition region CE of Fig. 1—and these changes are reflected in similar behaviour of the other extensive thermodynamic properties of enthalpy and entropy— there must be changes in the molecular relaxational mechanisms.

Generally it has been supposed that in the glass-transition region large scale rotational and translational motion of the backbone chain segments of the macromolecule become frozen-in over a narrow range of temperature. Whether this freezing-in processes has its origins in the basic thermodynamics of the system or simply in the availability of space for the molecules in which to move or in kinetic phenomena is a matter of argument and debate.

Calculations based on the hindered rotational movements of carbon–carbon single bonds in the main backbone of polymer molecules certainly suggest that the activation energies involved in such processes are adequate to explain the occurrence of a glass–rubber transition at the temperatures which are normally involved. What is difficult to explain is the apparent narrow region over which the change of slope of the volume–temperature plot occurs. Typically for a normal linear amorphous polymer this range is not more than 5°C. However, other types of measurement, for example the variation of tensile modulus with temperature indicate a much wider range, perhaps 50–60°C, over which changes in the structural arrangement of the sample are possible. It should be remembered that in this case the imposed stress during the measurement may itself be bringing about an effective structural rearrangement which perhaps would not be apparent in a strictly static measurement. Many dynamic measuring methods may also precipitate premature molecular rearrangements that would not be observed in stress-free conditions. Rotational isomerism of the main chain is brought about by the mobility of single bonds in the molecular backbone and if this were a purely intramolecular process, should result in a normal Arrhenius activation energy relationship with temperature. Instead, as we shall see later, the dependence of activation energy with temperature is nonlinear and is of the WLF type.

Co-operative intermolecular motion has been suggested as a possible reason for both the anomalous activation energy dependence and for the sharp nature of the volume transitions. Quantitative theories have been held up by the difficulties created in assumptions of co-operative motion, but these general concepts have recently gained in credance from the work of Adam and Gibbs.[19]

What is clear is that transitions in polymers are relaxational processes at which the relaxation times of a movement of a part or of the whole of a polymer chain are comparable with the experimental time of the process by which the transition is observed. Approaches in which single relaxation times are assigned to the transition process do not give results in accordance with observations. Generally infinitely broad relaxation time spectra are required in order to equate to the experimental observations.

Many types of molecular motion may give rise to transitions or relaxations of one kind or another, their effect being manifest by anomalies in the physical or mechanical behaviour of the material or by the absorption of energy by the polymer. It follows that there should be observable effects for each and every type of molecular motion in the material provided that the temperature and observational time scale are such that the effects are observable under the conditions of the experiment.

The presence of relaxational processes of various kinds within a polymer and their associated effects on all the major physical, mechanical, electrical and energy absorption behaviour explains why these processes have come under the closest investigation in recent years. The industrial importance of these effects is of considerable concern and is perhaps sufficient reason to add to the already large list of reviews of this subject.

3.2.2   Relaxational processes at the crystal melt temperature

Above the melt temperature T_m the structure of a crystallisable polymer melt should be that of a random liquid. In practice it is well known that to destroy evidence of previous crystallinity or existing nucleation centres then the melt must be maintained at temperatures appreciably above T_m for some time. For the majority of crystallisable polymers the predominate mode of crystal habit is that of the folded chain lamella, the length of fold period being primarily governed by the crystallisation temperature and degree of supercooling, the perfection of structure being related to the regularity of molecular order in the polymer and on the time available during the crystallisation for a regular lattice packing to be achieved.

As a crystallisable melt is cooled along *AI* in Fig. 1 sporadic nuclei of a folded chain structure will begin to form, and provided that the energetics of the system are favourable, will become stabilised on reaching a minimum critical size which will then grow by accretion of polymer at the crystallisation temperature T_c.

For an undercooling of $\Delta T (= T_m - T_c)$ we may relate the fold period of a critical sized nucleus ζ to the surface free energy of chain folds (σ_e) and the latent heat of fusion ΔH_u by the following relationship.[20]

$$\zeta = \frac{4\sigma_e T_m}{\Delta H_u \Delta T} \tag{1}$$

As can be seen the size of folded chain crystallites will be extremely sensitive to the degree of supercooling ΔT particularly as this gets smaller. At T_m the fold period becomes infinite but the rate of nucleation proceeds infinitely slowly. At the crystallisation temperature T_c which will generally be a few degrees $(T_m - T_c)$ below the melting temperature of the crystallites, there is a structural change from a random state of a disordered liquid to the relative perfection of the cystalline state. This is a typical first-order thermodynamic phase transition and is associated with abrupt discontinuities in the extensive thermodynamic variables of volume, enthalpy and entropy.

The perfection of lattice order within the crystallites will vary considerably from that of the polymer single crystals, formed in dilute solution and having few structural defects, to a very imperfect and small crystallite structure which may consist of only a few molecular segments. Between these two extremes of order we may visualise a crystalline state in which perfection of lattice order is marred only by a few defects or a state of disorder in which some slight degree of local order exists.

Commonly a clear demarcation between amorphous and crystalline regions in a polymer is supposed to exist. This, on a current view seems untenable, at least for a reasonably crystalline material. The most that can be foreseen is an interruption of the crystalline process of a given chain by entanglement, structural irregularity, defect or chain end, each chain meandering between embryonic folded chain structures. Some movement of molecules, resulting from local reorganisation of structures, will result, particularly from annealing processes in which the packing of molecules and the movement of defects will result in more perfect folded chain structures with a fold period that will correspond to the annealing temperature. Movements of this sort are responsible for some of the secondary relaxation processes that occur, for example in polyethylene.[21]

In a similar fashion a polymer that does not crystallise in the accepted sense to give crystallites of a size recognisable by the classical tools of X-ray diffraction or optical birefringence is classified as amorphous. It is implied that such a material, because of steric interference, high melt viscosity, structural or tactic defect is incapable of structural organisation of a perfection necessary for a normal description of crystallinity. This cannot be so. Atactic polymers must, by the very nature of statistical probability, exhibit local regions of structural regularity which, if not crystallising in the accepted sense, can locally associate to form some ordered regions. It appears that apart from low-angle X-ray diffraction and light scattering we do not have suitable tools to investigate structures of this kind.

Just as there are structural regions existing above the melt temperature in a crystallisable polymer so we may have order of a kind existing in otherwise amorphous polymers at temperatures below the crystalline melt temperature of the crystalline variety. Attention has been drawn to the existence of these structures by a number of authors, notably Boyer.[13] These structures, probably helical in arrangement and capable of forming or reforming, give rise to relaxational processes which are indicated at *B* in Fig. 1. A detailed discussion will be reserved until Section 3.2.3.

A variety of molecular motions are possible at and near to the crystal melting temperature. The major process occurring, of course, is the ordering and arrangement of molecular segments into the crystalline lattice. Considerable translational and rotational movement is involved which becomes largely stabilised on attaining a crystal lattice structure. As crystallisation proceeds, further rearrangement of macromolecules becomes difficult; a single polymer molecule may be involved in several different crystalline areas. For a polymer, the crystal-melt transition can hardly be expected to be as sharp as that for a low molecular weight substance, nor indeed is it. For many materials, notably the hydrocarbon polymers for which the interchain forces are comparatively weak, reorganisation of structure may take place below the melt transition; annealing or pre-melting effects are the results of such movements.

On annealing at temperatures below the melt temperature T_m, imperfect crystal arrays have the opportunity to gain perfection by local adjustments of structure. Pre-melting effects are essentially the dissolution of imperfect crystallites, brought about by the reduction of T_m with decreasing fold period (*see* eqn. (1)). The effects of annealing or pre-melting can often be observed in a crystalline polymer, particularly since the advent of differential scanning calorimetry. These effects, now well documented for many polymers, can be all too readily misinterpreted as transition processes.

The effects of crystallisation on the volume of a crystallising material are shown schematically in Fig. 1 as the line *AIJL*; the rounding at the upper and lower ends of the vertical at *A* and *K* is more pronounced as the rate of cooling increases. Rapid cooling through T_c (quenching) can, with some crystallisable polymers, result in glass formation rather than crystallisation (*e.g.* polyethylene terephthalate). Rate effects, due possibly to the viscosity or structural nature of the material, intervene and obscure the crystallisation even though the thermodynamic conditions exist for crystallisation to occur. It is interesting to compare this with the situation envisaged by Gibbs (see Section 3.2.4) in which he supposes that kinetic effects always intervene and obscure the 'true' thermodynamic character of a glass transition.

3.2.3 Relaxations in the amorphous state above T_g and below T_m

Occasionally, in the literature, anomalous transitions have been reported for both bulk and dissolved polymers for which the reported temperatures are in excess of the normal values for the glass-transition T_g. Evidence for the existence of such transitions has accumulated, and Boyer[13] has attempted to review this knowledge.

Relaxational regions at temperatures between the normal glass transition T_g and the crystalline melting temperature T_m have been reported for both amorphous and partially crystalline polymers. Boyer[3] has suggested that these transitions may be of four general types;

(i) For crystallisable polymers, first-order transitions involving a modification of the crystalline phase.

(ii) Amorphous transitions between one liquid structure and another.

(iii) Interactions between amorphous and crystallite regions.

(iv) Pre-melting phenomena.

One might expect transition processes which involve modifications of the crystal phase from a less stable to a more stable configuration on cooling below T_m but above T_g. In this temperature region major molecular motion in the amorphous phase is still possible, and some changes in crystalline structure can no doubt occur. We have already seen examples of this in the reorganisation from an imperfect lattice structure to a more ideal state. Other examples whereby there is a definite change from one lattice structure to another are known, for example the change from a triclinic to hexagonal unit cell in polytetrafluorethylene at 19°C.[22,23] Other transitions thought to be of the crystal$_1$ → crystal$_2$ type have been observed for 1,4-polybutadiene, poly-1-butene and polychlorotrifluoroethylene. Recent work by Lord[24] has cast doubt on the origin of the transitions for various nylons that occur in the 40–60°C temperature region; his evidence suggests that these transitions are a change from one intermolecularly hydrogen-bonded structure to another and take place at temperatures above the normal T_g for the material.

It is clear that for crystal–crystal transitions of this kind the magnitude of the effect will be substantially changed with degree of crystallinity.

Boyer,[13] in reviewing the experimental evidence for transitions above T_g, has suggested that the transition occurring in polystyrene at $T_g < T < T_m$ may be a transition of type (ii) above in which there is a change in liquid structure at the transition. Connor[25] has recently obtained further evidence for the existence of this transition in polystyrene and has advanced an explanation similar to that used by Boyer that the relaxation at about 160°C in polystyrene is a true liquid–liquid transition in which a gradual removal of restraints from the ends of individual molecules leads to the possibility of relative translational movement of whole molecules. Boyer initially postulated that the $T_g < T < T_m$ relaxation represented a condition in which the centre of gravity of the polystyrene molecules becomes able to move and could be regarded as a 'melting point' of the polymer, which of course being amorphous does not have a true first-order melting point corresponding to the dissolution of crystallites.

Interactions between amorphous and crystalline areas within a polymer may also give rise to transitions in the temperature interval $T_g > T > T_m$. In amorphous polymers, and particularly in those amorphous regions of partially crystalline polymers that have not, for reasons of insufficient order or lack of time during the crystallisation process, been able to crystallise, there may exist regions of local regularity in which helical or imperfect folded chain segments may exist. These imperfect helical arrangements may not have the perfection of order either within a single chain or in their inter-helical disposition to be classified as crystalline but they nevertheless lie roughly parallel in adjacent chains. There would exist in these regions the same type of inter- and intra-chain arrangements that exist in crystallites but imperfect in character. It is conceivable that relaxation processes involving the transition from a folded or helical arrangement to a random coil situation could be responsible in certain cases for transitions in the temperature interval between the melt and the major glass transition. A process of this kind involving a helix–coil transition could also be observed in atactic polymers where the degree of chain regularity or the presence of structural defects is likely to lead to the formation of only imperfect helices. It would be perfectly reasonable to expect such structures to 'melt' at temperatures much below the normal T_m. The range of sizes of helical or folded chain fragments could account for the lack of sharpness of the observed dispersion regions and the lack of perfection of crystallites would result in only low energies being involved in the observed transitions. An alternative molecular motion that could give rise to an apparent relaxation process above T_g is the occurrence of pre-melting effects. In a partially crystallised polymer in which molecular chains meander between locally disorganised amorphous areas and more ordered folded chain regions the effect of motion of the amorphous segments at temperatures above the T_g on the crystallised regions could be to reduce the T_m locally and induce a pre-melting effect. This effect could be supported by the relaxation being more readily observable in 50% crystallised samples for measurements which involve some mechanical deformation of the polymer.

At this point in time it would appear that there is some body of evidence for a liquid–liquid transition at $T_g < T < T_m$ in polystyrene. The work of Spencer and Dillon[11] on the melt viscosity anomalies for a polystyrene of $\bar{M}_n = 360\,000$ when replotted by Boyer[13] reveals a transition region at 192°C with activation energies of flow of 41 kcal/mol below the transition and 22 kcal/mol above 192°C. Similar data of Fox and Flory[12] when re-examined by Boyer suggest that there is a transition region at 162°C for a polymer of molecular weight 4300.

Thermal expansion, heat capacity, X-ray diffraction, differential thermal analysis as well as melt viscosity measurements have all shown indications

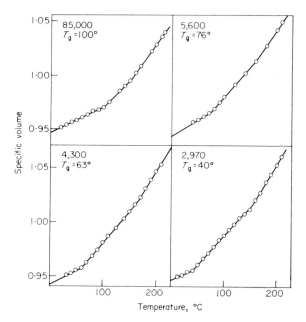

Fig. 3. Specific volume–temperature relationships for polystyrene obtained by Fox and Flory[12] clearly indicating an inflection in the curve at about 160°C. The various curves illustrate the effect of molecular weight on the transition process.

of the existence of a transition in the melt state for polystyrene. The specific volume–temperature data of Fox and Flory[12] reproduced in Fig. 3 illustrate clearly the existence of a changed slope above 160°C. The coefficients of expansion of specific volume are $7 \cdot 0 \times 10^{-4}$ K^{-1} above 160°C, $5 \cdot 5 \times 10^{-4}$ K^{-1} between T_g and 160°C and $2 \cdot 5 \times 10^{-4}$ K^{-1} below T_g. While the two latter values are independent of molecular weight, the high temperature expansion coefficient is found to increase with decreasing molecular weight. Comparison of the intensities of the two broad amorphous X-ray diffraction halos of polystyrene melts by Krimm and Tobolsky[10] supports the general view that a change of conformation of the chain is taking place at about 160°C as indicated in Fig. 4.

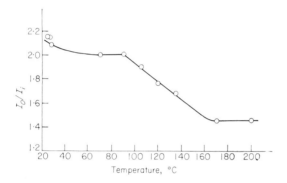

Fig. 4.   *X-ray scattering behaviour of polystyrene at high temperatures. The figure plots the ratio of the intensities of the two amorphous halos (I_o/I_i) as a function of temperature. (Krimm and Tobolsky.[10])*

The observation by Fox and Flory[12] that the expansion coefficient at the upper transition processes was increased as the molecular weight decreases supports the view that the observed relaxation could be due to the motion of whole molecules acting as a unit in view of the high available free volume and enhanced chain mobility at the elevated temperatures. In this connection it should be noted that cross-linking suppresses the occurrence of a liquid–liquid transition while at lower molecular weights a merger of the liquid–liquid transition with T_g occurs.

Some recent work on the diffusion of n-pentane into polystyrene at elevated temperatures by Duda and Vrentas[26] indicates the presence of a transition at elevated temperatures. As can be seen in Fig. 5 there is a sharp break in the diffusion coefficient at temperatures close to 150°C. Interaction of the penetrating molecule with the polystyrene had little

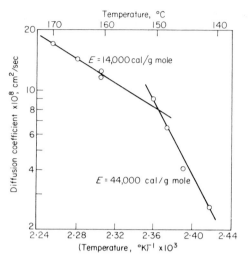

Fig. 5.   Diffusion coefficient for n-*pentane in polystyrene plotted as a function of reciprocal temperature. Energies of activation are shown for the two slopes of the curve. (Duda and Vrentas.*[26]*)*

influence on the transition, similarly little difference was seen as the molecular size of the penetrant was varied. Other measurements of Duda and Vrentas on the solubility of *n*-pentane in polystyrene also showed a distinct break at 152°C as indicated in Fig. 6. These changes in the slopes of diffusion coefficient-temperature and solubility-curves are seen as

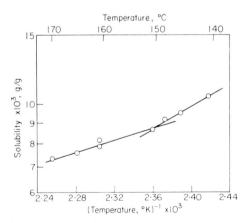

Fig. 6.   A plot of the solubility of n-*pentane polystyrene system as a function of reciprocal temperature at* 1 *atmosphere pressure. (Duda and Vrentas.*[26]*)*

supporting the concept of a structural change at this temperature. Probably of differing origin from those of polystyrene, relaxation regions have been observed for polyacrylonitrile at temperatures above its normal T_g of 100°C. Kimmel and Andrews[27] and Schmeider and Wolf[28] have reported a transition in polyacrylonitrile at 140°C. A transition has recently been detected at 125°C by Cotton and Schmeider[29] by dynamic mechanical measurements. Some measurements of the vibrational shifts of the nitrile group in polyacrylonitrile by Ogura, Kawamura and Sohne[30] have detected the presence of four transition regions at 90°, 110°, 120° and 140°C.

Andrews[31] has put forward the interesting suggestion that polyacrylonitrile is a 'doubly bonded single phase' with molecules held together by van der Waals' forces and also by dipole–dipole association between nitrile groups. The glassy phase will then show a two-step glass transition as the thermal energy overcomes in turn the two types of cohesive bonding. The lower transition temperature near to 100°C results from a loosening of the van der Waals' interactions while the higher value at 140°C results from a breakdown of the polar interactions between nitrile groups. The short-range order resulting from dipolar interaction between nitrile groups 'melts out' giving unrestricted mobility to molecular chains. An explanation of this sort is supported by the work of Beevers[32] in which stray molecular association in polyacrylonitrile solutions results from the formation of strong nitrile dipole-pair bonds. Movement of the nitrile groups are also implied from the infra-red vibrational studies of Ogura et al.[30] mentioned above.

A slightly differing explanation of the occurrence of relaxations in the temperature range starting at some 15–25° above the primary glass transition in butadiene–acrylonitrile copolymers has been advanced by Geiszler et al.[33] They speculate that there is a degree of ordering of the poly-cis-1,4-butadiene units in the chain and that these are in a mesomorphic state above the main glass-transition temperature.

Whatever the origins and explanations of the various transitions and relaxation processes that appear to occur in several polymer and copolymer systems above their normal T_g it is clear that much further work needs to be done in this area. Not only are the basic experimental facts far from clear but the very existence of these liquid–liquid transitions is not yet firmly established. Part of the difficulty may lie in the choice of experimental method, these transitions appear to be more easily detectable at very low frequencies, at shorter times the liquid transitions appear to merge with the primary glass transition.

Little is currently known about the effect of either internal structural features on the scope and nature of the transition and the effects of diluents, cross-linking, M_W etc. are as yet unproven. What is clear, however, particularly by analogy with other comparatively well understood transitions, is that on close examination many polymers will be found to display such relaxation processes and different explanations will be offered by each investigator.

3.2.4 Relaxational processes at the glass transition

In the glass-transition region many thermodynamic, physical, mechanical, electrical, chemical and aesthetic properties of polymers undergo striking changes. Perhaps the most obvious are the changes that occur in some of the mechanical properties in which for example the tensile modulus changes by a factor of 10^3 over the glass-transition interval. The general phenomenology of the glass transition has been extensively reviewed by a number of authors[3,4] and the general results are well established.

The experimental time scale of observation has a considerable effect on the process, the observed transition temperature may be shifted depending on the time scale employed. We have already some evidence of this from the work of Kovacs[14] shown in Fig. 2 in which an increased rate of cooling clearly shifts the apparent transition towards higher temperatures as the cooling rate increases (*see also* Section 1.1).

An examination of the changes that occur at the glass transition show that not only are static and thermodynamic properties affected, but that rate and relaxation properties are also markedly influenced at the T_g. It is this dual characteristic of glass transition that over the years has been the cause of considerable controversy over the development of a satisfactory theoretical explanation of the glass transition. Much of this difficulty has been in trying to adopt a quantitative approach to a phenomenon which affects the thermodynamic quantities and, at the same time, shows a great or overriding influence on rate effects. This has naturally given rise to theories which have their origin in either thermodynamic or kinetic explanations.

The various thermodynamic explanations seek to liken the glass transition to an underlying but 'true' thermodynamic transition of the second order while the kinetic explanations for the glass transition rely on relaxational processes existing in the material which, because of the difficulty in making measurements at very long times, gives rise to an artefact which is observed as a transition.

Neither of these separate explanations can be fully correct—probably he truth lies in a blend of each theory. Certainly, even if there were an underlying second-order transition temperature, the approach to it would be dominated by the near impossibility of attaining equilibrium conditions in a finite time scale.

Interpretations based on a molecular relaxational mechanism have many qualitative attractions and are probably basically correct, although there are many difficulties associated with a quantitative analysis using this type of theory.

Largely because of the quantitative difficulties experienced in the early uses of either approach an easier to handle but more arbitrary theory— the free-volume approach—became generally used after its introduction by Fox and Flory.[12] This theory has been remarkably successful in quantifying many of the effects and characteristics of transition behaviour, and it still has its value. However, it is to be regarded as one of the effects of the glass transition rather than one of its causes.

There is no doubt of the importance of rate phenomena in determining the overall state and characteristics of the glass-transition region. It is obvious that much molecular mobility has in fact been lost in the glassy state and that the structure of the glassy state in large measure derives from the previous thermal and temporal history.

Relaxational Theories of the Glass Transition

The glass transition generally becomes observable when the time scale of the experimental arrangement becomes comparable with the relaxation times of the molecular processes responsible for the transition. Generally these molecular motions are concerned with the changing conformational state of the assembly. Changes in conformation within an individual molecule are brought about by the rotation of backbone atoms within the macromolecule. Usually we are concerned with the rotational isomerisation about carbon–carbon single bonds in the main backbone of the molecule.

There are energy barriers that restrict motion about such single bonds even in simple molecules such as ethane or butane. The variation of the potential energy $U(\varphi)$ of the molecule as a function of the angle of rotation (φ) about the central carbon–carbon single bond in butane is shown in Fig. 7. In the gaseous state the height of the energy barriers restricting the free rotational motion between one isomeric state and another is generally a few kilocalories per mole. Similar barriers, but probably of a greater complexity, may also be present in the liquid or solid states.

At low temperature, the energy barrier height ΔU may be considerably in excess of the available thermal energy kT and the molecule will be effectively frozen into whichever isomeric state that the molecule happens

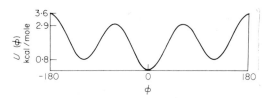

*Fig. 7. Potential energy functions for the rotational isomers of butane. The diagram illustrates the differences in the energy levels between the various isomeric states. φ is the angular displacement about the central carbon bond in butane. (McCoubrey, J. C. and Ubbelohde, A. R., Quart. Rev., **5**, 364.)*

to find itself at that period in time. Generally, however, this will be in the lower energy state representing the most stable conformation.

For isolated molecules in the gas phase the rate of change k_r from one rotational isomeric conformation to another will be given by the usual Arrhenius activation energy concept,

$$k_r = A \exp\left(-\frac{\Delta U}{kT}\right) \tag{2}$$

where A, the pre-exponential factor has its usual significance. Unfortunately an extension of this simple energy barrier concept to the isomerism of groupings in condensed systems does not fit with the observed behaviour. In common with the viscosity of simple liquids a simple energy barrier theory of the Arrhenius type breaks down and fails to fit the experimental facts except at temperatures far above T_g.

No single value of the activation energy will enable an equation of the Arrhenius form to express the rate of change of volume (or viscosity) with temperature. It requires an increasing activation energy to overcome the energy barriers restricting mobility as the temperature approaches the glass transition. A single energy barrier model for the rotational conformation changes will result in a single relaxation time; it has been demonstrated on numerous occasions that a wide spectrum of relaxation times is necessary to properly express the relaxational behaviour of a polymer at its T_g.

Many approaches have been made in recent years to develop multi-relaxational time models to enable calculations to be made of glass-transition effects. These include attempts by Hoffman[34] in which a spectrum of relaxation times was shown to result from a single simple axis rotator with several potential energy wells. This approach has been particularly useful for relaxations in semi-crystalline polymers.[21] Other, more numerous attempts, to quantify the relaxation treatment result from what amounts to curve fitting procedures in which a suitable combination of Voigt or Maxwell models is used in some suitable array. A Voigt element, consisting of an elastic component and a viscous component in parallel, has a relaxation time τ which corresponds to the time taken for a deformation to decay to $1/e$ of its original value when the stress is suddenly removed. A series of n such Voigt models as shown in Fig. 8 may then be constructed to give a spectrum of relaxation times. For example the creep compliance function $J(t)$ for such a model may then be represented by

$$J(t) = \sum_{i=1}^{n} J_i[1 - \exp(-t/\tau_i)] \tag{3}$$

where J_i represents the elastic compliance of the ith model. An elegant exposition of this approach on which the phenomenological theory of linear viscoelasticity is based is given by Ferry.[35]

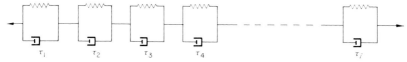

τ_1 $\qquad$ τ_2 $\qquad$ τ_3 $\qquad$ τ_4 $\qquad$ τ_j

Fig. 8. A series of Voigt spring and dashpot models each having a characteristic relaxation time τ , arranged in series.

What is clear, however, is that conformational changes in the shape of a molecule brought about by the ability of individual segments to rotate about the macromolecular axis are basically responsible for the observed character of the glass transition. It is equally apparent that our energy barrier theory of the simple Arrhenius type is insufficient by itself to explain the experimental facts in a quantitative fashion. In a condensed system in which molecules are in close proximity to one another temporary bonding may occur. Even though the thermal energy available to a molecular segment is in excess of the energy barrier restricting rotation there are considerations of packing and interactive forces with other molecules to take into account. It is these factors that the free-volume theory of Fox and Flory[12] attempts to rationalise in a readily understood fashion.

Free Volume Theories of the Glass Transition
Although one is continually groping for a true molecular interpretation of the glass transition the one outstandingly successful approach to the problem has been the free-volume theory advocated initially by Fox and Flory.[12]

A liquid, or for that matter a solid, has its volume partly occupied by molecules and part consists of 'free' or unoccupied volume. This unoccupied volume is supposed to consist of 'holes' of molecular sizes or imperfections in the packing order of molecules which arise from their random array. It is into this unoccupied volume that molecules must be able to move in order to adjust from one conformational state to another.

This free volume was regarded by Fox and Flory as being an essential prerequisite for molecular motion by rotation or translation to occur. A minimum level for the free volume in reality will fix the point at which a glass structure will be frozen into the matrix. The glass temperature then for any polymer will be that temperature at which the 'free volume' reaches a critical value below which there is insufficient room for molecular manoeuvre.

In the glassy state the free volume will be frozen in and will remain at a constant value, the 'hole' size and distribution of free volume within the glass will similarly remain fixed below the glass-transition temperature. The glass will, however, contract or expand with decreasing or increasing temperature due to the normal expansion processes of all molecules which result from the changing vibrational amplitudes of bond distances. Above the glass transition, in addition to the normal expansion process there will be an expansion of the free volume itself which will result in a larger expansion of the rubber than of the glass. The situation is as represented in Fig. 9. If V_o is the occupied volume of the glass at the absolute zero and V_g is the total volume at the glass-transition temperature T_g, then we have that

$$V_g = V_f + V_o + \left(\frac{dV}{dT}\right)_g T_g \qquad (4)$$

where V_f is the frozen-in excess volume which is frozen in because of molecular immobility in the glassy state (*see* p. 156). Similarly at a temperature above the glass transition $(T > T_g)$ then we have that the volume is

$$V_r = V_g + \left(\frac{dV}{dT}\right)_r (T - T_g) \qquad (5)$$

where the subscript r refers to the liquid (or rubbery) state. The expansion of free volume alone is represented by the difference in expansivities of the liquid and glassy states, *i.e.* $(dV/dT)_r - (dV/dT)_g$. If

$$\alpha_r = \frac{1}{V_g}\left(\frac{dV}{dT}\right)_r \quad \text{and} \quad \alpha_g = \frac{1}{V_g}\left(\frac{dV}{dT}\right)_g$$

represent the volume expansion coefficients at the glass-transition temperature then $\alpha_r - \alpha_g = \Delta\alpha$ may be used to represent the volume expansion
of free volume close to the T_g. Individual polymers do show some considerable range in values. Boyer[3] has indicated that there is a pronounced
relationship between the volume expansion $\Delta\alpha$ and the structure of the
polymer. Evidence for this view is given by the striking relationship between

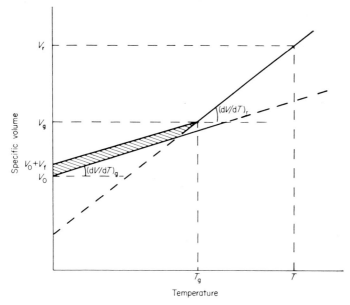

Fig. 9.   *A schematic illustration of the free volume and expansivities* $(dV/dT)_g$,
$(dV/dT)_r$ *in the glassy and liquid states respectively. The shaded area represents the
available free volume* (V_f) *in the glassy state.*

$\Delta\alpha$ and the reciprocal T_g as shown in Fig. 10. Various authors have used
differing definitions of the free volume and there is still some confusion
about its definition and measurement. For example, Simha and Boyer[36]
have suggested that the free volume of the glass at $T = 0$ should be
obtained from the difference between the occupied volume of the glass
and the extrapolated value of the liquid volume at $T = 0$. In this case

$$V_f = V_g(1 - \alpha_g T_g) - V_g(1 - \alpha_r T_g) \qquad (6)$$

or

$$V_f = V_g(\Delta\alpha T_g) \qquad (7)$$

The fractional free volume at temperatures below the glass temperature T_g is then

$$\frac{V_f}{V_g} = \Delta \alpha T_g \tag{8}$$

It is evident from the data of Boyer in Fig. 10 that an expression of this kind for the fractional free volume is supported to some extent by experimental evidence. A mean value of the fractional free volume obtained in

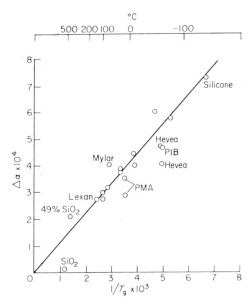

Fig. 10. *Differences in the expansion coefficients* ($\alpha_r - \alpha_g$) *plotted against the reciprocal absolute temperature. Some of the more widely deviant polymers have been named. The value of the fractional free volume obtained from the slope of this line is* 0·113. (*After Boyer.*[3])

this way is 0·113, a figure obtained for polymers with a molecular weight greater than 10 000 and relatively free from motions attributable to side groups. Motions of this kind might increase the effective value of the free volume below T_g. Individual values for V_f/V_g range from 0·082 for natural rubber to 0·13 for a polyurethane in which one might anticipate additional molecular processes to be operative.

An alternative and perhaps more widely used definition of the free volume of a polymeric glass arises from the important work of Williams *et al.*[37] This work relating mechanical and electrical relaxation times at a temperature T to a standard reference temperature (usually T_g) for a series of polymers enabled empirical correlations to be obtained. This work has now been developed until it now has some theoretical backing and is without doubt a most significant advance in our use and understanding of glass-transition phenomena. It enables us to rationalise the viscoelastic and time-dependent mechanical behaviour of polymeric materials close to their transition temperature. The empirical relationship developed by Williams, Landel and Ferry (the WLF equation) gives a_T, the ratio of relaxation time at a temperature T to the transition temperature T_g for a polymer in the temperature interval T_g to $T_g + 100$.

For a large number of polymers the following expression holds

$$\log a_T = \frac{-17 \cdot 44 (T - T_g)}{51 \cdot 6 + T - T_g} \tag{9}$$

the numerical constants being established by experiment. The viscosity of a liquid can be expressed in terms of the Doolittle equation[38] as

$$\ln \eta = \ln A + B V_{occ}/V_f \tag{10}$$

where V_{occ} is the occupied volume at the appropriate temperature and A and B are empirical constants. Without appreciable loss of accuracy V_f/V_{occ} can be replaced by V_f/V the fractional free volume (f) for temperatures greater than T_g. The Doolittle expression can be rearranged to give the ratio of viscosities at some temperature T above the T_g to that of the viscosity at the reference temperature T_g.

$$\ln \frac{\eta}{\eta_g} = \ln a_T = B \left(\frac{1}{f} - \frac{1}{f_g} \right) \tag{11}$$

where f, f_g are the fractional free volumes at temperature T and in the glassy state respectively.

Since we can write that

$$f = f_g + \Delta\alpha (T - T_g) \tag{12}$$

we have

$$\ln a_T = \frac{B}{f_g} \left(\frac{T - T_g}{f_g/\Delta\alpha + T - T_g} \right) \tag{13}$$

This is of the same form as the WLF equation and assuming that $B \approx 1$ as was the case in Doolittle's work on simple liquids, we can calculate f_g. Comparing the coefficients with the WLF expression we find that the fractional free volume $f_g \approx 0.025$ and $\Delta\alpha \approx 4.8 \times 10^{-4} \ K^{-1}$. These values then begin to take on the appearance of universal constants of general applicability. As with other general theories where there is a striking correspondence between theory and experiment, there are exceptions and a close examination of the $\Delta\alpha$ values for a range of polymers shows that this quantity is by no means constant. Observed values for $\alpha_r - \alpha_g$ vary between 2.9 and 7.0 $\times 10^{-4} \ K^{-1}$, values which would give fractional free volumes between 0.015 and 0.036.

Williams[39] has considered the WLF approach in detail with respect to polystyrene and has found that the constant B used in the Doolittle equation should have a value of 0.91 and that its value is temperature and molecular-weight independent. The empirical constant A is, however, strongly molecular-weight sensitive up to a molecular weight of about 35 000.

The WLF equation and its subsequent developments to temperatures greater than the limit of $T_g + 100$, proposed by Ferry et al., by Fox and Allen[40] has been significant. The latter authors have utilised an Arrhenius activation energy term in addition to the WLF expression in order to explain the behaviour of materials at elevated temperatures.

Below the glass-transition temperature in the glassy state there should be little observable collapse in free volume with decreasing temperature. However, Rusch[41] has recently used the WLF approach with success in interpreting the relaxational behaviour of polstyrene in the glassy state.

Thermodynamic theories of the glass-transition
Although now there is little doubt that the glassy state represents a situation of frozen-in disorder, because of its quasi-equilibrium state there is confusion over the applicability of the normal laws of thermodynamics to the system. Is there in fact a true equilibrium glassy state—which certainly could not be reached because of the impossibly slow rates of approach to equilibrium—rather than the liquid-like structure that happens to be preserved on glass formation? (*See* Chapter 1.)

Thermodynamic properties of glass forming simple liquids were first investigated by Simon[42] who used glycerol as a typical glass former. From specific heat–temperature data obtained from measurements made on the glassy and crystalline states at temperatures down to 10°K, Simon calculated that at the absolute zero the entropy of the glass was greater than that of the crystal by some 5.0 cal mol^{-1} K^{-1}, a result not unexpected in view of the lack of order in the metastable glassy state. Kauzmann in 1948,[43] in an analysis of Simon's and other available thermodynamic data for various glass-forming materials showed that the extrapolated entropy of the supercooled liquid at the absolute zero was less than the crystal. The point of intersection of the entropy–temperature curves for the supercooled liquid and crystalline state which will lie between $0°K$ and T_g may be regarded as a thermodynamic glass-transition temperature. This temperature would not be experimentally realisable because of the intervention of rate effects. If experiments were carried out infinitely slowly then the observed T_g would approach the underlying thermodynamic transition. Experiments of Oblad and Newton[44] in which the specific heats of supercooled glycerol were measured down to $175°K$, allowing up to five days between measurements, decreased the observed T_g by some $15°$ supporting this conclusion. A transition such as we have been discussing may represent a true thermodynamic transition of the second order of the type envisaged by Ehrenfest.[45] According to Rehage, however (p. 66), true second-order transitions would not be expected to give the general phenomenological relationships for volume, enthalpy, expansion coefficient and specific heat that are normally observed at a T_g.

Recently Gibbs and DiMarzio[46,47,48,49] have advanced a novel approach to the Kauzmann dilemma. For polymeric materials for which it is usually not practicable to measure and compare the specific heats of the crystalline and supercooled liquid states, they have assumed that there will be a second-order transition at a temperature T_2 at which the configurational entropy of the system becomes zero. The number of conformations available to the macromolecule as the temperature is lowered become fewer and in consequence the molecule appears stiffer and motion slower as T_2 is approached.

Gibbs and DiMarzio have used a Flory quasi-lattice model to calculate the configurational partition function in terms of the hindered rotation about the main chain bonds in the molecule. The theory enables a prediction of T_2 to be made in terms of the intramolecular bond rotational energy (ε), the energy for hole formation (α) and the degree of polymerisation of a polymer of a given co-ordination number. It should be pointed out that T_2 is not directly experimentally relatable to T_g but factors influencing T_2 may be expected to affect T_g in a similar fashion.

The Gibbs–DiMarzio theory is successful in describing the relation of molecular weight to transition temperatures and has had considerable success in describing the effects of copolymerisation, plasticisation and cross-linking on transitions. However, many workers including Rehage (*see* p. 80) do not subscribe to this theory as they are unable to find direct evidence for an underlying thermodynamic transition temperature T_2.

The hole energy (α) is relatively unimportant in determining T_2 while intermolecular attractions appear to be of only minor importance; the predominate variable affecting the transition temperature is the intramolecular rotational energy barriers.

More recently Adam and Gibbs[50] have extended these concepts to relate relaxational properties to the more fundamental thermodynamic property T_2 rather than the quasi-static T_g. Adam and Gibbs formulate the transition probabilities for a liquid in terms of an isothermal–isobaric ensemble of small systems of the size of a co-operatively rearranging region. This 'co-operating rearranging' region is the smallest unit that can undergo a transition to a new configuration without simultaneous configurational change on or outside its boundary. The temperature dependence of the size of this critical unit can then be calculated. At T_2, the co-operatively rearranging region must comprise the whole sample since when the configurational entropy is zero there will be only one configuration available to it. However, at higher temperatures a larger number of configurations is available and allows for individual rearrangements into different configurations for microscopic co-operative regions.

If z is the number of monomeric segments in a co-operative region, for an energy barrier between different configurational arrangements of $\Delta\mu$ we have the transition probability

$$W(T) = A \exp\left(-z\Delta\mu/kT\right)$$

On summation over all sizes of co-operative regions from the smallest size that permits a transition z^* to $z = \infty$ we find that the average transition probability is given by

$$\bar{W}(T) = \bar{A} \exp\left(-z^*\Delta\mu/kT\right)$$

This result implies that the overwhelming majority of transitions are undergone by regions whose size differs negligibly from the smallest size z^* that permits a transition at all. Alternatively this result can be expressed as

$$\bar{W}(T) = \bar{A} \exp\left(-\Delta\mu s^*_c/kTs_c\right) = \bar{A} \exp\left(-C/TS_c\right)$$

where s^*_c is the critical configurational entropy of smallest co-operatively rearranging region and S_c is the molar configurational entropy of the macroscopic sample.

Since the relaxational time of a system $\tau(T)$ is reciprocally related to the transition probability

$$\tau(T) = \frac{1}{\bar{W}(T)}$$

the shift factor a_T, used in the WLF relation may be expressed as

$$\log a_T = \log \frac{W(T_s)}{W(T)}$$

from which it follows that

$$\log a_T = 2 \cdot 303 \left(\frac{\Delta \mu s^*_c}{k} \right) \left[\frac{1}{T_s S_c(T_s)} - \frac{1}{T S_c(T)} \right]$$

where T_s is a reference temperature.

Allowing for the variation of S_c with temperature this expression can be transformed into an expression similar to the WLF relationship.

$$-\log a_T = a_1 \frac{(T - T_s)}{[a_2 + (T - T_s)]}$$

in which

$$a_1 = 2 \cdot 303 \frac{C}{\Delta C_p T_s \ln (T_s/T_2)}$$

and

$$a_2(T) = \frac{T_s \ln (T_s/T_2)}{\ln (T_s/T_2) + [1 + T_s/(T - T_s)] \ln T/T_s}$$

These expressions are supported by experimental estimations of T_2 for a number of polymers and the constancy of the parameters in the WLF expression, (eqn. (9)) are shown to depend on the constancy of values of $\Delta \mu s^*_c/\Delta C_p$ for common glass-forming polymers.

It is clear that these theories of Adam and Gibbs provide an alternative approach to the development of WLF type expressions to account for the observed behaviour of polymers close to the glass-transition temperature and which do not rely on free volume assumptions. In this way the difficulties surrounding the free volume figure of 0·025 (*see* pp. 25–39) may be avoided.

3.2.5 Relaxations in the glassy state

As the range of sophisticated experimental techniques for examining the mechanical, physical and electrical properties of polymers have advanced, enabling experimenters to carry out measurements over a wide temperature and frequency range, it has been realised that the majority of polymers exhibit a multiplicity of relaxational processes below T_g. There are appreciable difficulties in experimental investigations of this kind in relating dispersion regions located with one type of measurement at one frequency range to measurements made with a different technique in a different area of the frequency–temperature spectrum. Comparison of the results of different workers also raises problems because although using nominally the same material, polymers are inevitably of differing molecular weight, molecular weight distribution, structural geometry, orientation, crystallinity and with a different thermal history. Even for the glassy state of an amorphous polymer there can be substantial density and orientational changes depending on the manner in which the sample was prepared.

Static measurements, for example, of volume–temperature relationships can be used to detect relaxational processes below T_g. Dynamic methods, with a mechanical, electrical or thermal excitation of the sample are more commonly used to investigate secondary relaxation processes, although for some dispersion regions sensitivity is lost at the higher frequencies. The available frequency regions over which useful measurements may be made cover a range for both mechanical and electrical techniques from near static to several hundred megahertz. The simultaneous scan over a temperature range, particularly down to near the absolute zero is an invaluable advantage for any dynamic apparatus. Whatever the molecular origin of a particular secondary relaxation process the effect is observed as a small change or discontinuity in the observed parameter as the relaxation time of the molecular motion responsible for the transition matches the observational frequency at the temperature of the experiment. Associated with these relaxations there are usually energy losses which may be useful indicators of the presence of a secondary relaxation, particularly in dynamic experiments. At higher frequencies and elevated temperatures there is often a pronounced merging of relaxations that are discriminated at lower frequencies and temperatures.

Nomenclature of secondary relaxation processes
Many attempts have been made over the years to systematise the approach to the naming of the many observed secondary relaxation processes occurring below T_g in polymeric materials. Following the practice of Deutsch, Hoff and Reddish[51] the various dispersion regions in an amorphous polymer are usually designated by letters of the Greek alphabet, α representing the highest temperature transition observed at a fixed frequency or observational time, with β, γ, δ, ε, etc. representing other dispersion regions in decreasing order of temperature.

For amorphous polymers generally the α relaxation region is associated with major backbone chain movements and is the primary glass transition T_g. With polymers of different structures and composition and with several dispersion regions it is unlikely that the resulting relaxations, even though designated by a similar notation, will represent similar molecular motions. Each polymer system needs to be investigated individually and and assignment of molecular motion attached to each of the dispersion modes.

Although in this account we are not primarily concerned with crystalline or crystallisable polymers a similar nomenclature is used although in this case, the α relaxation implying the highest temperature relaxation process is normally associated with the crystalline–amorphous first-order phase transition T_m. In the case of some partially crystalline polymers (e.g. polyethylene) the occurrence of other transitions below T_g in the crystalline–glassy matrix is common and may partially result from the two-phase nature of the material.

A schematic diagram showing the designations of the various dispersion regions in both an amorphous and semi-crystalline polymer is shown in Fig. 11. Here the various loss regions in the mechanical spectra obtained at 1 Hz are shown as a function of the reduced temperature T/T_m. In the case of the semi-crystalline polymer, additional curves are included that

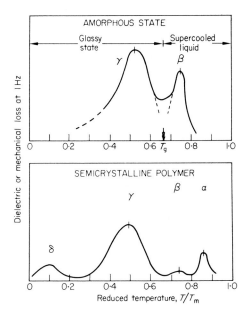

Fig. 11.   The various loss regions in the mechanical spectra at 1 Hz for an amorphous and a semicrystalline polymer plotted against the reduced temperature T/T_m. (Adapted from Hoffman et al.[21])

are representative of the effect of changing the degree of crystallinity of the material.

These diagrams illustrate the confusion that can easily arise in the α, β, γ notation. Many workers would, for an amorphous polymer, designate the transition region associated with the glass–rubber transition as an α-process, ignoring the fact that the majority of amorphous polymers can now be obtained in crystallisable forms with an associated T_m. However, this practice of nomenclature has gone so far now that any reader of an original paper must beware the pitfalls and draw his own conclusions about the nomenclature adopted by that particular author.

Boyer in his extensive review article on relaxation processes[3] has attempted to classify the various relaxations that can occur in polymer systems but he did not succeed in devising an acceptable unambiguous classification of mechanism and nomenclature. Molecular movements in polymers can be studied over a wide frequency range by dynamic mechanical techniques of various kinds, by dielectric methods or by nuclear magnetic resonance. Each of these methods influences the force field on the molecules in different ways and the responses of the system to the stimuli may be very different. Dielectric measurements, although capable of being carried out over an extremely wide frequency spectrum require a polymer having a degree of polarisability, whereas mechanical measurements may reveal the presence of completely non-polar groupings. Mechanical measurements, however, fail to detect motions which lead to completely equivalent positions in the molecule. Such movements, particularly rotational movements, while easily detected by n.m.r. methods are not detectable by dynamic mechanical techniques.

It is apparent then that the choice of experimental method for the detection of a particular type of molecular motion is critical if the experiment is to be successful. However, for the successful identification of a molecular motion with a particular dispersive region information from at least these three types of measurement is essential. Also desirable are activation energies, for the various relaxation processes. Certain of the modes of molecular movement have characteristic levels of activation energies and a particular dependence of activation energy on temperature.

With the wide variety of frequency–temperature information now available on many polymer systems, some convenient form of frequency–temperature correlation procedure must be adopted. McCrum et al.[7] along with many other prominent workers[32] in this field make extensive use of relaxation maps. Log (frequency) is plotted against the reciprocal absolute temperature at which a dispersion region occurs as in Fig. 12.

Here is displayed a range of data obtained by a variety of experimental methods for polyisobutylene, clearly showing the correlation between dielectric, mechanical and n.m.r. measurements for two dispersion regions.

Clearly as the frequency decreases, the dynamic data for the α process (the glass transition) is tending towards the static value for the glass-transition temperature of $-71°C$. Characteristically these values lie on a

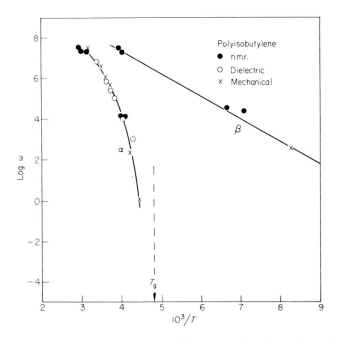

Fig. 12. *Frequency–temperature correlation map for dynamic mechanical, dielectric and n.m.r. measurements on polyisobutylene. The α and β relaxation regions are shown. (Slichter.[53])*

curve rather than a linear plot as do the results for the lower temperature β relaxation. A curved result of this kind is to be expected for a main chain relaxation because of the strong temperature dependence of the activation energy. The results fit an expression of the WLF type rather than a simple Arrhenius expression.

It should be noted that at the higher frequencies and higher temperatures resolution between the various dispersion regions becomes less.

Effect of secondary transitions on the physical properties of glasses
Although we must expect the glass-transition region to be associated with
very substantial changes in the majority of physical and mechanical properties of a polymer, there are still very important changes attributable to the
various secondary relaxations.

Volume dilatometry has been widely used in investigations of the primary
glass transition and also, on occasions, for the detection of various
secondary relaxations. At the glass transition there are abrupt changes in
the magnitude of the volume expansion coefficients, the difference $\Delta\alpha$

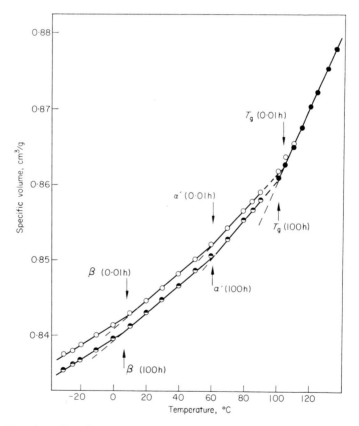

Fig. 13.   *Specific volume–temperature relationships obtained after two different
experimental times for a polymethylmethacrylate containing 56% syndiotactic and
33% heterotactic triads. Three transitions at 104°C, 60°C and 8°C are shown clearly
as breaks in the curve. (Wittmann and Kovacs.*[54])

between the expansivities of the liquid (α_r) and glass (α_g) states, attributable by some to the expansion of free volume, amounts to some $5 \times 10^{-4}\,K^{-1}$. The changes that occur in the neighbourhood of a β relaxation are generally smaller as are those which may or may not be detectable at lower temperatures.

An example of the type of behaviour of polymers at secondary relaxation regions is given by the careful dilatometric work of Wittmann and Kovacs.[54] These authors have investigated the volume–temperature changes for a series of polymethylmethacrylates having differing syndiotactic, isotactic and heterotactic triad contents. Figure 13 shows results for

TABLE 1
RELAXATION TEMPERATURES FOR POLYMETHYLMETHACRYLATE
SAMPLES OF VARYING TACTICITIES

Tacticity			Relaxation temperatures $°C$		
Isotactic	Syndiotactic	Heterotactic	T_g	α'	β
0·95	—	0·05	—	41·5	—	8·0
0·59	0·11	0·30	48·0	61·5	1·0
0·06	0·56	0·37	104·0	60·0	8·0
0·10	0·70	0·20	119·5	57·0	0
0·09	0·53	0·38	120·0	68·0	

After Wittman and Kovacs (1969). *J. Poly. Sci.* **16C**, 4443.

a polymethylmethacrylate having a 56% syndiotactic and 33% heterotactic triad content. Transitions are shown quite clearly for this polymer at 104°C (the α process or main glass transition), at 60·0°C (α') and 8°C (β). These measurements were made with an experimental time scale of 100 h between measurements. A shorter time scale of 10 h moves both T_g and the secondary relaxations to slightly higher temperatures. The values of dV/dT are also shown in the article for the various transitions, the change in dV/dT at T_g is some five-fold greater than those at the two secondary relaxation regions.

As indicated in Table 1 there are significant and interesting differences in the magnitudes of the various volumetric transition temperatures for polymers of differing tacticity. For highly isotactic materials the T_g may be as low as 41·5° while the relaxation at around 60°C appears to depend on the movement of heterotactic sequences in the material. This transition is conspicuously absent in predominantly isotactic material. The very low transition near to 0°C may be attributed to the freezing-in of ester side group motion. The linear expansion of polymers may of course also be used to detect secondary transition behaviour. This technique is now gaining in popularity with the advent of automatic equipment for taking the measurements.[55] Halden and Simha[56] have found breaks in the linear expansivity–temperature curve for polymethylmethacrylate as shown in Fig. 14 corresponding to the T_g and to a transition process at

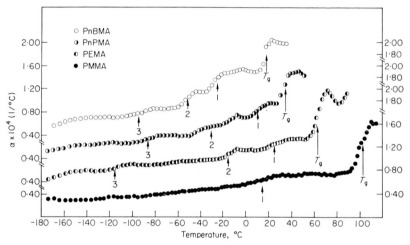

Fig. 14. *Linear expansion coefficient as a function of temperature for polymethylmethacrylate (●); polyethylmethacrylate (◑); poly-n-propyl methacrylate (◐); poly-n-butylmethacrylate (○). The various transition regions are indicated.*
(Halden and Simha.[56])

15°C and a further lower temperature peak at −130°C. Boyer[8] suggests the presence of a further break in the Halden and Simha data at about −50°C. This latter observation appears to correspond to the −40°C change in slope of the specific volume–temperature curves of Martin *et al.*[57]

Expansivity–temperature relationships for several other methacrylates are also shown in Fig. 14 from the data of Halden and Simha. These curves demonstrate the usefulness of this static method in obtaining information on the relaxational behaviour of polymers.

Provided that changes in volume are observed for the various relaxational regions then corresponding changes should be observable in other dependent physical properties, for example in refractive index which has been used extensively to detect T_g, for example by Beevers and White[58] in the case of polymethylmethacrylate.

The compressibility of polymethylmethacrylate similarly can be used to detect relaxational behaviour. The temperature–compressibility data of Heydemann and Guicking[59] shows several breaks in the isobaric compressibilities as shown in Fig. 15. These breaks at 103°C, 62°C and at −7°C correspond to those discussed above for the glass transition and two secondary relaxations. Confirmation of breaks in the compressibility coefficient at 67°C and 0°C are provided by the work of Becker[60] and by Nitsche and Wolf[61] respectively. An interesting feature of this work is that the glass-transition temperature is moved to higher temperatures with increasing hydrostatic pressure, the pressure coefficient of T_g is +0·18°C/atm. In contrast, neither of the two reported secondary transitions are pressure dependent as is apparent from Fig. 15. These results

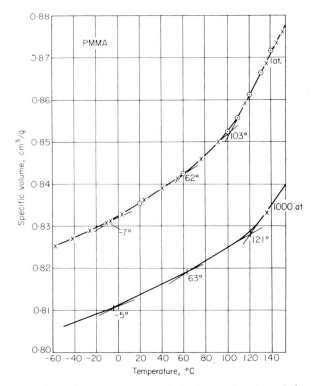

Fig. 15. Specific volume–temperature behaviour of polymethylmethacrylate obtained at 1 atm and 1000 atm by Heydemann and Guicking.[59] Transitions can be seen at 103°C, 62°C and at −7°C at 1 atm pressure. (Reproduced by permission of Dr Deitrich Steinkopff, Darmstadt.)

have been confirmed independently by dielectric constant measurements by Koppelmann and Gielessen.[62] This result surely implies that the molecular motions responsible for these transitions do not depend on free volume for their mobilities. In considering the validity of any particular approach to the investigation of particular transition regions it must be remembered that not all relaxational processes can be expected to give rise to changes in available volume as a result of the relaxation. Molecular movements involving segmental motion should, of course, be associated with volume changes, but processes involving only small group rotations, for example, methyl group rotation, would be unlikely to cause any observable change in volume.

Effect of secondary transitions on the mechanical properties of glassy polymers

At the glass transition stage all the mechanical properties show substantial changes in their behaviour; in the glassy state, however, it has been usual to assume that there are no abrupt changes in the mechanical behaviour of polymers. Closer investigation shows that this is certainly not so, the mechanical properties of organic glasses are affected by the presence of secondary relaxation regions.

Some of the stimulus for investigations of this kind came from the early observations of Buchdahl and Nielson[63] who reported that low-temperature dynamic loss peaks in rubber-modified polystyrenes were influencing their impact strength. For a while the impact strengths of glassy materials were related to the appearance and magnitude of low-temperature energy dissipative relaxation processes in the dynamic mechanical spectra of such materials. While the presence of such loss peaks in glasses is probably beneficial they are certainly not sufficient to confer impact resistance on an otherwise brittle material. Rubber–latex-modified polystyrenes have higher impact strengths by virtue of a change in the craze and crack propagation mechanism rather than in direct energy absorption (*see* Chapter 8).

Dynamic mechanical measurements have of course been extensively employed in the investigation of relaxation processes in polymers. It is perhaps worth considering why this should be and what nature of information one can obtain by the utilisation of such techniques.

For an elastic solid there is a unique relationship for the small strain elastic deformation of the material. Hooke's law

$$\sigma = E\varepsilon \qquad (14a)$$

relates the time independent stress (σ) to the corresponding strain (ε) through the elastic tensile modulus E.

A corresponding relationship

$$f = G\gamma \tag{14b}$$

applies for the shear deformation of the material, where f, γ are the shear stress and shear strain respectively and G is the shear modulus.

These simple relationships hold for isotropic materials, the small-strain elastic response to stress being characterised by only two elastic constants. In the more general case of an anisotropic body (which most fabricated polymers are) a generalised Hooke's law

$$\sigma_{ij} = C_{ijkl}\varepsilon_{kl} \qquad (i, j, k, l = 1, 2, 3) \tag{15}$$

may be used to relate the stress and strain components through a fourth rank stiffness tensor.

Polymeric materials, even in the glassy state are time dependent in their mechanical response to a deformation. Creep and stress relaxations are familiar manifestations of this time dependence (*see* Chapter 4).

For a tensile creep process in which a constant stress (σ_0) acts on a sample the strain becomes time dependent $\varepsilon(t)$, giving rise to a creep compliance which is itself a time dependent function $D(t)$, related in the following way:

$$\varepsilon(t) = D(t)\sigma_0 \tag{16}$$

Similarly if a constant strain ε_0 is retained on the sample then the initial stress σ_0 required to sustain the strain will reduce with time in an approximately exponential manner, the relationship between stress and strain being governed by a time dependent stress-relaxation modulus $E(t)$ given by

$$\sigma(t) = E(t)\varepsilon_0 \tag{17}$$

Although in the glassy state both the creep compliance and stress relaxation modulus are much less time variable than their corresponding values above T_g they are still appreciable. It is, however, in the regions of secondary relaxation processes that we should examine for evidence of a change in the creep or stress relaxation functions as has been done for example by Rusch[41] in the case of polystyrene and by Sherby and Dorn[64] for polymethylmethacrylate.

Although it is apparent that secondary relaxation regions do influence the creep and stress-relaxation properties of glassy polymers and may be of considerable importance in determining the long term stability of rigid polymers used for constructional purposes, the use of these properties for the detection of dispersion regions is far from easy. The long times required for evaluation of the WLF master curves are partially responsible for the relatively small amount of work carried out in this area compared with the extensive amount done on the dynamic mechanical response of polymers to oscillatory stresses of various kinds.

The use of periodic stress or strain functions to determine the time dependent mechanical response of a viscoelastic polymeric material is attractive. It can lead not only to additional data in the form of energy losses in dispersion regions but is also more sensitive than 'static' mechanical methods. When an applied oscillatory function is in resonance with the particular molecular motion responsible for a dispersion region then, in general, there will be an exchange of energy and a relaxation will result.

Dynamic mechanical methods are capable of operating over a very wide frequency spectrum and in consequence may be used to supplement static measurements for molecular motions that are insensitive to volume changes.

If a sinusoidal strain of angular frequency ω and of maximum strain amplitude ε_0 is imposed on the sample then the strain at any time t will be given by

$$\varepsilon = \varepsilon_0 \sin \omega t \tag{18}$$

The resulting stress (σ) for a viscoelastic or glassy solid which results may be described by

$$\sigma = \sigma_0 \sin (\omega t + \delta) \tag{19}$$

where δ is a phase angular difference between stress and strain.

This latter expression may be expanded and rewritten as

$$\sigma = \sigma_0(\cos \delta \sin \omega t + \sin \delta \cos \omega t) \tag{20}$$

which implies that the stress may be resolved into components in-phase and out-of-phase with the strain.

Defining E' as the ratio of the in-phase stress to the in-phase strain and E'' as the ratio of amplitudes of the stress $\frac{1}{2}\pi$ out-of-phase to the strain amplitude we have

$$E' = \frac{\sigma_0}{\varepsilon_0} \cos \delta \tag{21}$$

$$E'' = \frac{\sigma_0}{\varepsilon_0} \sin \delta \tag{22}$$

The ratio of the maximum amplitudes of stress and strain during a cycle can be defined as a complex modulus E^* and

$$E^* = \frac{\sigma_0}{\varepsilon_0} \qquad (23)$$

or may be alternatively expressed in complex notation as

$$E^* = E' + iE'' \qquad (24)$$

Of course, the phase angle δ in the form of the useful parameter $\tan \delta$ may be expressed as

$$\tan \delta = \frac{E''}{E'} \qquad (25)$$

The use of dynamic oscillatory mechanical techniques operating over a range of frequencies and temperatures can therefore give information about the time and temperature dependence of the real and loss components of the complex modulus. More importantly perhaps for the present purpose the method may be used to locate the regions of energy dissipation in the sample.

Oscillatory experiments may be of a forced vibration or of a resonance kind. Very useful reviews of the general experimental techniques available for carrying out mechanical spectrographical measurements are given by Ferry[35] and by McCrum et al.[7]

Simple resonance techniques using the torsion pendulum[65] have been extensively employed in the frequency range of 0·1–10 Hz. The equipment is robust, simple to set up and operate. Many useful papers utilising this technique have been published by Heijboer.[66,67]

In many cases the parameter most frequently measured and plotted is the logarithmic decrement (Δ). For a decaying resonance oscillation, as in the torsion pendulum device, the logarithmic decrement is the natural logarithm of the ratio of amplitudes of successive oscillations (θ_i).
Then

$$\Delta = \ln \frac{\theta_1}{\theta_2} \qquad (26)$$

The logarithmic decrement is a useful measure of the energy dissipated in the sample and can be related to the shear loss modulus G'' and to $\tan \delta$ by

$$\tan \delta = \frac{G''}{G'} = \frac{4\pi\Delta}{4\pi^2 - \Delta^2} \qquad (27)$$

For small loss angles then the latter expression reduces to Δ/π. It should be noted that peaks in tan δ — T curves do not necessarily correspond with the maxima in G'' — T curves, usually, particularly for polymers having a wide distribution of relaxation times the peak in tan δ — T appears at a higher temperature than the peak in the G'' — T curve. Heijboer[66] has

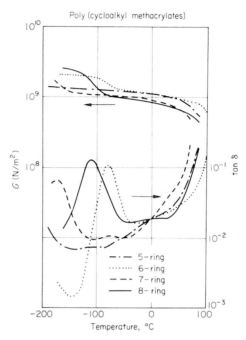

Fig. 16.   *Shear modulus and loss factor tan δ obtained by torsion pendulum studies at 1 Hz for polycyclopentylmethacrylate* (_ . _ . _ .); *polycyclohexylmethacrylate* (. . . . .); *polycycloheptylmethacrylate* (_ _ _ _); *polycyclo-octylmethacrylate* (————). (*Heijboer*[67].)

carried out much of the pioneering work in evaluating the effect of secondary dispersion regions on the dynamic mechanical response of polymers, particularly at low frequencies. The elegance of the results achievable by this dynamic mechanical approach is illustrated in Fig. 16 taken from Heijboer's recent work[67] on the low frequency mobility of several cycloaliphatic substituted polymethacrylates. From the tan δ peaks in Fig. 16 it can be inferred that a cycloaliphatic group undergoes a flexible transition at temperatures below the normal glass transition of the polymer. The mobility of the cycloaliphatic rings increases in the sequence six, eight, seven, five-membered ring. The dispersion is the largest for the eight-membered ring; it has the highest damping peak and the corresponding drop in modulus is highest.

It is in correlating the vast amount of dynamic mechanical data that the frequency–temperature relaxation maps of McCrum et al.[7] are so useful. Figure 17 taken from their book effectively correlates all the mechanical

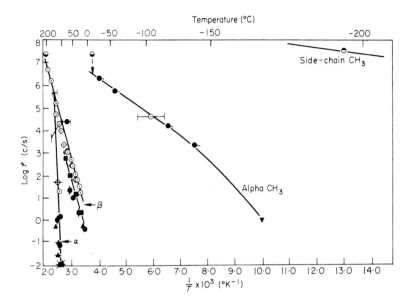

Fig. 17. *Frequency–temperature correlation map for polymethylmethacrylate. Dynamic mechanical measurements are indicated by filled points and dielectric measurement are open points. The glass transition (α); ester group rotation (β); α-methyl group rotation (γ) and side chain methyl group motions (δ) are shown. (From* Anelastic and Dielectric Effects in Polymeric Solids *by N. G. McCrum, B. E. Read and G. Williams. Copyright © 1967 John Wiley and Sons Inc., by permission of John Wiley and Sons Inc.).*

spectroscopy data available for polymethylmethacrylate, together with some dielectric and n.m.r. data.

It can be readily seen from this map that the use of low frequencies in dynamic mechanical spectroscopy can be exceedingly useful in discriminating between various relaxational processes. A discussion of the various observed relaxations will be deferred until later. Impact properties of polymers are of course a form of dynamic property, the deformation occurring in a very short period of time and is generally of large displacement. It is generally not possible to correlate the small strain elastic response obtained in a conventional dynamic experiment with the large strain result of an impact failure. In an impact failure generally the stress will not be homogeneous throughout the sample, stress concentrating factors arising from flaws or notches will introduce macroscopic features into consideration. The shape and area under the stress–strain curve and the occurrence of yield will have great bearing on the impact strength of polymers. To what extent the existence of secondary transitions lying below the T_g influence yield and ultimate failure properties is not easy to ascertain. There is certainly some influence, as the informed review by Boyer[8] makes clear. In a two-phase material represented by the rubber-modified polystyrenes Keskkula et al.[68] have compared damping-peak heights and areas with impact strength. They conclude that while the presence of a dispersion region in the glassy state is necessary for toughening, its size was not relatable to the degree of toughness.

Yield stress behaviour of glass thermoplastics does appear to show some dependence on the presence of secondary dispersion regions. Bauwens-Crowet et al.[69] have indicated that the yield stress behaviour of polymethylmethacrylate shows evidence for the existence of a local relaxation mode. Similar work[70] on a bisphenol A polycarbonate and on PVC

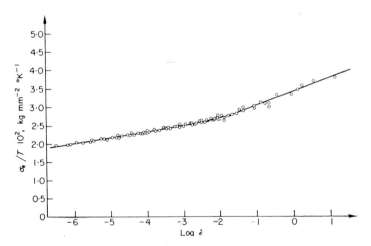

Fig. 18.   Master yield stress–strain rate curve for polyvinylchloride reduced to a temperature of $0°C$ showing evidence of a β relaxation corresponding to $-30°C$ at 10 Hz and having an activation energy of 14 kcal/mol. (Bauwens-Crowet et al.[70])

reveals the existence of a β transition process. Evidence for this is given in the yield stress–strain rate master curve for PVC reduced to a temperature of 0°C shown in Fig. 18. The break in the yield stress curve shown in Fig. 18 can be related to the observed local mode relaxation of PVC as revealed by measurements at -30°C of mechanical losses at 10 Hz.

Boyer has also discussed[8] the evidence that crazing in polystyrene and polystyrene blends can be influenced by the presence of low temperature secondary transition processes.

Effect of secondary transitions on the electrical properties of glassy polymers

At the glass transition there are pronounced changes in the various electrical properties of polymers. Most noticeably the dielectric constant ε' and the associated dielectric loss ε'' undergo large changes on passing through a temperature region appropriate for the frequency of measurement. There are also changes in the volume and surface resistivity as well as changes associated with the generation of static charges. Similarly we anticipate changes in all these properties on passing through a secondary relaxation region.

Particularly for those polymers that contain a group with an appreciable dipole moment the use of dielectric relaxation methods has proved of great value in elucidating the various molecular motions in the glassy state.

In a fashion similar to that used in Section 3.2.5 we may define a complex dielectric constant as

$$\varepsilon^* = \varepsilon' - i\varepsilon'' \tag{28}$$

and a loss tangent

$$\tan \delta = \frac{\varepsilon''}{\varepsilon'} \tag{29}$$

Provided that the motion responsible for a given relaxation is capable of a dielectric response then similar loss peaks will appear in the dielectric loss spectrum as would be seen in the results of dynamic mechanical measurements.

The dielectric relaxation time is a useful parameter that may additionally be recovered from dielectric measurements. Similar to the mechanical relaxation and retardation times this is the time taken for the polarisation of a polymer dielectric to decrease to $1/e$ of its original value. The dielectric relaxation time is of course directly relatable to the motion of the polarised group. In general, however, there will be a spectrum of relaxation times associated with any particular molecular motion and more complex methods are required to extract the information from experimental results. These techniques have been fully discussed from both the practical and theoretical view points by McCrum et al.[7] and the reader is referred there for further information.

Examples of the use of dielectric methods in obtaining information about the relaxation behaviour of various polymers are shown later (Section 3.3).

Nuclear magnetic resonance is also a particularly useful technique for observing secondary transitions, and the information obtained by this method is often complementary to dielectric results. The line width or second moment of the steady n.m.r. signal from glassy polymers usually exhibits a line broadening as particular molecular motions are frozen out. The line widths in a typical polymer above T_g are usually between 0·1 and 1 gauss. In the glassy state, however, line widths of 2–8 gauss are normal. At lower temperatures, on passing through secondary relaxation regions associated with side chain movement, further line broadening is observed and may be used to identify the particular motion. The line narrowing occurs when the frequency of the molecular motion becomes equal to the frequency of the line width, usually 10^4–10^5 Hz at the temperature of the sample.

Changes in both the spin lattice relaxation time T_1 and in the rotating frame relaxation times T_{1_p} have also been extensively used in detecting the presence of secondary relaxation processes in solid state polymers. Useful reviews of these techniques are given by Connor[71] and by Allen.[72]

An equilibrium may be set up between the spin system and the lattice involving a first-order energy exchange process characterised by a spin-lattice relaxation time T_1. This relaxation time will pass through minima as the rates of the various molecular motions become comparable with T_1. These relaxation times are normally measured at temperatures which will allow relaxations to occur at frequencies of 5–100 MHz. The rotating frame relaxation technique permits spin lattice relaxation times to be measured in the local fields existing between dipoles. The effective frequency at which these measurements are made are usually about 10^4 Hz and can therefore be correlated directly with dynamic mechanical or dielectric measurements.

Correlation of molecular motion with secondary relaxation processes
At temperatures below the glass-transition temperature the main chain segmental motion is frozen-in. However, there are still many localised molecular motions possible within the glassy matrix. These motions, as we

have seen, have considerable importance in determining the energy dissipative regions in the thermal, mechanical and dielectric spectra.

Commercially, particularly for those polymers widely used as dielectrics, the presence or absence of such regions may be of considerable technological benefit. For many reasons, both practical and academic, it is necessary to review the origin in molecular terms of the various relaxation processes that occur in organic glasses.

Among the non-crystallisable polymers secondary relaxations are exhibited by linear polymers without side groups and also by macromolecules in which side groups have an independence of motion irrespective of the main chain mobility. Polymers with side groups generally have a more complex relaxation spectrum than those without. Some β relaxation processes in non-substituted polymers must therefore be clearly associated with the backbone structure in some way unless the relaxation can be shown to be connected with the presence of impurities or end groups. The latter is unlikely; several studies, for example that of Ishida[73] on polyvinylchloride, have shown that the β relaxation is not molecular weight dependent.

The secondary relaxation in non-substituted polymers must arise from a backbone motion that differs from the micro-Brownian movement of the main chain characteristic of the T_g. Motion over restricted lengths of some few (six to eight) carbon atoms must be occurring in some way and this results in an observable relaxation. The following theories have been proposed.

(i) Local relaxation mode theories

If rotational movements involving the resistance of a rotational energy barrier as at T_g are to be avoided then small-scale motions of short chain segments can occur only by a limited vibrational oscillation about their mean position. Theories of this kind initially suggested by Okano[74] and developed by Yamafugi[75,76] have been reviewed by Saito et al.[77]

Because of the large number of internal degrees of freedom of the backbone of a polymer molecule the frequency spectrum of normal vibrations will be wide. The characteristic frequency of the μth normal mode is given by

$$\omega_\mu = \left(\frac{C_\mu}{m}\right)^{\frac{1}{2}} \tag{30}$$

where C_μ is the vibrational force constant for a group of mass m.

Statistical mechanics can be used to show that the r.m.s. amplitude of the μth vibrational mode is given by

$$\bar{\varphi}_\mu = \left(\frac{2kT}{M\omega_\mu^2} \cdot \frac{h\omega_\mu/kT}{\exp(h\omega_\mu/kT) - 1} \right)^{\frac{1}{2}} \tag{31}$$

Hence the amplitudes of the skeletal vibrational modes will cover a wide range from small amplitudes at the highest frequencies to large amplitudes at the lower frequencies. The modes at the lowest frequencies are considered to result from torsional oscillations about the carbon–carbon bond where the force constant is small compared to the force constants for bond stretching and valence angle deformation. In the glassy state, in view of the high internal friction, the low frequency torsional modes will be strongly damped resulting in a relaxational or a periodic character. The low amplitude high frequency modes will retain their vibrational character.

It is the molecular motions of the aperiodic kind that are responsible for local mode relaxational processes and which differ from the transitional modes or micro-Brownian motions responsible for the T_g.

Calculations of activation energies for the local mode relaxation for polyethylene give a figure of about 10 kcal/mol in reasonable agreement with experiment.

The breadth of the mechanical and dielectric loss curves in the β relaxation region can be readily understood in terms of the wide frequency distribution of the vibrational modes. The normal Arrhenius dependence of activation energy and the insensitivity of some β relaxations to pressure[59] can also be inferred from the local mode relaxation theory.

(ii) The 'Crankshaft' theory of Boyer and Schatzki

In view of the observation of Willbourn[78] that many amorphous polymers containing more than three or four $-CH_2-$ groups in sequence exhibited dynamic mechanical dispersions at temperatures of about $-120°C$ at 1 Hz, Schatzki[79,80] proposed that these loss regions originated in a common mechanism. He suggested that when the first and seventh bonds of a methylene sequence were collinear, the intervening atoms (see Fig. 19(a)) could rotate about this axis without disturbing any chain atoms further along the chain. Assuming that the normal tetrahedral bond angle of $109\frac{1}{2}°$ and that the trans, gauche$^+$ and gauche$^-$ positions of 120° apart are maintained then the activation energy for the 'crankshaft' rotation is about 11–15 kcal/mol. This value is in agreement with observed values. Schatzki suggests that this activation energy arises from a contribution due to an intrachain rotational energy barrier assumed to be twice the value for butane ($= 7.5$ kcal/mol) together with a term due to the van der Waals'

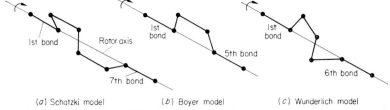

(a) Schatzki model   (b) Boyer model   (c) Wunderlich model

Fig. 19. 'Crankshaft' models of rotatability of main chain according to (a) *the Schatzki model in which rotation is about the first and seventh bond;* (b) *the Boyer model in which rotation is about the first and fifth bond;* (c) *the Wunderlich helix model in which rotation is about the first and sixth bond.*

interaction of the surrounding matrix. This latter, estimated from the cohesive energy density is about 5–6 kcal/mol. In the crystalline state, because the normal configuration of a $-(CH_2)_n-$ chain is all *trans* then crankshaft motion of the Schatzki kind is not possible. Schatzki has suggested that crankshaft motion will also take place for molecules containing side groups (*e.g.* methyl) providing that the group is not too large.†

Boyer[3] has proposed a model similar to Schatzki's except that only two carbon atoms join to form the crankshaft. However, this model utilises the energetically unfavourable *cis* conformation in the central bond and is much less probable than the four carbon model of Schatzki. An alternative structure using three carbon atoms between the collinear carbon atoms has been proposed by Wunderlich.[81] This model, in the form of a tight helix, is of a low energy conformation.

A serious disadvantage of the crankshaft theories, despite much circumstantial evidence, is that in each case free volume requires to be created in order that the crankshaft may rotate. We have seen evidence that, unlike T_g, the secondary transitions are insensitive to a reduction in free volume on increase of pressure and the temperature dependence of activation energy is of a normal Arrhenius form.

(iii) Association–dissociation theories

In the view of this theory, advanced by Andrews,[82] solid state transitions represent merely the loosening of various types of secondary intermolecular cohesive bonding in the solid state. The association–dissociation processes that are involved are governed by ordinary thermodynamic equilibria. If the transition is regarded as a thermodynamic equilibrium phenomenon, then the frequency dependence associated with the transition must be regarded as being associated with the transport rate in the two directions

† Schatzki in recent work (*Bull. Am. Phys. Soc.* **16**, 364, 1971) has largely discounted the value of the crankshaft concept for secondary relaxation interpretation.

of such an equilibria. Andrews and Kimmel[27] have used this theory to explain the two transitions that occur at 90 and 140°C in polyacrylonitrile on the basis of two types of association–dissociation forces, the lower transition supposedly being due to a dissociation of van der Waals' forces forming an intermolecular network. The well-known β transition in polymethylmethacrylate can also be explained on the basis of a dipole–dipole association existing between the ester side groups in this material.

It is apparent that this theory can be extended to cover the T_g as well as other secondary transitions. It is not necessary to have polar groups present. Andrews and Hammack[83] have used the dissociation of a particular type of van der Waals' bond between gauche conformations of adjacent chains to explain the familiar loss peak at -120°C for polymers containing ethylenic sequences.

It does seem probable, however, that the transition in nylon 6 at around 50°C which is moisture sensitive, is the result of a breakdown of a hydrogen bonded structure between amide groups in amorphous regions.

Not all the secondary relaxation processes occurring in glasses arise from the movement of short lengths of the molecular chain. Many such dispersion regions arise from a side group motion often referred to as a γ relaxation. If the side group is a flexible one with a long pendent chain, then it is possible that a local mode type of motion will be able to occur irrespective of the main chain mobility. There is evidence that the substitution of long alkyl groups into the poly(n-alkyl) methacrylates has a dispersion region arising from this cause. Side groups somewhat smaller in size, for example the ester groups in polymethylmethacrylate and polyvinylacetate, may undergo a limited torsional or vibrational motion giving rise to a dispersion region. The amplitude and frequency of these side-chain motions will clearly depend on the size and nature of the group and of its interactions with its neighbouring units in the main chain. The techniques that are used to detect such movements need to be chosen such that they will respond to a motion of the particular group involved in the movement.

Many side-chain movements arise from a structural peculiarity of the side group; perhaps the best known example is that of the cyclohexyl ring which may undergo transition between its isomeric conformations giving rise to a relaxation region in polymers of which it is part. Heijboer's classic work on the dynamic mechanical behaviour of cyclohexyl methacrylate is an example of motion of this kind.[66,84] These polymers have a damping peak at about -80°C at 1 Hz which is surprisingly unaffected by the local molecular environment of the cyclohexyl group. The activation energy for the 'flipping' of the ring between the two isomeric chain conformations calculated from an Arrhenius plot is 11·5 kcal/mol.

As we shall see later, aromatic rings are also associated with a limited motion of various kinds which can induce a small relaxation peak into the mechanical spectrum.

3.3 SECONDARY RELAXATION REGIONS IN TYPICAL ORGANIC GLASSES

It would be out of place in the present context to give more than a brief review of some of the more important transitions affecting those organic glasses which form the main subject matter of this book. Aspects of the dielectric and mechanical relaxations of many common polymers have been more than adequately reviewed in the book by McCrum et al.,[7] a collected source of information from which any account must inevitably draw.

3.3.1 Secondary relaxation regions in polyvinylchloride

Although polyvinylchloride has a glass-transition temperature of about 82°C it finds wide use as a flexible polymer in the plasticised form. When, as usually, prepared by free radical emulsion polymerisation techniques, steric and energy considerations favour a syndiotactic arrangement of monomer units in the chain, the polymer may approach an overall 65% syndiotactic placements. The polymer is not, however, particularly crystalline except when the chain regularity is improved; such crystallites as are formed are small and not well developed. It is to be regarded as an amorphous polymer but with strong electrostatic forces between chains.

In addition to its glass-transition temperature of 82°C as measured by volume dilatometry,[59,85] polyvinylchloride exhibits a further β relaxation region at $-26°C$ at atmospheric pressure. These two transition regions are clearly shown in Fig. 20 which records the specific volume–temperature–pressure relationships for polyvinylchloride obtained at various pressures up to 1000 atm under isobaric conditions. The glass-transition temperature clearly increases with increasing pressure, the pressure coefficient of T_g, $dT_g/dP = 0.014$ K/atm. The temperature for the β relaxation also appears to shift to higher temperatures with increasing pressure, a result differing from that for polymethylmethacrylate. Similar work was carried out by Heydemann and Guicking for polyvinylchloride plasticised with dioctylphthalate. The surprising result noticed was that while incorporation of plasticiser lowered the T_g the temperature of the secondary relaxation *increased* with increasing amounts of plasticiser until at about 30%

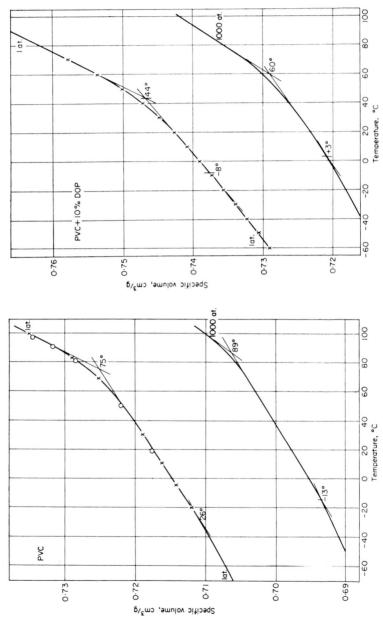

Fig. 20. Specific volume–temperature behaviour for polyvinylchloride and for polyvinylchloride plasticised with 10% dioctylphthalate at 1 and 1000 atm.[59] (Reproduced by permission of Dr Deitrich Steinkopff, Darmstadt.)

dioctylphthalate the two transitions merged into one. Whatever the cause of the β relaxation in this case, it is obviously hindered by the presence of the plasticiser molecules.

Yield stress behaviour,[70] dynamic mechanical and dielectric measurements in polyvinylchloride readily show the presence of a single β relaxation process at about $-30°C$ at 10 Hz with an activation energy of about 15 kcal/mol,[86,87] although Tanaka[88] from measurements in the frequency range 116–2320 Hz has estimated a value of 13 kcal/mol for the activation energy. There is extensive work available covering the dielectric and mechanical effects of plasticisers on polyvinylchloride particularly at T_g; much of this work is summarised by McCrum et al. Apart from the movement of the T_g towards lower temperatures which is usually observed for all plasticisers, non-polar plasticisers appear to cause a narrowing of the dispersion region. This narrowing may be due to a reduction in the interaction between crystallite and amorphous regions in the material. Incorporation of polar plasticisers into polyvinylchloride modifies the relaxation behaviour considerably. By dielectric measurements two loss regions are sometimes observed, one due to the plasticiser and one for the main chain. The whole character of the relaxation process of the main chain is modified by the bound plasticiser molecules that are associated with the main chain: Curtis[89] has reviewed this area.

Plasticiser molecules also affect the secondary relaxation regions to some extent. Saito[90] found that the intensity of the β relaxation peak decreases with increasing dioctylphthalate concentration (0–9%). However, at constant temperature the peak frequency of the relaxation does not vary. Fuoss[91] has also reported on dielectric loss data for polyvinylchloride plasticised with diphenyl. Recently Pezzin et al.[92] have indicated the results of dynamic mechanical measurements at frequencies of 1·5–2·8 Hz for polyvinylchloride plasticised with dioctylphthalate. A plot of tan δ against temperature for samples plasticised with 0–12% dioctylphthalate is given in Fig. 21. On the low temperature side of the β peaks, the curves are superimposed and the plasticiser modifies only the right-hand part of the curve. The tan δ of the minimum above the relaxation increases gradually and T_β decreases accordingly with increasing plasticiser content. The overall effect of the plasticiser on the β peak appears to be to reduce the motions of chain segments responsible for mechanical absorptions in the range -80 to $20°C$. This conclusion of Pezzin et al. is in agreement with the conclusions of Hedemann and Guicking in which the relaxation temperature as measured by volume changes actually increased with increasing amounts of plasticiser.

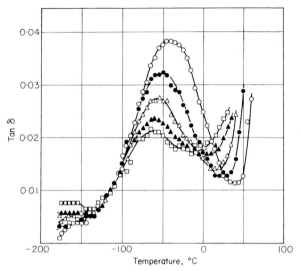

Fig. 21. Effect of plasticisation of polyvinylchloride by dioctylphthalate on the primary and secondary relaxation regions observed at 1·5–2·8 Hz. ○ 0% *Dioctylphthalate;* ● 3% *Dioctylphthalate;* Δ 6% *Dioctylphthalate;* ▲ 9% *Dioctylphthalate;* □ 12% *Dioctylphthalate. (Pezzin et al.*[92]*)*

The increased rigidity of the polyvinylchloride chain with the incorporation of small amounts of plasticiser, associated with the reduction in the β loss peak may be the cause of the lowered impact strength previously reported.[93,94]

There is no substantial difference between the dynamic behaviour of a normal amorphous PVC and a more crystalline sample, the relaxation loss peak and T_β being similar and reacting in the same way with plasticiser.

Hellwege *et al.*[85] have shown by linear expansion measurements that cold drawing does not affect the β relaxation in any way. Pezzin *et al.*[92] show that although T_β remains constant the minimum in the tan δ curve above T_β is reduced by as much as 35° on using an oriented sample, this decrease corresponding to the increased free volume resulting from the lowered density of the drawn sample.

Copolymerisation and chemical modification can of course affect the glass transition of a polymer very considerably. By incorporation of copolymer units into an otherwise stiff polyvinylchloride backbone the T_g can be lowered. Some effects may also be observed on the β relaxation process. For example copolymerisation of 5 and 13% ethylene into PVC displaces the β relaxation temperature to lower regions while the intensity is not appreciably altered. As shown in Fig. 22 there is also the appearance of a new dispersion region represented by the shoulder at $-160°C$ attributable to the motion of $-(CH_2)_n-$ sequences as mentioned earlier. Similar results are observed for vinylchloride–ethylhexylacrylate copolymers.

Reddish[95] has examined the effect of chlorination on the dielectric constant–temperature behaviour of PVC. The glass transition moves towards higher temperatures with increasing chlorine content but the transition peak decreases in size; the low temperature transition T_β is little affected by chlorination. The mechanical data of Pezzin et al., however, suggests that the β peak too is reduced in magnitude, broadened and displaced towards higher temperatures.

It would appear that the experimental data concerning the dielectric and mechanical relaxational behaviour of polyvinylchloride in the glassy state are consistent with a local mode relaxation theory for the β relaxation. Evidence for the participation of free volume effects, unlike that for the α

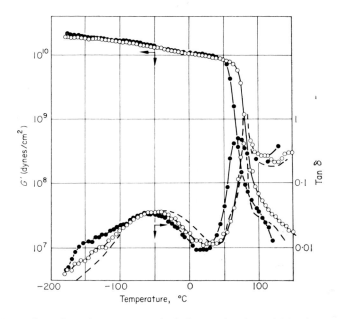

Fig. 22. *Effect of copolymerisation of ethylene with polyvinylchloride on primary and secondary relaxation regions. Shear moduli and tan δ values were obtained in a dynamic mechanical experiment at 1·5–2·8 Hz by Pezzin, Ajroldi and Garbuglio.[92] Polyvinylchloride (– – – – – –); polyvinylchloride with 5% ethylene (○); polyvinylchloride with 13% ethylene (●).*

transition is, in general, lacking. However, many of the results could be considered in terms of Andrews[82] association–dissociation theory.

3.3.2 Secondary relaxation regions in polystyrene

Polystyrene as normally prepared is essentially linear and atactic. Isotactic polymers can, however, be made by the use of organometallic co-ordination catalysts and this material is available either in the quenched amorphous or crystalline states so that it is possible to separate the effects of tacticity from those of crystallisation. Generally, however, we are concerned with amorphous atactic material prepared by free-radical catalysis. Materials obtained from differing sources will have a variety of end groups and the molecular weights and molecular weight distributions may well differ. Anionically initiated polystyrenes usually have a very narrow

TABLE 2

SELECTED VALUES OF RELAXATION TEMPERATURES,
ACTIVATION ENERGIES AND POSTULATED MODES OF
MOLECULAR MOTION FOR POLYSTYRENE

Relaxation temperature (°K)	Activation energy (kcal/mol)	Molecular motion
T_g		
atactic, 377	80, WLF type	main chain relaxation
isotactic, amorphous, 373–83[99,100]		
isotactic, annealed, oriented 386[99]		
T_β		
atactic, 300[101]	30[98], 33[97]	local mode relaxation
isotactic, transition not observed[98]		
T_γ		
atactic, crosslinked, 153(1 Hz)[102] 138(1 Hz)[103]	8[102], 9[98]	restricted phenyl group rotation
isotactic, transition less marked and displaced to higher temperatures[100,103]		
T_δ		
atactic, 50(10 kHz)[104] 51(6·3 kHz)[105] 38(5·59 Hz)[106]	2·0,[a] 1·6[98]	phenyl oscillation

[a] Estimated from results of McCammon[105] and Sinnott.[106]

distribution of molecular weights. M_w/M_n ratios are often close to the theoretical value of 1 for a monodisperse material.

Even in an essentially atactic material there may exist limited local regions of a helical ordered structure and as we have previously seen a limited helix–random coil transition process may take place.

Linear, amorphous, atactic polystyrene exhibits four relaxation regions in the glassy state when examined by static and dynamic mechanical techniques. For this polymer, in view of its non-polar character, dielectric relaxation methods, whilst used, are not so useful as for many other polymers. These relaxations together with the appropriate activation energy and the suggested modes of molecular motion are shown in Table 2.

Apart from the sharp change in the expansion coefficient at the glass-transition temperature for polystyrene it is not easy to see evidence for lower temperature transitions from volumetric data. Martin et al.[57] have examined the specific volume–temperature behaviour of atactic polystyrene over the range −180 to 180°C and show that the plot is curved below T_g and they hesitate to pick out any other transition regions. With hindsight one could now discern a transition at about 140°K corresponding to the γ transition. Recently Saba[96] has examined the thermal expansion of polystyrene over a temperature range from 4°K up to room temperature. He indicates a fairly large change in expansion coefficient in the 4–40°K region, probably indicative of the onset of the δ relaxation. The expansion coefficient remains broadly constant over the range 80–200°K. Moraglio and Danusso[107] have, however, found a peculiarity in the expansion of polystyrene between 47 and 55°C, and in the same article Bianchi and Rossi[108] indicate an anomaly in the internal pressure of polystyrene around 50°C.

Much of the discussion of the early work on the dynamic properties of polystyrene has been given by McCrum et al.[7] and by McCall[52] and by Boyer.[9] Recently Connor[97] and Yano and Wada[98] have considerably extended our knowledge of this area. The following correlation map (Fig. 23) has been compiled from their diagrams. As shown, the frequency–temperature correlation map indicates the usual nature of the α transition (T_g) curve, corresponding to a temperature sensitive activation energy of the WLF type. Polystyrene has a β relaxation peak which appears just below the glass transition; this relaxation is apparent in both the dynamic mechanical loss spectrum and in dielectric loss measurements. A narrowing of the n.m.r. line-width signal at about 350°K may also be attributable to the β process.

As Illers[103] has reported, at frequencies higher than 40 Hz the β

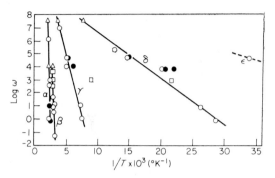

Fig. 23. Frequency–temperature correlation map for polystyrene. (○, ●)
mechanical loss peaks; (□, ■) *dielectric loss peaks;* (Δ, ▲) *n.m.r. narrowing and*
T_1-*minima for* (○, □, Δ) *atactic and* (●, ■, ▲) *isotactic polystyrenes.* (*From*
Yano and Wada.[98])

relaxation peak merges with the primary relaxation. Takayanagi[109]
has observed the β relaxation in the mechanical loss spectrum at 100 Hz
when it is apparent as a shoulder on the primary glass transition peak.

This merging of the α and β relaxation regions at higher frequencies is a
tendency that is noticed for several other polymers. The two α and β
transition lines in Fig. 23 effectively encompass the principal results of
dielectric, mechanical (dynamic shear and dynamic tensile) and n.m.r. spin
lattice relaxation time measurements.

Illers and Jenckel[102] have attributed the β relaxation to a rotation of
some phenyl groups about the main chain, which because of their local
environment are less sterically hindered than others. Vol'kenshtein[110,111]
has, however, shown that a narrowing of the fluorine n.m.r. absorptions of
poly-fluorostyrenes occurs for substitution in the *ortho* and *meta* positions
but not when the fluorine atom is in the *para* position. Clearly, if correct,
this observation supports the phenyl group rotational theory of Illers and
Jenckel. Yano and Wada[98] have carried out dielectric loss measurements
in the neighbourhood of the β relaxation. For a monodisperse polystyrene
a loss peak is observed at 340°K (110 Hz) and for atactic polystyrene an
indication of a β relaxation as a shoulder on the α peak at 320°K (110 Hz)
is seen. For an isotactic polystyrene no significant dielectric relaxation in
this region is observed. Rotation of phenyl groups should not result in a
change of polarisation and a dielectric relaxation should not be seen if
Illers and Jenckel's mechanism is correct. However, a local mode relaxation in the backbone would result in a change of polarisation if the vector
sum of the dipoles of phenyl groups in the segment does not vanish. For an

isotactic polystyrene with a 3_1 helix no resultant dipole would result. Takayanagi[109] has suggested that the β relaxation is due to a local mode twisting of the main chains. Odajima et al.[112] have shown that the second moment narrowing of the n.m.r. absorption spectrum of polystyrene in the β relaxation region is $\frac{2}{3}$ gauss which is reasonable for a backbone vibrational mode. The evidence of Vol'kenshtein quoted above has been disputed by Tanaka et al.[113] who have detected line narrowing for poly(p-fluorostyrene).

The available evidence suggests that the β relaxation in polystyrene results from a local mode relaxational behaviour as discussed earlier, rather than from a phenyl group rotation.

The γ relaxation in polystyrene which is shown clearly from the results of dynamic mechanical experiments but not from dielectric relaxation measurements has an activation energy of 7·6–9 kcal/mol. The magnitude of the dynamic loss peak for the γ process is extremely small and some authors (e.g. Chung and Sauer[114]) doubt its existence. However, Illers and Jenckel[101,102] using a torsion pendulum located γ relaxations at a frequency of 0·5–1 Hz on both linear and cross-linked polystyrenes and a sample that had been oriented by drawing up to 100% extension. Illers and Jenckel further found that the γ loss peak was unaffected by water, monomer or the previous thermal and mechanical history of the sample. Additionally it was pointed out that Wall et al.[100] had found that the loss peaks from atactic polystyrenes were larger than those from isotactic material.

Illers and Jenckel[102] suggested that the γ relaxation resulted from irregularities in the structure of the molecule associated with the presence of 'head-to-head'

$$-CH-CH_2-CH_2-CH-$$

units in the polymer chain. These units should of course be absent in an isotactic material accounting for the observations of Wall et al. Recent observations by Yano and Wada,[98] however, indicate that an anionically prepared monodisperse polystyrene, in which there are presumably no 'head-to-head' segments shows a pronounced γ relaxation at around 200°K (34 kHz).

It has also been suggested by Takayanagi[109] that the γ relaxation was associated with a restricted phenyl group rotation.

Yano and Wada using a composite oscillator method at 34 kHz have obtained mechanical loss spectra on atactic, monodisperse and isotactic polystyrenes which clearly show both the γ and δ relaxation peaks. These are shown in Fig. 24. There is no difference in the behaviour of the three types of polystyrene in their mechanical relaxational behaviour over this temperature range. Corresponding experiments in which dielectric constant and dielectric loss were measured over a comparable temperature region show no dispersions attributable to the relaxation. High-resolution n.m.r. has not proved useful in interpreting the chain motions of atactic polystyrene even at 220 MHz. The narrowing of the n.m.r. second-moment signal for polystyrene in the γ region is approximately 1 gauss[115,116] which is reasonable for a phenyl group rotation. Odajima et al.[116] show that this narrowing only occurs in para substituted polystyrenes but not for ortho and meta substituents probably because of a steric hindrance to rotation in the latter case. Hunt et al.[117] have observed a minimum in the spin lattice relaxation time T_1 at 260°K (21·5 MHz) which they attribute to the γ relaxation. Connor[97] has also observed a minimum at 223°K (64 kHz) by spin lattice relaxation measurements which is undoubtedly due to the γ process. Connor suggests that Hunt's result does not quite fit with a γ relaxation.

The mechanism of the γ relaxation process in polystyrene is still somewhat in doubt; it appears that the relaxation could be caused by phenyl group motion, possibly a rotational movement, with an exchange of energy

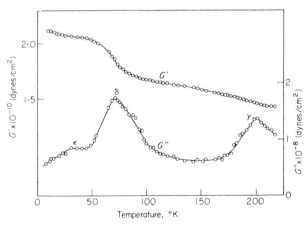

Fig. 24. Complex shear moduli for atactic polystyrene obtained at 34 kHz by Yano and Wada[98] as a function of temperature. γ, δ and ε transitions are clearly shown in the loss data.

between the phenyl group and backbone chain.[98] The peak height in isotactic polystyrene is smaller than for atactic material and also shifts towards lower temperatures, possibly because phenyl groups in the atactic chain exert strong interactions with other phenyl groups or backbone chains.

Polystyrene exhibits a very prominent δ dispersion region at about $40°K$ (1 Hz). Sinnott[106] attributed the relaxation that he observed using the torsion pendulum at $38°K$ (5·59 Hz) to a phenyl group motion. By the use of a longitudinal vibration apparatus Crissman and McCammon[118] have detected a δ peak at $48°K$ (6294 Hz) while McCammon et al.[119] have shown that the dielectric loss associated with this relaxation is slight. Whilst Hunt et al.[120] have observed a small depression in the spin lattice relaxation at about $130°K$ which may be associated with the δ process, Connor[97] has not been able to confirm this.

The effect of tacticity on the mechanical δ relaxation is not appreciable, but for an isotactic material the peak is narrower and not quite so pronounced as for the atactic sample.[98,121]

In a study of substituted polystyrenes and of polyvinyl benzoates, Baccaredda et al.[122] and also Pizzirani et al.[123] indicate that ortho and meta substituted polystyrenes do not exhibit a δ relaxation whereas para substituted polystyrenes do. These latter materials have a δ relaxation that is shifted towards higher temperatures and the size of the peak depends on the nature, number and position of the substituents. A higher activation energy is also associated with substitution. Polystyrenes substituted in the α position have δ relaxations that occur at somewhat higher temperatures compared with polystyrene. Similar results are seen for the polyvinyl benzoates. Baccaredda et al. suggest that the motion responsible for the relaxation is associated with the phenyl ring but is probably more complicated than a simple rotation around the carbon–carbon bond which links it to the main chain. A wagging movement as already suggested by Sinnott is not excluded.

Yano and Wada[98] speculate that the δ relaxation may have its origins in a defect model. In an isotactic polystyrene crystallised in a perfect 3_1 helix the phenyl groups are successively arranged, and a strong intermolecular interaction exists through van der Waals' forces between phenyl groups. In the glassy phase the arrangement may locally be similar to the crystal but when a defect in tacticity is introduced into the chain the helical conformation of the chain must change sense at that point. There will be a resulting misfit of phenyl groups with the surrounding chains and these will be in a complicated potential energy field which may well have one or more metastable states. It is the transition from one of these minimum energy states to another that results in the observed δ relaxation. It is suggested by Yano and Wada that this mechanism is consistent with the observed facts that (i) the peak height is small for an isotactic sample where the defect density is small; (ii) the peak is specific to polystyrene and similar compounds because it is due to an interaction between side chain phenyl groups; (iii) only a small relaxation is observed in the dielectric spectrum, because the phenyl group has only a small dipole moment; (iv) uniaxially stretched polystyrene has only a small δ peak for torsional movements about the stretching axis.[124]

Other relaxation processes have been observed for polystyrene; among these are a γ' process at 97°K (10 kHz) and an ε process at 25°K (10 kHz).[98] However, these processes have not been adequately confirmed but may arise from chain defects.

3.3.3 Secondary relaxations in polymethylmethacrylate
Polymethylmethacrylate as normally prepared by free radically initiated suspension or bulk polymerisation is non-crystalline although it may have

TABLE 3

RELAXATION TEMPERATURES, ACTIVATION ENERGIES AND
POSTULATED MODES OF MOLECULAR MOTION FOR
POLYMETHYLMETHACRYLATE

Relaxation temperature (°K)	Activation energy (kcal/mol)	Molecular motion
T_g		
(isotactic = 326[125])	55[125] WLF type	main-chain relaxation
(syndiotactic = 388–93[125])	68[125] WLF type	
(stereoblock = 333[78])		
(free radical = 387[58])	80[51], 245[126] WLF type	
$T_{\alpha'}$		
59% (syndiotactic) = 301[129], 335[59]	42·2[129]	local mode relaxation?
T_β		
(isotactic = 273 (1 Hz))[127]		ester group rotation
(syndiotactic = 303 (3 Hz),[125] 305 (0·9 Hz))[128]	18·7	
(free radical = 283 (1 Hz))[127]	17–30[a]	
T_γ		
100 (1 Hz)[130] unaffected by tacticity	3·1[b]	methyl group rotation
T_δ		
4·2 (1 Hz)[132], 15 (10 Hz)[131]	0·75[131]	ester methyl group rotation

[a] Values quoted in reference 7, p. 258.
[b] Mean of several values from reference 131.

an appreciable syndiotactic content. The use of lower temperatures for a free radical polymerisation may lead to high syndiotactic contents and the material may be crystallisable. Isotactic polymethylmethacrylate may be made with the use of stereospecific catalysts while isotactic–syndiotactic block copolymers are also known.

There are large differences in the packing of the two stereoisomers, isotactic polymethylmethacrylate has a helical arrangement of monomer residues in the ordered chain, there being five monomer units in a two-turn helix. Syndiotactic material has a stiffer structure resulting from ten monomer units arranged in a helix of four turns. On account of its greater flexibility, the isotactic material has a lower T_m and correspondingly lower T_g.

In common with many other polymers, polymethylmethacrylate has, in addition to its normal glass–rubber transition temperature, various secondary relaxation processes occurring below T_g. Table 3 lists some of these transitions together with the appropriate values of the activation energies associated with each transition. Specific volume–temperature relationships for polymethylmethacrylate as we have already seen from the data of Heydeman and Guicking[59] in Fig. 15 show the existence of two relaxation regions below T_g at 62°C and 7°C which are essentially unchanged with hydrostatic pressure up to 1000 atm. Martin et al.[57] report volumetric transitions at 15°C and −30°C while Halden and Simha[56] indicate the presence of transition regions at −130°C and at approximately −50°C in addition to one at 15°C. A number of other authors using dilatometric techniques have also shown the existence of transition processes in the 20–70°C range.[64,129,133,134,135,136,137]

Whilst the reported volumetric transitions falling just below room temperature may be associated with the β relaxation attributed to side group motion the transitions reported between 20° and 70° are more difficult to reconcile. The slow-rate mechanical properties of polymethylmethacrylate are considerably affected by the presence of secondary relaxations below the glass transition. The increased mobility afforded by these relaxations gives enhanced creep and stress relaxation effects in the otherwise rigid glass. Early creep studies by Sato et al.[138] had suggested that the activation energy for creep in the glassy state was 30 kcal/mol, a value substantially higher than those found from internal friction measurements by Deutsch et al.[51] and Heijboer[66] who gave results of 18 kcal/mol. Morris and McCrum[139] using shear creep compliance measurements over a temperature range of −30 to 40°C have calculated an activation energy for the creep process in this temperature range of 19 kcal/mol, a result in agreement with other methods of determination.

Sherby and Dorn[64] found that the activation energy for creep was constant over the temperature range $-10°$ to $50°C$ but that above $50°C$ the activation energy increased rapidly with temperature. They analysed their data in terms of two slightly overlapping T_g and T_β relaxations having activation energies of 100 and 20 kcal/mol respectively. However, there is evidence in the data of Sherby and Dorn of a relaxation at between 40 and $80°C$. A slightly higher value of 24 kcal/mol has recently been used by Roetling[140] to analyse the yield stress behaviour of polymethylmethacrylate at various strain rates between $30°$ and $90°C$.

A relaxation process can be estimated to occur at about $60°C$ from the creep data of Becker[141] gathered over the temperature range $20-140°C$. Similar evidence for a secondary relaxation just below T_g also comes from tensile energy experiments carried out on polymethylmethacrylate at various strain rates from $0.0025-500$ cm/sec by Maxwell and Harrington[142] (*see* Boyer[8]). The existence of a brittle–ductile transition for polymethylmethacrylate about $60°C$ may also be associated with a transition below T_g but above T_β. A recent determination of the shear and tensile creep compliances for polymethylmethacrylate between -150 and $75°C$ by Thompson[129] has enabled the β relaxation to be located at $-35°C$ but has also indicated the presence of a further relaxation at about $28°C$ having an activation energy of 42.2 kcal/mol. Thompson has also reviewed the extensive evidence for the existence of a relaxation process occurring in the temperature range $20-70°C$. Quite clearly there is a considerable body of evidence from dilatometric, creep and stress relaxation and calorimetric measurements to support this view. However, Thompson does not speculate on the molecular origins of the relaxation which he refers to as the α' process.

The α' relaxation does not appear to be observed during dynamic mechanical experiments. This transition may be due to a local mode relaxation similar to those discussed for polyvinylchloride (Section 3.3.1) and polystyrene (Section 3.3.2) which merges with the relaxation at higher frequencies, rather than the ester side group motion usually associated with the β relaxation. The relaxation time spectrum of the β relaxation has been reported to be abnormally wide[143] which could result from an overlap of a local mode relaxation with the ester group rotation.

A possible further explanation of the inflection in Heydeman and Guicking's specific volume curves at $62°C$ and the other reported transitions in this temperature range is that this represents the T_g for an isotactic component of the polymethylmethacrylate. Glass-transition temperatures for isotactic materials have been reported variously as $60°C$

(1 Hz),[144] 70°C (1 Hz),[127] 53°C (static),[125] which are certainly close to the relaxations reported by Heydeman.

The β relaxation in polymethylmethacrylate which shows up clearly in dynamic mechanical experiments as an energy loss near to room temperature (10°C/1 Hz) is generally held to be due to a movement associated with the ester group in the polymer. McCrum et al. have reviewed the data pertinent to the β relaxation and the frequency–temperature correlation map taken from their account, shown in Fig. 17, effectively summarises the available information.

Associated with the dynamic mechanical loss peaks are analogous dielectric loss peaks which would be consistent with an ester group rotational mechanism for the β process. Heijboer[66,127] has presented some evidence for this assignment from studies on various polyalkylacrylates and methacrylates. In order for a secondary β relaxation peak to be present, rotation of the methoxylcarbonyl group must be possible but such movement should not be too easy. There should be some resistance to motion by steric hindrance from the neighbouring α–Me group on the main chain. If rotation is blocked, for example with a polyphenylmethacrylate, or if there is no restricting α–Me group as in polymethylacrylate there is no β relaxation or it is severely depressed in magnitude. These conclusions have been broadly supported by n.m.r. and the mechanical loss measurements of Powles et al.[145] and by others.

Although the available evidence is consistent with the β relaxation, being due to a movement associated with the methoxycarbonyl group, the exact mechanism is not clear and it is uncertain to what extent the main chain is involved in the process. According to Illers,[146] Heijboer,[127] and Mikhailov[147] the β relaxation in polymethylmethacrylate is strongly affected on copolymerisation, for example with methyl acrylate and styrene. The energy loss peak shifts to lower temperatures with increasing co-monomer concentration and the activation energy decreases. Even for only 10 mole % co-monomer there are significant effects ruling out any nearest-neighbour-only interaction or suggesting a main-chain involvement in the β process. Kawamura et al.[148] have further investigated the copolymerisation of methylmethacrylate with n-butylmethacrylate and other monomers by dielectric methods at frequencies between 30 Hz and 1 MHz. They find that the loss peak temperature attributed to side group motion in polymethylmethacrylate varies with co-monomer ratio when the co-monomer does not have an α–Me group but remains unchanged for co-monomers which have an α–Me group. For both types of monomer a reduction in the intensity of the relaxation is seen on copolymerisation. It is suggested as a result of these experiments that the moving unit concerned in the β process consists of a single side chain together with a segment of the main chain. Increased mobility of the main chain results from copolymerisation with a monomer which does not have an α–Me group. The fact that the rotational movement of the side group is predominantly governed by the intrachain potential[149] is supported by the fact that the effect of plasticiser on the β relaxation is slight,[66,150] that pressure dependence on relaxation time is small[151,152] and that the volumetric transitions reported by Heydeman and Guicking[59] are almost negligible.

According to Read[143] who has used dynamic birefringence as a useful tool for investigating the motion of side groups, there are two possible types of movement. These are (i) torsional oscillations of limited amplitude about the carbon–carbon bonds attaching the ester side groups to the main chain of the type considered by Saito et al.[77] (ii) Hindered rotations within the –COOMe group. These two processes may be considered to occur either independently or co-operatively, in the latter case a broad spectrum of relaxation times would be expected. Read has found that the shorter relaxation times are associated with a relaxation of the strain–optical coefficient (at 8 Hz) while the longer relaxation times in the spectrum result in a relaxation of the stress–optical coefficient at constant strain. The strain–optical relaxation may be associated with side group internal rotations and the stress–optical relaxation may tentatively be associated with the torsional mode process (i). An interesting account by Havriliak[153] suggests on the basis of infra-red absorption studies as a function of temperature that there is only a 0·8 kcal/mol difference in the energies between two discrete positions of the ester side group in syndiotactic polymethylmethacrylate. He concluded that the β transition with its high activation energy could not be due to an ester group rotation relative to the main chain but could result from a twisting of the main chain about its longitudinal axis.

The glass-transition temperature of isotactic polymethylmethacrylate, for which the most reliable value is 48·3°C for material of infinite molecular weight,[154] is appreciably lower than that of either a syndiotactic polymer or a free radical polymer. For 100% syndiotactic polymethylmethacrylate an estimate of 160°C has been made for high molecular weight material[154] while free radically initiated polymer has a T_g of 114°C.[58] The isotactic chain is therefore considerably more flexible than that of the syndiotactic arrangement and this is reflected in a slight lowering of the corresponding T_β to 0°C (1 Hz) as reported by Heijboer[127] and supported by the dielectric loss measurements of Mikhailov and Borisova.[155] Recently, however, Havriliak[125] pointed out that the resolution of the relaxation data of Mikhailov and Borisova for isotactic polymethylmethacrylate into two components was rather arbitrary and with other data of Havriliak[156] it could be represented by a single relaxation. In contrast, syndiotactic polymethylmethacrylate displayed a very obvious β relaxation at about 30°C (3 Hz)[125] and 32°C (0·9 Hz)[128] by mechanical relaxation and a corresponding dielectric loss peak is also observed. The shift towards slightly higher temperatures of this β relaxation is no doubt due to the stiffer chain structure of the syndiotactic arrangement. Absence of the β peak for the isotactic material observed in some studies is probably a result of merging of T_β with the much larger glass-transition peak which has been shifted to much lower temperatures (48·3°C). An interesting discussion on the structure–β dispersion relationships for polymethylmethacrylate is to be found in the paper by Havriliak[125] but clearly this is still a problem that remains to be solved.

As already indicated in the frequency–temperature correlation map in Fig. 17 and in Table 3 for polymethylmethacrylate there are two further relaxation processes occurring at lower temperatures. The γ relaxation at a temperature of 100°K (1 Hz) has been observed by Sinnott[130] using dynamic mechanical experiments and by Hendus et al.[157] at temperatures between 123 and 253°K for frequencies in the range of 10^3 to 10^6 Hz. This relaxation which does not show up in dielectric relaxational observations has been attributed to the rotation of α-methyl groups attached to the main backbone chain of the molecule. This has been confirmed by n.m.r. line narrowing studies notably by Powles[158] and by spin-lattice relaxation time minima by Kawai[159] and by Powles, Hunt and Sandiford.[145]

These latter authors find a minimum in T_1 at 260°K (30 MHz) which they assume is caused by an α-methyl group reorientation without main-chain motion. Such T_1 minima are present in many polymers containing an α-methyl group such as polyethylmethacrylate, poly-n-butylmethacrylate, polyphenylmethacrylate and polycyclohexylmethacrylate. Minima are absent when the α-methyl group is replaced by H, C_2H_5 or Cl groups as in polymethylacrylate, polyethylacrylate, polymethylmethacrylate and polymethylchloroacrylate.

Line narrowing measurements by Powles and Mansfield[131] for the γ process in polymethylmethacrylate obtained at an effective frequency of 21·5 MHz indicate an activation energy for the process of 2·5 kcal/mol. Kawai[159] finds a value of 3·6 kcal/mol; a mean of values obtained by various authors[131] is 3·1 kcal/mol.

Recent studies[160] on the dependence of the ability of the methyl group to rotate in the stereospecific forms of poly-n-butylmethacrylate suggest that there is little difference in the location of the relaxation or in the activation energies for the γ process in the stereo-isomers and that it is unaffected by the mobility of the backbone. For both syndiotactic and isotactic poly-n-butylmethacrylate Ochiai, Shindo and Yamamura find an activation energy of 6·7 kcal/mol for the γ loss at $-155°C$ (30 Hz).

A relaxation region at $15°K$ (10 Hz) has been inferred for polymethylmethacrylate by Powles and Mansfield[131] from spin-lattice relaxation time measurements at higher frequencies. Sinnott[130] has detected a narrowing of the second moment of the n.m.r. signal of both the methyl esters of polyacrylic and polymethacrylic acids near to 77°K, which could be attributed to the rotation of a methyl group at frequencies of 10^4–10^5 Hz. The activation energy of this relaxation is very low having a value of 0·75 kcal/mol[131] and has been attributed to a rotational movement of the methyl group in the ester side group.

REFERENCES

1. Brandrup, J. and Immergut, E. H. (1966). *Polymer Handbook*, John Wiley and Sons Inc., New York.
2. Lee, W. A. (1965). *RAE Tech. Rpt*, 65151.
3. Boyer, R. F. (1963). *Rubb. Chem. Technol.*, **36**, 1303.
4. Shen, M. C. and Eisenberg, A. (1966). *Progress in Solid State Chemistry*, Pergamon Press, Oxford, vol. 3, p. 407.
5. Gibbs, J. H. (1960). *Modern Aspects of the Vitreous State*, ed. J. D. Mackenzie, Butterworth, London, vol. 1.
6. Goldstein, M. (1964). *Modern Aspects of the Vitreous State*, ed. J. D. Mackenzie, Butterworth, London, vol. 3, p. 90.
7. McCrum, N. G., Read, B. E. and Williams, G. (1967). *Anelastic and Dielectric Effects in Polymeric Solids*, John Wiley and Sons Inc., London.
8. Boyer, R. F. (1968). *Polymer Eng. Sci.*, **8**, 161.
9. Boyer, R. F. (1970). *Papers presented at 160th Meeting of ACS, Chicago, Organic Coatings and Plastics Chemistry*, **30**, No. 2.
10. Krimm, S. and Tobolsky, A. V. (1951). *J. Poly. Sci.*, **6**, 667.
11. Spencer, R. S. and Dillon, R. E. (1949). *J. Colloid Sci.*, **4**, 241.
12. Fox, T. G. and Flory, P. J. (1948). *J. Am. Chem. Soc.*, **70**, 2384; (1950). *J. Appl. Phys.*, **21**, 581.
13. Boyer, R. F. (1966). *J. Poly. Sci.*, C, **14**, 267.
14. Kovacs, A. J. (1958). *J. Poly. Sci.*, **30**, 131.
15. Barton, J. M. (1969). *Polymer*, **10**, 151.
16. Gee, G. (1970). *Contemp. Phys.*, **11**, 313.
17. Allen, G., Ayerst, R. C., Cleveland, J. R., Gee, G. and Price, C. (1968). *J. Poly. Sci.*, C, **23**, 127.
18. Bianchi, U., Pedemonte, E. and Rossi, C. (1965). *Preprints*, **P.286**, High Polymer Conference, Prague.
19. Adam, G. and Gibbs, J. H. (1965). *J. Chem. Phys.*, **43**, 139.

20. Mandlekern, L. (1964). *Crystallisation of Polymers*, McGraw-Hill, New York.
21. Hoffman, J. D., Williams, G. and Passaglia, E. (1966). *J. Poly Sci., C,* **14,** 173.
22. Rigby, H. A. and Bunn, C. W. (1949). *Nature,* **164,** 583.
23. Quinn, F. A., Roberts, D. E. and Work, R. N. (1958). *J. Appl. Phys.,* **22,** 1085.
24. Lord, F. (1970). Private communication.
25. Connor, T. M. (1970). *J. Poly. Sci.,* A2, **8,** 191.
26. Duda, J. L. and Vrentas, J. S. (1968). *J. Poly. Sci.,* A2, **6,** 675.
27. Kimmel, R. M. and Andrews, R. D. (1965). *J. App. Phys.,* **36,** 3063.
28. Schmeider, K. and Wolf, K. (1953). *Kolloid Z.,* **134,** 149.
29. Cotten, G. R. and Schmeider, W. C. (1963). *Kolloid Z.,* **192,** 16.
30. Ogura, K., Kawamura, S. and Sohne, H. (1971). *Makromolecule,* **4,** 79.
31. Andrews, R. D. and Kimmel, R. M. (1965). *J. Poly. Sci.,* B, **3,** 167.
32. Beevers, R. B. (1967). *Polymer,* **8,** 463.
33. Geiszler, W. A., Kowtsky, J. A. and DiBenedetto, A. T. (1970). *J. Appl. Poly. Sci.,* **14,** 89.
34. Hoffman, J. D. (1954). *J. Chem. Phys.,* **22,** 156.
35. Ferry, J. D. (1961). *Viscoelastic Properties of Polymers*, John Wiley and Sons Inc., New York.
36. Simha, R. and Boyer, R. F. (1962). *J. Chem. Phys.,* **37,** 1003.
37. Williams, M. L., Landel, R. F. and Ferry, J. D. (1955). *J. Amer. Chem. Soc.,* **77,** 3701.
38. Doolittle, A. K. (1951). *J. Appl. Phys.,* **22,** 1471.
39. Williams, M. L. (1958). *J. Appl. Phys.,* **29,** 1396.
40. Fox, T. G. and Allen, V. R. (1965). *J. Chem. Phys.,* **41,** 344.
41. Rusch, K. C. (1968). *J. Macromol. Sci.-Phys.,* **B2,** 179.
42. Simon, F. E. (1930). *Ergebn. exact. Naturwiss,* **9,** 244.
43. Kauzmann, W. (1948). *Chem. Rev.,* **43,** 219.
44. Oblad, A. G. and Newton, R. F. (1937). *J. Amer. Chem. Soc.,* **59,** 2495.
45. Ehrenfest, P. (1933). *Leiden Comm. Suppl.,* 756.
46. Gibbs, J. H. (1956). *J. Chem. Phys.,* **25,** 185.
47. Gibbs, J. H. and DiMarzio, E. A. (1958). *J. Chem. Phys.,* **28,** 373.
48. Gibbs, J. H. and DiMarzio, E. A. (1963). *J. Poly. Sci.,* A, **1,** 1417.
49. Gibbs, J. H. and DiMarzio, E. A. (1964). *J. Res. Nat. Bur. Stds.,* **68A,** 611.
50. Adam, G. and Gibbs, J. H. (1965). *J. Chem. Phys.,* **43,** 139.
51. Deutsch, K., Hoff, E. A. W. and Reddish, W. (1954). *J. Poly. Sci.,* **13,** 565.
52. McCall, D. W. (1969). In *Molecular Dynamics and Structure of Solids*; NBS Special Publication, Washington, **301,** p. 475.
53. Slichter, W. P. (1966). *J. Poly. Sci., C,* **14,** 40.
54. Wittmann, J. C. and Kovacs, A. J. (1969). *J. Poly. Sci., C,* **16,** 4443.
55. Du Pont, Differential Thermal Analyser.
56. Halden, R. and Simha, R. (1968). *J. Appl. Phys.,* **39,** 1890.
57. Martin, G. M., Rogers, S. S. and Mandlekern, L. (1956). *J. Poly. Sci.,* **20,** 579.
58. Beevers, R. and White, E. F. T. (1960). *Trans. Farad. Soc.,* **56,** 744.
59. Heydeman, P. and Guicking, H. D. (1963). *Kolloid Z.,* **193,** 16.
60. Becker, G. W. (1955). *Kolloid Z.,* **140,** 1.
61. Nitsche, R. and Wolf, K. A. (1962). *Kunstoffe Struktur, physikalisches Verhalten und Pruefung*, Bd. 1, 186, Springer-Verlag, Berlin.
62. Koppelmann, J. and Gielessen, J. (1961). *Kolloid Z.,* **175,** 97.
63. Buchdahl, R. and Nielson, L. E. (1950). *J. Appl. Phys.,* **21,** 482.
64. Sherby, O. D. and Dorn, J. E. (1958). *J. Mech. Phys. Solids,* **6,** 145.
65. Nielson, L. E. (1962). *Mechanical Properties of Polymers*, Reinhold, New York.
66. Heijboer, J. (1956). *Kolloid Z.,* **148,** 36.
67. Heijboer, J. (1968). *J. Poly. Sci., C,* **16,** 3413.

68. Keskkula, H., Turley, S. G. and Boyer, R. F. (1971). *J. Appl. Poly. Sci.*, **14**, 351.
69. Bauwens-Crowet, C. and Homes, G. A. (1964). *Compt. Rendu*, **259**, 3434.
70. Bauwens-Crowet, C., Bauwens, J. C. and Homes, G. A. (1969). *J. Poly. Sci.*, A2, **7**, 735.
71. Connor, T. M. (1971). *NMR-Basic Principles and Progress*, Vol. 4, Springer, New York, p. 247.
72. Allen, G. in *Molecular Spectroscopy*, ed. P. W. Hepple, Institute of Petroleum, London, p. 395.
73. Ishida, Y. (1960). *Kolloid Z.*, **171**, 71.
74. Okano, K. (1960). *Rept. Prog. Polymer Phys. Japan*, **3**, 71.
75. Yamafuji, K. (1960). *J. Phys. Soc. Japan*, **15**, 2295.
76. Yamafuji, K. and Ishida, Y. (1962). *Kolloid Z.*, **183**, 15.
77. Saito, N., Okano, K., Iwayanagi, S. and Hideshima, T. (1963). *Solid State Physics*, vol. 14, ed. H. Ehrenreich, F. Seitz and D. Turnbull, Academic Press, New York.
78. Willbourn, A. H. (1958). *Trans. Farad. Soc.*, **54**, 717.
79. Schatzki, T. F. (1962). *J. Poly. Sci.*, **57**, 496.
80. Schatzki, T. F. (1965). *Polymer Preprints*, **6**, 646.
81. Wunderlich, B. (1962). *J. Chem. Phys.*, **37**, 2429.
82. Andrews, R. D. (1966). *J. Poly. Sci.*, C, **14**, 261.
83. Andrews, R. D. and Hammack, T. J. (1965). *J. Poly. Sci.*, B, **3**, 659.
84. Heijboer, J. (1960). *Kolloid Z.*, **171**, 7.
85. Hellwege, K. H., Hennig, J. and Knappe, W. (1963). *Kolloid Z.*, **188**, 121.
86. Ishida, Y. (1960). *Kolloid Z.*, **168**, 29.
87. Pezzin, G. and Paglian, A. (1966). *Chim. Ind.* (*Milan*), **48**, 458.
88. Tanaka, K. (1962). *Rept. Prog. Polymer Phys. Japan*, **5**, 138.
89. Curtis, A. J. (1960). *Progress in Dielectrics*, **2**, 31.
90. Saito, S. (1964). *Rept. Res. Electrotech. Lab. No.* 648, Japan.
91. Fuoss, R. M. (1941). *J. Am. Chem. Soc.*, **63**, 378.
92. Pezzin, G., Ajroldi, G. and Garbuglio, C. (1967). *J. Appl. Poly. Sci.*, **11**, 2553.
93. Bohn, L. (1963). *Kunstoffe*, **53**, 826.
94. Horsley, R. A. (1957). *Plastics Progress* (*London*), 77.
95. Reddish, W. (1966). *J. Poly. Sci.*, C, **14**, 123.
96. Saba, R. (1967). Ph.D. Dissertation, Pennsylvania State University.
97. Connor, T. M. (1970). *J. Poly. Sci.*, A2, **8**, 191.
98. Yano, O. and Wada, Y. (1971). *J. Poly. Sci.*, A2, **9**, 669.
99. Newman, S. and Cox, W. P. (1960). *J. Poly. Sci.*, **46**, 29.
100. Wall, R. A., Sauer, J. A. and Woodward, A. E. (1959). *J. Poly. Sci.*, **35**, 281.
101. Illers, K. H. and Jenckel, E. (1958). *Rheol. Acta.*, **1**, 322.
102. Illers, K. H. and Jenckel, E. (1959). *J. Poly. Sci.*, **41**, 528.
103. Illers, K. H. (1961). *Z. Elektrochem.*, **65**, 679.
104. Baccaredda, M., Butta, E. and Frosini, V. (1965). *J. Poly. Sci.*, B, **3**, 189.
105. McCammon, R. D. cited by A. E. Woodward. (1960). In *Trans. N.Y. Acad. Sci.*, **24**, 250.
106. Sinnott, K. M. (1962). *SPE Trans.*, **2**, 65.
107. Moraglio, G. and Danusso, F. (1963). *Polymer*, **4**, 445.
108. Bianchi, U. and Rossi, C. (1963). *Polymer*, **4**, 447.
109. Takayanagi, M. (1963). *Rept. Progress Polymer Phys.* (*Japan*), **6**, 121.
110. Abrashitov, R. A., Baghenov, N. M., Vol'kenshtein, M. V., Kol'tsov, A. I. and Khachaturov, A. S. (1964). *Vysokomol. Soedin*, **5**, 405; (1965). **6**, 1871.
111. Vol'kenshtein, M. V., Kol'tsov, A. I. and Khachaturov, A. S. (1965). *Vysokomol. Soedin*, **7**, 296.
112. Odajima, A., Sohma, J. and Koike, M. (1957). *J. Phys. Soc. Japan*, **12**, 272.

113. Tanaka, K., Yano, O., Maru, S. and Magao, R. (1969). *Repts. Progress Polymer Phys. Japan*, **12**, 379.
114. Chung, C. I. and Sauer, J. A. (1971). *J. Poly. Sci.*, A2, **9**, 1097.
115. Wada, Y. (1966). *J. Poly. Sci.*, C, **15**, 101.
116. Odajima, A., Sauer, J. A. and Woodward, A. E. (1962). *J. Poly. Sci.*, **57**, 107.
117. Hunt, B. I. and Powles, J. F. (1966). *Proc. Phys. Soc.*, **88**, 513.
118. Crissman, J. M. and McCammon, R. D. (1962). *J. Acoust. Soc. Am.*, **34**, 1703.
119. McCammon, R. D., Saba, R. G. and Work, R. N. (1969). *J. Poly. Sci.*, A2, **7**, 1721.
120. Hunt, B. I., Powles, J. G. and Woodward, A. E. (1964). *Polymer*, **5**, 323.
121. Crissman, J. M., Woodward, A. E. and Sauer, J. A. (1965). *J. Poly. Sci.*, A, **3**, 2693.
122. Baccaredda, M., Butta, E., Frosini, V. and Magagnini, P. L. (1966). *J. Poly. Sci.*, A2, **4**, 789.
123. Pizzirani, G., Magagnini, P. and Guisti, P. (1971). *J. Poly. Sci.*, A2, **9**, 1133.
124. Frosini, V. and Woodward, A. E. (1969). *J. Poly. Sci.*, A2, **7**, 525.
125. Havriliak, S. (1968). *Polymer*, **9**, 289.
126. Sasabe, H. and Saito, S. (1968). *J. Poly. Sci.*, A2, **6**, 1401.
127. Heijboer, J. (1965). In *Physics of Non-crystalline Solids*, North Holland, Amsterdam.
128. Gall, W. G. and McCrum, N. G. (1961). *J. Poly. Sci.*, **50**, 489.
129. Thompson, E. V. (1968). *J. Poly. Sci.*, A2, **6**, 433.
130. Sinnot, K. M. (1960). *J. Poly. Sci.*, **42**, 3.
131. Powles, J. G. and Mansfield, P. (1962). *Polymer*, **3**, 336.
132. Sinnott, K. M. (1959). *J. Poly. Sci.*, **35**, 273.
133. Wada, Y. and Yamamoto, K. (1956). *J. Phys. Soc. Japan*, **11**, 887.
134. Rogers, S. S. and Mandelkern, L. (1957). *J. Phys. Chem.*, **61**, 985.
135. Wada, Y., Hirose, H., Asano, T. and Fukutomi, S. (1959). *J. Phys. Soc. Japan*, **14**, 1064.
136. Holt, T. and Edwards, D. (1965). *J. Appl. Chem.*, **15**, 223.
137. Atkinson, H. F. and Grant, A. A. (1966). *Nature*, **211**, 627.
138. Sato, K., Nakane, H., Hideshima, T. and Iwayanagi, S. (1954). *J. Phys. Soc. Japan*, **9**, 413.
139. Morris, E. L. and McCrum, N. G. (1963). *J. Poly Letters*, **1**, 393; (1964). *Proc. Roy. Soc.*, A.**281**, 258.
140. Roetling, J. A. (1965). *Polymer*, **6**, 311.
141. Becker, G. W. (1955). *Kolloid Z.*, **140**, 1.
142. Maxwell, B. and Harrington, J. (1952). *Trans. Amer. Soc. Mech. Engrs.*, **74**, 2579.
143. Read, B. E. (1967). *J. Poly. Sci.*, C, **16**, 1887.
144. Nagata, N., Hikichi, K., Kaneri, M. and Furuichi, J. (1963). *Rept. Progress Polymer Phys. Japan*, **6**, 235.
145. Powles, J. P., Hunt, B. I. and Sandiford, D. J. H. (1964). *Polymer*, **5**, 505.
146. Illers, K. H. (1966). *Ber. Bunsenges, Physik. Chem.*, **70**, 353.
147. Mikhailov, G. P. (1964). *Soviet Physics*, USPEKHI, **7**, 375.
148. Kawamura, Y., Nagai, S., Hirose, J. and Wada, Y. (1969). *J. Poly. Sci.*, A2, **7**, 1559.
149. Havriliak, S. and Roman, N. (1966). *Polymer*, **7**, 387.
150. Jenckel, E. and Illers, K. H. (1954). *Z. Naturforsch.*, **9a**, 440.
151. Williams, G. (1965). *Trans. Farad. Soc.*, **61**, 2091.
152. Sasabe, H. and Saito, S. (1968). *Rep. Progress Polymer Phys. Japan*, **11**, 373.
153. In Roetling, J. A. (1965). *Polymer*, **6**, 311.
154. Thompson, E. V. (1966). *J. Poly. Sci.*, A2, **4**, 199.
155. Mikhailov, G. P. and Borisova, T. I. (1958). *Sov. Phys. Tech. Phys.*, **3**, 120.
156. Havriliak, S. and Negami, S. (1966). *J. Poly. Sci.*, C.**14**, 99.

157. Hendus, H., Schnell, G., Thurn, H. and Wolf, K. (1959). *Ergeb. Exakt. Naturw.*, **31**, 5, 220.
158. Powles, J. G. (1956). *J. Poly. Sci.*, **22**, 19.
159. Kawai, T. (1961). *J. Phys. Soc. Japan*, **16**, 1220.
160. Oshiai, H., Shindo, H. and Yamamura, H. (1971). *J. Poly. Sci.*, A2, **9**, 431.

CHAPTER 4

CREEP IN GLASSY POLYMERS

S. TURNER

4.1 INTRODUCTION

Creep in plastics is one manifestation of their viscoelastic nature, which is, in turn, a characteristic feature of the macroscopic deformation behaviour of polymeric materials in general. The term 'creep' was adapted from its use in relation to the behaviour of metals, for which it designates the time-dependent component of the strain that is observed as a result of prolonged stressing. The initial, nearly instantaneous, strain is elastic in nature and that which develops later is very largely 'plastic', or irreversible. No such convenient and logical subdivision of the deformation of plastics is possible. Most aspects of their deformational behaviour are so severely time-dependent that the isolation of a distinct elastic component or a region of genuinely constant modulus is possible only under very special experimental conditions and 'creep' means the entire strain caused by an applied force. In contrast to its use in relation to metals, there is no implication that the deformations are irreversible, despite the broad classification of 'viscoelastic' in which the conjunction of 'visco' and 'elastic' could be taken to imply a viscous, or irreversible constituent. It is apparent that words and definitions are often chosen for their pictorial quality rather than for their explicit meaning, even in scientific contexts.

Leaving aside semantic quibbles, two quite distinct approaches to the study of creep may be discerned. One starts with molecular concepts and considers the macroscopic strain as the consequence of the diffusion-type movement of molecular segments. The other disregards the molecular texture and treats strain merely as a geometric statement of the consequence of applying forces to a continuum whose nature is specified by a constitutive equation. Some interconnection between these two theories develops

at isolated points but they never truly coalesce. The first class of theories
is of great relevance to the development of new or improved plastics and
the second class provides quantitative rules by which the deformation of
plastics articles in service can be predicted from basic physical measurements on the materials. Both are preoccupied with the overwhelming fact
that plastics are much more easily deformed than most of the more tradi-
tional materials of construction. This deficiency persists even when allowance is made for their low densities by the use of 'specific modulus'.
Typical values of modulus for plastics and other materials are given in
Table 1.

TABLE 1

APPROXIMATE VALUES OF MODULUS, AND DENSITY (20°C)

Material	Young's modulus (GN/m^2)	Relative density
Carbon steel	200	7·8
Rolled copper	120–130	~8·9
Cast iron	85–100	~7·7
Cast aluminium	55–75	2·7
Polyester resin + 87% w/w uniaxially orientated glass filament	52	2·2
Polyester resin + 60% w/w glass cloth	21	1·7
Polyester resin + 30% w/w glass fibre mat.	10·5	1·3
Nylon 66 + 33% w/w glass fibres (dry)	10[a]	1·4
Oak (dry)	~10	~0·7
Polymethylmethacrylate	3[a]	1·2
Propylene homopolymer (sp. density 0·907)	1·5[a]	0·9

The data in this table must be treated with reserve. The properties of metal alloys
depend on the thermal history, those of plastics depend on temperature, time, strain,
etc., to such a degree that the values given here are merely rough indices of a complex
physical property. The properties of oak are similarly dependent on several variables.

[a] Creep moduli measured at a specific time and a specific strain. These will be numerically different from
moduli measured by another method. (*See* also Introduction, Table 5, p. 43.)

The cause of the modulus deficiency, and the predominant viscoelastic
characteristics, of plastics is undoubtedly the loose packing of the molecules. Marked improvements of this can be effected only by radical
chemical modifications that simultaneously produce changes in other
properties and effectively create a new class of material. Thus the essential
problem is to understand the deformation properties in order that they
can be accommodated within a technology. Such understanding requires
the critical analysis of accurate experimental results and these require sound
testing techniques. The best guide to good experimental technique is a
respectable theory and that is fortunately available. It starts with what

is known as the phenomenological theory of viscoelasticity, which is actually a theory of linear systems, extends it to nonlinear viscoelasticity and finally formulates a working compromise between that and a range of semi-empirical 'creep equations'. Those parts of the mathematical background essential to any discussion of creep are outlined in Section 4.2, in just sufficient detail to indicate the relationships between creep and other deformation phenomena. Only a few references are made to original papers, and those are to specific items of special relevance to the topics discussed in later sections. A more comprehensive guide to the literature would be largely irrelevant to the main discussion of creep in glassy polymers, and would be cumbersome if it were to be useful, because the modern theory is the result of many extensions to, and refinements of, the basic theory. However, as a partial compensation for this omission, a number of useful review papers on the subject of viscoelasticity are cited in the bibliography.

4.2 PHENOMENOLOGICAL THEORY OF CREEP

4.2.1 Linear theory
The phenomenological theory of linear viscoelasticity is directly analogous to the theory of linear elasticity. The earliest analyses were based on model combinations of Hookean springs and Newtonian dashpots but the modern treatment is more general, postulating stress–strain–time relationships of the form

$$a_n \frac{\partial^n \sigma}{\partial t^n} + a_{n-1} \frac{\partial^{n-1} \sigma}{\partial t^{n-1}} + \cdots + a_0 \sigma = b_m \frac{\partial^m \varepsilon}{\partial t^m} + \cdots + b_0 \varepsilon \qquad (1)$$

where σ = stress, ε = strain, t = time.

In the most general anisotropic case twenty-one such relationships are required for a complete characterisation.

The coefficients $a_0, \ldots a_n$ and $b_0, \ldots b_m$ have the status of material coefficients. The Hookean solid, the Newtonian liquid, the Maxwell, Voigt and other elementary model materials are special cases of eqn. (1) that are obtained when most of the coefficients are equated to zero; the remaining coefficients are then identifiable as simple physical entities.

The response of a linear viscoelastic system (*i.e.* of one representable by eqn. (1)) to a sinusoidal excitation, of either stress or strain, defines a 'complex modulus function' and the response to a step excitation defines a 'creep compliance' or a 'relaxation modulus' function. These functions completely characterise the linear viscoelastic behaviour and the problem of materials evaluation may be regarded as being the tabulation of the coefficients. The fundamental significance of a sinusoidal excitation is easily seen. If the excitation is a stress

$$\sigma = \hat{\sigma} \exp{(j\omega t)}$$

it is easily shown that the complex modulus, $M^*(\omega)$, of a material representable by eqn. (1) is given by

$$M^*(\omega) = \frac{b_m(j\omega)^m + b_{m-1}(j\omega)^{m-1} + \cdots + b_0}{a_n(j\omega)^n + a_{n-1}(j\omega)^{n-1} + \cdots + a_0} \tag{2}$$

and clearly incorporates all the material coefficients. Its reciprocal is $C^*(w)$, the complex compliance function.

The creep compliance function is generated by a step-function excitation and similarly incorporates all the coefficients, though this is not so immediately apparent by inspection. It is defined by

$$C_c(t) = \frac{\varepsilon(t)}{\sigma_0}$$

and Laplace Transformation† gives

$$\bar{C}_c(p) = \frac{\bar{\varepsilon}(p)}{\sigma_0}$$

which can be written

$$\bar{C}_c(p) = \frac{\bar{\varepsilon}(p)}{p\bar{\sigma}(p)}$$

whence, from eqn. (1),

$$\bar{C}_c(p) = \frac{a_n p^n + a_{n-1}p^{n-1} + \cdots + a_0}{p(b_m p^m + b_{m-1}p^{m-1} + \cdots + b_0)} \tag{3}$$

which, in principle, can be transformed back to give an expression for $C_c(t)$ which is completely general.

Equation (3) is much more significant than a formal statement. A new quantity, the 'transform compliance' denoted by $\bar{C}_c$, is defined by

$$\bar{C}_c = \frac{a_n p^n + a_{n-1}p^{n-1} + \cdots + a_0}{b_m p^m + b_{m-1}p^{m-1} + \cdots + b_0} \tag{4}$$

† The Laplace Transformation is defined by the equation
$$\bar{f}(p) = \int_0^\infty f(t) \exp{(-pt)} \, dt$$

and it can be shown that, for a viscoelastic material, there is a whole set of such transform compliances and transform moduli corresponding completely to the elastic compliances and moduli of an elastic material. Furthermore, the relationships between the transform moduli correspond exactly to those between the elastic moduli so that viscoelastic problems are resolvable if the corresponding elastic solution is known. The importance of the creep compliance functions is that they are simply related to transform compliances (eqns. (3) and (4)) and are therefore similarly analogous to their elastic counterparts.

The complex compliance is related to the creep compliance by

$$C^*(\omega) = \int_0^\infty \dot{C}(t) \exp{(\mathrm{j}wt)}\, \mathrm{d}t \tag{5}$$

and there is a similar relationship between complex modulus and relaxation modulus.† This link between sinusoidal and step function data is a crucial part of the background theory; it enables a creep function to be converted into the corresponding sinusoidal compliance function, some features of which may be directly relatable to specific molecular relaxation processes.

The creep compliance function can be assumed to consist of three components, namely

$$C(t) = C_0 + \psi(t) + \frac{t}{\eta} \tag{6}$$

where
C_0 = a time-dependent component
$\psi(t)$ = a time-dependent component, which is relatable to the differential equation
η = a 'viscosity' coefficient.

Amorphous plastics at a temperature near to their glass–rubber transition temperature may exhibit the full range of behaviour represented by this equation but if the service temperature is well below the transition only part of the $\psi(t)$, and probably none of the third term, will contribute to the compliance.

It is generally assumed that $\psi(t)$ is of the form

$$\psi(t) = \int_0^\infty \mathrm{f}(\tau)[1 - \exp{(-t/\tau)}]\, \mathrm{d}\tau \tag{7}$$

† The relaxation modulus is not the reciprocal of the creep compliance; the transform modulus is the reciprocal of the transform compliance and hence $p\overline{C}_c(p) = 1/p\overline{M}_r(p)$.

where

τ = retardation time
$f(\tau)$ = a distribution function of retardation times.

It may be shown that this expression is equivalent to the differential equation, to which it is a superior alternative when the creep compliance function extends over many decades of log time. The distribution of retardation times is a popular concept because it must be directly related to the actual molecular relaxation processes. Thus it brings a simple physical reality to what is otherwise only a mathematical model, and a logical link between the different viscoelastic functions. In principle, $f(\tau)$ can be derived from one type of experiment and then substituted into the integral equation appropriate to a different experimental situation, but the process is not simple because the unknown $f(\tau)$ in the first instance is under the integral sign, and the empirical quantity $\psi(t)$ is never measured over the complete range of integration. These mathematical difficulties are circumvented by practical approximations; the integral may be inverted by a numerical method and the effective time range over which $\psi(t)$ is measured may be extended artificially by time-temperature superposition.[1] The superposition technique exploits the sensitivity of the molecular relaxation processes to temperature; a long duration experiment may be replaced by one of much shorter duration at a higher temperature and, under certain simplifying assumptions, a quantitative equivalence between elapsed time and temperature difference may be established.

The two manipulations are successful where the viscoelastic functions are very sensitive to elapsed time, i.e. within a main transition, but they are not satisfactory for polymers in their glassy state. Only a small part of the distribution function is effective in that region and there is little point in manipulations related directly to the integral equations. On the other hand, the duration of experiments could be reduced dramatically by time–temperature superposition if it were not particularly susceptible to two severe errors in the glassy region. One is experimental–manipulative in origin. The constituent creep compliance vs. log time curves obtained at different temperatures have to be moved relative to one another along the log time axis until they superpose into a master curve, but there are no unambiguous criteria of what constitutes acceptable superposition and when the curves are relatively featureless and of low slope, as they are in the glassy region, a small experimental error, which is always along the ordinate, transforms into a large error in the displacement along the abscissa. The other source of error is fundamental; the glassy-state creep response is often the combined effect of the early stages of the main relaxation process and a secondary process associated with short relaxation times (or high relaxation frequencies). The relative contributions of the two processes change with temperature, and the secondary process is preferentially susceptible to extraneous factors such as water, soluble additives, etc., so that the basic premise of the time–temperature superposition principle is violated; a change of temperature does not correspond to the operation of a simple 'shift factor'.

Recent refinements to the technique[2] minimise the second difficulty by introducing an adjustment to the compliance values, but this need not be pursued because a separate overriding factor severely restricts the direct usefulness of the equations listed above. The restriction arises because the equations are linear whereas the deformation behaviour they should represent is nonlinear. The term 'nonlinear' may be defined in several ways. The most practical definition is that at any particular time the strain is not proportional to the stress.

Most practical deformations are outside the realm of linear viscoelasticity but, even so, the linear theory plays a significant role in the development of the theory of deformation. It demonstrates that creep data, or relaxation data, have a fundamental significance as characterising functions, and it provides a starting point for the more complex equations that are required for a proper representation of nonlinear behaviour.

4.2.2 Nonlinear theory—creep equations

In principle, it should be possible to postulate an equation of sufficient generality to account for all the observed deformation phenomena, but it is extremely unlikely that such an equation would be tractable or physically significant and the trend has therefore been towards special equations of limited applicability. Innumerable equations have been proposed to account for creep, particularly creep in tension; some are frankly empirical, others have some theoretical basis for their form, all are inexact, to varying degrees; despite their wide variety of form, they fall into two classes:

$$\text{(i)} \quad \varepsilon = g(\sigma) \cdot f(t)$$

and

$$\text{(ii)} \quad \varepsilon = F(\sigma, t) \tag{8}$$

where the symbols have the same meaning as for eqn. (1).

The first equation is by far the easier to manipulate. A simple check for the separability of the variables is that curves of log strain vs. log time with stress as parameter, will be parallel, displaced relative to one another along the log strain axis without change of shape.

Families of creep curves of glassy amorphous plastics often show this simple regularity at strains below about 0·01 (1 %) but not at large strains, where severe viscoelastic nonlinearities cause effects phenomenologically similar to, though physically different from, the large plastic deformations observed in metals. The two regions are clearly distinguishable in Fig. 1.

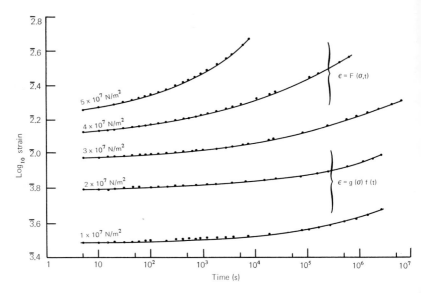

Fig. 1.   Creep at 20°C, glassy amorphous polymer. The stress-dependence and the time-dependence are separable at low strains, inseparable above about 0·01.

However, diverging log strain vs. log time curves are not an infallible means of discrimination because eqn. (8) incorporates an oversimplification. There are good physical reasons for expecting there to be a component of strain that is independent of time, as in eqn. (6). Thus, if

$$\varepsilon(t, \sigma) = f_1(\sigma) + f_2(\sigma)F(t) \tag{8a}$$

is the proper form for the creep equation, the appropriate quantity to plot against the logarithm of the time would be $\log [\varepsilon - f_1(\sigma)]$ rather than $\log \varepsilon$. The value assigned to $f_1(\sigma)$ can affect the slope, or the shape, of the curve significantly, as is shown in Fig. 2. The test material here was polypropylene, which has a relatively simple time-dependence, and the objective was to assign an appropriate value to $\varepsilon_0 = f_1(\sigma)$ in order to straighten out the early part of the creep curve so that the data could be

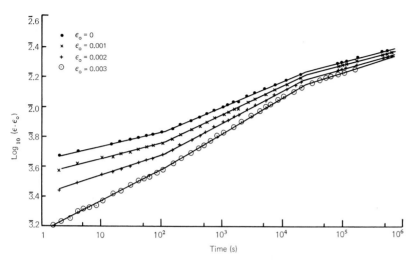

Fig. 2. The manipulation of creep data. If $\varepsilon_0 + a\mathrm{F}(t)$ is assumed, an appropriate choice for ε_0 can simplify the form of $\mathrm{F}(t)$. ε_0 is not necessarily meaningful physically. (See eqn. (8a).)

analysed in terms of a power-function dependence on time. The value by which this was achieved implies an 'instantaneous' compliance of about 5×10^{-10} m^2/N which is too high, by a factor of at least 3, to be physically justifiable; alternatively the power-law time-dependence may be abandoned.

One of the more widely used creep equations is the hyperbolic sine equation, introduced for plastics by Findley.[3] This has the form

$$\varepsilon = a \sinh b\sigma + ct^n \sinh d\sigma \qquad (9)$$

where a, b, c, d, n are materials coefficients.

Findley tabulated the values of the coefficients for a wide range of plastics and, just as for Fig. 2, the empirical values of the first term imply unreasonably high values for the 'instantaneous' compliance. Even so, this equation merits special mention because it is a reasonably good representation of the creep behaviour of many plastics and has some theoretical basis as a general creep law. This can be seen by considering the potential energy field associated with a particular molecular segment. If one supposes that a shear stress f_0 is applied in the x direction and that molecular movements are restricted to the parallel and antiparallel directions then the argument proceeds, in relation to Fig. 3, as follows:

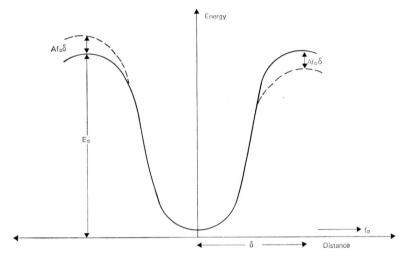

Fig. 3. *Potential energy diagram for derivation of hyperbolic sine creep law (eqn. (11)).*

The randomly distributed movements of segments, due to thermal vibrations, are biased under the influence of an applied stress. Thus, for a stress f_0, the energy required for a left to right transition is $E_0 - Af_0\delta$, where δ is the displacement of a mobile unit and A is its effective cross-sectional area; for a right to left transition it is $E_0 + Af_0\delta$. Replacing the product $A\delta$ by v, since it has the dimensions of volume:

Probability of a left to right transition is $\propto \exp\left[-(E_0 - vf_0)/kT\right]$

Probability of a right to left transition is $\propto \exp\left[-(E_0 + vf_0)/kT\right]$

and hence the net flow from left to right will be proportional to

$$\exp\left(-E_0/kT\right)\left[\exp\left(f_0 v/kT\right) - \exp\left(-f_0 v/kT\right)\right] \qquad (10)$$

On average, f_0 is proportional to the macroscopic stress, σ, and the net flow is proportional to the strain, ε. Therefore

$$\varepsilon \propto \exp\left(\frac{E_0}{kT} \sin h\, \frac{\alpha\sigma}{kT}\right) \qquad (11)$$

where α is a constant. This equation is often referred to as the Eyring equation after its originator.[34]

Few of the creep equations are as soundly based as the hyperbolic sine creep law, but a lack of physical significance may be unimportant. Their main purpose may be a concise representation of many data, but if the equation is a complicated one, as it invariably must be if it is to be an accurate representation, this advantage is lost in comparison with the convenience of graphical presentations, which readily lend themselves to quick comparisons between materials and to quick data abstraction for substitution into design formulae. Superficially, nonlinearity is a relatively simple issue, the complication merely being that more than one experiment is needed to characterise the behaviour. Similarly, the substitution of such data into design calculations is not intrinsically difficult, even though the actual computations may be complicated, provided that the applied stress does not vary with time.

When the stress does change, the standard creep functions, whether analytical, graphical or numerical in form, are inadequate, because they are not equations of state, i.e. the relationship between the variables is not unique. This is their serious weakness; they present strain as a function of elapsed time for a step excitation function of stress but they do not contain an intrinsic superposition rule, such as is inherent within the mathematics of linear systems, by which the response to an arbitrary excitation function can be calculated if the response to a step excitation function is known.

4.2.3   Nonlinear theory—superposition rules
Boltzmann's Superposition Principle[4] states that for a linear viscoelastic material the strain response to an arbitrary stress excitation function, $\sigma(t)$, is given by

$$\varepsilon(t) = \int_{-\infty}^{t} C(t - u) \frac{d\sigma(u)}{du} \, du \qquad (12)$$

where $C(t)$ = the creep compliance function. There are several alternate forms of eqn. (12), easily derivable by integration by parts and change of variable. It is a general result for linear systems that may be derived analytically from eqn. (1) or by a physical argument in which the only supposition is that the response to an additional excitation is independent of, and can be linearly added to, any prevailing response. In many instances the equation can be replaced by graphical superposition which is far more convenient to use.

The early attempts to formulate a superposition rule for nonlinear materials could be described as linear manipulations of a nonlinear creep equation. Findley and Khosla formulated three superposition rules.[5] The simplest was a variant of Boltzmann's Principle which assumed that the creep of a material subjected to stress σ_1 from the time zero to time τ, and subsequently subjected to a stress σ_2 was given by the sum of the creep which would occur under constant stress σ_1 and the creep which would occur under a stress $(\sigma_2 - \sigma_1)$ applied from $t = T$ onwards. For such conditions eqn. (9) becomes

$$\varepsilon = a \sinh b\sigma_1 + a \sinh b(\sigma_2 - \sigma_1) + ct^n \sinh d\sigma_1$$
$$+ c(t - T)^n \sinh d(\sigma_2 - \sigma_1) \qquad (13)$$

The other two rules were obtained by differentiation with respect to time after prior manipulations to eqn. (9). This gave creep rate as a function of stress and time (time-hardening equation), as a function of stress and strain (strain-hardening equation) and as other more complicated combinations. The predictions of these rules for various stress histories did not agree well with the experimental results. The authors reported average errors of 10%, 13% and 36% for the superposition, strain-hardening and time-hardening rules respectively.

Such theories have given way to the multiple integral theory. The form corresponding to eqn. (12) is

$$\varepsilon(t) = \int_0^t C_1(t - u) \frac{d\sigma}{du} du + \int_0^t \int_0^t C_2(t - u_1, t - u_2) \frac{d\sigma}{du_1} \frac{d\sigma}{du_2} du_1 du_2$$

$$+ \int_0^t \int_0^t \int_0^t C_3(t - u_1, t - u_2, t - u_3) \frac{d\sigma}{du_1} \frac{d\sigma}{du_2} \frac{d\sigma}{du_3}$$

$$\times du_1 du_2 du_3 + \cdots \qquad (14)$$

where the lower limit has been taken as zero without loss of generality.

The kernel function $C_1(t)$ is merely the linear creep compliance function the others, C_2, C_3, etc. are similar in nature but are multiple functions of time, and they provide for the cross-dependence of the response to a new additional excitation on the history of all earlier excitations and the associated responses.

During the last few years the multiple integral theory has been a popular research topic and it is well established as a mathematical tool. Its practical usefulness is less certain at present. The available evidence suggests that the prediction of the response to an increase of stress can be accurate even if relatively crude approximations are made, whereas the prediction of the response to a decrease of stress is very unreliable, probably because the increasing strain in a creep experiment takes the specimen into a region of even easier deformation (because of the nonlinearity) whereas the decreasing strain in a recovery experiment takes the specimen into a region of less easy deformation. Until this inadequacy is resolved there is probably n alternative to direct measurements of recovery, *i.e.* the decrease of the strain if the stress is removed, and of the strain response to intermittent stressing, both of which are important practical situations. A major handicap to progress is the very high experimental accuracies that are required if the various working hypotheses are to be checked and compared. Too often in the past such comparisons have been vitiated by the coincidence of complementing experimental errors. Working approximations to the full theory are required if its cumbersome nature is to be confined within realistic bounds. The first question to be resolved is the order of the integral series. This depends on the complexity of the basic creep curves because for a single step stressing history eqn. (14) reduces to the relatively simple form

$$\varepsilon(t) = \int_0^t C_1(t) \frac{d\sigma}{du} \, du + \int_0^t \int_0^t C_2(t, t) \frac{d\sigma}{du_1} \frac{d\sigma}{du_2} \, du_1 \, du_2 + \cdots$$

$$= C_1(t)\sigma + C_2(t, t)\sigma^2 + C_3(t, t, t)\sigma^3 + \cdots \qquad (14a)$$

The first approximation, therefore, is the choice of the lowest order of polynomial in stress that will represent the creep behaviour. The series is usually truncated after the cubic term, not because that provides a very good fit for the experimental data but because the later manipulations of the integral series is otherwise too complicated. The complexity is immediately evident from inspection of the expression for the residual strain after the creep stress has been removed at time T.

From eqn. (14), if creep stress σ is removed at $t = T$ the residual strain is

$$\varepsilon_r(t) = \sigma[C_1(t) - C_1(t - T)] + \sigma^2[C_2(t, t) - 2C_2(t, t - T)$$

$$+ C_2(t - T, t - T)] + \sigma^3[C_3(t, t, t) - 3C_3(t, t, t - T)$$

$$+ 3C_3(t, t - T, t - T) - C_3(t - T, t - T, t - T)] \qquad (14b)$$

In this expression six terms are known from the creep experiments but the three with nonsymmetrical arguments, *i.e.* $C_2(t, t - T)$, etc., have to be derived from other experiments, and it may be claimed, therefore, that theory is of little practical value even for relatively simple stress histories such as recovery after creep. On the other hand, once the constituent parts have been evaluated the equations have wide generality. They can be derived from a set of experiments in which the stress is changed abruptly, either upwards or downwards, at various values of T. The derivation involves the addition and subtraction of experimental quantities such as $\varepsilon(t)$, procedures that are equivalent in some respects to differentiation and involve similar loss of precision. Another source of error in this class of experiment is interspecimen variability; even when it is low, it may constitute a large error in some of the constituent experiments or during the subsequent manipulations.

There is also a fundamental difficulty. The early part of the creep response contains information that is vital to the successful application of the multiple integral theory and yet it is experimentally inaccessible unless the excitation function is a close approximation to a step. This is very difficult to achieve mechanically and current equipment is really incapable of bridging an important gap in the information available. This is discussed in greater detail in Section 4.3.2.

4.3 APPARATUS AND EXPERIMENTAL METHODS

4.3.1 General principles

Creep experiments are simple in principle; a force, or a system of forces, is applied and the deformation is measured as a function of the elapsed time. In practice it is difficult to avoid interactions between the apparatus and the specimen, in particular to ensure that the stress system is exactly what is stipulated or supposed, and to measure the strain accurately without imposing a restraint on the specimen at the same time. The strain in glassy amorphous plastics is usually too small for elementary methods of measurement† and yet the specimens are insufficiently robust to support the elaborate devices used on metal specimens. The standard techniques to achieve progressive alignment of a metal specimen/test machine assembly are similarly unsuitable for plastics because of their relatively low moduli.

Uniaxial tension is the commonest deformation mode employed, partly because tensile apparatus is relatively simple and partly because there have been sound reasons for the fashion in metals testing to be followed. The main features of apparatus for accurate uniaxial tension measurements are:

(i) The force must be applied symmetrically along the geometric axis of the specimen, otherwise the accuracy at low strains may be poor and a brittle specimen may break prematurely.

(ii) The extensometer must combine low mass with high mechanical

---

† The range 0–0·02 (2%) is the one of greatest interest, but experiments up to 0·05 are commonplace.

stability. It must consistently record the deformation in the specimen without imposing any restriction on it.

Several accurate tensile creep machines have been described recently.[6,7] Used in accordance with highly refined operating procedures that were developed subsequently, such machines have elevated the experiments from a technological to a scientific status.

The requirements for uniaxial compression are very similar[8] but it is more difficult to attain a truly uniaxial stress in compression than in tension because friction between the end faces of the specimen and the thrust plates restrains the lateral expansion near the ends. The corresponding effect in tension would be restriction of the lateral contraction by the clamps, which is avoided by the use of a long slender specimen; the same solution is not possible for compression because long slender columns are unstable under longitudinal compression. The specimen shape is thus a compromise between the high length–diameter ratio required for true uniaxial compression and the low ratio necessary for stability. In practice ratios between 4 and 8 are satisfactory though the higher values can be used only if the apparatus is very accurately aligned and if the specimen has been machined to a commensurate close tolerance. An alternative method is to prevent the buckling of a slender specimen by lateral restraints.[9] The overwhelming advantage of this is that the same specimen can be used for tension and compression.

Flexure has been a popular deformation mode in creep experiments, partly because the application of a small force produces a relatively large deflection. These apparent practical advantages are very largely illusory because the deflections have to be very small if a high accuracy is required and this, in turn, imposes stringent requirements on the apparatus.[10] If large strains are permitted, as in simple tests such as ASTM D790–66, purely geometrical effects contribute to the deflection of the beam. These are compensated for in the formulae of the theory of large elastic deflections, but the nonlinear viscoelastic characteristics of the specimen cannot be encompassed because the stress system in a bent beam is not uniform, nor can the change in the applied stress that results from the increasing deflection during creep under constant load conditions.

There is no serious difficulty in the measurement of shear creep if the material is soft. If it has a high modulus, shear is usually achieved through torsion. A hollow tube is the ideal specimen but it is difficult to prepare to the requisite precision and is susceptible to buckling as the angle of twist increases. A solid prism of circular cross-section is better in these respects but it is only suitable for experiments at very small strains, where the stress–strain relationships are approximately linear. A specimen of rectangular cross-section, though very much easier to prepare, has the same disadvantage plus the geometric one that all plane sections perpendicular to the specimen axis distort under torsion. Apparatus suitable for the direct measurement of shear creep in high modulus materials has been developed recently.[11] An annular gauge section is machined from a flat circular disc, the rim of which is then rotated in relation to the centre section. The profile of the gauge section is such that the shear stress is uniform throughout for a constant applied torque.

4.3.2 Special experimental requirements

At small elapsed times

In an elementary creep experiment a specimen can be stressed simply by the manual application of a force through some mechanical system. Such a procedure corresponds only very approximately to the step-function excitation by which the creep compliance functions are defined. This would not be particularly important were it not for the very wide range of the molecular response times, *i.e.* of the $f(\tau)$ of eqn. (7), because of which some strain is manifest during the loading period, no matter how short it is. The discrepancy between the observed response and the step-function response decreases as the elapsed time grows large in relation to the loading time, until it is quite insignificant. Some error in the measured response at short times is tolerable when the main preoccupation is the response at long times, but it can be a major deficiency in some experiments.

The loading force cannot be applied instantaneously because of the mechanical inertias in the system. Even so, rapid loading rates can be achieved fairly easily and the practical limitation is usually vibrations in the specimen or mechanical disturbance of the extensometer. The design objective is the best compromise between high loading rate, freedom from shock and reproducibility, for a wide range of specimen characteristics. The discrepancy can hardly be classed as an error; it is more in the nature of an example of the uncertainty inherent in all our observations of physical phenomena. Its magnitude can be estimated from calculations for a model linear viscoelastic material. It can be shown that such a material, with distribution of retardation times $f(\tau)$, subjected to a constant loading rate $\dot{\sigma}_c = (\sigma_0/t_0)$ (henceforward referred to as a ramped step, amplitude σ_0, loading time t_0) has a strain response

$$\varepsilon(t) = \frac{\sigma_0}{t_0} \int_0^\infty f(\tau)\{t - \tau[1 - \exp(-t/\tau)]\}\, d\tau \quad \text{for } t \le t_0$$

and

$$\varepsilon(t) = \sigma_0 \int_0^\infty f(\tau) \left[1 - \exp\left(-t/\tau\right) \left(1 + \frac{t_0}{2!\tau} + \frac{t_0^2}{3!\tau^2} + \cdots \right) \right] d\tau$$

$$\text{for } t \geq t_0 \quad (15)$$

The first of these equations is very different from eqn. (7), not surprisingly, since the applied stress is changing throughout the period up to $t = t_0$, but the second part differs only by the quantity $\Delta\varepsilon$ where

$$\Delta\varepsilon = -\sigma_0 \int_0^\infty f(\tau) \exp\left(-t/\tau\right) \left(\frac{t_0}{2!\tau} + \frac{t_0^2}{3!\tau^2} + \cdots \right) d\tau \quad (16)$$

which, clearly, tends to zero as $t_0 \to 0$, as $t \to \infty$ and for $t_0 \ll \tau$.

To provide some physical picture of eqn. (15) the strain has been calculated for a particular distribution function. The one chosen was a 'logarithmic box' distribution, defined by

$$L(\ln \tau) = A \quad \text{for } \frac{t_0}{10} \leq \tau \leq 10t_0 \left.\right\}$$

$$\quad (17)$$

$$L(\ln \tau) = 0 \quad \text{for } \frac{t_0}{10} > \tau > 10t_0 \left.\right\}$$

where $L(\ln \tau) = \tau f(\tau)$.

The distribution function of a real material would be much wider than this but the calculation is nevertheless valid, mainly because the term $[1 - \exp\left(-t/\tau\right)]$ ensures that the response at any time t' is almost independent of any retardation time greater than $10t'$ and that there will be virtually no response if t' is less than 0·1 of the smallest retardation time, i.e. the response at t_0, the main point of interest, is dominated by the retardation spectrum between $\tau = t_0/10$ and $\tau = 10t_0$. Furthermore, the correction terms t_0/τ, t_0^2/τ^2, etc. in eqn. (16) become small as τ increases relative to t_0. Thus, the results of the arbitrary calculation should correspond fairly closely to the behaviour of any linear viscoelastic material stressed by a ramped step, and not very dissimilar in general form from the behaviour of a nonlinear viscoelastic material for which the corresponding calculation is at present impossible. The results of the calculation are shown in Fig. 4; the upper curve is the response to a step-function excitation and the lower one is the response to the ramped step-function excitation postulated above. At elapsed times near to t_0 the discrepancies are large but they decrease rapidly with increasing time, e.g. at $t = t_0$ the discrepancy is

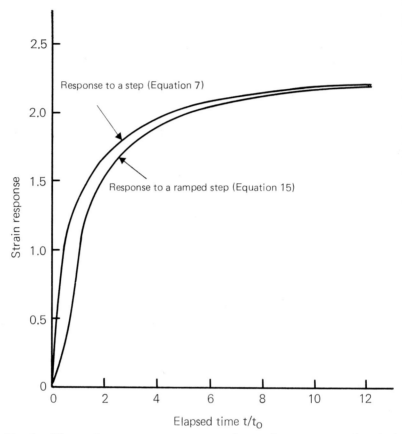

*Fig. 4.   The strain response to a true step input of stress compared with the
response to a ramped step. (Full stress applied within $t = t_0$.)*

31 % of the true step response, at $t = 5t_0$ it is about 2 % and at $t = 10t_0$
it is less than 0·5 %.

As a good working rule, creep data for elapsed times less than about
ten times the loading period should be treated with reserve. Where strain
vs. log time curves appear to be convex upwards at short times the explanation is almost certain to be a lengthy loading period or ambitiously
early strain readings.

At large elapsed times
If the observed creep curve is to be a genuine measure of the effect of
elapsed time, any inherent changes in the sample must be eliminated or

corrected for. They may be either dimensional changes, due to the slow redistribution of the internal stresses set up during the moulding and other fabrication processes, or changes in the molecular state of the sample. In either case, the rate of change is governed by the same molecular mobilities that control the creep rates and hence they are likely to become manifest during creep or other long duration experiments.

It is standard practice to monitor the change of dimensions on an unstressed control specimen during creep experiments and to correct the experimental curve appropriately when necessary. Whenever it is feasible, sufficient time should be allowed for most of the change to occur before the experiments begin; sometimes the process may be accelerated by a mild thermal treatment, though this practice is not to be recommended unreservedly (see Section 4.4.2).

Changes in the molecular state are less easily handled. From a scientific viewpoint, the best procedure is to confine the experiments to samples that are in a stable state. Special annealing procedures may be used to give at least an approximation to stability, though the associated properties are often atypical (but see Section 4.4.2).

If the programme is dominated by severely practical requirements, it may be argued that a sample in some 'average' state is the only proper one. This argument is superficially reasonable but it is actually of dubious merit because it cannot resolve the important issue of how that average state should be defined. Where it prevails, the progressive change in the material state should be registered by independent tests at intervals throughout the duration of the creep experiment. These independent tests may primarily reflect either a change in sample state or a change in sample properties. They need not be complicated.

Both the dimensions and the molecular state may be affected by the test environment, if it interacts with the specimen. For instance, the properties of some polymers are very sensitive to water. The rate of equilibration is governed by the rate of diffusion. It is often very slow and special conditioning procedures have been adopted to hasten the process. However, they give only approximations to equilibrium and the results obtained on such samples are much less regular and reproducible than corresponding results on materials for which equilibration with the environment is immaterial. In practice, an extreme state, such as nominally wet or nominally dry, is much less difficult to attain and offers the prospect of reproducible results. On the other hand, reproducibility is then achieved at the expense of realism. This problem has received spasmodic attention for many years and remains unresolved.

Accuracy in creep testing

The accuracy with which any measurement can be made is related fairly directly to the degree of refinement of the apparatus and the skill with which it is manipulated. In creep experiments, as in many others, it is influenced by many factors which interact in a complex way. Thomas and Turner discussed various aspects of this problem,[12] especially the experimental technique for tensile creep, in relation to a strain measurement accuracy of $\pm 1\%$ at a strain of 0·005. This accuracy level is a compromise between what is realistic for practical evaluations of materials and what is desirable for scientific measurements. British Standard Recommendation 4618, sub-section 1.1.1 limits its quantitative proposals to a classification of the sensitivities of the extensometers, simply because many of the relevant factors cannot be stipulated in general terms. However, it proposes the following useful rule: 'The scale used for plotting the strain should be such that the discrimination against the grid corresponds fairly closely with the measurement discrimination.' This is merely sound experimental practice, of course.

Creep data for plastics are usually plotted as strain vs. log (elapsed time) or log strain vs. log (elapsed time) in contrast to the usual practice for metals of plotting strain vs. elapsed time. This difference in procedure is necessitated by the very early creep response of many plastics.

Against a log time abscissa, creep curves are mainly devoid of sudden irregularities; if individual points at long times are erratically positioned the cause may be either reading error or temperature fluctuation, though good laboratory practice detects and counters both;† erratic data at short times will not be due to temperature fluctuations.

If the extraneous experimental errors have been eliminated and if interspecimen variability has been restricted by appropriate control of the fabrication stages, duplicated tests should yield curves that are identical within close limits, at least for times less than 10^4 seconds and strains less than 0·02 (approximate bounds). However, repeatability in itself is no guarantee of accuracy in the widest sense, it may merely be indicative of good control of the variables of the experiment, and one must question the physical reality of the data. Major sources of discrepancy have been discussed above. These are particularly important in that they produce changes in the shape of the curves and hence also in the inferences that may be drawn from them. For instance, the derivative of the creep compliance function with respect to log time is a first-order approximation to

---

† A reading at high values of elapsed time should be repeated once or twice at intervals of about ten minutes.

the distribution of retardation times,[13] *i.e.*

$$\frac{dC(t)}{d \log t} \doteq [L(\log \tau)]_{t=\tau} \tag{18}$$

where

$$L(\log \tau) = \frac{1}{2 \cdot 303} L(\ln \tau)$$

and

$$\frac{d \log C(t)}{d \log t} = \frac{2}{\pi} \tan \delta \tag{19}$$

where

$$\tan \delta = \frac{\text{Imaginary part of the complex compliance}}{\text{Real part of the complex compliance}}$$

(*See* eqn. (2)). Graphical differentiation is itself a notorious source of error and the overall consequence is that inferences about the shape of the distribution function or the loss processes themselves should be subject to reservations, particularly when long-term data are involved. Other factors than the slow change in the dimensions or the molecular state must contribute to inaccuracies at high elapsed times, because duplicate tests often give creep curves that coincide at short times but diverge later. The divergence is small when the strain is small (*see* the bounds above). There are two plausible explanations. The first is that specimens may differ in their molecular state in such a way that only large strain properties show variability, and the second is that the increasing strain during creep is the result of, or at least is accompanied by, the formation of small zones of plastically deformed material which initiate at defects in the specimen and are statistically distributed so that some scatter in the data is inevitable. The available experimental evidence is inconclusive, with some support for each hypothesis. This last type of inaccuracy is less serious than the others because the shape of the creep curves is not changed to any marked degree and therefore it does not lead to fundamentally incorrect inferences, though extrapolations to longer times may be inexact. In practice, however, the hazards of extrapolation are well known, and the results are amenable to correcting adjustments, so much so that small discrepancies between duplicate curves are much less troublesome than scattered datum points in a single experiment. The phrase 'correcting adjustments' carries undertones of unrespectable or unscientific practices, but the practice is sound. The adjustments rely on the results of short subsidiary experiments and the judicious, interchangeable use of strain and log strain as the ordinate. A discussion of their validity and the mutual enhancement of interconnected experiments is given by Thomas and Turner.[12]

4.3.3 Special experiments

The isochronous experiment

An evaluation of the creep characteristics of a nonlinear viscoelastic material requires experiments at several stress levels, from which, if desired, analytical representation of the form summarised in eqn. (8) may be deduced. However, a full evaluation is expensive and may even be over-elaborate for some purposes, and there is some need for an alternative, such as the isochronous experiment. This eliminates elapsed time as a variable and provides a relationship between the applied stress and the consequent strain (at any specific time). Thus, it constitutes an elementary index of nonlinearity.

The excitation function for the isochronous experiment is shown in Fig. 5(*a*); it is extremely simple in principle and in execution, but under the practical restrictions, such as the desirability of using a single specimen throughout, whenever possible, the simplicity gives way to an elaborate formality if accuracy is to be preserved. The details of the experiment, a full discussion of which has been published,[12] need not be pursued here.

The applied stress plotted against the resulting strain is a straight line for a linear viscoelastic material, and deviation of the data towards disproportionately greater strains is the usual manifestation of nonlinearity. If there is experimental scatter in the data it may be better for them to be plotted as log stress vs. log strain, because the linearity criterion is then a straight line of unit slope. Figure 6 shows 100-second tensile isochronous data for a typical amorphous polymer in its glassy state plotted in two forms. There is an abundance of tensile isochronous data; as log stress vs. log strain they lie almost invariably on straight lines of slope slightly less than unity (generally between 0·95 and 0·80) up to a strain of about 0·005, and above that on curves of steadily decreasing slope. If the material is ductile the slope ultimately approaches the horizontal. Very similar results have been obtained in the less numerous experiments based on other deformation modes, shear,[11] uniaxial compression[8] and combined stress.[14] However, what is observed as an apparent phenomenon may really be the consequence of an extraneous experimental factor and it is disturbing to note that friction, which can never be entirely absent from an apparatus, will lower the slope of the log stress vs. log strain curve owing to the disproportionate effect of a frictional resistance when the applied force is small. The uniaxial compression data show the same type of nonlinearity.

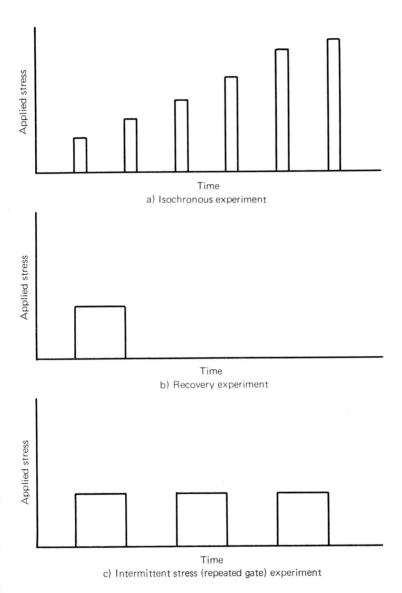

Fig. 5. Special excitation functions for creep studies.

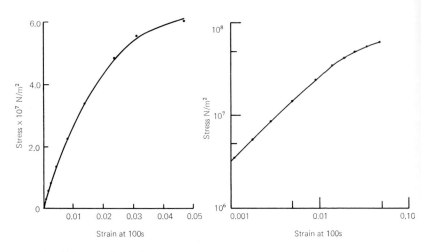

Fig. 6. 100-*second tensile isochronous stress–strain data for a commercial grade of poly(methylmethacrylate).*

Most of the experimental evidence suggests that there is no genuine linear region. However, any error due to friction will be greatest at very small strains and the possibility that there is a small linear region cannot be discounted. There is support for this possibility in the results of very accurate measurements on a beam in flexure. For small deflections, corresponding to maximum skin strains of 0·0005, an isochronous loading procedure gives load–deflection data that lie very accurately on a straight line. Unfortunately a flexure experiment cannot give an unambiguous indication of the extent of the linear region, if one exists, because geometric nonlinearities develop as the deflection increases.

The high practical value of the isochronous experiment is quite independent of the outcome of such speculations. A strain–stress ratio taken at some point on the curve is a creep compliance for that particular value of elapsed time, and its reciprocal may be termed a creep modulus, which is not the same as the relaxation modulus (*see* p. 227). This compliance or modulus is a function of the applied stress, and/or the strain, if the material is nonlinear. Standard practice clearly dictates that it should be plotted against stress, the independent variable, but it transpires that strain, the dependent variable, is far more satisfactory. Plotted against strain, compliance data for different grades of a polymer, different thermal histories and different temperatures show recurrent regularities and patterns; against stress no such patterns can be discerned. This is not surprising from a physical viewpoint, for one would expect the spatial distribution of the molecules, rather than the excitation producing that distribution, to be the prime factor governing the properties, but it is a great analytical inconvenience because it imposes an intractable form on the creep equations.

The concept of modulus or compliance is inherently a linear one; the six independent components of the stress tensor are each assumed to be a linear function of the six components of the strain tensor in the most general case and the number of coefficients reduces to two under the simplifying assumption of isotropy. Viscoelastic nonlinearity, as discussed here and demonstrated in Fig. 6, is a breakdown of the proportionality between stress and strain, a violation of the entire physical situation in which modulus is definable. The retention of modulus as an entity is therefore justifiable only on severely practical grounds; it is a quantity that can be manipulated in calculations, within an existing formulation, and it is one that is conveniently concise. Even so, whenever it is used, the strain should be stipulated.

Complete isochronous data are clearly preferable to single values of modulus or compliance, because they contain much more information, and a family of isochronous curves, for different values of elapsed time, are even better. A family of isochronous curves are equivalent to a family of creep curves. Creep behaviour in polymers may be discussed in terms of a family of creep curves, an isochronous curve or a single compliance datum, depending on whether a comprehensive or a concise measure is required. All three levels will be used later in the chapter.

The recovery experiment
The recovery experiment is basically simple; after a period of creep the applied force is removed smoothly and rapidly to give the excitation function depicted in Fig. 5(b). The residual strain decreases with the passage of time, along a course which is essentially a creep curve in reverse. It is an important adjunct to creep studies because it distinguishes between reversible and irreversible creep strains, *i.e.* between viscoelastic and plastic deformations. If materials were linear viscoelastic such experiments would not be needed because the recovery characteristics could be predicted from the creep compliance function by means of the Boltzmann Superposition Principle but, in the absence of an equivalent rule for nonlinear materials, direct measurements are necessary. Because of this, recovery data are an essential part of the evaluation of nonlinear viscoelastic materials.

The data can be plotted in several different ways and the choice depends on the ultimate use to which they are to be put. The time origin may be taken as the moment at which the preceding creep period started or as the moment at which the recovery period itself started. The alternative visual displays are very different when the elapsed time is plotted on the usual logarithmic scale, Fig. 7.

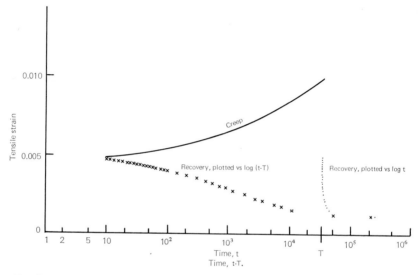

Fig. 7.   *Presentation of recovery data. Creep terminated at elapsed time T. (Propylene–ethylene copolymer at 20°C.)*

The discrepancies between the residual strain observed and that predicted by linear superposition is a sensitive check on the linearity of the system. The differences are almost undetectable if the creep strain has not exceeded 0·005 but they are pronounced after greater creep. When the deformation is viscoelastic, the nature of the discrepancy is always the same; during the early stages, the strain recovered is always greater than linear superposition would predict, as in Fig. 8, and during the later stages it is usually less, though as recovery progresses and the strain becomes small the observed residual strain conforms fairly closely to the prediction of linear superposition. The general pattern is in accord with a strain-softening model, *i.e.* one where the resistance to an incremental deformation decreases as the strain in the specimen increases; this is because the initial stages of recovery occur with the specimen in a strain-softened state, but

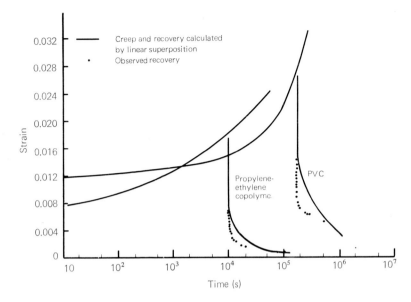

Fig. 8. Recovery in nonlinear materials.

as the recovery proceeds the strain-softening process is reversed. Creep equations to represent such behaviour can be formulated but not with sufficient generality to account quantitatively for the recovery after several different creep histories. A major obstacle to the accurate specification of such equations is the experimentally inaccessible region of the response at short times. The exact course of a significant proportion of the creep and recovery are never known and any estimates of the relative roles of strain-softening and time-dependence are correspondingly imprecise.

As a further complication, analysis of the discrepancy at long times, *i.e.* where the strain is low, is hampered by the possibility of experimental error due to friction in the machine. The small but inevitable frictional resistance mentioned in this section may be completely insignificant during a creep experiment yet a major factor when the retractive forces in the specimen decrease towards zero with the residual strain.

The high stress experiment
High stress creep experiments differ from those discussed above in that the strain may be so large that the specimen suffers irreversible changes. There may be the appearance of 'stress whitening', the formation and growth

250   THE PHYSICS OF GLASSY POLYMERS

of cracks or crazes, the development of deformation bands, necking or complete rupture. The more innocuous of these manifestations are often referred to as pre-failure phenomena and they mark the boundary between viscoelastic and rupture behaviour (*see* Chapters 5–7). In such experiments the visual appearance of the specimen is often more important than an accurate strain measurement.

The creep strain measured by an extensometer is a mean value over a finite gauge length and may bear little relationship to the local strains at defects in the specimen. Such defects may be inherent in the sample, *e.g.* contaminating particles or deliberately introduced heterogeneities, or they may be surface imperfections originating from the fabrication processes. In either case, the best specimens for high stress experiments are often significantly different in shape from those best suited for accurate strain measurements at lower stresses. One specimen geometry that is highly

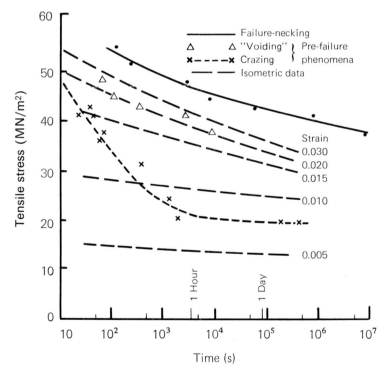

Fig. 9.   Creep at high stress ends in failure. Lifetime envelopes and isometric data.
(*PVC,* 20°C, 65% *RH.*)

favoured for tension studies has no parallel-sided gauge section; the sides of the specimen are circular arcs which are easily machined to a fine surface finish and the profile is such that the failure phenomena are confined to a small region near the cross-section of minimum area which may be closely inspected throughout the experiment. A simple machine with no special refinements for alignment is adequate for ductile failures because the associated strains are large, but apparatus of similar precision to the creep machines is preferable if brittle failure or the onset of crazing is to be studied.

At any specific stress there is a distribution of elapsed times for the onset of the various phenomena. In turn, this must depend on the distribution of the severities of the defects and on the reliability and constancy of the subjective criteria by which the phenomena are identified. There is, therefore, a significant difference in the underlying philosophy as well as in the mechanical details of experiments at high stress. In particular, the 'scatter' of statistically distributed events is superposed on the regularity of the standard creep curves and there is correspondingly a greater emphasis on the number of individual experiments than on their separate accuracy. In fact, the accuracy of long-term failure experiments has never received the close quantitative attention that was devoted to the creep experiments, and the sources of the distribution of the failure times have never been identified unambiguously. Even so, long-term strength and creep phenomena are intimately related. For any specific polymer, the graph of applied stress vs. log (time to fail by necking rupture) has a shape very similar to that of the isometric curves,† as is shown by Fig. 9. Pre-failure phenomena and brittle failure may also be displayed in this way, though the picture is then less regular.

4.4   CREEP PHENOMENA IN GLASSY POLYMERS

4.4.1   Typical creep behaviour

The salient features of the creep behaviour of amorphous polymers well below their glass–rubber transition temperature are illustrated in Fig. 10, by a family of tensile creep curves for a slightly modified polymethylmethacrylate at 20°C. The individual datum points lie accurately on smooth curves; the spacing between the curves is such that a stress–strain section at constant time shows the characteristic nonlinearity of Fig. 6;

† An isometric curve is a stress-time section at constant strain across a family of creep curves.[15]

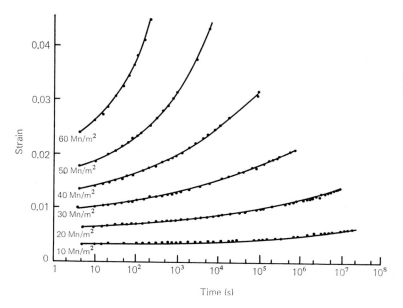

Fig. 10.   Typical tensile creep behaviour of a glassy amorphous polymer. (A modified PMMA at 20°C.)

the high stress curves swing sharply upwards in their approach to the region of ductile failure.

The same characteristics, including the nonlinearity, have been observed in shear and under hydrostatic compression by Mallon,[11] some of whose results are shown in Fig. 11. Mallon has measured the creep of glassy polymers under several stress systems in a study of the interrelationships between the basic nonlinear viscoelastic functions. His interest was primarily the development of working rules for the manipulation of those functions in engineering calculations but clearly such results may give valuable information on the mechanism of creep, and particularly on the role of free volume.

Many creep equations, of varying degree of complexity, have been proposed for PMMA. None of them is completely satisfactory and all are much more cumbersome to use than the graphical presentation. Even the early work compared creep under various stresses. Marin *et al.*[16] used tension, compression, torsion and flexure; they concluded that tensile and compressive creep were not necessarily identical. It has since been ascertained that for polymers in general the resistance to creep in uniaxial

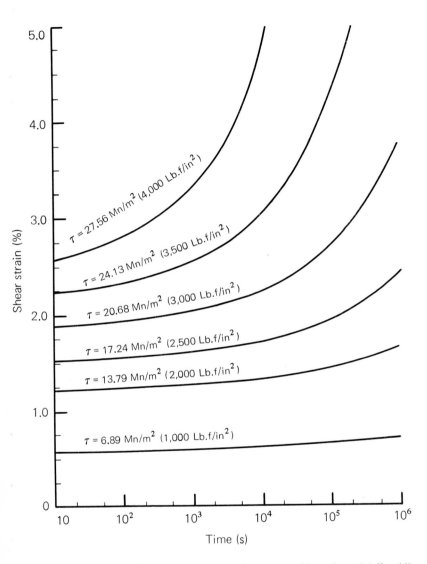

Fig. 11.   *Shear strain response of PVC to pure shear stress. (Data due to Mallon.* [11])

compression is superior to the resistance to creep in tension,[8,9] and this is similar to the situation at yield (Chapter 5).

Each class of polymer has its own particular creep characteristics, which differ from one another significantly despite the nominally universal applicability of Findley's equation. Thus, for instance, polymethylmethacrylate and unplasticised PVC behave similarly at low stresses and differently at high stresses, *see* Fig. 12. Recent work by Benham and

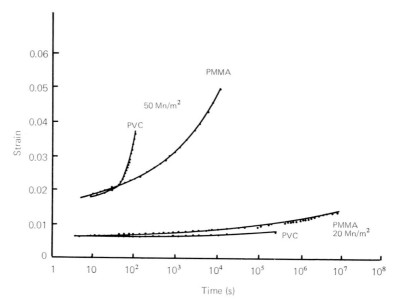

Fig. 12.   Comparisons between tensile creep at 20°C of unplasticised PVC and PMMA.

McCammond[17] has detected a significant difference in the behaviour of these polymers. They measured the transverse strain in addition to the axial strain and showed that after the initial strain response the creep in PMMA occurred without change in volume whereas that in PVC was accompanied by an increase in volume. One possible explanation is that the increase in volume is merely indicative of the formation of microvoids, or zones of reduced density, because the sample was seen to stress whiten at high stress.

The slope of a creep curve does not necessarily increase continuously with elapsed time. The shape depends on the form of the distribution of retardation times and its position in relation to the elapsed time of the experiment, as can be inferred from eqns. (18) and (19). Thus, McCrum and Morris[2] studied the creep of polymethylmethacrylate in the region of the β-process (the short-time, secondary process); they observed an inflexion point in log shear compliance vs. log elapsed time curves and were able to construct a master curve with the classical sigmoidal shape by means of a modified time–temperature superposition technique. The creep curves in Fig. 10 are influenced by the end of the β-process and the beginning of the α-process; this circumstance obscures the sigmoidal shape, but an additional factor is the imminent onset of yielding. In contrast, the yield strain of crystalline polymers is usually greater than that of glassy, amorphous polymers and therefore the purely viscoelastic effects are not so thoroughly overwhelmed by the preliminaries to yielding. Apart from this, crystalline polymers are commonly used above their glass–rubber transition temperature because the crystals mitigate the physical changes associated with the transition by lowering the compliance in what would otherwise be the rubbery region. Thus, if the test conditions are appropriate a pseudo-equilibrium region, manifest as a marked decrease of slope on a log strain vs. log time graph, is reached. Polyethylenes exhibit a particularly abrupt change of slope which has been a convenient focal point in studies of the effect of fabrication variables and structure on the deformation properties.[18]

The tedious nature of creep tests, coupled with the practical usefulness of the results has encouraged the study of extrapolation–prediction methods. Time–temperature superposition has not been very successful for glassy polymers, partly because of the phenomena discussed in the next section. Simple extrapolation, unsupported by other experimental results, would be highly erroneous in the neighbourhood of a transition, but stress–time superposition incorporates the necessary safeguards and is a potentially useful technique. Bergen described the use of creep equations incorporating stress-dependent shift factors for ABS and unplasticised PVC;[19] he found good agreement between experimental results over an elapsed time of three years and the prediction from an equation of the form

$$\varepsilon = \varepsilon_0 + \sigma/A\{1 - \exp[-(a_s t)^{\frac{1}{3}}] + ka_s t\} \qquad (20)$$

the constants of which were derived from creep experiments of a few days. It was Bergen's intention that some of the experiments should continue for several years, in order that the prediction could be checked more rigorously still.

4.4.2   Creep at elevated temperatures

The creep of glassy amorphous polymers has naturally been studied mainly at room temperature, standardised at 20°C, 23°C or 25°C, but the phenomenon becomes increasingly important in practice as the service temperature is raised towards the glass–rubber transition temperature and data for high temperatures are now in demand. Experiments at elevated temperatures pose some technical problems, particularly the close control of the specimen temperature. This is often necessitated by a high sensitivity of the deformation characteristics to temperature and is hampered by the low thermal conductivity of polymers. Temperature gradients are difficult to eliminate when the test machine is massive, as it has to be for accurate measurements, but the problems are nevertheless resolvable and are not fundamental in nature. On the other hand, the creep behaviour of a polymer depends on its molecular state, which changes slowly during storage at room temperature and more rapidly at higher temperatures. Such changes are likely to occur during a creep experiment at high temperature, and what is observed is therefore not necessarily the genuine time-dependence. The interpretation of such compound results can be very difficult and the only reasonable recourse is to minimise or eliminate the change by an appropriate thermal conditioning period prior to the experiment. This establishes a more stable molecular state than that produced by the normal moulding processes, though the sample is then in an artificial state.

The use of a conditioning period prior to a test is artificial in relation to actual service performance, which will always contain a hidden component attributable to changes in properties due to the operating environment. The counter argument is that service conditions are almost infinitely variable and an evaluation can do no more than measure properties under fixed conditions, from which the performance under varying conditions may be estimated. A sample that changes during the experiment violates this requirement and any results obtained on it are correspondingly difficult to interpret and have no general applicability.

The relationship between heat treatment and properties is simpler for crystalline polymers than it is for amorphous polymers, despite the fact that annealing produces complex changes in the degree of crystallinity and in the crystalline texture. The resistance to deformation increases markedly with the degree of crystallinity in a polymer above its glass–rubber transition temperature; the texture is of secondary importance. Simple models of a crystalline polymer, for example that due to Bueche,[20] predict a modulus/crystallinity relationship similar to what is usually observed, but not with any quantitative certainty. On the other hand, the inadequacy of the theoretical models is offset by a regularity in the phenomenological effects of changes in the crystallinity. It transpires that, to a good first approximation, an increase of crystallinity changes the creep strain by a simple factor that is nearly constant for all elapsed times. It is therefore possible to derive the relevant factor in an experiment of short duration rather than to evaluate the whole creep function. The isochronous

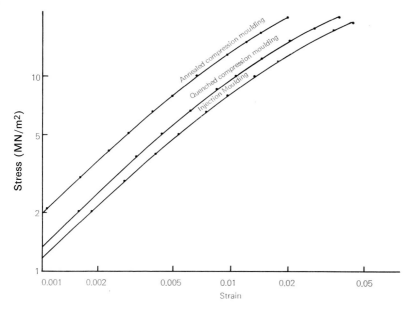

Fig. 13.   *Simple regularity in deformation behaviour of a crystalline polymer.* (*A high density polythene at* 20°*C.*)

experiment is invaluable for such derivations because it embraces a wide strain range. It usually shows that the modulus at low strains increases by a slightly larger factor than the yield stress for a particular increase in crystallinity, *i.e.* the factor is strain-dependent. Typical results are shown in Fig. 13, in which, because of the logarithmic axes, a constant factor is represented by a constant distance. Corresponding isochronous sections for a higher value of elapsed time show a very similar convergence.

Amorphous polymers in their glassy state do not show the same regularity. A thermal conditioning period decreases the short-term creep compliance slightly (more commonly it is said that the modulus is increased) but changes the long-term creep behaviour in a totally disproportionate manner. The results shown in Fig. 14 are quite typical. They are for an unplasticised PVC stored for different periods at the test temperature, 60°C, prior to the start of the experiment. The parameter is storage time. There is obviously no possibility of conversion from one curve to another by a simple factor.

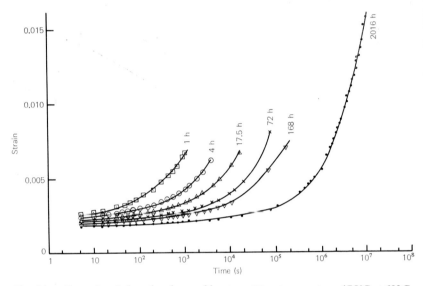

Fig. 14.   Creep just below the glass–rubber transition temperature. (PVC at 60°C. Storage at test temperature prior to the experiment changes the strain response. Storage time in hours.)

Similar results have been observed for many amorphous polymers and also changes in other properties, but the work has been spasmodic and uncoordinated so that, until recently, the phenomena were commonly interpreted in specific terms, e.g. the growth of crystallites, the loss of water or other diluents. However, McLoughlin and Tobolsky[21] observed that rapid cooling from above T_g changed the stress relaxation characteristics of polymethylmethacrylate. They postulated that it resulted in slightly more 'uncollapsed free volume', and it is now widely accepted that the properties of a glassy amorphous polymer are strongly influenced by the 'free volume' which, in turn, depends on the thermal history. Rapid cooling from the processing temperature produces a highly disorganised molecular assembly which subsequently changes towards a more orderly state at a rate which is governed by the temperature. At temperatures well below T_g the molecular mobilities are low and the rate of reorganisation is so slow that the changes of property are detectable only by the most refined methods. At temperatures near T_g the mobilities are much higher and significant property changes are detectable. These changes can be reversed by a relatively short period at a temperature within the conventionally accepted glass–rubber transition region for short-term phenomena, presumably because the newly-ordered state of the molecules has been disrupted by the brief excursion into a region of significantly higher molecular mobility.

The stability of the molecular state of a crystalline polymer is governed mainly by the crystallinity. Once this is established by a thorough annealing procedure there is little further change; the temperature of a sample may be changed, as the exigencies of the experiment demand, with little disturbance of the crystallinity provided that the annealing temperature is not reached. In contrast, the stability of the molecular state of a glassy amorphous polymer is governed by the free volume or the molecular order, the equilibrium value of which is different at each temperature so that there must always be a period of re-equilibration after any change of temperature, irrespective of the thermal history. This basic difference between the two classes of polymer is reflected in the practical conduct of creep experiments at elevated temperatures; for crystalline polymers an overriding annealing treatment can be applied but for amorphous polymers the conditioning temperature should always be identical to the test temperature.

The rate at which volume equilibrium is reached is governed by the same energy considerations as the processes underlying creep and hence one would expect that conditioning periods of about the same duration as the creep experiment would be required. Although the short-term response is affected less severely, compliance or modulus obtained from a short duration isochronous curve derived after different periods of conditioning can be used to monitor the approach to equilibrium. If the isochronous experiment is limited to strains no greater than 0·004 the specimen apparently suffers no damage and can be re-tested at intervals during the conditioning procedure; this eliminates the risk of scatter from interspecimen variability. Figure 15 shows the change of modulus with storage time for several polymers at temperatures a few degrees below their T_gs. A close approach to equilibrium is achieved within a few days at these temperatures; with PVC the process requires many years at 20°C.

The increased resistance to deformation is accompanied by a decrease in toughness in an impact test and a deterioration in long-term strength.

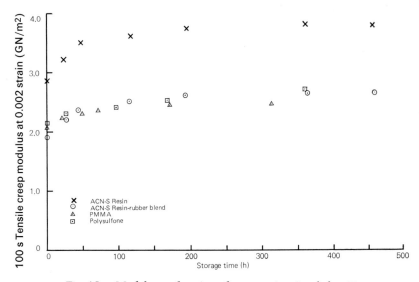

Fig. 15.   Modulus as function of storage time just below T_g.

The strain at which crazing develops decreases with increased conditioning time but the resistance to deformation increases and hence the 'lifetime', as judged against the compounded criteria of excessive deformation and failure, is affected in a most complex manner. Thus, the relatively rapid creep of a specimen that has not been preconditioned may embrace strains two or three times as great as those at which a conditioned specimen will break after a much longer period of creep at the same stress. The general details depend on the molecular weight, however, because this affects the failure characteristics much more than it affects the creep.

The full evaluation of the deformation characteristics of a polymer over a temperature range entails an evaluation of the stress–strain–time function at several temperatures. This tedious and expensive procedure is often severely abbreviated by the use of a creep modulus as a replacement for the full function. A graph of creep modulus vs. temperature shows the major transition regions and demonstrates their relative importance. It is also a convenient means by which important phenomena such as the high temperature storage effect may be monitored. Thus, for instance, prolonged storage at an elevated temperature changes the shape of the curve, particularly where the glassy state slips towards the transition. In this region a threefold increase in the modulus has been observed. On the other hand, such abbreviated evaluations may mislead, because the

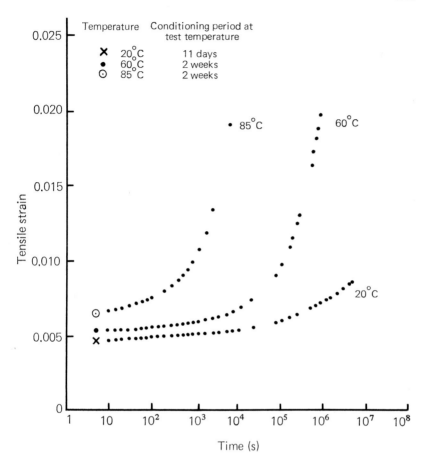

Fig. 16. *Effect of temperature on creep.* (*ABS resin–rubber blend at* 10 *MN/m²*.)

results show only a limited region of the deformation function. This is illustrated by Fig. 16 which shows creep curves at different temperatures. Even a casual inspection of the curves suffices to rule out the possibility of time–temperature superposition into a master curve and hence there can be no reliable substitute for experiments of long duration at selected temperatures. The results in Fig. 14 give a similar warning of the restricted nature of the information available for short-term experiments. The principal cause for concern is that in both diagrams the picture changes radically with elapsed time and, in particular, the strain increases in a manner disproportionate to that which is manifest at short times. The upswing of the curve can be attributed either to the proximity of a transition or to the preliminary stages of ductile failure. At first sight it would appear possible to distinguish between these alternatives by crucial experiments, either creep at very low strains, where ductile failure would be excluded, or recovery experiments, where ductile failure would be manifest as unrecovered strain, but ambiguities persist, mainly because of the nonlinear phenomena. The only reliable discrimination seems to be via the identification of changes in appearance, *i.e.* stress whitening, crazing, deformation bands, etc., and the only safe procedure is to regard the upswing as defining a practical service limit beyond which excessive deformation and failure of a component can be expected.

4.4.3   Creep in anisotropic samples

Molecular orientation in a plastic causes anisotropy in many of the physical properties, including the creep resistance. An obvious consequence of anisotropy is that the creep behaviour cannot be fully characterised by two independent viscoelastic functions such as suffice to characterise an isotropic sample, so that more experiments are required. A less obvious consequence is that the interaction between the specimen and the apparatus is more complicated for anisotropic specimens than for isotropic ones, so that there is an increased chance of experimental error unless more elaborate apparatus is used.

Anisotropy is enhanced if the plastic contains short fibres with high Young's modulus because they tend to align parallel to the molecular orientation and provide local stiffening in the axial direction. In plastics containing many long fibres, *e.g.* glass-fibre reinforced resins, the fibres dominate completely and unidirectionally reinforced composites show extreme anisotropy. In the direction parallel to the fibres the properties are essentially those of the equivalent fibre bundle so that the modulus is given by the simple addition rule:

$$E_C = E_F V_F + E_M(1 - V_F) \qquad (21)$$

where

E_C = Young's modulus of the composite
E_F = Young's modulus of the fibre
E_M = Young's modulus of the matrix
V_F = Volume fraction of the fibres

and there is insignificant creep. In torsion about an axis parallel to the fibres the matrix dominates and the shear creep of the composite is little different from that of the polymer.

For a composite containing only short fibres the theory is much more complicated. A very crude approximation modifies eqn. (21) to

$$E_C = \varphi E_F V_F + E_M(1 - V_F) \tag{21a}$$

where φ may be regarded as an efficiency coefficient. For small deformations the 'inefficiency' is simply that there must be some series addition of matrix and fibre components as well as the parallel addition, but for larger deformations, say tensile strains greater than 0·005, there is a genuine inefficiency that becomes worse as the strain increases.

The creep behaviour of a short-fibre composite is essentially that of the matrix, modified by the fibres to a degree that reduces as the creep strain increases. It is never dominated by the fibres even when they are favourably oriented. Thus the short-term modulus of some plastics can be increased to about the level of aluminium by the incorporation of a sufficiently large volume fraction of fibres but the equality disappears after a short period under stress as creep in the matrix develops. The minimum creep strain to be expected is that of the unreinforced base polymer reduced by a factor which has been termed an 'enhancement factor' and a 'stiffness factor'. Enhancement factors greater than about 3 are not common for glassy polymers because the requisite higher fibre concentrations would impair some of the other physical properties and the processing characteristics, and even this unremarkable improvement is not always achieved, for instance if the fibres are not efficiently coupled to the matrix. Particulate fillers are still less effective.

There have been remarkably few studies of creep in anisotropic systems. One important reason for this has been the severely practical one that it is difficult to prepare controlled anisotropic samples sufficiently wide to provide transversely oriented specimens of the long, slender shape recommended for accurate tensile creep specimens. Special moulds, designed to give uniform and highly directional flow paths, have been used with some success, but sample preparation is no longer a major difficulty, thanks to apparatus developed recently by Darlington and Saunders[22] which is highly accurate even for specimens of gauge length 15 mm.

Their results for a highly oriented polyethylene[23] show the main characteristics of a sample with hexagonal symmetry, as do results for glass-fibre reinforced polymers injection-moulded into rectangular flash-gated plaques. Their experiments were an elaborate† sequel to those of Raumann and

† The apparatus provides simultaneous measurements of axial extension and lateral contraction.

Saunders[24] in which it was first established that simple modulus measurements on a highly drawn polyethylene sample show this type of anisotropy. E_θ, the tensile modulus at an angle of θ to the direction of orientation, is given by the expression

$$\frac{1}{E_\theta} = \frac{\sin^4 \theta}{E_{90}} + \sin^2 \theta \cos^2 \theta \left(\frac{4}{E_{45}} - \frac{1}{E_{90}} - \frac{1}{E_0}\right) + \frac{\cos^4 \theta}{E_0} \quad (22)$$

where the suffices 0, 45 and 90 are specific values of θ. The effect of draw ratio on the level of anisotropy is shown in Fig. 17(a), taken from the Raumann and Saunders paper.

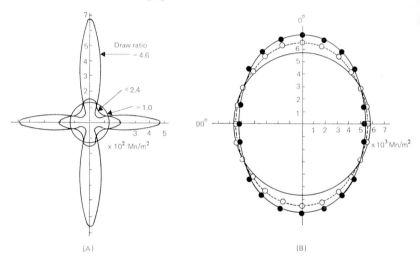

(A)   (B)

Fig. 17.   The effect of molecular orientation on the deformation characteristics of plastics. (a) Crystalline polymer, after Raumann and Saunders.[24] (b) Glassy amorphous polymer, after Wright.[25]

Similar results have been reported recently for glass-fibre reinforced nylons and polypropylene but there appears to be no such strong effect of orientation in glassy, amorphous polymers. Moduli measured by ultrasonic wave propagation in polystyrene and polymethylmethacrylate oriented to various degrees lie on a nearby circular polar diagram, *see* Fig. 17(b), due to Wright.[25] Presumably, data at higher strains and longer elapsed times, *i.e.* creep moduli, would be similarly insensitive, though it is possible that significant differences emerge under extreme creep conditions. There has been other indirect evidence of the insensitivity of the creep of glassy, amorphous polymers to orientation. Bonnin et al.[26] discussed the use of accurate measurements in flexure and torsion, from which the tensile and shear creep moduli at very small strains can be calculated. From such results the Poisson's Ratio can be derived to high accuracy, provided the assumptions of linear, isotropic viscoelasticity theory are not seriously violated. The only important violation is anisotropy, as a result of which the calculated value of Poisson's Ratio is usually high. In tests on specimens cut from injection moulded, ASTM Type I tensile bars, in which there is usually some molecular orientation in the axial direction, values between 0·5 and 1 are common for crystalline polymers above their nominal glass–rubber transition temperature, whereas values greater than about 0·4 are unknown for amorphous polymers, irrespective of moulding conditions or the flow characteristics. The explanation of this difference is probably that the movements of side groups or small main-chain segments that govern the creep of glassy, amorphous polymers are affected only slightly by large-scale orientation of the backbone chains. The moduli of crystalline polymers below their transition temperature show a sensitivity to orientation intermediate to that of the polyethylenes and the glassy amorphous polymers.

4.4.4 Recovery behaviour

Data on recovery are far less numerous than those on creep and it is correspondingly more difficult to derive the general pattern of behaviour, particularly for glassy amorphous polymers. A complicating feature is that the course of recovery depends on the duration of the preceding creep period and the strain reached therein, as well as on the elapsed recovery time, *i.e.* there is one more controlling variable than there is for creep. For the practical display of recovery data it has been found convenient to define two derived quantities, as follows:

$$\text{Fractional Recovery (F.R.)} = 1 - \frac{\text{residual strain}}{\text{maximum creep strain}}$$

$$\text{Reduced Time } (t_R) = \frac{\text{recovery time}}{\text{preceding creep time}}$$

This allows the recovery function to be represented by a family of simple curves. It was initially hoped that all the data would condense onto a master curve but the individual curves do not superpose exactly. The trend of the discrepancies is well illustrated by some results for a propylene homopolymer (Fig. 18). In one experiment several specimens were subjected to different stresses, the recovery phase being started when the creep

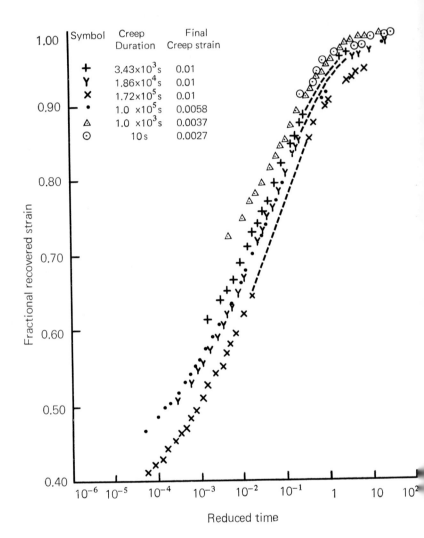

Fig. 18.   *Typical recovery behaviour. Propylene homopolymer*
(20°C; *see Section* 4.4.4).

strain reached 0·01, and in another experiment the same stress was applied for different times, so that the final creep strain varied.† The deviation from superposition into a master curve becomes more pronounced as either the final creep strain or the creep duration increases. These polypropylene results, and many others besides, fall within the framework of viscoelasticity theory and are explicable in terms of the nonlinear superposition integrals, but there are some apparent anomalies, particularly in the recovery characteristics of glassy amorphous polymers. On close examination these anomalies may be explained by simple physical arguments. For instance, full recovery may be observed in specimens that have crazed during creep, even though the crazes are known to be discontinuities bridged by drawn material; the crazes tend to disappear as the strain decreases after the stress is removed. The early stages of stress whitening are similarly reversible but, on the other hand, the heavy stress whitening that lies within Luders bands originating at edge defects or at points of stress concentration do not disappear, and are associated with a significant proportion of unrecoverable strain. The factor controlling the degree of recovery is probably the proportion of crazed or stress-whitened material. An isolated craze is a region of local plastic deformation within an elastically deformed matrix; the elastic stored energy causes the craze to close when the external force is removed, either by a reversed deformation or, more probably, by buckling collapse of the fibrils bridging the gap. Crazes are of little significance in relation to creep because they obviously originate at small defects where the local stress field exceeds the yield stress even when the average stress is well below it; they bear only a diffuse statistical relationship to the nominal stress and strain of the experiment. Another anomaly is that the recovery after creep at high temperatures (but well below the glass–rubber transition) is often very much poorer than is usual for thermoplastics tested at room temperature. The results in Fig. 19 are typical. They were obtained on a sample of 'Noryl'‡ that was conditioned at the test temperature, 85°C, before the experiments began. The creep curves are shown in the left-hand section of the diagram to emphasise that the unusually poor recovery of one specimen is associated with a long time under stress rather than with a large creep strain. The inferior behaviour is not attributable to phase separation in a

---

† In the latter one specimen was used throughout to eliminate interspecimen variability. Long rest periods between each stage and successively higher stresses exclude any possible viscoelastic memory effects.

‡ 'Noryl' is a blend of PPO and polystyrene.

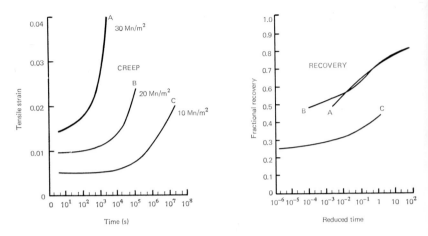

Fig. 19. *Recovery after creep at high temperature. 'Noryl' at 85°C, specimens conditioned at test temperature for four weeks prior to creep. (Recovery after creep of long duration is poor.)*

polymer blend, nor is it associated in other polymers with crazing or other pre-failure phenomena; it is presumably another consequence of the molecular reordering process occasioned by a high test temperature and, since it proceeds under a stress field during the creep experiments, the conditions are favourable for the development of 'permanent set'.

4.4.5 Creep under intermittent stress

The basic recovery experiment is not ideal, for the reasons outlined on pp. 248, 249, nor does it correspond very closely to actual service. A variant and improvement is an experiment in which creep and recovery periods are repeated regularly, *i.e.* one in which the excitation is a repeated gate, as depicted in Fig. 5(c). There is the minor advantage that such an excitation is marginally closer to service conditions than an isolated creep–recovery situation, but the main attraction is that the overall response during the recovery periods is less subject to experimental error because the individual errors in each cycle combine in a random manner and should be mutually compensating. Errors due to frictional resistance will not be additive and should contribute progressively less to the response in the later recovery cycles. These benefits accrue only if the results can be interpreted within quantitatively established theory, *i.e.* where linear superposition is applicable. Where the creep strains are so large that the response deviates significantly from linear, for example in the manner depicted in Fig. 8, interpretation of the results is more difficult and the main recourse is to empiricism. The general form of the response remains similar to that predicted by the Boltzmann Superposition Principle, though there is no quantitative correspondence and there are some interesting irregularities.

The general case, in intermittent stress experiments, is when there is a residual strain at the end of the $(n - 1)$th recovery period. According to viscoelasticity principles, this residual strain will continue to decrease during all succeeding cycles irrespective of any new creep or recovery period and will supplement any residual strain arising from later cycles. In principle, the response of a linear material to a repeated gate function can be predicted if the linear creep compliance function is known, and the response of a slightly nonlinear material can be calculated from the creep in one cycle plus the complete curve of recovery following the same creep conditions. As the degree of nonlinearity increases the elementary methods become increasingly unsatisfactory and the multiple integral theory has to be used; this is sufficiently general to accommodate even secondary effects though not conveniently and concisely.

The present position is that the response to a repeated gate is studied directly rather than being calculated from the basic viscoelastic functions, creep and recovery in particular, or being used conversely to calculate those functions. Nor has the multiple integral theory been applied to the problem. A simple method of calculation which assumes a power law of time for creep and a Boltzmann type superposition[27] has given good predictions for two crystalline polymers under various conditions of stress level and periodicity, and there is no obvious reason why it should not be suitable for glassy amorphous plastics.

The experimental results are both interesting and simple; a graph of maximum strain reached during the nth creep period vs. the logarithm of the cycle number, n, or vs. the total time under stress, is a nearly straight line which curves upwards at high values of the abscissa. The overall effect is impressively regular and simple; it has been verified in detail for polypropylene,[27] and for acetal copolymer, at several stress levels and for different cycles. Typical results are shown in Fig. 20. It is demonstrated by the results, and there is confirmation from the model, that the upward trend at long times originates from the residual strain. The behaviour of amorphous polymers has not been recorded in the same detail as has that of crystalline polymers, but Benham and Hutchinson have published a few similar results for unplasticised PVC and many results for tension–compression cycles.[28] They observed runaway creep phenomena at high stress and there was clear evidence of associated increases in the temperature of the specimens. The rise in temperature was deemed to be a consequence of the large strains rather than their prime cause. A further complication is the propensity of glassy amorphous plastics to crazing. A craze grows much more rapidly under intermittent stress than under steady stress and therefore there is a greater probability of premature failure. Thus the intermittency of stress confers the same viscoelastic advantage for

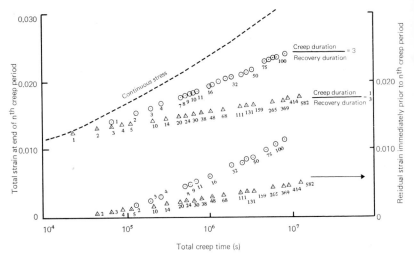

Fig. 20.   Creep under intermittent stress, durnal cycles. Polypropylene, 20°C, 10 MN/m². Numbers indicate cycle number (n).

amorphous polymers as it does for crystalline ones but introduces the risk of failure through dynamic fatigue. This can be seen from the results in Fig. 21, which are apparently typical of materials that craze, though the specimen subjected to 40 MN/m² intermittent stress did not fail prematurely. This apparent anomaly is not necessarily at variance with the probable explanation for early failure under intermittent stress, which follows work by Vincent.[29] During an unloaded period a large proportion of the creep strain disappears and the size of the plastic zone at the craze tip also decreases. Successive loadings do little more than re-establish the strain state that existed during earlier creep periods and the conditions in which the craze grows are nearly constant during successive cycles. During steady stress creep this retraction mechanism is absent and, in fact, the plastic zone size, and hence the fracture toughness, increases. The specimen

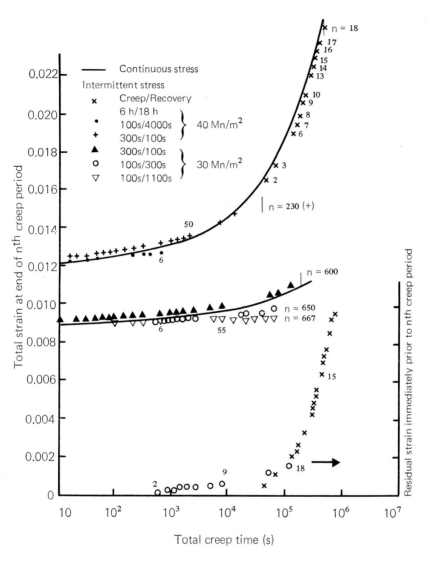

Fig. 21. Creep under intermittent stress. Unplasticised PVC 20°C. Numbers indicate cycle number (n).

stressed intermittently at 40 MN/m^2 retracted during the recovery periods far less, relatively, than those stressed at 30 MN/m^2; the maximum strain in each creep cycle did not fall below the steady stress creep curve and, presumably, the plastic zone increased in size more or less as in a steady creep situation. It is as though the specimen did not know that the stress reduced to zero periodically.

The apparently successful method for calculating the response assumes that the response to a period of stress and the subsequent recovery are quite unaffected by the mechanical history and the current strain. This is, of course, an assumption of linearity and it is adequate for nonlinear systems only because of the interaction of several competing factors. However, the new creep strain in successive cycles is not absolutely constant. The usual behaviour is that the maximum creep strain increases during the first few cycles and decreases during later cycles, though a steady decrease from the beginning has been observed occasionally. The phenomenon is apparently unrelated to the residual strain because it has been observed even when the residual strain had decreased to zero before the start of a new creep period. [30] This last result is rather disconcerting because it implies that a unique mechanical zero state cannot be identified by physical observation. Other, rather similar complications are discussed in the next section.

4.4.6 Creep under abrupt changes of stress

Evaluation of the multiple integral method of representation and the general characterisation of nonlinear systems require experiments in which the excitation function is varied, possibly several times, during the course of an experiment. Step-wise changes are the most convenient and many of the experiments reported in the literature have employed staircase functions, both ascending and descending. It is difficult to gauge the success achieved; it seems to be the general consensus that there is a closer agreement between predicted and experimental results when the stress is increased than when it is reduced. In principle, close agreement between prediction and actual behaviour could be achieved simply by increasing the number of integral terms, and at first sight, therefore, it would seem that the limitations are experimental rather than theoretical. There is the difficulty that relatively small errors are magnified by some of the manipulations and there is also the disadvantage that the number of experiments necessary to evaluate the kernel functions increases disproportionately to the order of the integral series. Mainly because of this escalation of experimental effort, it is usual for the integral series to be truncated at the third term; this implies that the creep strain under steady stress is a third order polynomial in stress (eqn. 14(a)) which is a gross approximation for most materials, seventh or higher order polynomials being more appropriate. It is obvious, therefore, that the general problem abounds with ill-defined practical and mathematical difficulties, but there is also a more fundamental reason for the incomplete success of the theory. This is that our basic model of nonlinear viscoelasticity is merely an explicit constitutive equation relating stress, strain, time and temperature (where necessary). It is accepted that slow changes in structure during an experiment of long duration may change the constitutive relationship to some degree but there has been far less widespread appreciation that such changes may be accentuated and modified by the stress or strain state of the specimen. The effect of conditioning periods at high temperatures and the poor recovery after creep in some circumstances are manifestations of this extra complexity, and there is some evidence to suggest that similar factors have intruded into the experiments with varying stress. The main experimental evidence of odd nonlinear phenomena has come from experiments in which the stress was increased temporarily from one level to another at various elapsed times, T_i at the lower stress. The response to the additional stress would be expected to change with the elapsed time, primarily because the creep strain due to the maintained lower stress would be increasing continuously, but the behaviour is more complicated than might reasonably be expected.

The first experiments were carried out on polypropylene[31] but it is more appropriate here to describe more recent results on an unplasticised PVC. The excitation function was ostensibly of the form shown in Fig. 22, but several specimens were used so that none was subjected to many, or to closely spaced, changes of stress, and hence the new response to the gate excitation between σ_L and σ_H could be identified as a function of T rather than as a function of several previous such steps. The higher stress was maintained for 100 seconds each time and the additional strain $\Delta\varepsilon$ was measured immediately prior to the reduction of stress, i.e. at an elapsed time of $(T_i + 100)$, and is therefore designated $\Delta\varepsilon(T_i + 100)$. The original experiments were expected to show $\Delta\varepsilon(T_i + 100)$ increasing with T_i, because of the seemingly reasonable assumption that the specimen would exhibit something akin to strain-softening as the creep strain increased under the steady stress σ_L. The polypropylene data showed that $\Delta\varepsilon(T_i + 100)$ vs. log T_i increased slightly at first and then decreased sharply. The general trend was such that the increase at low values of log T_i could have been dismissed as experimental error but subsequent results substantiated

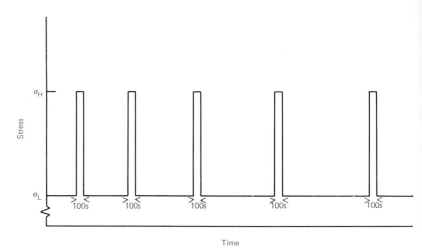

*Fig. 22.   Excitation function for complex stress history experiments. ($\sigma_H = 2\sigma_L$
in experiments discussed in Section 4.4.6.)*

it completely. Figure 23 shows results for unplasticised PVC; several
levels of σ_L and σ_H have been used but $\sigma_H = 2\sigma_L$ in all the experiments.
The datum points for the highest stress are scattered; because at low
values of T_i the additional strain was so large that local yielding occurred
erratically in the specimen. Beneath the scatter and the interspecimen
variability at the highest stress, and in the experiments at lower stresses,
the effect first observed in polypropylene is clearly discernible. It has also
been observed in uniaxial compression[32] and in shear.[14]

Lockett has shown that the results are accountable by the multiple
integral theory and that they impose certain restraints on the kernel
function.[33] Unfortunately, the duration of stressing at σ_H was always 100
seconds in these experiments and hence the conclusions he was able to
make were limited in their scope. Furthermore, it is in no sense an
'explanation'. The results suggest that the specimen responds to a change
of stress imposed at long elapsed times as though it were free of all strain
or strain history whereas it responds in a grossly nonlinear fashion to a
change imposed at short elapsed times. However, the picture presented in
Fig. 23 is incomplete. $\Delta\varepsilon(T_i + 100)$ is specific and limited, and should be
replaced by $\Delta\varepsilon(T_i + t)$; for instance, if the higher stress was maintained
for a far longer time than T_i the resulting total response would
presumably become indistinguishable from the creep response to steady
stress σ_H after a sufficiently long time, i.e. the slope of $\Delta\varepsilon(T_i + t_j)$ vs.

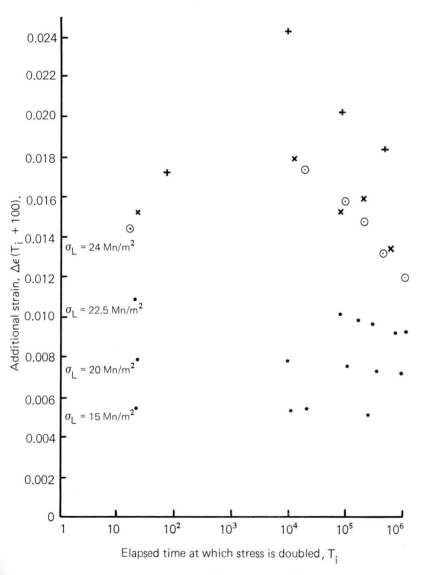

Fig. 23. *Effect of abrupt changes of stress from σ_L to $2\sigma_L$. (PVC at 20°C. Three specimens (•, ×, +) demonstrate interspecimen variability due to incipient yielding at highest stress.)*

log T_i would be positive for sufficiently high values of t_j. At this stage speculation is unrewarding. No immediate explanations or solutions are available and there is only a low probability that nonlinear creep behaviour can ever be adequately represented by a constitutive equation sufficiently simple to be readily usable.

4.5 FINAL COMMENTS

As a tool in polymer physics, straightforward creep experiments on glassy amorphous polymers are virtually useless. Unlike the complex modulus or complex compliance functions, the creep compliance function lacks identifiable features that can be located with precision and associated with molecular relaxation processes. On the other hand, as a guide to service performance they are invaluable. Creep data are essential in the quantitative, engineering design process by which the size of the critical cross-sections of plastics components is determined. The design calculations generally incorporate a number of idealisations and the final computations are only approximations to the truth, but the creep data themselves should be accurate, for a number of interconnected reasons that appeal to the physicist rather than to the engineer. One is that creep is a function of several variables, some of which may vary inadvertently during an experiment, with confusing results unless accurate definitive experiments can be arranged. Another is that the overall value of a creep curve is enhanced if it can be seen as part of a viscoelastic function and in proper relation to the other parts; such an integration is possible only if the constituent parts are known with high precision.

Physics should contribute more than mere experimental refinements, of course. Even though quantitative rules are elusive, it is nevertheless necessary for the relationships between the creep properties and the molecular structure to be pursued. The current knowledge of this for glassy polymers amounts to no more than empirical rules and associations between concepts. For instance, it is known that benzene rings in the backbone chain of a molecule confer a high T_g, which varies in a predictable way with the proportion of benzene rings and the type of linking atoms or chain segments; on the other hand, the magnitude of the creep modulus in the wide, featureless glassy region cannot be predicted. The reason for this difference is that T_g is dominated by the chain structure, whereas the glassy modulus is a function of the structure and the molecular order which, in turn, is sensitive to the thermal history and to small proportions of extraneous material, *e.g.* monomer, water and other impurities. Recovery after creep similarly defies quantitative rationalisation within the accepted polymer physics framework and it seems possible, therefore, that progress in understanding the behaviour of glassy amorphous plastics will be through the adoption of models borrowed from metallurgy rather than through the usual concepts of polymer physics.

REFERENCES AND BIBLIOGRAPHY

1. Williams, M. L., Landel, R. F. and Ferry, J. D. (1955). 'The temperature dependence of relaxation mechanisms in amorphous polymers and other glass-forming liquids', *J. Am. Chem. Soc.*, **77**, 3701.
2. McCrum, N. G. and Morris, E. L. (1964). 'On the measurement of the activation energies for creep and stress relaxation', *Proc. Roy. Soc.*, A, **281**, 258.
3. Findley, W. N. (1944). 'Creep characteristics of plastics', ASTM Symposium on Plastics, p. 18.
4. Boltzmann, L. (1876). 'Zur Theorie der elastischen Nachwirkung', *Pogg. Ann. Physik.*, **7**, 624.
5. Findley, W. N. and Khosla, G. (1955). 'Application of the superposition principle and theories of mechanical equation of state, strain, and time hardening to creep of plastics under changing loads', *J. App. Phys.*, **26**, 821.
6. Findley, W. N. and Gjelsvik, J. (1962). 'A versatile biaxial testing machine for investigation of plasticity, creep or relaxation of materials under variable loading paths', *Proc. ASTM*, **62**, 1103.
7. Mills, W. H. and Turner, S. 'Tensile creep testing of plastics'. Paper 23, Symposium on 'Development in Materials Testing Machine Design'. Manchester, 7–10 September, 1965.
8. Thomas, D. A. (1969). 'Uniaxial compressive creep studies', *Plastics and Polymers*, **37**, 485.
9. O'Connor, D. G. and Findley, W. N. (1962). 'Influence of normal stress on creep in tension and compression of polyethylene and rigid poly(vinyl chloride) copolymer', *J. Eng. Ind.*, **84**, 237.
10. Dunn, C. M. R. and Turner, S. 'Apparatus and technique for the accurate measurement of modulus and creep in flexure'. To be published.
11. Mallon, P. J. Ph.D. Thesis, Queen's University of Belfast, 1970; Mallon, P. J. and Benham, P. P. (1972). 'The development and results of a shear creep for plastics'. *Plastics and Polymers*, **40**, 22.
12. Thomas, D. A. and Turner, S. (1969). 'Experimental technique in uniaxial tensile creep testing', Chapter II of *Testing of Polymers*, vol. IV, ed. W. E. Brown, Interscience, New York.
13. Andrews, R. D. (1952). 'Correlation of dynamic and static measurements on rubber-like materials', *Ind. Eng. Chem.*, **44**, 707.
14. Ewing, P., Turner, S. and Williams, J. G. (1972). 'Combined tension/torsion studies on polymers. Apparatus and preliminary results for polythene', *J. of Strain Analysis*, **7**, 9.
15. Turner, S. (1968). 'A system of deformation data for rational engineering design with plastics', *Polymer Eng. & Science*, **8**, 101.

16. Marin, J., Pao, Y.-H. and Cuff, G. (1951). 'Creep properties of Lucite and Plexiglas for tension, compression, bending and torsion', *Trans. Am. Soc. Mech. Engs.*, **73**, 705.
17. Benham, P. P. and McCammond, D. (1971). 'Studies of creep and contraction ratio in thermoplastics', *Plastic & Polymers*, **39**, 130.
18. Turner, S. (1964). 'Creep in thermoplastics. Polythene', *British Plastics*, **37**, 501.
19. Bergen, R. L. (1967). 'Creep of thermoplastics in the glassy region. Stress as a reduced variable', *SPE Journal*, **23**, 57.
20. Bueche, F. (1956). 'Young's modulus of semi-crystalline polymers', *J. Poly. Sci.*, **22**, 113.
21. McLoughlin, J. R. and Tobolsky, A. V. (1952). 'The viscoelastic behaviour of polymethylmethacrylate', *J. Coll. Sci.*, **7**, 555.
22. Darlington, M. W. and Saunders, D. W. (1970). 'An apparatus for the measurement of tensile creep and contraction ratios in small non-rigid specimens', *Journal of Physics E: Scientific Instruments*, **3**, 511.
23. Darlington, M. W. and Saunders, D. W. (1971). 'Creep in oriented thermoplastics', *J. Macromol. Sci. Phys.*, **B5(2)**, 207.
24. Raumann, G. and Saunders, D. W. (1961). 'The anisotropy of Young's modulus in drawn polyethylene', *Proc. Phys. Soc.*, **77**, 1028.
25. Wright, H. M.Sc. Thesis, UMIST, 1967.
26. Bonnin, M. J., Dunn, C. M. R. and Turner, S. (1969). 'A comparison of torsional and flexural deformations in plastics', *Plastics and Polymers*, **37**, 517.
27. Turner, S. (1971). Journal of Applied Polymer Science Symposia No. 17. Mechanical Performance and Design in Polymers, p. 213.
28. Benham, P. P. and Hutchinson, S. J. (1970). 'Cyclic creep and fracture of polyvinyl chloride', *Plastics and Polymers*, **38**, 259.
29. Vincent, P. I. 'Localised plastic deformation and fracture', T.R. No. 97, Division of Polymer Science, Case Western Reserve University, Cleveland, Ohio.
30. Lockett, F. J. and Turner, S. (1971). 'Non-linear creep of plastics', *J. Mech. Phys. Solids*, **19**, 201.
31. Turner, S. (1966). 'The strain response of plastics to complex stress histories', *Polymer Engineering and Science*, **6**, 306.
32. Thomas, D. A. Unpublished results.
33. Lockett, F. J. Private communication.
34. Eyring, H. (1936). *J. Chem. Phys.*, **4**, 283.

The following contain many references to earlier sources and are useful reviews of many aspects of viscoelasticity theory:

Passaglia, E. and Knox, J. R. (1964). 'Viscoelastic behaviour and time–temperature relationships', Ch. 3, *Engineering Design for Plastics*, ed. Baer, Reinhold, New York.
Hilton, H. H. 'Viscoelastic analysis', Ch. 4, *ibid.*
Alfrey, T., Jnr (1948). 'Mechanical behaviour of high polymers', Interscience, New York.
Leaderman, H. (1958). 'Viscoelasticity phenomena in amorphous high polymeric systems', Ch. 1, *Rheology*, VII, ed. Eirich, Academic Press, New York.

CHAPTER 5

THE YIELD BEHAVIOUR OF GLASSY POLYMERS

P. B. BOWDEN

5.1 INTRODUCTION

When a glassy polymer starts to deform plastically under an applied stress it is said to have yielded. Yield leads to a change in the shape of the specimen as a whole. Other processes such as crazing and voiding (strain whitening) may also take place when a polymer is deformed but these involve only local deformations and are not a necessary part of the general yield process. They are often the prelude to fracture and as such they form part of the subject matter of Chapter 7 and to a lesser extent of Chapter 6. Here we shall deal solely with the process of yield, which is of interest because it is the factor limiting the strength of the polymer if brittle fracture can be suppressed; a polymer must have a high yield stress in order to be strong. Another reason for studying the yield behaviour is that the question as to whether or not brittle fracture occurs depends on the detailed interaction of the bulk yielding and fracture processes. If bulk yielding occurs the polymer is likely to be tough.

When it comes to an exact definition different writers mean different things by yield. What follows is a description of yield behaviour using one particular set of definitions as a framework for discussion; it is hoped that the various other definitions used, and the differences between them, will become clear in the process.

5.2 EXACT DEFINITIONS

To define yield precisely we have to examine the intrinsic behaviour of glassy polymers in response to an applied stress under precisely defined

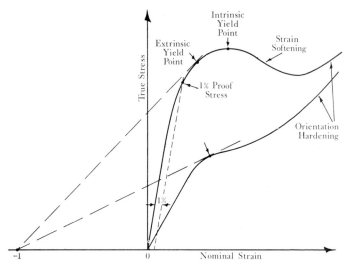

Fig. 1. Schematic true stress *versus* nominal strain *curves for amorphous glassy polymers. A tangent to the curve through the point on the abscissa $\varepsilon_n = -1$ is Considères construction and defines the extrinsic yield point of a sample tested in tension (5.2.4).*

conditions. An example of a test in which the conditions are fully specified would be the measurement of the *true stress as a function of nominal strain for a sample of material deforming homogeneously at a constant strain rate with a constant deformation-rate tensor at constant temperature and pressure.* This test is the determination of a conventional stress–strain curve with the difference that all possible test variables have been brought under control. Many of these specifications are self explanatory. Stress, strain and the deformation-rate tensor are dealt with below. The conditions for homogeneous deformation are dealt with more fully in Section 5.5.

Such a stress–strain curve is a property of the material and will not be affected by the details of the test method. It is an abstraction, since for one reason or another in any experimental test the conditions will deviate from the specifications, but it is a useful abstraction since it is simple to understand and interpret; and in many cases it is possible to obtain experimental curves that approach quite closely to it. Two schematic curves of true stress versus nominal strain for amorphous glassy polymers are shown in Fig. 1.

5.2.1 Stress

True stress is the load divided by the instantaneous cross-sectional area of the sample. *Nominal (or Engineering) stress* is the load divided by the initial (undeformed) cross-sectional area. It is preferable to use true stress when considering the intrinsic properties of the material. Nominal stress is more convenient when considering the properties of the sample as a whole. For instance when the nominal stress is a maximum the sample is carrying its maximum load.

5.2.2 Strain

Nominal strain is the change in length divided by the original length. *True strain* is the integral of this quantity:

$$\varepsilon_n = \frac{(l_1 - l_0)}{l_0} = \frac{\Delta l}{l_0}; \qquad \varepsilon_t = \int_{l_0}^{l_1} \frac{dl}{l} = \ln\left(\frac{l_1}{l_0}\right)$$

The two quantities are identical at small strains and the divergence only becomes serious at strains above about 0·1. Nominal strain is the simpler to compute and use.

5.2.3 The deformation-rate tensor

Different types of mechanical test produce different changes in the shape of an element of the sample. Figure 2 shows four simple deformations produced by commonly used mechanical tests in terms of the change in shape of an initially cubic element. Other intermediate types are possible but all the simple ones are shown. In all cases the same deformation can be produced in a plastic material by more than one applied stress system. For instance the deformation in Fig. 2b can be produced by a uniaxial compressive stress, a biaxial tensile stress, or a combination of both. All these changes of shape are at constant volume. The question of volume changes during yield is considered specifically in Sections 5.4.8 and 5.7.3.

These shape changes can be defined in terms of the deformation-rate tensor necessary to produce them. To specify the tensor for a given deformation it is first necessary to define a set of axes fixed in space as is done in Fig. 2. The nine components of the tensor describing a general deformation are most conveniently written in the form of a three-by-three matrix which for a general deformation has the form

$$\begin{vmatrix} \dot{\varepsilon}_{11} & \dot{\gamma}_{12} & \dot{\gamma}_{13} \\ \dot{\gamma}_{21} & \dot{\varepsilon}_{22} & \dot{\gamma}_{23} \\ \dot{\gamma}_{31} & \dot{\gamma}_{32} & \dot{\varepsilon}_{33} \end{vmatrix}$$

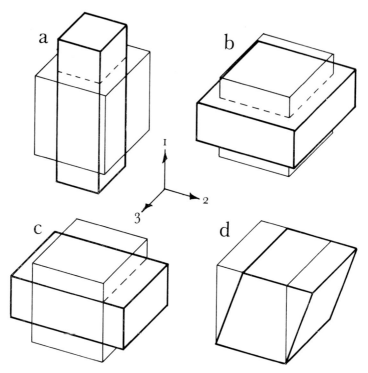

Fig. 2. Four different possible plastic deformations of an initially cubic element deforming at constant volume: (a) *uniaxial extension or biaxial compressions;* (b) *uniaxial compression or biaxial extension;* (c) *plane strain extension or compression;* (d) *simple shear.*

The epsilons are normal strain rates and the gammas are shear strain rates. The first subscript of each term indicates the plane whose movement is being considered (the plane normal to the axis indicated by the subscript) and the second subscript the direction in which movement is taking place.[†] The dot indicates differentiation with respect to time; $\dot{\varepsilon} = d\varepsilon/dt$, $\dot{\gamma} = d\gamma/dt$.

All nine terms in the tensor can vary independently except that if the deformation is at constant volume then the rate of volume dilatation, $\dot{v}/v$, which is equal to $(\dot{\varepsilon}_{11} + \dot{\varepsilon}_{22} + \dot{\varepsilon}_{33})$, must be zero. The shape changes in Fig. 2 can be produced by the operation of the following deformation-rate tensors which are written for the set of axes shown in the figure.

[†] The way in which strain tensors are defined and manipulated are described in detail in p. 92 ff. of reference 32 and Chapter 2 of reference 35.

$$(a) \begin{vmatrix} \dot{\varepsilon} & 0 & 0 \\ 0 & -\dfrac{\dot{\varepsilon}}{2} & 0 \\ 0 & 0 & -\dfrac{\dot{\varepsilon}}{2} \end{vmatrix} \quad (b) \begin{vmatrix} -\dot{\varepsilon} & 0 & 0 \\ 0 & \dfrac{\dot{\varepsilon}}{2} & 0 \\ 0 & 0 & \dfrac{\dot{\varepsilon}}{2} \end{vmatrix}$$

$$(c) \begin{vmatrix} \dot{\varepsilon} & 0 & 0 \\ 0 & -\dot{\varepsilon} & 0 \\ 0 & 0 & 0 \end{vmatrix} \quad (d) \begin{vmatrix} 0 & \dot{\gamma} & 0 \\ 0 & 0 & 0 \\ 0 & 0 & 0 \end{vmatrix}$$

Unlike a strain tensor, a strain-rate tensor need not be symmetrical. If it is non-symmetrical ($\dot{\gamma}_{ij} \neq \dot{\gamma}_{ji}$) then the flow is not purely *extensional* but there is a *rotational* component known as the *vorticity* of the deformation. Simple shear (Fig. 2*d*) is the sum of a pure shear and a rotation

$$\begin{vmatrix} 0 & \dot{\gamma} & 0 \\ 0 & 0 & 0 \\ 0 & 0 & 0 \end{vmatrix} = \begin{vmatrix} 0 & \dfrac{\dot{\gamma}}{2} & 0 \\ \dfrac{\dot{\gamma}}{2} & 0 & 0 \\ 0 & 0 & 0 \end{vmatrix} + \begin{vmatrix} 0 & \dfrac{\dot{\gamma}}{2} & 0 \\ -\dfrac{\dot{\gamma}}{2} & 0 & 0 \\ 0 & 0 & 0 \end{vmatrix}$$

| Simple shear | Pure shear | Rotation (vorticity) |

In the elastic region the strains are small, the rotation is small, and a test in simple shear is identical to one in pure shear apart from the fact that the sample has twisted slightly in space. (The tensor describing the pure shear component can be made of the same form as (*c*) above, with $\dot{\varepsilon} = \dot{\gamma}/2$, by referring the deformation to a set of axes at 45° to the original ones.) However, in the plastic region rotating the material while continuing to deform it may well affect its stress–strain behaviour.

Differences in stress–strain behaviour dependent on the form of the applied deformation-rate tensor have never been specifically looked for in glassy polymers, but they certainly exist in other systems. A viscoelastic liquid formed from a mixture of glycerol (49 %), water (49 %) and Separan

(2%) becomes more fluid at large strains if it is deformed in simple shear but stiffer and less fluid if it is deformed in uniaxial extension.[1] In this case the effect only appears after large shear strains of the order of 2 or more.

5.2.4 The yield point

In Fig. 1 the various regions of interest on the stress–strain curve are indicated. In the elastic region the material is deforming elastically or viscoelastically and the deformation is essentially recoverable on unloading. At some point beyond this it yields. As deformation proceeds further, the sample may or may not exhibit strain softening. At strains over about 0·3 most glassy polymers exhibit orientation hardening.

The conventional concept of a yield point is the point beyond which the deformation ceases to be entirely elastic. At the yield point the material starts to deform plastically. This concept is based on experience with metals where it is convenient since the mechanisms causing the two types of deformation, lattice distortion and dislocation motion, are clearly distinct. It is difficult to apply it precisely to polymers. Experimentally the distinction between elastic (recoverable) and plastic (permanent) deformation is not clear cut and it is quite possible that there is no sharp distinction in mechanism either.

A number of different criteria are used to define a yield point and they are set out below. Care is needed when reading the literature as the terms 'yield stress' and 'yield point' are used by different authors to describe different things. The nomenclature used below is self-consistent and as far as possible consistent with that used to describe yield in non-polymeric materials.

The maximum true stress—the intrinsic yield point
For polymers which exhibit a true stress versus strain curve with a maximum similar to that of the upper curve in Fig. 1, the *intrinsic yield point* can conveniently be defined as this maximum point. The yield stress and yield strain then correspond to the values at this maximum. This is the practical definition of the term *yield point* adopted in this chapter because the maximum does appear to correspond to the onset of permanent plastic deformation at any rate for PMMA (*see* Section 5.4.1). We will call it an intrinsic yield point as it is intrinsic to the material and should not be a function of any of the geometrical features of the test. For polymers which have a true stress–strain curve that does not pass through a maximum this definition does not work, but an intrinsic yield point (the onset of a

permanent plastic deformation) can generally be located in the region of a kink in the true stress–strain curve.

The maximum nominal stress in tension—the extrinsic yield point
When a sample is tested in tension the deformation becomes unstable at a point defined by Considère's construction (*see* Sections 6.3.1 and 5.5) and a neck develops. This construction is illustrated in Fig. 1. For a material whose flow stress is independent of strain rate the load carried by the sample passes through a maximum at this point and the sample as a whole can be said to have yielded. We will call the point at which the load goes through a maximum the *extrinsic yield point* since it is related to the geometry of the deformation of a tensile sample and only indirectly to the intrinsic properties of the material being tested.

In a strain-rate sensitive material such as a polymer although the deformation becomes unstable at the point given by Considère's construction the rate at which the instability develops can be slow (Section 5.5.1) with the result that the extrinsic (apparent) yield point can occur at a later point on the curve than is indicated by Considère's construction and so can approach the intrinsic yield point. From the geometry of Considère's construction it is never possible for the extrinsic yield stress, σ_y^e to be very much less than the intrinsic yield stress, σ_y^i; the maximum possible value of $(\sigma_y^i - \sigma_y^e)$ is $\varepsilon_n \sigma_y^e$ where ε_n is the nominal strain at the intrinsic yield point. In practice the difference will be much less.

It will be appreciated that the extrinsic yield point is the one generally referred to as the yield point in most of the literature on plastics, as is done in Chapter 6.

The 1% proof stress
The term *proof stress* is used primarily by metallurgists and engineers and is defined as the stress necessary to produce a specified amount of plastic deformation. It is determined in practice by drawing a straight line parallel to the initial elastic portion of the stress–strain curve but offset by the specified strain (*e.g.* 1%) and noting the stress at which this line intercepts the stress–strain curve. The construction is shown in Fig. 1.

In materials where the elastic response is known to be linear the construction is justified. In polymers where the initial response is viscoelastic and the stress–strain curve can be curved in the region where the deformation is fully recoverable its use is more doubtful. The construction does not define the stress level at which the specified amount of permanent plastic deformation has been produced since at all strains less than the intrinsic yield strain there may be no permanent plastic deformation.

The limit of proportionality

The limit of proportionality is defined as the point at which the stress–strain curve departs from a straight line. In practice it is very difficult to locate such a point reliably or reproducibly and this is the reason that the concept of a proof stress was introduced. For polymers it seems doubtful whether the limit of proportionality has any basic significance.

5.2.5 Nomenclature for deformation processes

After yielding has taken place most glassy polymers retain an apparently permanent deformation. However, as will be described in Chapter 6 this deformation is generally reversible when the polymer is heated above its glass-transition temperature. It has been recognised for some time that the reversion process is associated with a deformation of the polymer coils which tend to go back to their originally statistically-preferred forms when the internal viscous forces in the polymer glass are reduced, for example by raising the temperature. When moulding operations are carried out above the T_g it is generally desirable to effect a permanent relative movement of the centres of gravity of the molecules which may retain the form of a statistically random coil. Mouldings of this type are inherently more stable than those in which substantial molecular orientation is retained. In practice this often means that compression mouldings which are made over relatively long times are more stable to heat than injection mouldings[91] which are made by a fast flow process and in which cooling of the melt generally takes place before the molecules in the melt have had time to relax to their preferred statistical configurations. Thus most injection mouldings exhibit observable birefringence and will change their shape when warmed to the neighbourhood of their T_g.

To cover these effects polymer scientists and technologists have for some time distinguished broadly between 'flow' meaning a permanent relative displacement of the centre of gravity of the polymer molecules, and other types of deformation which involve a change in the configuration of the molecular coils.[92] During the yield process as observed in a glassy polymer under normal conditions this distinction is not obvious. The deformation that takes place after yield is of a type which many metallurgists or materials scientists would regard as (plastic) flow, yet it is not flow as it would be understood by a polymer technologist which is displacement of the centre of gravity of the molecules as described above.

5.3   MECHANICAL TESTS

Before considering the yield behaviour in detail it is necessary to look at the types of test that have been used to obtain stress–strain curves as the curve obtained and the behaviour observed depend to some extent on the test method used. For theoretical analysis one would like an intrinsic stress-versus-strain function for the material obtained under conditions specified as rigorously as those laid down at the beginning of Section 5.2. Deviation from these conditions during the test will complicate the analysis. In any practical experiment deviation is almost inevitable. In the following sections the principal features of the common mechanical tests are summarised.

5.3.1   The tensile test
This is the most widely used test. The arrangement is shown schematically in Fig. 3(a). Provided the specimen continues to elongate uniformly there is no basic difficulty in carrying out a precise analysis.

Stresses are easiest to obtain as nominal stresses, but the true stress can be determined by measuring the cross-sectional area under load. Because of machine elasticity the strain rate in the specimen will not match that calculated from the cross-head speed of the testing machine except when

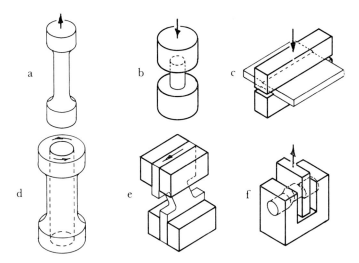

Fig. 3.   Mechanical tests used to study yield in polymers: (a) *tensile test;* (b) *uniaxial compression test;* (c) *plane strain compression test;* (d), (e) *and* (f) *tests in simple shear.*

the sample is deforming at constant load, but this is not a serious difficulty. In practice it is sometimes difficult to measure the strain reliably. The strain can be evaluated from the displacement of the cross-head of the testing machine only if the specimen is relatively long so that end corrections are unimportant. Otherwise it is necessary to fit a strain gauge (which can be awkward) to the central portion of the sample under test.

The two drawbacks of the tensile test for studying the yielding of glassy polymers are firstly that in many plastics the tensile stress can lead to fracture before yield occurs and secondly that it is only the extrinsic yield point as defined in Section 5.2.4 that can be readily investigated. This may be a perfectly satisfactory way of defining a yield stress since the extrinsic and intrinsic yield stresses can never be far apart. However, once the specimen has formed a neck, as it will generally do at the extrinsic yield point, it is very difficult to work back to obtain the intrinsic stress–strain function for the material, since the stress and strain in the neck are difficult to measure with any precision and the strain rate has increased locally.

5.3.2   The uniaxial compression test
The experimental arrangement for this test is shown schematically in Fig. 3(b).

A practical difficulty that arises is that if the diameter-to-height ratio is too small the sample is liable to buckle elastically or plastically, while if it is large, friction between the dies and the sample (which can never be completely eliminated even with good lubrication) will introduce a constraint. This constraint can be corrected by obtaining a yield stress for a series of samples of different diameter-to-height ratios and extrapolating to the value for a ratio of zero. A second difficulty is that as the strain is increased the diameter-to-height ratio increases, the frictional constraint increases, and it is not possible to apply large strains before the frictional constraint gets out of hand.

However, within these limitations this is a useful test for studying yield since, because the stress is compressive, tensile fracture is suppressed and plastic yielding can be obtained in a material that under most other conditions is brittle. An initial diameter-to-height ratio of about 0·5 is a good compromise. The yield stress measured in a compression test is the intrinsic yield stress of the material since there is no geometrical reason for the deformation to become unstable.

Since the cross-sectional area of the specimen increases as the test proceeds, the true stress in a compression test is always less than the nominal stress; in a tensile test the true stress is always the greater. If the strain at yield is large this effect can lead to appreciable differences between the nominal-stress values of the intrinsic yield stress determined in a tensile and a compression test, even though the intrinsic yield stress may be essentially the same in both cases. If, at yield, the strain transverse to the axis of the specimen is 4% in both cases then in tension the cross-sectional area will be 8% smaller (in compression 8% larger) than the unstressed cross-sectional area. This would lead to a 16% difference between the nominal-stress values of the intrinsic yield stress determined in tension and compression.

5.3.3 The plane strain compression test

The experimental arrangement is shown in Fig. 3(c). The same general considerations apply as apply to the uniaxial compression test. The problem of frictional constraint at large strains is not quite so serious since the area of the specimen in contact with the dies remains constant as the deformation proceeds. It is necessary to test specimens of different widths using dies of different breadths to correct for frictional constraint and effects at the edges of the specimen and the edges of the dies where the deformation is complex and not plane strain.[2] For many polymers these corrections are small. One effect to be avoided is an anomalously low yield stress due to reflected shear zones which form in some materials when the ratio of die breadth to specimen thickness at yield is an integer.[2]

Advantages of this test are that specimen preparation is simple, and since the deformation is always stable it is the intrinsic yield stress of the material that is measured. An additional advantage is that since the area of the specimen under the dies remains constant during the test the stress most readily calculated is the true stress.

5.3.4 Tests in simple shear

Three different methods that can be used to obtain a simple shear deformation are shown in Fig. 3.

Twisting a tube of the material (Fig. 3(d)) is a very satisfactory test. The stress and strain can be precisely determined. However, instabilities are likely to develop if the wall is too thin relative to the tube diameter. A serious disadvantage of this method is the difficulty of preparing samples.

Shearing an initially symmetrical waisted specimen clamped between steel blocks as shown in Fig. 3(e) can work satisfactorily, although the shear strain in the waisted region is not always uniform. The blocks have to be constrained to move parallel to each other.

Symmetrically shearing a plug of the material (Fig. 3(f)) is a quick and easy test but it is not amenable to precise analysis. Even if the dies are carefully made the thickness of the regions being sheared is not well defined so it is difficult to specify the shear strain.

5.3.5 Machine elasticity

In practice, no testing machine or testing arrangement is ideally 'hard' in the sense that its elastic deflection is negligible, and this can affect the observed behaviour of materials whose flow stresses are strongly strain-rate dependent, such as polymers.

Under the widely used testing condition of constant cross-head speed the (nominal) strain rate in the specimen will not be constant unless the sample is deforming at constant load. If the load is increasing some of the cross-head movement will be absorbed in an increasing machine deflection and the strain rate in the sample will be reduced. It is possible to overcome this difficulty by using an extensometer on the sample to control the cross-head speed of the machine in order to give the desired constant specimen strain rate. However, very little work has been done on polymers under these conditions and so when interpreting data it is necessary to remember that the strain rate in the sample may be varying during the test.

5.3.6 Drawing at constant load

In all the tests described above the sample is brought to yield by imposing a more-or-less constant strain rate. An alternative test which can be used to study yield in materials such as polymers where the flow stress is highly strain-rate sensitive is a test at constant stress, or in practice at constant load. By 'flow' in this context is meant the complex viscoelastic–plastic response to an applied stress of a polymer in its glassy state; not simple viscous flow of the type observed in a polymer above its T_g (*see* Section 5.2.5). This type of test has been used by Ender[3] to study yield in poly-methylmethacrylate.

When the stress is applied the specimen does not yield immediately. The strain at first increases rapidly as shown in Fig. 4(a), then increases more slowly as the specimen yields (the strain rate goes through a minimum), and subsequently increases more rapidly again. Figure 4(b) shows schematically the reason for this behaviour. A constant-stress path on the flow-stress surface in Fig. 4(b) will go through a minimum in strain rate at the point where a conventional stress–strain curve (a path at constant strain rate) would go through a maximum in stress.

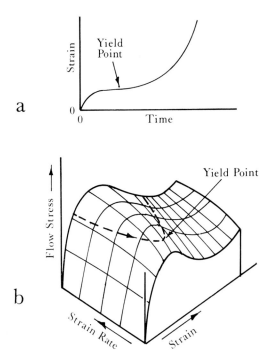

Fig. 4. (a) *Schematic variation of strain with time observed in a polymer sample held at a constant stress.* (b) *Schematic variation of the flow stress of a polymer sample with strain and strain rate. The dotted line is the constant-stress trajectory followed by the sample in Fig. 4(a).*

5.4 CHARACTERISTICS OF THE YIELD PROCESS

In this section we will concentrate on the intrinsic material behaviour of glassy polymers in the region of the yield point, and will postpone for the moment a consideration of the various models that have been proposed to explain that behaviour. A great deal can be deduced about the yield processes in a polymer from stress–strain curves similar to those in Fig. 1. Although such 'ideal' curves are not available any form of stress–strain data can be used provided that the effect of any departure from ideality is taken into account in the interpretation of the results.

5.4.1 The yield point and the yield stress

Figure 5(a) shows a stress–strain curve obtained from a PMMA sample deformed in plane strain compression at a constant cross-head speed.

Initially the stress rises linearly with strain. The deformation is elastic and recoverable on unloading. As the strain increases the gradient of the curve decreases until it becomes horizontal, at which point the sample is flowing at constant stress. As the strain increases further the flow stress decreases slightly (strain softening is taking place) and then increases again (orientation hardening).

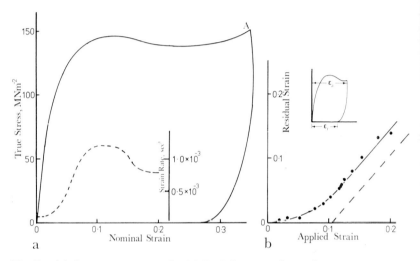

Fig. 5. (a) *Stress–strain curve for PMMA determined in a plane strain compression test. The dashed curve shows the variation of the strain rate during the test.*[4] (b) *The residual strain, ε_r, as a function of the applied strain, ε_a, immediately after unloading* (*continuous curve*) *and after recovering for* 1 *week* (*dashed curve*).[4]

At the point A the direction of travel of the cross-head of the testing machine was reversed to unload the sample. The load immediately started to fall, but the strain continued to increase very slightly as deformation could still take place (at a lower strain rate) at the lower stress. This effect is a consequence of the strong strain-rate sensitivity of the flow stress and machine elasticity. The lower portion of the unloading curve shows a strong curvature because of the viscoelastic nature of the recovery process.

The intrinsic yield point as defined in Section 5.2.4 is the point beyond which the deformation ceases to be recoverable on unloading. In Fig. 5(b) the residual strain measured immediately after unloading, ε_r, is plotted as a function of the applied strain, ε_a. The deformation continues to recover with time and the values of ε_r after a week are indicated by the dotted line. It is evident from these results that something irreversible (at any rate irreversible after a week at room temperature) is happening in the region of the maximum in the stress–strain curve. This is the evidence on which the definition of the intrinsic yield point as the maximum in the true stress is based.

Even if yield is defined as the onset of permanent (plastic) deformation there is no sharply-defined yield point for PMMA. An arbitrary decision has to be taken as to the time scale on which the permanence is to be judged. Even if a time scale is defined, the point at which residual strain first becomes detectable is not always sharply defined as is shown by the values obtained immediately after unloading. However, in spite of the viscoelastic nature of the yield process the results do seem to indicate that for this polymer, which has a true stress versus strain curve that passes through a maximum, yield occurs in the vicinity of this maximum. It follows that the yield stress is a well-defined quantity although the yield strain is not.

It can be seen in Fig. 5 that the strain rate was not constant during the test. The steep increase in strain rate just before yield is a direct consequence of machine elasticity as described in Section 5.3.5. At and after yield where the stress is approximately constant the strain rate is constant and corresponds to that calculated directly from the cross-head speed. Experiments in which the cross-head speed is controlled to give a constant strain rate throughout the test show that the value of the yield stress is unaffected and depends only on the value of the strain rate at yield. The general features of the curve are unaltered but the maximum is shifted to slightly larger strains.[4]

5.4.2 The yield strain

The strain at which yield occurs in Fig. 5 is a nominal compressive strain of 0·13. This implies a shear strain of 0·21 if Poisson's ratio is taken as 0·4. Yield has been observed in a specimen of PMMA tested in simple shear at a shear strain of 0·25. (Refer to the curve at 0·69 kbar in Fig. 11.) It is necessary to take this curve since 0·65 kbar is approximately the magnitude of the hydrostatic component of the stress tensor at yield in Fig. 5 (*see* Section 5.4.6). These values of the yield strain are very large when compared with those for crystalline materials. Most metals flow plastically at elastic strains of 0·01 or less. PMMA may be exceptional in that its yield strain in plane strain compression appears to be about twice that of a number of other glassy polymers which yield at strains of around 0·06[5] but high values have also be observed for polyethylene terepthalate.[6] The variation of the yield strain with the testing conditions, in particular temperature and pressure, is considered below.

5.4.3   Strain softening and orientation hardening

The strain softening illustrated in Figs. 1 and 5(a) appears to be a general feature of the behaviour of amorphous glassy polymers.[7,8] It appears that once the structure has yielded and started to flow some structural change has taken place which allows flow to continue at a lower stress. This softening is an intrinsic property of the polymer and is preserved even if the sample is temporarily unloaded during the test, as can be seen from Fig. 6(a) and as was noted by Lazurkin and Fogel'son.[7]

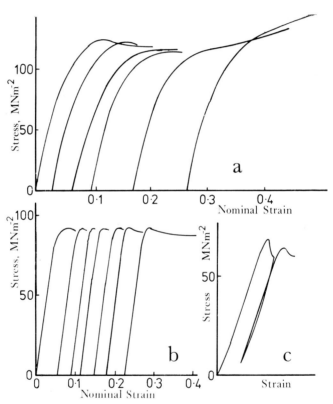

Fig. 6. (a) *Stress–strain curves obtained on a sample of PMMA in plane-strain compression. The test has been interrupted and the load reduced to zero five times during the test. The unloading paths are not plotted.* (*Reproduced from reference 9 by permission of the Editor of* Polymer.) (b) *Similar test on polystyrene at room temperature.*[10] (c) *Test on polyethylene terepthalate in uniaxial compression.* (*Reproduced from reference 8 by permission of John Wiley and Sons Inc.*)

In Figs. 6(*b*) and (*c*) examples are given of polymers showing strain softening which is *not* preserved after unloading. In both cases microstructural examination shows that these materials are deforming inhomogeneously by the formation of micro shear bands and the strain softening is now related to the ease of dynamic nucleation of these bands. However, the reason that these materials deform inhomogeneously in the first place is that the intrinsic material stress–strain curves show so much strain softening that homogeneous deformation is unstable. The conditions for the development of micro shear bands are considered in Section 5.5.

No isotropic amorphous glassy polymer has been shown to have a true-stress versus strain curve similar to the lower curve in Fig. 1 showing no strain softening at all (except close to the glass transition temperature where there appears to be no definite yield point[12]). This type of curve, where rapid orientation hardening masks any possible strain softening, appears to be given only by crystalline polymers or fibre-forming glassy polymers which crystallise on drawing. Cellulose nitrate is an amorphous polymer that, when orientated, hardens very rapidly, but even here there is a small amount of strain softening, except at very low strain rates.[13]

It should be emphasised again that the strain softening we are talking about here is a true-stress effect intrinsic to the material. A sample with an intrinsic stress–strain curve similar to the lower curve in Fig. 1 (no strain softening) will form a neck in a tensile test and at this point a plot of nominal stress will show a drop.

Strain hardening in amorphous glassy polymers tends to occur only at large strains of the order of 0·4 or more as orientation develops. Cellulose nitrate which starts to strain harden at a strain of about 0·1 is an exception (*see* Chapter 6).

5.4.4   The strain-rate dependence of the yield stress

Flow in amorphous glassy polymers appears to be a viscous process and the yield stress is strongly strain-rate dependent. For many polymers a plot of the yield stress against the logarithm of the strain rate is linear so that the gradient $(\partial \sigma_y / \partial (\ln \dot{\varepsilon}))_T$ is a constant. It is this gradient that determines the activation volume in the Eyring equation (Section 5.8.4) and strain rate sensitivity is often discussed in terms of it. In the following sections data that has been obtained on a number of materials is summarised. It will be appreciated that when yield–stress data is quoted below, as it is in Sections 5.4.4 and 5.4.5, the value of the yield stress corresponds to that at the intrinsic yield point for tests in compression and the extrinsic yield point for tests in tension.

Polymethyl methacrylate
This polymer has been more widely investigated than any other and
Fig. 7 gives selected data obtained by five different workers. It can be seen
that there is considerable variation in the absolute magnitudes of the yield
stresses reported but much of this variation can be attributed to differences
in test method. Curve III (uniaxial compression) is expected to fall as it

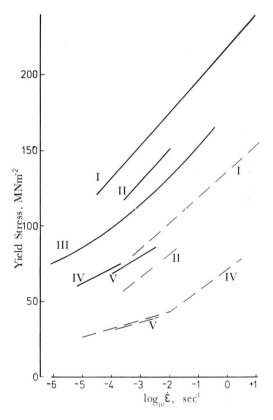

*Fig. 7.   Variation of the yield stress with strain rate for PMMA at 22°C (continuous
curves) and 70°C (dashed curves). The results were obtained by five different
workers using different techniques and materials as follows: (I) Uniaxial compression (nominal stress), Plexiglas II.[14] (II) Plane strain compression (true stress),
Perspex.[11] (III) Uniaxial compression (true stress), Perspex.[15] (IV) Uniaxial
extension (true stress), specially-prepared sample with no stabilisers or lubricants.[16]
(V) Uniaxial extension (true stress), Perspex.[17] In some cases a small extrapolation
has been used to obtain results at a homologous temperature.*

does slightly below curve II (plane strain compression) because of the extra constraint in a plane strain compression test (Section 5.7.6). Curve I is expected to be 10% or so above curve III because the results are plotted in terms of nominal stress; it falls 35% above III and the additional discrepancy may be due either to sample variation or possibly to less-perfect lubrication during the test. However, as far as the strain-rate dependence of the flow stress is concerned all three sets of data obtained in compression agree very well and show that the gradient $(\partial\sigma_y/\partial(\ln\dot\varepsilon))$ is approximately constant over the range of strain rate investigated with a slight decrease at low strain rates, and also that the value of the gradient increases as the test temperature is decreased.

There is a large discrepancy in the magnitude of the yield stress between results obtained in tension tests and results obtained in compression. Results IV and V (uniaxial tension) fall approximately 30% below III (uniaxial compression). Part of the difference is certainly due to the differing hydrostatic component of the stress system in the two cases which for PMMA might be expected to make the tensile yield stress about 18% lower than the compressive one (Section 5.4.6). The remaining discrepancy may be due to sample variation, less-than-perfect lubrication in the compression test and possibly to the fact that in tension it is the extrinsic yield stress of the sample that is measured, which is always less than the intrinsic yield stress of the material, although the difference in practice is likely to be small. All samples tested in tension crazed before they yielded but there is no evidence that this affected the yield stress significantly. The strain-rate sensitivity of the tensile yield stress $(\partial\sigma_y/\partial(\ln\dot\varepsilon))$ is approximately the same at high strain rates as that of the compressive yield stress. At low strain rates and high temperatures it is significantly smaller.

Polycarbonate and polyvinylchloride

Two other amorphous polymers whose yield stress in tension has been investigated in detail as a function of strain rate are polycarbonate and polyvinylchloride.[18] For polycarbonate the gradient $(\partial\sigma_y/\partial(\ln\dot\varepsilon))$ is independent of strain rate and, in contrast to PMMA, increases as the temperature increases. Bauwens-Crowet et al.[18] have shown that the quantity $(1/T)[\partial\sigma_y/\partial(\ln\dot\varepsilon)]$ is a constant over the full range they have investigated. For polyvinylchloride the general pattern of behaviour is similar although there is some variation of the gradient with strain rate.[12,18]

The yield stress of these two polymers appears to be considerably less dependent on strain rate than is the case for PMMA although the literature for polycarbonate shows considerable variation in reported values.[79] Table 1 gives the strain rate sensitivity of the yield stress for all three polymers at 22°C at a strain rate of 10^{-3}/sec.

TABLE 1

THE STRAIN RATE DEPENDENCE OF THE YIELD STRESS AND THE CORRESPONDING EYRING ACTIVATION VOLUME v (SEE SECTION 5.8.4) FOR TESTS AT 22°C AT A STRAIN RATE OF 10^{-3}/SEC. THE LOGARITHMS ARE NATURAL LOGARITHMS

Polymer	Test	$\partial\sigma_y/\partial(\ln \dot{\varepsilon})$, MN/m^2	v $(nm)^3$	References
PMMA	Uniaxial extension	5·2	3·13	16, 17
	Uniaxial compression	9·3	1·75	11, 14, 15
PC	Uniaxial extension	1·26	12·9	12
PVC	Uniaxial extension	1·81	9·0	12

5.4.5   The temperature dependence of the yield stress and the yield strain
The yield stress
Figure 8 shows yield-stress values obtained by a number of authors as a function of temperature in tests on PMMA at a strain rate of 10^{-3}/sec or close to it. As in Fig. 7 tests in tension (IV, V) give appreciably lower values than tests in compression but the trend with temperature is similar. The yield stress tends to zero in the region of the T_g and rises rapidly as the temperature is decreased. At -120°C for Perspex it is in the region of 420 MN/m^2 which is an impressive figure for a polymer, being slightly above the room-temperature yield stress of mild steel. The results obtained by Beardmore (VIII) are significantly lower than those reported by other workers, in particular the temperature dependence of the yield stress is lower, indicating the grade of PMMA that he tested (Lucite) behaves in a markedly different manner from Perspex. The reasons for the difference are not clear at the time of writing.[†]

Additional results obtained by Vincent[19] on four other methacrylate

† Molecular weight determinations by gel permeation chromatography have now been carried out on samples of the materials used to obtain results VII and VIII. The values obtained were as follows:

VII ('Perspex')   Mn = 0·71 · 10^6 a.m.u., M_n/M_w = 5·5
VIII ('Lucite')   Mn = 0·34 · 10^6 a.m.u., M_n/M_w = 4·7

The factor of two difference in molecular weight is of course only one possible reason for the observed differences in yield stress.

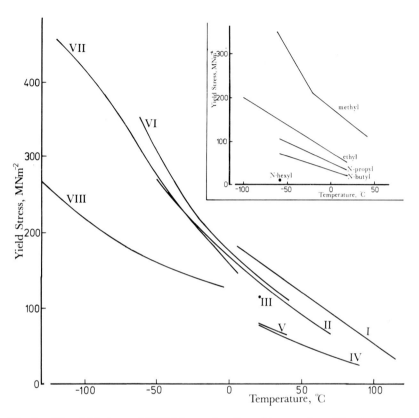

Fig. 8. The yield stress of PMMA as a function of temperature. The strain rate is 10^{-3}/sec unless otherwise indicated. (I to V) as in Fig. 7. (VI) Uniaxial compression (nominal stress), strain rate 10^{-2}/sec, Perspex.[19] (VII) Uniaxial compression (nominal stress), Perspex.[20] (VIII) Uniaxial compression (nominal stress), strain rate $7 \cdot 10^{-4}$/sec, Lucite.[21] Inset: Yield stress in uniaxial compression (nominal stress) of five methacrylate ester polymers.[19] (Reproduced by permission of the Editor of Europlastics Monthly.)

ester polymers are plotted in the inset in Fig. 8 and show the dramatic effect on the yield stress of increasing the size of the ester side group.

Figure 9 shows results obtained on two other glassy polymers, PVC and polycarbonate. Again the yield stress tends to zero in the region of the T_g and rises rapidly at lower temperatures, but the increase in yield stress at low temperatures is not nearly so marked as it is for PMMA. An additional difference is that both PVC and polycarbonate will yield in tension at low temperatures without fracture.

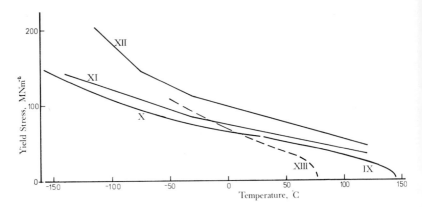

Fig. 9. Yield-stress values for polycarbonate (continuous curves), and PVC (dashed curve) at a strain rate of $1.4 \cdot 10^{-4}/sec$ unless otherwise indicated. (IX) Uniaxial tension (nominal stress), Macrolon P.C.[12,18] (X) Uniaxial tension (nominal stress), Merlon P.C.[22] (XI) Uniaxial tension (nominal stress), strain rate $4.16 \cdot 10^{-3}/sec$, Macrolon P.C.[23] (XII) Uniaxial compression (nominal stress), strain rate $4.15 \cdot 10^{-3}/sec$, Macrolon P.C.[23] (XIII) Uniaxial tension (nominal stress), strain rate $2 \cdot 10^{-3}/sec$, Solvic 227PVC.[12,18]

The yield strain

Figure 10 shows stress–strain curves for PMMA in uniaxial compression at a series of temperatures. It can be seen that as the temperature is decreased the shape of the stress–strain curve changes. The modulus of the material (the initial slope of the curve) increases markedly, the strain at which yield occurs decreases very slightly, and strain softening after yield becomes more pronounced.

In contrast, for polycarbonate tested in tension the yield strain increases significantly at low temperatures.[22]

5.4.6   The effect of hydrostatic pressure on the yield stress and yield strain

The question of the dependence of the yield stress of glassy polymers on hydrostatic pressure is tied up with the general question of pressure-dependent yield criteria, but we will consider the direct effect of hydrostatic pressure first.

Tests under hydrostatic pressure

Early work by Ainbinder et al.[24] and by Holliday et al.[25] showed that if amorphous glassy polymers were tested in compression or tension in a sealed chamber in which the pressure could be raised to a few kbar

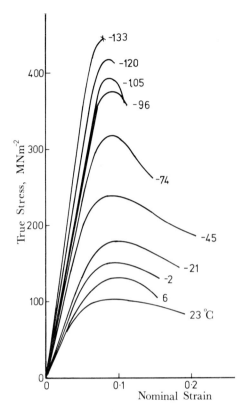

Fig. 10. Stress–strain curves for PMMA obtained in uniaxial compression at a strain rate of $10^{-3}/sec$ at the temperatures indicated. The stress has been converted to true stress on the assumption that the deformation is occurring at constant volume.[20] (I am grateful to Mr J. L. Henshall for permission to publish this data.)

(1 kbar = 100 MN/m^2) then their yield stresses were increased very significantly and normally brittle polymers such as polystyrene yielded in a ductile manner in tension without fracture.

A more recent experiment by Rabinowitz et al.[6] is simple to interpret and demonstrates the effects clearly. They tested tubes of PMMA in simple shear (see Fig. 3(d)) in an environment where the hydrostatic pressure could be increased to 7 kbar. The particular advantages of a test in simple shear in this instance were firstly that the shear strain applied could be deduced accurately from the angle of twist and, secondly, that since a shear stress has no hydrostatic component the hydrostatic stress

acting on the material was solely that due to the environment (castor oil
and brake fluid).

Some of their results are shown in Fig. 11. The shear-stress values are in
terms of true stress, corrected for the change in cross-sectional area that
occurs on pressurisation. The curve obtained at 0·69 kbar has essentially
the same yield stress and yield strain as the curve determined for PMMA
in plane strain compression, Fig. 5, so both sets of results are consistent.

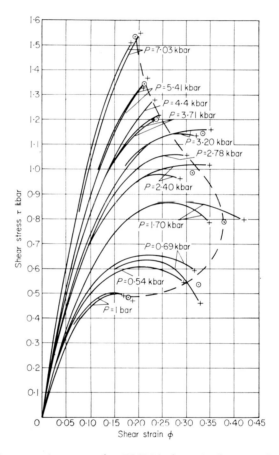

Fig. 11. *Stress–strain curves for PMMA determined in simple shear under
different hydrostatic pressures at 22°C at a strain rate of approximately* $4 \cdot 10^{-4}/$
*sec. Pressures and stresses are in kbar (1 kbar = 100 MN/m²). (The diagram is
reproduced from reference 6 by permission of the authors and Chapman & Hall
Ltd.)*

It can be seen in Fig. 11 that both the yield stress and the yield strain increase as the hydrostatic pressure is increased. The shear modulus at small strains, which is given by the initial slope of the stress–strain curves, also increases with pressure.

For PMMA the shear yield stress τ increases linearly with the hydrostatic pressure, P, according to the relation

$$\tau = 50\cdot3 + 0\cdot204P \ \text{MN/m}^2$$

This type of linear variation of the yield stress with pressure, of the general form $\tau = \tau_0 + \mu P$, has been found to be obeyed for all amorphous glassy polymers for which it has been tested. The dimensionless constant of proportionality μ, which we will refer to as the *coefficient of internal friction* following the usage in Soil Mechanics, has a value of between about 0·1 and 0·25 depending on the polymer. Values of μ for crystalline polymers tend to be lower.[6,22]

The strain at which yield occurs in PMMA also increases as the hydro-static pressure is increased. It can be seen in Fig. 11 that the shear strain at yield increases from a value of 0·15 at atmospheric pressure to about 0·30 at 3·2 kbar. This increase with pressure appears to be a general phenomenon. The nominal tensile strain at the extrinsic yield point of tensile specimens of polycarbonate increases from 0·08 to 0·25 between 1 bar and 8 kbar.[22]

Finally, it can be seen in Fig. 11 that the shear modulus of PMMA, which is given by the initial slope of the stress–strain curve, increases with pressure. The increase is approximately linear, from 0·7 GN/m² at 1 bar to 1·3 GN/m² at 7 kbar.

It is perhaps worth pointing out that it is reasonable that the physical properties of amorphous glassy polymers should undergo significant changes under these relatively small hydrostatic pressures. Their bulk moduli are small when compared with those of metals, about 5 GN/m² for PMMA compared with 124 GN/m² for copper, which is another way of saying that the volume changes they undergo on pressurisation are much larger. The pressures we are talking about are of the order of the yield stress (1 kbar is 100 MN/m²) which is why, unlike metals, glassy polymers need a pressure-dependent yield criterion to describe their behaviour.

The hydrostatic component of the stress tensor

If a hydrostatic stress affects the yield stress and other properties of an amorphous glassy polymer then the hydrostatic component of any applied stress tensor must do so also. Any applied stress system except pure shear has a hydrostatic component. For example in a plane-strain compression test if yield occurs at a compressive stress of $\sigma_1 = \sigma$ (σ is a negative number) then the applied stress tensor can be split into a deviatonic and a hydrostatic component as follows:

$$
\begin{vmatrix} \sigma & 0 & 0 \\ 0 & 0 & 0 \\ 0 & 0 & \dfrac{\sigma}{2} \end{vmatrix} = \begin{vmatrix} \dfrac{\sigma}{2} & 0 & 0 \\ 0 & -\dfrac{\sigma}{2} & 0 \\ 0 & 0 & 0 \end{vmatrix} + \begin{vmatrix} \dfrac{\sigma}{2} & 0 & 0 \\ 0 & \dfrac{\sigma}{2} & 0 \\ 0 & 0 & \dfrac{\sigma}{2} \end{vmatrix}
$$

| Plane-strain compression | Deviatonic component pure shear | Hydrostatic component, a pressure of $\sigma/2$ |

(The additional term of $\sigma_{33} = \sigma/2$ in the stress tensor for plane strain compression arises because a restraining stress of this magnitude in the σ_{33} direction is necessary to make the deformation plane strain.[5]) It can be seen that the stress system is identical to that in the Rabinowitz et al.[6] experiment when the shear stress is equal in magnitude to the hydrostatic pressure. The behaviour of the material should therefore be the same. For tests in tension σ would be positive, the hydrostatic component would become a tension and on the basis of the observations made under hydrostatic pressure a significantly lower yield stress, yield strain and modulus might be expected.

In so far as these predictions have been tested they have been found to be true. For a concise interpretation of experiments carried out under different states of stress it is necessary to have a yield criterion as a framework for the interpretation, and there is still discussion as to which form of criterion is most appropriate for glassy polymers. However, all yield criteria so far proposed incorporate pressure dependence of the yield stress in one form or another. Consideration of results obtained in experiments under different states of stress is postponed until yield criteria are discussed in Section 5.7.

5.4.7 The effect of polymer structure on the yield stress

By 'structure' in this context is meant the molecular weight, lubricant content, annealing treatment, etc. of a particular polymer. An important parameter that characterises a polymer is its molecular weight. The molecular weight must have a certain minimum value for the polymer to behave as a rigid glassy material, but for most commercial materials this minimum value is comfortably exceeded. The yield stress is insensitive to differences in molecular weight above this minimum, or at any rate large differences in yield stress due to differences in molecular weight distribution have never been reported. It is just possible that the large discrepancy in yield stress between Lucite and Perspex at low temperatures (Section 5.4.5) is due to such differences but if so it is the first clear instance to come to the writer's attention.

Factors other than molecular weight are considered below.

Annealing effects

In inorganic glasses it is possible to produce changes in density of 1 % or more by changing the rate at which the sample is cooled through the glass transition region. These density differences produce significant differences in the mechanical properties of the glass, in particular in the creep rate under load. On annealing below the glass transition temperature the density tends towards a maximum equilibrium value.

It appears to be possible to produce similar effects in organic polymeric glasses although the density changes are not so large. Struik[26] has recorded density transients in quenched samples of polystyrene involving density changes of up to 0·2%, and has shown that the creep rate in the region of 80°C is very sensitive to the annealing treatment after quenching.

The yield stress is also sensitive to the annealing treatment. Raha[10, 11] prepared samples of polystyrene by quenching into iced water from 110°C, and found that the intrinsic yield stress measured in plane-strain compression at 22°C was 12 % lower than the yield stress of samples annealed at 110°C and slowly cooled to room temperature over 24 h. The density difference was 0·2%, only just detectable by the method used. The properties of the quenched material changed appreciably over a period of several hours immediately after the quenching treatment. The results quoted were obtained after storing at room temperature for two days. Golden et al.[88] have reported increases in the tensile yield stress of polycarbonate of up to 15 % on annealing quenched samples, associated with a density increase of about 0·2%. Brady and Yeh have carried out a detailed study of the effect of quenching and annealing on the properties of both polystyrene and polycarbonate.[27]

Experiments by Ender[28] on quenched and annealed PMMA tested at 80°C under constant load (Section 5.3.6) also indicate that the yield stress is reduced by any quenching treatment. Ender found that at constant load the time to yield was decreased and the strain rate at the yield point was increased for the as-quenched samples. Referring to the schematic diagram in Fig. 4(b) it can be seen that these results indeed imply that the yield stress is lower.

The effect of additives

The effect on the yield stress of additives such as small amounts of plasticiser or lubricant, and the effect of small differences in molecular weight such as exist between equivalent grades of the same polymer produced by different manufacturers or processes has never been carefully assessed. Experience of testing different grades, and the comparison of results obtained by different workers on different grades, suggests that on the whole differences in yield stress are small and of the same order as those produced by different annealing treatments (that is maximum differences of 20%, not factors of 2). Larger differences do exist in some cases such as the case of Lucite mentioned in Section 5.4.5; a detailed investigation of the structural reason for such differences would be of great interest.

One obvious way to lower the yield stress significantly is to add a large amount of plasticiser. Even then the changes *can* be small provided the material is still essentially a glass and has not been shifted into the transition region. An increase in the plasticiser content of an epoxy resin from 16 to 24 wt%, sufficient to decrease the softening temperature from 75°C to 45°C, caused only a 5% decrease in the intrinsic yield stress determined in a plane-strain compression test at room temperature.[5]

Conversely the yield stress (and modulus) of polymers such as polycarbonate can be raised by 30% or so by adding an antiplasticiser.[89] The increase in yield stress so obtained is in addition to and independent of the increase that can be obtained by annealing.[90]

5.4.8 Volume changes at yield

The question of whether small volume changes occur during the plastic flow of glassy polymers has been investigated in detail because a number of explanations for yield, including explanations for the pressure-dependence of the yield stress, are based on the occurrence of such volume changes.

Recent work has shown that plastic deformation of amorphous glassy polymers produces a small *increase* in density of about 0·25 % irrespective of whether the deformation is compressive or tensile[27] and that this small compaction occurs at yield.[29] Flow after yield occurs at essentially constant volume.[29,30] These results indicate clearly that the pressure-dependence of the yield stress of these materials cannot be attributed to volume changes during flow[29] and that some other explanation is needed (*see* Section 5.7.3).

This increase in density is associated with the deformation of the material in shear. It is not possible to produce a permanent volume compaction by loading to a high hydrostatic pressure[6] as is possible with some inorganic glasses. However, it is possible to produce a compaction of a per cent or so in an amorphous polymer by cooling it through the glass transition under a hydrostatic pressure of a few kilobars and subsequently releasing the pressure.[31]

5.4.9 The Bauschinger effect

If, after a material has been made to yield plastically, it is found subsequently that it is easier than it would otherwise have been to make it yield plastically in the reverse direction, then the material is said to display a Bauschinger effect.[32] Such effects are thought to be due to self-stresses set up internally in the body when it is first deformed which make the reverse deformation easier. Amorphous polymers oriented by hot or cold drawing show strong Bauschinger effects. Rider and Hargreaves[33] have investigated the yield behaviour of polyvinylchloride oriented by drawing in tension and have found that in order to explain the yield stresses they observe in compression and tension at room temperature they have to postulate an internal tensile stress in the draw direction that can be as high as 40 MN/m².

Amorphous glassy polymers that have been deformed plastically will revert to their undeformed shape if they are heated above their glass transition temperature (Section 6.1) and this recovery can perhaps be thought of as being due to the same self stresses that cause the Bauschinger effect. Incidentally polymers are not the only materials that can recover from large plastic deformations on heating. Some nickel–titanium alloys have this property.[34]

5.5 INHOMOGENEOUS DEFORMATION

A number of materials when deforming plastically do not always deform homogeneously. The strain in certain local regions increases more rapidly than it does in the specimen as a whole. In a limiting case plastic strain may occur *only* in certain local regions. The study of the development of these inhomogeneities in strain is of interest in its own right, but if one wishes to study the intrinsic stress–strain behaviour of the material in which they form they can be a nuisance since they can obscure it. In the following sections the characteristics of the various types of strain inhomogeneity that have been observed in polymers are described. None of them are exclusive to polymers. All of them have a close parallel in plastically deformed metals. The arguments below about the geometry of the deformation are based on the assumption that plastic flow is occurring at constant volume. The effects of a plastic volume change are considered specifically only where they affect the conclusions reached.

5.5.1 The reasons for inhomogeneous deformation

Inhomogeneous deformation occurs because homogeneous deformation has become unstable. There are two possible reasons for this instability, one geometrical and one structural, and they can both occur at once.

(*a*) *Considère.* An example of a geometrical instability is the formation of a neck in a specimen tested in uniaxial tension. If part of the specimen should happen to be slightly thinner than the rest then the stress there will be slightly higher. This will concentrate further deformation at that point and increase the local stress further unless the rate at which the material strain-hardens is sufficient to suppress the instability. The critical rate of strain hardening is given by Considère's construction (Sections 6.3.1 and 5.2.4).

(*b*) *Strain softening.* A second reason for instability is strain-softening of the material after the yield point as illustrated in Fig. 1. If locally the strain should happen to be slightly higher than elsewhere (possibly due to some fortuitous stress concentration) then the material will be softer locally and it will therefore deform to a higher strain than elsewhere and become softer still. This process can only be stopped by the eventual orientation hardening of the material.

Once the deformation becomes unstable the *rate* at which any inhomogeneity develops is limited by the strain-rate sensitivity of the flow stress $(\partial\sigma/\partial(\ln \dot{\varepsilon}))$. If this is small then a small local increase in stress or a small degree of local softening will cause a large increase in the local strain rate and the inhomogeneity will develop rapidly. If it is large then the local inhomogeneity will develop slowly.

5.5.2 The principle of maximum plastic resistance

An important point about the development of strain inhomogeneities is that they should always nucleate at essentially the same stress as that at which the rest of the material is deforming. It is true that the reason they nucleate is because locally the stress is slightly higher or the material is slightly softer than for the rest of the specimen, and the reason that they develop and grow is that these differences become large; but as they start to form such differences are negligible.

The principle of maximum plastic resistance[35] dictates that if a material is being deformed plastically with a given deformation-rate tensor by the appropriate stress tensor then the plastic resistance is a maximum and there is no other deformation that can absorb less work (occur more easily) at the same stress. This is a rather heavy statement but it is only saying that if any other deformation could occur more easily, it would. The principle means that if any inhomogeneity is to nucleate locally then the local deformation should initially have the same strain-rate tensor as the general deformation.

5.5.3 The geometry of inhomogeneous deformation

The various types of strain inhomogeneity that develop can be conveniently classified in terms of the degree of constraint imposed on the inhomogeneously deforming region by the surrounding material. For the inhomogeneity to develop the strain rate locally must become higher than that of the surrounding material. For the type of inhomogeneity we are talking about no discontinuity in strain develops between the inhomogeneity and the surrounding material. No fracture occurs and the strain varies continuously across the boundary between the inhomogeneity and the material around it. The surrounding material may therefore impose some restraint on the type of deformation that can develop locally and different types of strain inhomogeneity involve different degrees of restraint.

We said above that the deformation-rate tensor must be initially the same locally as in the surrounding material. An inhomogeneity can only start to form by a slight increase in the deformation rate locally without any other change in the deformation-rate tensor (which is specifically forbidden by the principle of maximum plastic resistance if the deformation is to occur at the same stress). If there is a restraint in any direction the form of the deformation-rate tensor will be altered unless the extension rate in this direction is zero. Therefore: *if the geometry of the formation of a strain inhomogeneity involves a restraint in any direction the extension rate must be zero in that direction for the inhomogeneity to nucleate at the same stress as obtains for general deformation.*

No restraint—neck

The only strain inhomogeneity that it is geometrically possible to form with negligible restraint in any direction from the surrounding material is

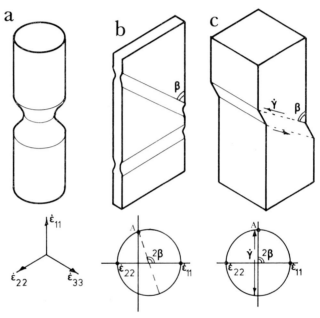

Fig. 12. (a) *Formation of a neck in a cylindrical tensile specimen.* (b) *Formation of an inclined neck in a flat strip tensile specimen together with the Mohr circle for strain rate.* (c) *Formation of a shear band.*

a symmetrically necked region in a sample tested in tension. The deformation is illustrated in Fig. 12(a). The deformation rate tensor is

$$\begin{vmatrix} \dot{\varepsilon} & 0 & 0 \\ 0 & -\dfrac{\dot{\varepsilon}}{2} & 0 \\ 0 & 0 & -\dfrac{\dot{\varepsilon}}{2} \end{vmatrix}$$

and it is possible for all three strain-rate components to increase locally provided that the region that is forming the neck is fairly large compared with the transverse dimensions of the specimen.

It is geometrically possible for an inhomogeneity similar to this to develop in a compression test in which case it would form as a local bulge rather than a neck. In that case the basic reason for the instability would have to be the strain softening of the material rather than the Considère geometrical effect (Section 5.5.1).

Restraint in one dimension—inclined neck
The only strain inhomogeneity that it is geometrically possible to form with restraint in only one direction is the locally-thinned band of material (an inclined neck) that can form in a strip specimen deforming in uniaxial extension. This is illustrated in Fig. 12(b). For such a band there is restraint in the direction along the length of the band. The deformation-rate tensor is the same as that in the previous section and for this tensor the extension rate along the length of the band becomes zero only if the angle β is 54·7° ($\cos 2\beta = -\frac{1}{3}$). The reason for this can be seen by referring to the geometry of the Mohr circle of strain rate in Fig. 12(b) and remembering that $\dot{\varepsilon}_{22} = -\dot{\varepsilon}_{11}/2$. The inclination of the neck is represented by the point A.

If the material should dilate plastically during yield the effect would be to modify the deformation-rate tensor:

$$
\begin{vmatrix}
\dot{\varepsilon} & 0 & 0 \\
0 & -\dfrac{\dot{\varepsilon}}{2} & 0 \\
0 & 0 & -\dfrac{\dot{\varepsilon}}{2}
\end{vmatrix}
+
\begin{vmatrix}
\dfrac{\dot{v}}{3v} & 0 & 0 \\
0 & \dfrac{\dot{v}}{3v} & 0 \\
0 & 0 & \dfrac{\dot{v}}{3v}
\end{vmatrix}
=
\begin{vmatrix}
\dot{\varepsilon} + \dfrac{\dot{v}}{3v} & 0 & 0 \\
0 & -\dfrac{\dot{\varepsilon}}{2} + \dfrac{\dot{v}}{3v} & 0 \\
0 & 0 & -\dfrac{\dot{\varepsilon}}{2} + \dfrac{\dot{v}}{3v}
\end{vmatrix}
$$

| Uniaxial extension | Volume dilation | Resultant |

The new values of $\dot{\varepsilon}_{11}$ and $\dot{\varepsilon}_{22}$ in the resultant tensor can be used in the Mohr circle of strain rate to obtain the new value of β. A positive value of $\dot{v}/v$ increases β.

This type of inclined neck normally only forms in a specimen tested in tension but, like a symmetrical neck, it could form in a specimen tested in compression if the material showed sufficiently rapid strain softening. Inclined necks of this type are sometimes referred to as shear bands in the literature but we will reserve the term for the inhomogeneity to be described in the next section. The distinguishing features of an inclined tensile neck are that the material relaxes inwards in the region of the neck and that there is no shear off-set of the top half of the specimen with respect to the bottom half.

As an illustration of the operation of the principle of maximum plastic resistance consider a neck forming with $\beta = 90°$ as illustrated at the bottom of the diagram in Fig. 12(b). The local deformation in the neck would have to change from uniaxial extension to plane-strain extension, which would require a higher stress unless the material obeys a yield criterion, for example the Tresca criterion, that permits both deformations at the same stress.

Restraint in two dimensions—shear band
A volume of material restrained in two dimensions cannot extend in any direction in a plane. The only deformations it can undergo are simple shear parallel to the plane and a volume dilation normal to it. A strain inhomogeneity forming with this restraint at constant volume (and therefore involving a simple shear deformation) is illustrated in Fig. 12(c).

A special point about this type of inhomogeneity is that since it involves no relaxation inwards of the sides of the specimen it can be a very thin region. Moreover, it can form as a disc-shaped region entirely inside the specimen providing that the lateral dimensions of the disc are large compared with the shear or normal displacement, in which case the strain discontinuity at the edge of the disc can then be accommodated elastically.[36] It is the only type of strain inhomogeneity that can form totally inside a body without a large elastic penalty. Two examples in polymers are crazes and micro-shear bands.

The deformation must be in plane strain and if it is occurring at constant volume it will be simple shear. Simple shear deformation of a band with $\beta = 45°$ as shown is equivalent to a plane strain extension with $\dot{\varepsilon}_{22} = -\dot{\varepsilon}_{11}$ and $\dot{\varepsilon}_{33} = 0$ as can be seen from the Mohr circle of strain rate. Since the deformation is simple shear not pure shear it has a rotational component (Section 5.2.3). The effect of a plastic volume change during yield is to change the value of β from 45° by changing the ratio of $\dot{\varepsilon}_{22}$ to $\dot{\varepsilon}_{11}$; a positive value of $\dot{v}/v$ will increase β.[5]

Since the deformation inside the band can only be plane-strain extension or compression such an inhomogeneity cannot nucleate at constant stress unless the deformation of the sample as a whole is plane-strain extension or compression. If the deformation of the sample is *uniaxial* extension or compression, bands can be nucleated only if there is a local stress concentration sufficiently large to raise the stress to the appropriate value for a plane-strain deformation. Such inhomogeneities can only form if the material is strain softening. There is no change in the cross-sectional area that can lead to a Considère type of instability. We will call them *shear bands* as they involve a simple shear deformation unlike the tensile neck and the inclined tensile neck described above. A distinguishing feature of shear bands is that they involve a shear offset of the top half of the specimen with respect to the bottom. Inclined tensile necks sometimes show a shear offset as well as local thinning in which case they are hybrid in character.

5.5.4 Strain inhomogeneities in polymers

The discussion in the previous sections applies to all materials whatever yield criterion they obey and whether or not they dilate during plastic deformation, as long as they are reasonably isotropic. Examples of all three types of strain inhomogeneity described have been observed in metals (*see* pp. 82, 281 and 322 of reference 37). The third type has been observed in soils where it is called a failure plane and where β deviates from 45° because of volume dilatation.[40]

All three types of inhomogeneity have been observed in polymers but we will restrict discussion here to the third type, shear bands, since necking is covered in Section 6.3.1.

The magnitude of the strain in a shear band

Shear bands will form if a material exhibits strain softening. Since all amorphous glassy polymers strain-soften to some extent they all have a tendency to form shear bands but in some polymers the tendency is much stronger than in others. Figures 13 to 16 show sections cut from four different polymers that have been deformed in plane-strain compression at room temperature. Shear bands are present in all cases but the magnitude of the strain in the band, judged from the birefringence, differs markedly in the four cases. PMMA forms broad diffuse bands and the strain in them is only a few per cent at most above that in the rest of the material. In PVC the strain in the bands is larger and they are more sharply defined. In an epoxy resin the strain in the bands is larger still[38] and the matrix material outside a band undergoes no permanent plastic deformation at all.

In amorphous polyethylene terephthalate and in polystyrene the bands have a markedly different character. They are very fine indeed and the strains in them are very large. The bands in polystyrene can be as thin as

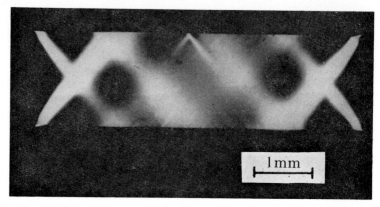

Fig. 13.   *Section cut from a sample of PMMA that has been deformed just past yield at 22°C in a plane strain compression test viewed between crossed polars. Strong shear bands have been nucleated at the corners of the dies. Figures 13 to 16 are reproduced by permission of Dr J. A. Jukes from his thesis.*[39]

50 nm and the shear strain in them is approximately 2·5.[11] The difference in character of the bands in all four materials arises from the differing rates at which bands are able to develop, which is controlled by the rate of strain softening and the strain-rate sensitivity of the flow stress. Bands will tend to develop rapidly if the rate of strain softening, the magnitude of the (negative) slope of the stress–strain curve, $-\partial\sigma_y/\partial\varepsilon$, is large. But the rate at which they can develop will be limited if the strain-rate sensitivity of the flow stress, $(\partial\sigma_y/\partial(\ln \dot{\varepsilon}))$, is large. It can be shown[36] that the rate at

Fig. 14.   *Section similar to Fig. 13 cut from a deformed sample of PVC.*

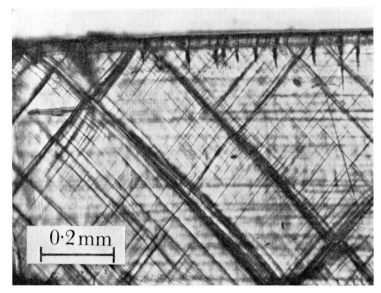

Fig. 15. *Section similar to Fig.* 13 *cut from a deformed sample of amorphous polyethylene terephthalate and viewed in white light.*

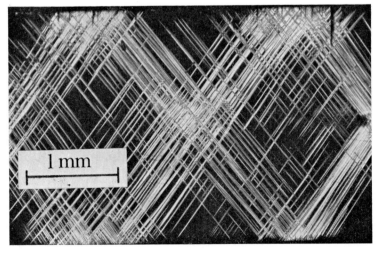

Fig. 16. *Section similar to Fig.* 13 *cut from a deformed sample of polystyrene.*

which they develop depends critically on the value of a material parameter
with the dimensions of strain which is defined by the relation

$$\varepsilon^* = -\frac{[\partial\sigma/\partial(\ln\dot\varepsilon)]_\varepsilon}{(\partial\sigma_y/\partial\varepsilon)_{\dot\varepsilon}}$$

The parameter ε^* has a value of 0·11 for PMMA at room temperature
where the bands are relatively diffuse.

Polystyrene deformed at 80°C also forms diffuse shear bands and at this

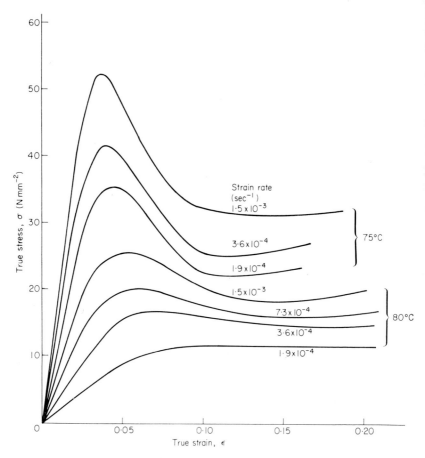

*Fig. 17. Stress–strain curves for polystyrene determined in plane strain com-
pression. (Reproduced from reference 11 by permission of Taylor and
Francis Ltd.)*

temperature ε^* is 0·2. As the temperature is reduced ε^* for polystyrene decreases rapidly, mainly because of the rapid increase in the amount of strain softening as illustrated in Fig. 17. At about 70°C when ε^* has decreased to 0·016 the bands have sharpened up considerably and now appear similar to those in PVC or an epoxy resin at room temperature. Below 70°C the character of the bands suddenly changes and they become similar to the micro shear bands in Fig. 16. The stress–strain curve loses its pronounced load drop and becomes similar to the curve in Fig. 6(b) since its shape is now determined by the kinetics of microband nucleation and not the intrinsic properties of the material. The reason for the sharpness of the transition and the extreme fineness of the bands is not immediately apparent. It may have to do with the effect of adiabatic heating once the deformation becomes sufficiently localised. A contributing effect might be additional strain softening induced by the vorticity of the simple shear deformation in the band (Section 5.2.3).

Whether or not a polymer deforms by the formation of micro shear bands depends not only on the temperature and strain rate of the test but on the annealing treatment given to the sample. A quenched sample is able to deform relatively homogeneously to a much lower temperature.[11,27]

The inclination of shear bands
The inclination of shear bands in amorphous glassy polymers differs from 45°, at any rate when measured in relaxed specimens. The value of β is always greater than 45°. For materials such as metals which deform at constant volume β is expected to be 45° and it is found experimentally that indeed β is very close to 45° if allowance is made for the elastic recovery that occurs on unloading (p. 278 of reference 37). For PMMA, amorphous polyethylene terephthalate and an epoxy resin it has been shown that the value of β is approximately 45° if a similar allowance is made.[5]

For polystyrene Argon et al.[41] measured a value of β of 53° for bands formed in compression near a stress-concentrating notch. An identical value was obtained in a plane-strain compression test[5] and it was shown that if due allowance is made for the elastic recovery the actual value of β under load when the bands formed is 50°. This behaviour is significantly different from that of metals.

For PVC a value of β of 55° has been obtained for samples deformed in tension[42] and for thin-walled tubes deformed in tension and torsion.[43] In plane-strain compression a value of 49° has been reported which converts to a value under load of approximately 46°.[5]

The deviation from 45° in the case of polystyrene is clear cut. A possible explanation is that there is a small transitory volume increase as yield occurs.[5] For PVC the position is not so clear. It may be that in tension the deformation has some of the characteristics of an inclined neck (Section 5.5.3) which would increase β.

5.6 STRUCTURAL OBSERVATIONS

A difficulty in working with amorphous materials rather than crystalline ones is that there are very few techniques available for studying changes in the molecular structure produced by deformation. X-ray diffraction can be used to obtain the nearest-neighbour spacings of atoms in the material, but it is doubtful if it is capable of detecting changes produced by deformation. Infra-red dichroism can pick up changes in the orientation of selected groups in the polymer[44] and is possibly a promising technique. Two difficulties at the moment are that the technique has only limited sensitivity at small degrees of orientation and that if an even moderately strong absorption is being studied the sample has to be extremely thin. Wide-line nuclear magnetic resonance absorption has been used to obtain orientation functions for oriented amorphous and crystalline polymers, but so far only for high degrees of orientation.[45] Two remaining techniques for investigating changes in the structure of glassy polymers at yield are birefringence and electron microscopy.

5.6.1 Birefringence

Figures 13 to 16 show that initially isotropic amorphous polymers become birefringent when deformed plastically. They also of course become birefringent when deformed elastically which is the basis for the technique of photoelastic stress analysis used by engineers to analyse stresses in complex structures.

The birefringence, Δn, is defined as the difference between the refractive indices n_1 and n_2 for light with its plane of polarisation respectively parallel and perpendicular to the maximum tensile strain in the plane of observation. If the maximum polarisability of the sample (the 'slow' direction) is parallel to the maximum tensile strain then the birefringence is positive.

If it is known that neither the sample as a whole nor any of the atomic bonds in it are under stress then the polarisability of the sample can be directly related to the sum of the polarisabilities of the individual bonds, which are known.[46] As a simple example the birefringence of oriented polyethylene is strongly positive since the polarisability of the molecule, which is due primarily to the polarisability of the carbon–carbon bonds in the chain backbone, is an ellipsoid with its maximum principal axis in the orientation direction.

If the sample is under stress or if there are any internal stresses in the structure due to interference between adjacent molecules then the polarisabilities of the bonds are altered and complicated effects can arise. Some progress has been made in analysing the behaviour of crystalline materials[47] but for amorphous polymers the problem is so far unsolved.

A great deal of work has been done on the birefringence of polymers, particularly for deformations in the elastic region. If the polymer is rubbery the stresses in the material are very small and the polarisabilities can be calculated reliably. The theory of the birefringence of deformed rubbers has been worked out by Treloar[48] and there is excellent agreement between theory and experiment. However, in the glassy region the stresses are larger and any interpretation of the results has to be more tentative.

For polystyrene, Rudd[49] measured the strain-optical coefficient ($\Delta n/\varepsilon$) at small strains for dynamic tests in tension. He found that the coefficient was positive at low temperatures, but decreased in magnitude as the temperature was increased and became negative in the region of the glass transition temperature. He attributed the change to a change in the mechanism of deformation arising from distortion of the phenyl side groups with respect to the main chain at low temperature to distortion of the chains as units (with the side groups at right-angles to them) at the higher temperature. Kolsky[50] held samples of polystyrene at constant stress in compression at 16°C and watched the birefringence decay with time. The birefringence was initially positive but for stresses in the region of the yield stress it decayed rapidly to a negative value. It has been shown more recently that this same transition in birefringence occurs as the strain is increased towards the yield strain in a plane-strain compression test.[11] The plastically deformed material in a shear band in polystyrene has a strong negative birefringence. Following Rudd these results could be interpreted as evidence that yield in polystyrene is associated with the breakdown under the applied stress of mechanical locking between phenyl groups on adjacent molecular chains.

For polymethylmethacrylate the birefringence is always negative. Read[51] has measured both the stress–optical ($\Delta n/\sigma$) and strain–optical coefficients as a function of temperature in a dynamic test in tension. He found that the strain–optical coefficient was essentially constant as the temperature was raised through the β transition and deduced that the methacrylate side groups were not distorted with respect to the main chain, that is that the chain and attached side groups were deforming as a unit. Raha[9,10] measured the residual birefringence of polymethylmethacrylate that had been plastically deformed at different temperatures. He found that the birefringence could be explained semi-quantitatively if the polymer structure was held together at a number of 'cohesion points' which could be broken down either by increasing the temperature or by an increase in the applied plastic strain.

Utsuo and Stein[53] have measured the birefringence of PVC deformed to small strains in tension. The birefringence was small and negative at room temperature, but became positive at 40°C for strains greater than 0·05.

It should be stressed again that any interpretation of the observed birefringence of polymer glasses can only be tentative. Complicated effects can arise. Besides the unknown effect of stress mentioned above the (stress-free) orientation birefringence of polymers such as PMMA is a reversible function of temperature probably due to changes in the conformation of the side groups.[54]

5.6.2 Electron microscopy

A number of effects have been observed in samples of amorphous glassy polymers examined in the electron microscope.

A fine nodular structure on a scale of about 10 nm has been seen in shadowed surface replicas of polyethylene terephthalate and polycarbonate[55] and there is evidence that in PET these nodules align themselves in short rows at about 40° to the draw direction in drawn samples.[56] A periodic structure on this scale has also been seen in iodine-stained PET which confirms that the structure is not an artifact of the shadowing procedure used for making replicas.[57] A periodic structure on a slightly smaller scale (2 to 5 nm) has been observed in films of amorphous polystyrene examined in dark field in the electron microscope.[58] It has been suggested that in all cases these nodules are regions where the molecules are to some extent aligned. Unfortunately the size of the nodules is close to the limit of resolution of the technique used to observe them, and while the evidence seems clear that they exist the evidence for changes brought about by annealing or deformation is more difficult to assess.

There is evidence for a larger nodular unit on the 30 nm scale in polyethylene terephthalate. It can be shown that in a completely amorphous un-annealed film of PET plastic deformation does not take place uniformly.[57] If such a film is decorated with small particles of gold and then drawn uniaxially, some areas appear completely free of gold while the spacing of the gold particles in the remaining areas is unaffected. It has been suggested that this is because deformation takes place by the movement of 30 nm nodular regions around each other without the nodules themselves being appreciably deformed. The gold-free regions in the drawn film would then be where nodules have come to the surface from the interior.

5.7   YIELD CRITERIA FOR POLYMERS

A yield criterion is a general condition that must be satisfied by the applied stress tensor for yield to occur. It is possible to define a criterion in terms of strain instead of stress, but since stress is related to strain through the elastic or viscoelastic properties of the material such a criterion could also be expressed in terms of stress.

A yield criterion expressed in terms of stress can be represented as a surface surrounding the origin in principal stress space. As the stress is increased from zero (the origin) yield does not occur until the stress has reached some point on that surface. It is only possible for the yield surface to be a single-valued function of stress if the yield stress is either independent of the loading path or the loading path is fully specified (for example loading at a constant rate with the principal stresses in fixed ratios to each other). For polymers and other materials whose properties are time-dependent it will, in general, be necessary to specify the loading path, although in particular cases it may be possible to show that the exact path is unimportant. For isotropic materials there can be no distinction between the three principal stress axes, and consequently the yield surface must have three-fold symmetry about the hydrostatic line, $\sigma_1 = \sigma_2 = \sigma_3$. Since yield always involves a change in the shape of a body a pure hydrostatic tensile or compressive stress can never produce yield. Consequently the yield surface approximates to an open-ended cylinder with axis along the hydrostatic line. Two yield surfaces are shown schematically in Fig. 18.

It is possible to measure the yield stress of a material under a large number of different states of stress and so to define the yield surface empirically. However, the principal aim in defining a yield criterion is to find some simple function or idea that defines the yield surface satisfactorily. This will make it simple to predict the yield stress for stress states that have not been specifically investigated. Also the form of the function will give an insight into the mechanism of yield.

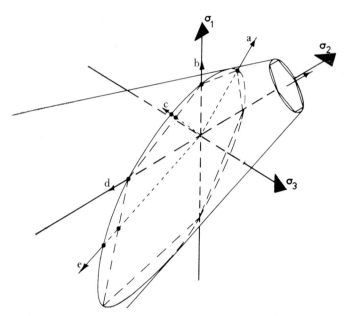

Fig. 18. Yield envelopes in principal stress space for the modified Tresca criterion (hexagonal pyramid) and the modified von Mises criterion (cone). The small arrows indicate the loading paths for tests in (a) biaxial tension, (b) uniaxial tension, (c) pure shear, (d) uniaxial compression and (e) plane-strain compression.

5.7.1 The Tresca yield criterion

The Tresca yield criterion is based on a simple concept which is that *yield will occur when the resolved shear stress on any plane in the material reaches a critical value.* It can be written

$$\sigma_1 - \sigma_3 = 2\tau_T \tag{1}$$

where σ_1 and σ_3 are the maximum and minimum principal stresses and τ_T is the critical shear stress which is a material constant. The yield surface is a hexagonal prism in principal-stress space with its axis lying along the hydrostatic line.

The criterion was originally proposed for metals, but most metals do not obey it as well as they obey the von Mises yield criterion described in the next section. An exception is mild steel, which obeys the Tresca criterion when it is deforming inhomogeneously by the formation of Lüders bands. It has been shown that this behaviour is expected of a material which obeys von Mises criterion when deforming homogeneously but which forms well-defined shear bands.[59]

5.7.2 The von Mises yield criterion

The von Mises yield criterion was originally proposed because it is awkward mathematically to deal with the discontinuities at the corners of the hexagonal Tresca yield surface; on the von Mises criterion the yield surface is a cylinder whose equation is

$$(\sigma_1 - \sigma_2)^2 + (\sigma_2 - \sigma_3)^2 + (\sigma_3 - \sigma_1)^2 = 6\tau_M^2 = 9\tau_{oct}^2 \qquad (2)$$

The constant τ_M is the shear stress for flow in pure shear. An alternative way of stating the criterion is to say that the octahedral shear stress, τ_{oct}, shall be a constant.[37] This criterion is obeyed fairly well by most metals.[35] It was later realised that the equation above is, for a linear elastic material, equivalent to the statement that *yield will occur when the elastic shear strain energy density reaches a critical value.*

On both the von Mises and the Tresca criteria the yield stress is independent of the hydrostatic component of the stress tensor so that they cannot be used to describe the behaviour of materials such as polymers where the hydrostatic stress affects the yield stress.

5.7.3 The Mohr–Coulomb yield criterion

In 1773 Coulomb proposed a simple criterion to predict the fracture of building-stone in compression.[60] It was later adopted under the name of the Mohr–Coulomb criterion to describe the failure of soils.[61] The criterion is that *failure will occur when the shear stress on any plane in the material reaches a critical value which varies linearly with the stress normal to that plane.* This criterion is similar to the Tresca criterion with τ which is now a function of the form

$$\tau_c = \tau_c^0 - \mu_c \sigma_n \qquad (3)$$

The quantity σ_n is the stress acting normal to the plane on which failure is occurring and μ_c is a constant referred to as the *coefficient of internal friction.* In soil mechanics τ_c^0 is known as the *cohesion.* It is envisaged in the definition above that failure occurs by shear on specific planes which are identified with the rupture surfaces observed in stone and soils. The criterion predicts the inclination of these planes, which is directly related to the value of μ_c. Although the shear stress is greatest on 45° planes the normal stress is reduced if β is a little larger. The exact value of β is given by the relation $-\cot 2\beta = \mu_c$.

A corollary was later added to this criterion by applying plasticity theory. If the material obeys St Venant's principle† then it must dilate

---

† For an isotropic body the principal axes of stress and strain rate coincide. In simple if inexact terms: the material must go the way it is pushed.

during plastic flow and μ_c is determined by the rate of dilatation.[62] μ_c is given by $\dot{v}/v\dot{\gamma}$ if $\dot{v}/v$ is the rate of dilatation and $\dot{\gamma}$ is the shear strain rate in simple shear. Experimentally μ_c is positive for soils and they do dilate to some extent during plastic flow.

Recent work in soil mechanics has shown that the Mohr–Coulomb criterion does not apply to soils in the form set out above. An excellent account of the current position has been given by Roscoe.[40] The main conclusions can be summarised as follows:

(i) The rupture planes in soils are regions of inhomogeneous deformation and form parallel to planes in which the extension rate is zero as described in Section 5.5.3. Their inclination is therefore determined by the rate of dilatation obtaining when they form ($\dot{v}/v\dot{\gamma} = -\cot 2\beta$). But the rate of dilatation is not related to the value of μ_c in eqn. (3).

(ii) The failure stress of soils depends on pressure not because they dilate during plastic flow but because the pressure changes the *state* of the material and so increases the yield stress.[63]

The concept of the pressure being able to produce a change in the state of the material is a very important one since it allows the flow stress to depend on pressure without the necessity of either invoking a continuously increasing dilatation during flow to account for the effect or violating St Venant's principle.

If the change in flow stress with pressure is due to a change in state and if St Venant's principle is obeyed then the flow stress cannot possibly be proportional to the *normal* pressure on the plane on which shear is envisaged as occurring. It must be proportional to some non-directional property of the stress tensor such as the hydrostatic stress. Criteria incorporating this dependence are considered below.

The conclusion of this section is that the Mohr–Coulomb criterion in its original form can only apply to materials for which the pressure-dependence of the yield stress is due solely to dilatation during flow, or materials which it can be shown do not obey St Venant's principle. It is known that polymers do not dilate continuously during flow (Section 5.4.8). It is possible that there may be some small deviation from St Venant's principle due to the anisotropy introduced by the elastic strains prior to yield but there is no experimental evidence to suggest that the deviation is sufficiently large to convert them into the 'frictional materials' proposed theoretically by de Jong[64] which are the only type of solid that could obey the Mohr–Coulomb criterion without dilating.

5.7.4 The modified Tresca criterion

The Tresca criterion in Section 5.7.1 can be modified by making the quantity τ_T in eqn. (1) depend on the state of the material as determined by the hydrostatic component of the stress tensor.

$$\tau_T = \tau_T{}^0 + \mu_T P, \qquad P = -\tfrac{1}{3}(\sigma_1 + \sigma_2 + \sigma_3) \tag{4}$$

The result is a criterion that is pressure-dependent like the Mohr–Coulomb criterion but that does not have the difficulties set out above.

The yield envelope is shown schematically in Fig. 18. If μ_T is constant it is a hexagonal pyramid with its axis along the hydrostatic line. It must be emphasised that this is not now a yield surface in the conventional sense, but an envelope of the yield surfaces appropriate to the material in the different states induced by the changing hydrostatic pressure. The argument is set out in detail in the book by Schofield and Wroth[63] where they emphasise the difference by calling it the Mohr–Coulomb envelope, not the yield surface.

Since the original Mohr–Coulomb criterion cannot be applied to polymers the choice appears to be between this modified Tresca criterion and a similarly-modified von Mises criterion.

5.7.5 The modified von Mises criterion

The von Mises criterion can be modified to incorporate the effect of pressure on the state of the material by substituting in eqn. (2) a value of τ_M that increases linearly with the hydrostatic component of the stress tensor

$$\tau_M = \tau_M{}^0 + \mu_M P \quad \text{or} \quad \tau_{oct} = \tau_{oct}{}^0 + \tfrac{2}{3}\mu_M P \tag{5}$$

The constant $\tau_M{}^0$ is still the yield stress for a test in pure shear since in that case P is zero. The yield surface is a right circular cone (if μ_M is constant) shown schematically in Fig. 18 where it has been matched to the modified Tresca criterion for tests in uniaxial tension and compression. As before it is a yield envelope rather than a conventional yield surface.

A von Mises criterion modified in this way was first suggested for polymers in a theoretical model by Bauwens,[42,43] and later independently by Sternstein et al.[65] who obtained more detailed evidence for it from tests on PMMA under combined stress. The constant A used by Bauwens and the constant μ used by Sternstein and Ongchin are both equal to $\tfrac{2}{3}\mu_M$ in the present treatment.

5.7.6 Choice of a yield criterion for polymers

To distinguish experimentally between two different proposed yield criteria it is necessary to fit both criteria to the measured yield stress for some particular states of stress—for example the yield stress in uniaxial tension—and then to determine the yield stress experimentally for stress states for which the predictions of the two criteria differ. For the 'modified' criteria described here a fit at two points is necessary in the first instance to determine both the parameters that define the yield surface.

Most practical experiments to distinguish between yield criteria are carried out in plane stress. In Fig. 18 it can be seen that in the σ_1–σ_2 plane the modified von Mises criterion makes a distorted ellipse, and the modified Tresca criterion makes a distorted hexagon which is inscribed in the ellipse if the yield stresses in uniaxial tension and compression are matched. In Table 2 analytical expressions are given for the yield stresses in a number of different tests according to the two criteria.

TABLE 2

Test (see Fig. 18):	a	b	c	d	e
Modified von Mises criterion	$\dfrac{\sqrt{3}\tau_M^0}{1+2\mu_M/\sqrt{3}}$	$\dfrac{\sqrt{3}\tau_M^0}{1+\mu_M/\sqrt{3}}$	τ_M^0	$\dfrac{-\sqrt{3}\tau_M^0}{1-\mu_M/\sqrt{3}}$	$\dfrac{-2\tau_M^0}{1-\mu_M}$
Modified Tresca criterion	$\dfrac{2\tau_T^0}{1+4\mu_T/3}$	$\dfrac{2\tau_T^0}{1+2\mu_T/3}$	τ_T^0	$\dfrac{-2\tau_T^0}{1-2\mu_T/3}$	$\dfrac{-2\tau_T^0}{1-\mu_T}$

Argon et al.[41] measured the yield stress of samples of polystyrene using tests b, c, d and e and in addition using a plane strain extension test. On the whole their results fall more closely on a distorted ellipse than a distorted hexagon.

By simultaneously twisting and pulling a tube of material it is possible to obtain yield for all states of stress between b (uniaxial tension) and c (pure shear), and tests of this type have been carried out on PMMA by Sternstein et al.[65] and on PVC by Bauwens.[43] Sternstein et al. showed that a plot of τ_{oct} against P was linear, which implies that the yield surface follows the distorted von Mises ellipse. In Fig. 19 data obtained by Bauwens on PVC[43] has been re-plotted in terms of the principle stresses and it can be seen that if the yield-stress values in uniaxial tension and pure shear are used to define the yield envelopes for the two criteria then the experimental points fall closer to the locus predicted on the modified von Mises criterion. In addition an unreasonably large value of μ_T is needed to fit the modified Tresca criterion.

Bowden and Jukes[5] have measured the yield stresses of PMMA and polystyrene in plane strain compression, uniaxial compression and pure

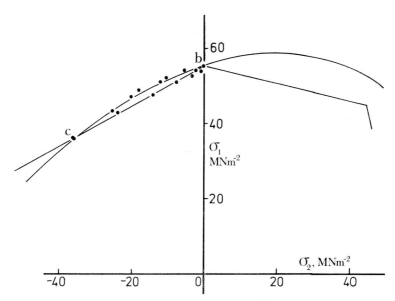

Fig. 19. Yield-stress data obtained by Bauwens[43] on PVC tubes tested in tension and torsion. The modified Tresca criterion and the modified von Mises criterion have been fitted at the points b and c using the parameters $\tau_M^0 = \tau_T^0 = 36\cdot0$ MN/m², $\mu_M = 0\cdot224$ and $\mu_T = 0\cdot453$.

shear. They found their results for PMMA were consistent with the modified von Mises criterion; but for polystyrene they were more consistent with the modified Tresca criterion and it was suggested that this was because under the experimental conditions used the polystyrene was deforming by the formation of shear bands (*see* Section 5.7.1).

5.8 MOLECULAR THEORIES OF YIELDING

The eventual object of any molecular theory of yielding must be to relate the observed yield behaviour to the detailed molecular structure of the polymer and to the local changes in molecular conformation that occur at yield. The behaviour to be explained might be summarised as follows:

When amorphous glassy polymers yield plastically they initially flow at constant stress. Deformations are essentially fully recoverable before this point is reached.

The strain at the yield point is large, a shear strain of 0·1 or 0·2.
After yield most polymers strain-soften, and some do so very rapidly.
The yield stress is sensitive to the applied strain rate.

The yield stress tends to zero in the region of the glass temperature and increases rapidly as the temperature is decreased. Any process or treatment which gives the molecular chains less room in which to move and so reduces their mobility (such as applying a hydrostatic pressure, annealing a sample to a higher density, or removing plasticiser) leads to a higher yield stress.

There is generally a small overall volume decrease after yield; there is no clear evidence for a volume increase during yielding.

Since, so far, no method has been found for deducing directly the changes in molecular conformation that occur locally in an amorphous polymer at the yield point, such changes can only be inferred from observations of the type listed above. Consequently, models to describe the yield behaviour of polymers are not yet as firmly based as are, say, models describing the yield strength of metals where the mechanism by which changes in the local atomic conformation occur on deformation (dislocation motion) is well established and in many cases can be observed directly. It is therefore not yet possible to decide firmly between many of the models and ideas that have been put forward to describe yield in polymers. Models have been proposed that are capable of describing different aspects of the yield behaviour, but so far no accepted unified quantitative treatment exists that can explain all aspects. For the quantitative models that do exist it is difficult to demonstrate the physical significance of critical parameters (such as activation volume and activation energy) and attempts to identify them closely with details of the molecular structure remain to some extent speculative. In the following sections some of the ideas that have been put forward to describe yielding in amorphous glassy polymers are described.

5.8.1   Reduction of the T_g by the applied stress

It has been suggested[66] that the effect of an applied stress (or its associated strain) is to reduce the glass transition temperature (to increase the mobility of the molecular segments) until at the yield stress the T_g is reduced to the test temperature, the segments become fully mobile and yield occurs. Andrews and Kazama[67] have expressed this idea more quantitatively. They tested rigid PVC in tension and obtained identical creep curves with different combinations of test temperature and applied stress (*e.g.* a low stress at a high temperature; a higher stress at a lower temperature). From these results they argued that either increasing the temperature or increasing the stress causes an increase in the segment mobility (an approach to the state at the glass–rubber transition temperature). They suggested that the glass–rubber transition should be regarded not as just a temperature but as a phenomenon that is a function of temperature, stress level and time.

There has been discussion as to whether the segmental mobility produced by the applied stress is a mobility in all directions that produces a rubber-like state analogous to a polymer at its T_g, or is a more restricted mobility permitting movement solely in the direction of the applied stress. The former has been argued on the basis of results obtained by Litt and Koch on oriented polycarbonate.[68] Sheets were oriented by rolling (equivalent to a plane strain extension) and samples were cut transverse to the orientation direction. On testing these samples in tension it was found that at the yield point the thickness of the sample *increased*. It was argued that the applied tension produces a rubber-like structure so that small internal compressive stresses in the orientation direction were then capable of producing the thickness increase.

However, consideration of plasticity theory suggests that there may be no distinction in an experiment of this type between general mobility and mobility only in the direction of the applied stress. Any isotropic rubbery or plastic solid must always deform so as to conform with the applied state of stress (St Venant's principle) so that if there is segment mobility it can only occur in the direction dictated by the applied stress tensor. An increase in thickness at yield can therefore only arise if the internal compressive stress in the sample in the orientation direction (which would produce a strong Bauschinger effect (Section 5.4.9)) is larger than the additional external tensile stress needed to produce yield.

5.8.2 Stress-induced increase in free volume

If stress induces an increase in chain segment mobility the next question is what is the mechanism by which this is brought about. A number of workers[69,70,71,72,73] have discussed quantitatively the possibility that under stress the volume of the sample increases and that the consequent increase in free volume (volume not occupied by a molecule) permits the increased mobility that leads to yield. It is certainly true that a hydrostatic pressure which decreases the volume of the sample causes a decrease in the segment mobility[74] and it might be expected that a hydrostatic tension should have the reverse effect. The difficulty with this approach as an explanation for yield is that yielding occurs in response to the deviatoric component of the stress tensor (which produces no elastic volume change) and can occur freely whether the hydrostatic component of the applied stress tensor is a tension or a compression. Careful measurements have shown that there is no evidence for a volume increase at any stage in a compression test and indeed that plastic flow in tension and compression generally involves a volume decrease (see Section 5.4.8).

The only way the approach can be justified is if the occupied volume can change under stress in such a way as to allow the free volume to increase without increasing the total volume.[22] A point in favour of any explanation of yield in terms of a stress- or strain-induced increase in free volume is that it could explain why strain-softening occurs after yield.

5.8.3   Break-down of entanglements under stress

Various authors[52,75,76,77] have envisaged yield as the progressive break-down of interaction points between adjacent molecules, either geometrical entanglements or secondary valence forces of some kind. It is very probable that such processes are involved, but it is not clear to what extent they determine the level of the yield stress. Such a picture would readily explain the rapid strain-softening that can occur after yield, and also the reason for the pressure-dependence of the yield stress, since extra space is needed locally to disentangle an entanglement.[41] The break-down of such interaction points need not be permanent but they may re-form after a rest period.[75]

5.8.4   The Eyring model

One of the earliest quantitative models used to describe the flow of polymers is that due to Eyring.[78] As described in Section 4.2.2 this model assumes that molecular segments are vibrating over an energy barrier (of height E_0) and that the effect of the applied stress is to reduce the height of the barrier for a jump in the forward direction and to increase it for a jump in the reverse direction. It is further assumed that the macroscopic strain rate of the sample is proportional to the net jump rate of the segments in the forward direction. This model then predicts that the macroscopic shear strain rate is given by an equation of the form

$$\dot{\gamma} = \dot{\Gamma} \exp\left(-\frac{E_0}{kT}\right) \sinh\left(\frac{v\tau}{2kT}\right) \tag{6}$$

which is analogous to eqn. (11), Chapter 4. The quantity $\dot{\Gamma}$ is a constant with the dimensions of strain rate, E_0 is the enthalpy of the process and v

is the activation volume. As mentioned in Section 4.2.2, v is a constant with the dimensions of volume although it is not in fact a volume. The quantity $(v\tau)$ has the dimensions of energy and is the work done on a mobile segment during a jump by the applied shear stress, τ. The Eyring equation describes a viscous process occurring at constant stress so it can be applied to yield if yield occurs at constant stress.

Equation (6) can be rearranged to give the flow stress

$$\tau = \frac{2kT}{v} \sinh^{-1}\left[\frac{\dot{\gamma}}{\Gamma}\exp\left(\frac{E_0}{kT}\right)\right] \tag{7}$$

For flow at low strain rates and high temperatures when the flow stress is small this relation predicts that the flow stress will be proportional to the applied shear strain rate (Newtonian Viscosity) since $\sinh^{-1} x \approx x$ for small x. In physical terms almost as many jumps are occurring over the barrier in the reverse as in the forward direction.

For flow at high strain rates and low temperatures the equation predicts that the flow stress will vary linearly with the logarithm of the applied shear strain rate since $\sinh^{-1} x \approx \log x$ for large x. In this region the number of jumps over the barrier in the reverse direction is negligible and differentiation of eqn. (7) then leads to the prediction that the flow stress should vary linearly with the logarithm of the strain rate and that the slope of such a plot should be proportional to the absolute temperature

$$\frac{\partial \tau}{\partial(\ln \dot{\varepsilon})} = \frac{2kT}{v} \tag{8}$$

The values of the activation volume, v, needed to fit the Eyring model are reasonable. A value of $(\partial\sigma/\partial(\ln \dot{\varepsilon}))$ of $5\cdot2$ MN/m^2 determined from tensile tests on PMMA at 22°C given in Table 1 implies a value of v of $3\cdot13$ (nm)^3 [1 (nm)$^3 = 1000$ (Å)^3]. It has been assumed that $\tau = \sigma/2$, which might indicate that a mobile segment consists of a few monomer repeat units. The other values of $(\partial\sigma/\partial(\ln \dot{\varepsilon}))$ in Table 1 would then show that v is smaller for PMMA in a compression test than in a tensile test, and considerably larger for polyvinylchloride and polycarbonate than for PMMA.

Unfortunately there is not yet sufficient evidence for a true physical interpretation of v.[27] As mentioned before, v is not a physical volume but the product of an area and a displacement, and it is not clear what area and what displacement might be involved. Attempts to correlate v with specific features of the molecular structure have had to remain speculative.

It can be shown that for most polymers v is from two to ten times larger than the volume of a statistical random link in solution[79] but there is no clear correlation of the size of one with the size of the other for different polymers.

For some materials, for example polycarbonate, v can be shown to be constant for a range of temperatures and strain rates[23] although it is increased if the sample is annealed before testing.[27] For others, notably PMMA and polyvinylchloride, it may vary by a factor of two or more.

The other parameter from the Eyring equation that should have physical significance is the activation energy, E_0, which can be determined from tests at different temperatures if v is known. Unfortunately the value obtained in many cases varies with the temperature range in which it is determined although near the glass transition it may approach the activation energy of the α (main chain) relaxation process.[27]

In cases where the simple Eyring equation cannot fit the data modified versions have been tried which take into account the possibility that other processes may be occurring. Crowet and Homès[17] have fitted tensile data on PMMA by assuming that v is proportional to the absolute temperature as suggested by Ree and Eyring[80] and assuming in addition that the number of segments carrying the load decreases linearly as the temperature is increased. Roetling[16] has fitted similar data by assuming, following Ree and Eyring,[80] that more than one type of molecular segmental motion is involved so that the applied stress τ is the sum of the stresses carried by the various processes, weighted according to the fraction of the shear plane, f_n, occupied by each type of segment

$$\tau = \sum_{1}^{n} f_n \tau_n \qquad (9)$$

For each process τ_n is given by eqn. (7) with independent values of v, $\dot{\Gamma}$ and E_0. The activation volume was again taken to be proportional to the absolute temperature. Roetling fitted his data by assuming that two independent processes were operating, which he identified with the α and β relaxations in PMMA on the basis of the values of E_0. Tensile data on polyvinylchloride has been interpreted in a similar manner.[18]

It can be seen that the Eyring equation is capable of accounting for the variation of yield stress with temperature and strain rate quantitatively if only semi-empirically. The effect of hydrostatic pressure can be incorporated by arguing that since a segment needs extra space to execute a jump then under pressure either E_0 will be increased or $\dot{\Gamma}$ will be reduced which, because of the form of the equation, are equivalent statements.

5.8.5   The Robertson model

In one sense the model developed by Robertson[81] is an attempt to express quantitatively some of the ideas set out in Section 5.8.1, namely that the applied stress causes the molecules to seek a new, more rubber-like conformation, and when the conformation becomes similar to that at the T_g yield occurs.

The details of this theory have been well set out by Robertson himself in a recent book.[82] In simple terms it is postulated that at any time the molecular segments making up the polymer are distributed between a population of *cis* (high energy) and a population of *trans* (low energy) conformations; that the population of *cis* segments in equilibrium at the glass transition temperature is frozen-in in the glassy state; and that the effect of the applied stress is to cause certain segments to change over from the *trans* to the *cis* conformation, increasing the population of *cis* sufficiently for yield to occur. The viscosity of the glass (and hence the yield stress) is obtained by taking a figure for the viscosity at the T_g (10^{13} poise) and multiplying it by a rate factor obtained by adapting the Williams–Landel–Ferry equation to take account of the fact that the structure is not the equilibrium structure at the test temperature. To get yield at temperatures below the T_g the population of *cis* segments has to be increased by the stress to a value considerably greater than that appropriate to the T_g.

A special feature of this model in its original form is that although six parameters are needed none of them are adjustable, since the magnitudes of all of them can be estimated independently. The two parameters that relate the model to a particular polymer are the glass transition temperature (which determines the temperature at which the yield stress tends to zero) and a parameter V which is the average volume of a chain segment containing two single non-collinear bonds (which effectively determines the rate at which the yield stress rises as the temperature is decreased—if V is large the rise is less rapid). Considering the simplifications inherent in the model it predicts the general features of the variation of the yield stress of a number of polymers with temperature and strain rate remarkably well.

The model has been extended by Duckett et al.[15] to incorporate the effect of the hydrostatic component of the stress tensor on the yield stress. They suggest that a pressure will increase the energy difference between the *cis* and *trans* conformations because a segment in a *cis* conformation is likely to pack less efficiently and to occupy a larger volume. By making adjustments to all (seven) parameters in the modified theory they are able to obtain an excellent fit to yield-stress data on PMMA and PET, while still keeping the magnitudes of all parameters reasonable.

5.8.6 The theoretical shear strength—Frank's modification of the Frenkel model

A different approach to the problem of understanding yield in amorphous glassy polymers is to ask what is the maximum possible strength of the structure. Frenkel, in 1926,[83] produced a simple argument for estimating the maximum theoretical shear strength of a crystal. The argument is illustrated in Fig. 20 and goes as follows. If the undistorted crystal lattice in Fig. 20(a) is sheared to a shear strain of unity (Fig. 20(c)) each atom has moved from one equilibrium position to the next. If it is sheared to a shear strain of 0·5 (Fig. 20(b)) each atom is balanced half way between

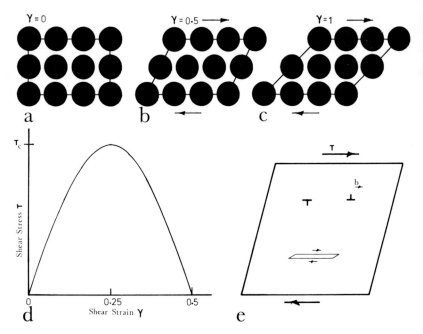

Fig. 20.   (a) *Undeformed primitive cubic lattice.* (b) *and* (c) *The same lattice deformed in simple shear to shear strains of* 0·5 *and* 1 *respectively.* (d) *Plot of shearing stress* versus *strain.* (e) *Configuration of dislocation loop nucleated under stress.*

one equilibrium position and the next and the shear stress to hold it in this position will be zero. The maximum shear stress will therefore occur when the applied shear strain is about 0·25 as shown in Fig. 20(d). The initial slope of the curve in Fig. 20(d) is known since it is G, the elastic shear modulus of the material. The simplest analytical function that has the general form of the curve in Fig. 20(d) is a sine curve and if this function is fitted to the elastic modulus the maximum shear stress, τ_c, becomes $G/2\pi \approx G/6$, at an applied shear strain of 0·25.

While the structure of an amorphous polymer is very different from that of a crystal it can be argued that the above general ideas are still valid. In the relaxed glass each molecular segment will be in some kind of equilibrium position. Under a sufficiently high applied shear strain they are all likely eventually to fall into new equilibrium positions (although the new positions may not correspond to such deep potential wells as the old). At an intermediate strain segments will be balanced between the two equilibrium positions; and at some lower strain the shear stress must pass through a maximum. The applied shear strain at which yield occurs in amorphous polymers is of the same order as the theoretical estimate of 0·25. It was suggested by Buchdal in 1957[84] that the yield stress of amorphous polymers could be explained on the Frenkel model; however, this model is for deformation without the aid of local thermal fluctuations and Buchdal did not specifically consider this effect.

Frank has shown how, for a crystal, the Frenkel model might be modified to take local thermal fluctuations into account and his treatment has been set out by Kelly.[85] In a crystal under stress it is possible for a dislocation loop to grow as illustrated in Fig. 20(e). As it expands the elastic energy associated with it first increases and then, beyond a critical radius, decreases. The height of the consequent energy barrier to expansion decreases as the stress is increased and this height can be calculated specifically if the shear modulus of the material and the burgers vector of the dislocation loop are known. At a given temperature dislocation loops will be nucleated and yield will occur when the applied stress reduces the height of the barrier sufficiently to make it comparable with the thermal energy available. The effect of thermal activation then is to reduce the yield strength from the maximum value of $G/6$ estimated above.

It may be questioned whether a dislocation loop is a valid concept in an amorphous material. If a small penny-shaped volume of material should shear as illustrated in the lower part of Fig. 20(e) the elastic strains would be almost identical to those of a dislocation loop and Frank's analysis would still apply. The magnitude of the shear displacement would become the burgers vector. A dislocation is only the elastic discontinuity at the boundary between a sheared and an unsheared region.

The numbers needed to fit a model of this type are reasonable. At room temperature PMMA has a shear modulus at small strains of about $1\cdot5\,GN/m^2$ and yields in pure shear at a shear stress of $50\,MN/m^2$ which is $G/30$. Thermal activation is capable of reducing the theoretical strength from $G/6$ at absolute zero to $G/30$ at room temperature if the burgers vector of the equivalent dislocation is $0\cdot3$ nm, which is a little smaller than the diameter of a molecular chain.

On the above model the variation of the yield stress with temperature and strain rate is partly due to the variation in the elastic modulus and partly because the process is a thermally activated rate process. Strain softening is expected since the production of 'dislocations' at the yield point will make subsequent deformation easy. An analogous effect is observed in crystalline materials. A special feature of 'dislocations' in amorphous material is that there is no reason for the dislocation to be conserved so that it may 'fade away' as the dislocation loop expands. Such an effect could explain the variations in the amount of strain softening observed in different materials.

5.8.7   Disclinations

Li and Gilman[86] have studied the elastic properties of *disclinations* which are the type of defect produced if one polymer chain in a parallel array of such chains contains a twist or kink. The elastic properties of these defects such as the stress field around them and their strain energy can be calculated if it is assumed that the surrounding material is an elastically isotropic continuum.

Argon[87] has used Li and Gilman's results to calculate the height of the energy barrier that opposes the flipping-over of a segment of molecular chain from one position to the next. The two kinks in the chain which form to permit this motion are treated as a pair of disclinations and the energy necessary to form them (the total elastic strain energy) is calculated. Argon goes on to develop a model to describe the yield behaviour of a glassy polymer. The comments at the beginning of this section about the difficulty of obtaining independent confirmation for any molecular theory for yield apply to this model also. Nevertheless it is an interesting approach as it is one of the few attempts to calculate directly the height of the energy barrier to the motion of a molecular segment that arises from interactions with adjacent molecules.

REFERENCES

1. Moore, C. A. (1971). Ph.D. Thesis, University of Cambridge.
2. Williams, J. G. and Ford, H. (1964). *J. Mech. Eng. Sci.*, **6**, 405.
3. Ender, D. H. (1968). *J. App. Phys.*, **39**, 4877.
4. Jukes, J. A. (1969). Ph.D. Thesis, University of Cambridge.
5. Bowden, P. B. and Jukes, J. A. (1972). *J. Mat. Sci.*, **7**, 52.
6. Rabinowitz, S., Ward, I. M. and Parry, J. C. S. (1970). *J. Mat. Sci.*, **5**, 29.
7. Lazurkin, Yu. S. and Fogel'son, R. A. (1951). *Zhur. Tech. Phys. USSR*, 3, **21**, 267.
8. Brown, N. and Ward, I. M. (1968). *J. Poly. Sci.*, A-2, **6**, 607.
9. Raha, S. and Bowden, P. B. (1972). *Polymer*, **13**, 174.
10. Raha, S. (1970). Ph.D. Thesis, University of Cambridge.
11. Bowden, P. B. and Raha, S. (1970). *Phil. Mag.*, **22**, 463.
12. Bauwens, J-C., Bauwens-Crowet, C. and Homès, G. (1969). *J. Poly. Sci.*, A-2, **7**, 1745.
13. Kirkland, J. T., Duncan, J. L. and Haward, R. N. (1970). *Polymer*, **11**, 562.
14. Holt, D. L. (1968). *J. App. Poly. Sci.*, **12**, 1653.
15. Duckett, R. A., Rabinowitz, S. and Ward, I. M. (1970). *J. Mat. Sci.*, **5**, 909.
16. Roetling, J. A. (1965). *Polymer*, **6**, 311.
17. Crowet, C. and Homès, G. A. (1964). *App. Mat. Research*, **3**, 1.
18. Bauwens-Crowet, C., Bauwens, J-C. and Homès, G. (1969). *J. Poly. Sci.*, A-2, **7**, 735.
19. Vincent, P. I. (1962). *Plastics*, **27**, August, 105.
20. Henshall, J. L. Private communication, unpublished data.
21. Beardmore, P. (1969). *Phil. Mag.*, **19**, 389.
22. Christiansen, A. W., Baer, E. and Radcliffe, S. V. (1971). *Phil. Mag.*, **24**, 451.
23. Bauwens-Crowet, C., Bauwens, J-C. and Homès, G. (1972). *J. Mat. Sci.*, **7**, 176.
24. Ainbinder, S. B., Laka, M. G. and Maiors, I. Yu. (1965). *Mekhanika Polimerov*, **1**, 65.
25. Holliday, L., Mann, J., Pogany, G. A., Pugh, H. Ll. D. and Gunn, D. A. (1964). *Nature*, **202**, 381.
26. Struik, L. C. E. (1966). *Rheologica Acta*, **5**, 303.
27. Brady T. E. and Yeh, G. S. Y. (1971). *J. App. Phys.*, **42**, 4622.
28. Ender, D. H. (1970). *J. Macromol. Sci.–Phys.*, **B4**, 635.
29. Pampillo, C. A. and Davis, L. A. (1971). *J. Appl. Phys.*, **42**, 4674.
30. Whitney, W. and Andrews, R. D. (1967). *J. Poly. Sci.*, C, No. 16, 2981.
31. Price, C., Williams, R. C. and Ayerst, R. C. (1972). *Amorphous Materials*, Ch. 12, ed. R. W. Douglas and B. Ellis, John Wiley and Sons Inc., New York.
32. Cottrell, A. H. (1964). *The Mechanical Properties of Matter*, John Wiley and Sons Inc., New York, p. 304.
33. Rider, J. G. and Hargreaves, E. (1969). *J. Poly. Sci.*, A-2, **7**, 829.
34. Buehler, W. J., Gilfrich, J. V. and Wiley, R. C. (1963). *J. App. Phys.*, **34**, 1475.
35. McClintock, F. A. and Argon, A. S. (1966). *Mechanical Behaviour of Materials*, Addison–Wesley, Reading, Mass., p. 285.
36. Bowden, P. B. (1970). *Phil. Mag.*, **22**, 455.
37. Nadai, A. (1950). *Theory of Flow and Fracture of Solids*, vol. 1, 2nd ed., McGraw-Hill., New York.
38. Bowden, P. B. and Jukes, J. A. (1968). *J. Mat. Sci.*, **3**, 183.
39. Jukes, J. A. (1969). Thesis, University of Cambridge.
40. Roscoe, K. H. (1970). *Geotéchnique*, **20**, 129.
41. Argon, A. S., Andrews, R. D., Godrick, J. A. and Whitney, W. (1968). *J. App. Phys.*, **39**, 1899.

338   THE PHYSICS OF GLASSY POLYMERS

42. Bauwens, J-C. (1967). *J. Poly. Sci.*, A-2, **5**, 1145.
43. Bauwens, J-C. (1970). *J. Poly. Sci.*, A-2, **8**, 893.
44. LeGrand, D. G. (1965). *J. Poly. Sci.*, A, **3**, 301.
45. Kashiwagi, M., Folkes, M. J. and Ward, I. M. (1971). *Polymer*, **12**, 697.
46. Le Fevre, C. G. and Le Fevre, R. J. W. (1956). *J. Chem. Soc.*, 1956.
47. Leigh, R. S. and Szigeti, B. (1967). *Proc. Roy. Soc.*, **301**, 211.
48. Treloar, L. R. G. (1958). *Physics of Rubber Elasticity*, Oxford University Press, p. 197.
49. Rudd, J. F. (1966). *Polymer Letters*, **4**, 929.
50. Kolsky, H. (1950). *Nature*, **166**, 235.
51. Read, B. A. (1967). *J. Poly. Sci.*, C, No. 16, 1887.
52. Raha, S. and Bowden, P. B. (1972). *Polymer*, **13**, 174.
53. Utsuo, A. and Stein, R. S. (1967). *J. Poly. Sci.*, A-2, **5**, 583.
54. Hammack, T. J. and Andrews, R. D. (1965). *J. App. Phys.*, **36**, 3574.
55. Yeh, G. S. Y. and Geil, P. H. (1967). *J. Macromol. Sci.–Phys.*, **B1**, 235.
56. Yeh, G. S. Y. and Geil, P. H. (1967). *J. Macromol. Sci.–Phys.*, **B1**, 251.
57. Klement, J. J. and Geil, P. H. (1971). *J. Macromol. Sci.–Phys.*, **B5**, 505.
58. Yeh, G. S. Y. (1972). *J. Macromol. Sci.–Phys.*, **B6**, 451.
59. Taylor, G. I. (1934). *Proc. Roy. Soc.*, **145A**, 1.
60. Coulomb, C. A. (1773). *Mém. Math. et Phys.*, **7**, 343.
61. Terzaghi, K. and Peck, R. B. (1948). *Soil Mechanics in Engineering Practice*, Chapman and Hall, London.
62. Drucker, D. C. (1953). *J. Mech. and Phys. of Solids*, **1**, 217.
63. Schofield, A. N. and Wroth, C. P. (1968). *Critical State Soil Mechanics*, McGraw-Hill, Maidenhead.
64. De Josselin de Jong, G. (1959). Thesis: *Statics and Kinematics in the Failable Zone of a Granular Material*, Uitgeverij Waltman, Delft.
65. Sternstein, S. S., Ongchin, L. and Silverman, A. (1969). *Applied Polymer Symposia No. 7*, Interscience, New York, p. 175.
66. Bryant, G. M. (1961). *Textile Research Journal*, **31**, 399.
67. Andrews, R. D. and Kazama, Y. (1967). *J. App. Phys.*, **38**, 4118.
68. Litt, M. H. and Koch, P. (1967). *J. Poly. Sci.*, B, **5**, 251.
69. Newman, S. and Strella, S. (1965). *J. App. Poly. Sci.*, **9**, 2297.
70. Eirich, F. R. (1965). *App. Poly. Symp.*, **1**, 271.
71. Nielsen, L. E. (1965). *Trans. Soc. Rheol.*, **9.1**, 243.
72. Rusch, K. C. and Beck, R. H. (1969). *J. Macromol. Sci.–Phys.*, **B3**, 365.
73. Litt, M. H., Koch, P. J. and Tobolsky, A. V. (1967). *J. Macromol. Sci.–Phys.*, **B1**, 587.
74. Sasabe, H. and Saito, S. (1968). *J. Poly. Sci.*, A-2, **6**, 1401.
75. Nielsen, L. E. (1962). *Mechanical Properties of Polymers*, Reinhold, New York.
76. Vincent, P. I. (1960). *Polymer*, **1**, 7.
77. Bartenev, G. M. and Zuyev, Yu. S. (1968). *Strength and Failure of Viscoelastic Materials*, Pergamon, Oxford.
78. Eyring, H. (1936). *J. Chem. Phys.*, **4**, 283.
79. Haward, R. N. and Thackray, G. (1968). *Proc. Roy. Soc.*, A, **302**, 453.
80. Ree, T. and Eyring, H. (1955). *J. App. Phys.*, **26**, 793.
81. Robertson, R. E. (1968). *App. Polymer Symp.* (7), 201.
82. Kambour, R. P. and Robertson, R. E. (1972). In: *Materials Science of Polymers*, ed. A. D. Jenkins, North Holland, Amsterdam, vol. I, p. 687.
83. Frenkel, J. (1926). *Z. Phys.*, **37**, 572.
84. Buchdal, R. (1958). *J. Poly. Sci.*, **28**, 239.
85. Kelly, A. (1966). *Strong Solids*, Oxford University Press, p. 22.
86. Li, J. C M. and Gilman, J. J. (1970). *J. App. Phys.*, **41**, 4248.
87. Argon, A. S. Private communication, to be published.

88. Golden, J. H., Hammant, B. L. and Hazell, E. A. (1967). *J. App. Poly. Sci.*, **11**, 1571.
89. Jackson, W. J. and Caldwell, J. R. (1967). *J. App. Poly. Sci.*, **11**, 211.
90. Robertson, R. E. and Joynson, C. W. (1972). *J. App. Poly. Sci.*, **16**, 733.
91. Boundy, R. H. and Boyer, R. F. (1952). *Styrene*, Reinhold, New York, p. 476.
92. Tuckett, R. F. (1943). *Chem. and Ind.*, **62**, 430.

CHAPTER 6

THE POST-YIELD BEHAVIOUR OF AMORPHOUS PLASTICS

R. N. HAWARD

6.1 GENERAL

In the previous chapter the yielding of glassy thermoplastics was described and the different yield criteria assessed. In this chapter we will be concerned with what happens next. It is clear that in some cases, and especially in tension, fracture intervenes, although, on the other hand, even under tension many plastic materials go on to exhibit large deformations at a temperature well below the glass transition temperature. It is, of course, also well known that brittleness and extensibility depend on the molecular weight of the polymer which needs to be above a certain level, characteristic of the particular polymer, for adequate mechanical properties to be attained. Naturally, the polymer glasses used commercially exceed this molecular weight, and when this criterion is met it seems that virtually all organic glasses are capable of showing yield phenomena under a suitable stress field.

On the other hand, even at high molecular weights several glassy polymers, typically polystyrene and polymethylmethacrylate at ambient temperatures, do not show large deformation under tension. Nevertheless, even with these materials the elongation at break is dependent on molecular weight and its distribution, as shown in Fig. 1,[1] *i.e.* 'brittleness' becomes more marked at low molecular weights. With other cases, where a rigid polymer glass will yield in tension it can be assumed that below a certain molecular weight a changeover to brittle behaviour will occur. Generally, however, such low molecular weight materials are not made commercially so that most polymer physicists find themselves working with materials having a near 'optimum' molecular weight.

As also explained previously (*see* Chapter 5), neither the ultimate

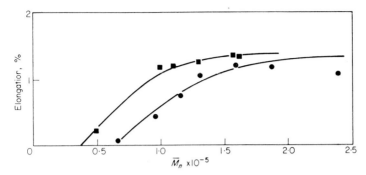

Fig. 1.   The effect of molecular weight on the elongation at break under tension of polystyrene. Plots of elongation at break against number average molecular weight for anionic (narrow molecular weight distribution) ■ *and thermal (wide molecular weight distribution)* ● *polystyrenes. (Reproduced from reference 1 by permission of John Wiley and Sons Inc.)*

strain nor the rate of strain at yield is proportional to the applied stress, and so most of the conventional spring and dashpot models do not apply to post-yield deformation. Further, after removal of the stress only a part (often only a small part) of the deformation is recovered. Thus at one time it was believed that actual flow of the material had taken place. However, if the deformed polymer is subsequently heated above its glass transition temperature it returns to its original dimensions, often with remarkable accuracy, as shown in Fig. 2.[2] This phenomenon has been known for a long time and was first reported by Gurevich and Kobeko in 1940.[3] Later Haward[4] and Hoff[5] described these effects with different materials and Hoff described a very striking case in which hollow cylinders of polymethyl-methacrylate were compressed and showed a recovery quite as drastic as that illustrated in Fig. 2. Clearly the deformation process cannot be one of flow as normally understood.

After the polymer starts to yield under the influence of an applied stress, the subsequent course of events is affected by a number of factors which are summarised in items 1–5 below.

(1) There may be a 'yield drop' (or 'strain softening') which can only be defined for the present as an unexplained fall in true stress after yielding starts. The phenomenon has analogies with that of thixotropy in colloidal systems.[6]

(2) Various types of plastic instability may occur of which the most well-known form is that generally described as 'necking'. However,

(a)

(b)

Fig. 2.   The thermal retraction of deformed polystyrene. Recovery of shear band.
(a) A broad shear band produced by the compression of a rectangular polystyrene
test-piece; (b) after heating 1½ hours at 110°C the original form of the test-piece is
recovered. (Reproduced from reference 2 by permission of John Wiley and Sons
Inc.)

other striking phenomena also take place, some of which have been described in the previous chapter (Section 5.5.4).

(3) Heat is generated and if it is not removed the temperature of the specimen will increase and it will become softer. This accentuates plastic instability, especially at high rates of strain.

(4) As the deformation increases some form of 'orientation hardening'[7] nearly always occurs, leading to an increase in stress.

(5) The test piece may break. Depending on the material used and the conditions of the test (*e.g.* temperature, geometry and strain rate) this may take place over a whole range of deformation levels.

The significance of these various factors will now be considered. Item (1) will, however, be dealt with only shortly since it has also been discussed in the previous chapter. Item (5) is of course the main subject of Chapter 7 and will be covered only so far as theories of deformation have been advanced to account for fracture.

6.2   THE PHENOMENA OF 'STRAIN SOFTENING'

The type of behaviour known as 'strain softening' may be defined as a fall in the true stress as deformation takes place at yield. In a tensile or compression test this means a fall in $\sigma_0(1 + \varepsilon)$ where ε is the tensile strain (negative in compression) and σ_0 the stress (engineering stress) calculated on the original cross-section of the test-piece. The term 'yield drop' was first applied by Brown and Ward[8] to describe this effect but 'strain softening' appears to be a more descriptive term and as it is a very convenient expression it is used here. The phenomena has however been known for some time and was noted by Lazurkin and Fogel'son.[9]

Probably all plastic materials show some form of strain softening, but its magnitude differs substantially from one plastic to another. Evidence showing the existence of strain softening may be obtained from several different types of experiments, but because of the geometrical features which occur in a tensile test, and tend to promote necking (*see* Section 6.3), tensile tests are generally less significant than measurements in compression or shear. Whenever there is a fall in applied stress under compression or in shear at reasonably low strain rates (isothermal conditions) it may be assumed that a genuine strain softening is taking place.

Experiments in compression by Binder and Muller[10] and others,[9,12] leave no doubt that both polystyrene and polymethylmethacrylate

show a substantial strain softening effect (Fig. 3). However, the magnitude
of the effect varies from one plastic to another; both PVC and polycarbonate
show smaller effects than the above two polymers, so also does cellulose
nitrate.[11,12] It is perhaps significant that tough materials are associated
with a small amount of strain softening.[2] For example polycarbonate and
cellulose nitrate may be compared with polystyrene and polymethylmethacrylate.[2,10] The former are tough materials and the latter relatively
brittle ones.

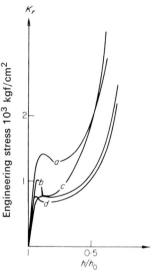

Fig. 3. Compression curves for different plastics. (a) *Polymethylmethacrylate;*
(b) *polystyrene;* (c) *polycarbonate;* (d) *polyvinylchloride (PVC). Note that the
amount of strain softening for* (a) *and* (b) *is significantly greater than for* (c) *and*
(d). *(Reproduced from reference 10 by permission of Dietrich Steinkopt Verlag.)*

Conclusive evidence for the occurrence of strain softening may also be
obtained from experiments in shear, as described by Brown and Ward[8]
for polyethylene terephthalate and by Sternstein and co-workers[13] for
polymethylmethacrylate. An example showing the occurrence of strain
softening in shear is shown in Fig. 4.[13] In carrying out this work Sternstein
and co-workers considered the possibility of a (second-order) correction
for a change in cross-sectional area during the shear experiment and
showed that it could not possibly account for the magnitude of the effect
observed. Polystyrene has also been reported by Vinogradov and Belkin
as showing strain softening in shear, even above its glass transition

temperature,[14] though the effect was greater when the temperature was not too high (160° compared with 210°C). Leonov and Vinogradov have also proposed a theoretical treatment of the phenomenon which is claimed to depend on a breakdown in structure.[15]

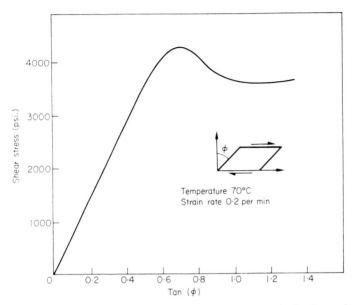

Fig. 4. Strain softening in shear. Typical stress–strain curve in shear obtained with polymethylmethacrylate. (Reproduced from reference 13 by permission of John Wiley and Sons Inc.)

Information indicative of the occurrence of strain softening may often be obtained from a study of tensile stress–strain curves. For example, polystyrene appears to show a large strain softening effect when subjected to a high hydrostatic pressure and tested in tension.[16] With natural rubber, however, under similar conditions strain softening, if present at all, is only small.[17] Here it will be appreciated that negative evidence that strain softening is either small or absent, is reasonably conclusive when obtained in tension, but when a positive strain softening effect is identified the effects of geometry have to be considered and the amount of the observed effect has to exceed the reduction in cross section.

Another phenomenon closely related to strain softening is that of the 'delay time' which is often observed when a plastic is tested under constant load.[18] The observed 'delay time' is a time which is measured after the application of the load, but before large strains are observed. Here geometric factors (though present) may still be reasonably small and can sometimes be allowed for.[4] Delay times can be characteristically measured with polystyrene and polymethylmethacrylate correlating with their known tendency to show strain softening. In a recent study of delay times Ender[19] showed that they could be increased by annealing the polymer and decreased by rapid cooling from its softening temperature.

He also found that the annealing procedure slightly increased the density of the polymer so that the increased delay time could be related to the need to disturb the close packing of the polymer chains. It would be reasonable to expect that similar effects would be seen in other experiments designed to measure the amount of strain softening.

Further evidence showing the importance of thermal history in yield phenomena has recently been reported by Brady and Yeh.[18a] They showed that an annealing process which caused a small increase in density, also led to a significant increase in yield stress. This was accompanied by an increased tendency to form small shear bands on the polymer surface which were visible in the electron microscope. Rapid cooling of the melt decreased the material density by about 0.04% and decreased the tendency for plastic strain to localise in narrow bands. In the case of polymethylmethacrylate the quenched polymer showed no shear bands at all. Such uniform deformation might be expected to correlate with a reduced strain softening and with a consequent greater stability in plastic deformation. (*See also* Chapter 5.)

6.2.1   Stress hardening

Some polymers which show strain softening also show a stress hardening effect. This was first described by Vincent in the case of PVC.[21] He found that if, in the course of measuring a stress–strain curve, the cross-head of the testing machine was stopped and then adjusted to allow the stress to fall to zero, on restarting the machine at the same speed as earlier the stress reverted quickly to the original level and the stress–strain curve was continued almost as if no interruption had occurred. However, when the machine was stopped if, instead of allowing the stress to fall to zero, a lower stress was maintained on the specimen, then, on restarting, the stress–strain curve showed a new peak only slightly smaller than that which was observed at the beginning of the test before the 'neck' (*see* next section) had been formed (Fig. 5). A similar result was reported by Whitney and Andrews[19a] using polyvinyl formal.

This phenomenon was later studied extensively by Kramer[19b] in the case of nylon filaments. He again found the same sort of effect as Vincent. When held under reduced load, which was insufficient to propagate the neck, the filament hardened so that a new peak occurred when the stress–strain test was restarted. Kramer studied this process quantitatively by means of its effect on delay times at constant load. He concluded that

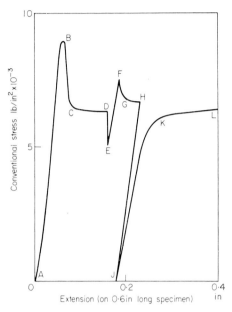

Fig. 5. Load–extension curve for polyvinylchloride at $3 \cdot 3 \times 10^{-4}$ *in/sec, interrupted twice. This shows the hardening effect when kept at a reduced stress.*

action of the stress caused the formation of small regions of better inter-chain packing (micro crystals) in nominally amorphous parts of the nylon. This conclusion is in line with the observation of Whitney and Andrews[19a] who showed that during the stress ageing of polyvinyl formal there was a reduction in volume. Thus Kramer's increased delay time, or a stress peak in a constant rate of extension test, was caused by the necessity to break down this more closely packed structure. A remarkable feature of this work was that the effect could be quickly eliminated if the stress on the filament was allowed to fall to zero.

At present it is not known how far this effect can be observed with amorphous polymers, other than PVC and polyvinyl formal.

6.3 PLASTIC INSTABILITY PHENOMENA

6.3.1 Plastic instability in tension

The most well-established phenomenon associated with plastic instability in polymer glasses is that of 'necking'. This occurs with most of the well-known amorphous polymers: PVC,[20,21] polycarbonate[20] and polymethylmethacrylate (under appropriate conditions).[22,9] Neck formations have also been reported with polystyrene when extension takes place under hydrostatic pressure.[16,23] The cellulose derivatives, however, generally extend in a rather uniform way. Examples showing the different types of behaviour are given in Fig. 6.

The basic theory of neck formation is relatively straightforward and is generally attributed to Considère, *e.g.* by Vincent[21] and by Nadai[24] whose treatment is followed here. When a tensile test-piece deforms plastically

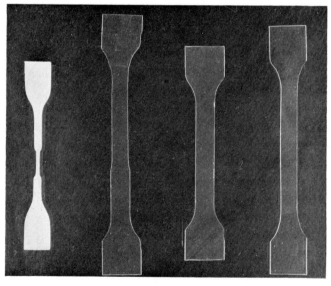

High density   Polycarbonate   Original   Cellulose
polyethylene   test piece   nitrate

Fig. 6. Different types of tensile behaviour in plastics. High density polyethylene forms a very marked neck. The polycarbonate forms a less marked but distinct neck while the cellulose nitrate extends uniformly. (In the case of the high density polyethylene the extension of the test-piece took place at a steady rate over a period of 16 hours.)

without changes in volume then the cross-section areas A, A_0, the lengths l, l_0 (where subscript 0 refers to the initial condition of the test-piece) and the plastic strain ε, are related as follows:

$$\frac{A}{A_0} = \frac{l_0}{l} = \frac{1}{1 + \varepsilon}$$

It follows that if σ_0 is the stress referred to the original cross-section of the test-piece then σ, the true stress, $= \sigma_0(1 + \varepsilon)$, from which it can be shown that

$$\frac{d\sigma_0}{d\varepsilon} = \frac{1}{(1 + \varepsilon)^2}\left[(1 + \varepsilon)\frac{d\sigma}{d\varepsilon} - \sigma\right]$$

Then at the point where σ is a maximum $d\sigma/d\varepsilon = \sigma/(1 + \varepsilon)$ and this corresponds to the tangent to the true stress–strain curve from an origin defined by $l = 0$, i.e. when plotted as described in Fig. 7. Thus, the maximum of σ_0 and the tangent to the true stress–strain curve occur at the

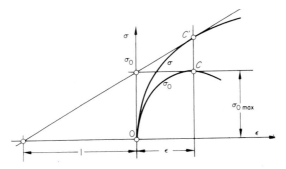

Fig. 7. Construction by Considère. The point C, which is a maximum on the engineering stress curve, (σ_0), is also a tangent from the point $l = 0$ on the true stress curve, (σ). (Reproduced from reference 24 by permission of McGraw-Hill Book Co.)

same elongation, and when the material has properties such that this can occur, then any further increase in elongation beyond this point leads to a fall in stress (σ_0).

If the test-piece was perfectly uniform in cross-section and composition it would, in principle, be possible for uniform extension always to take place. However, in practice this is never so; there is always a point in the test-piece where σ_0 passes the maximum first, and when this happens, the stress required to extend further at this point falls. Extension therefore continues there while the stress in other points of the test-piece falls below that required to pass over the yield point. A constriction, or neck, then develops. Once such a neck is formed it may get steadily thinner, with the load decreasing up to fracture (as is the case with copper or with PVC at high speeds) or the 'neck' may stabilise and extend throughout the test-piece.

In discussing these phenomena, Vincent[21] distinguishes three cases of tensile behaviour:

I
$$\frac{d\sigma}{d\varepsilon} > \frac{\sigma}{1 + \varepsilon}$$

in this case stable elongation takes place. A normal vulcanised rubber is a very good example of this type of behaviour.

II
$$\frac{d\sigma}{d\varepsilon} = \frac{\sigma}{1 + \varepsilon}$$

at one point. This leads to necking with thinning to failure. Finally

III
$$\frac{d\sigma}{d\varepsilon} = \frac{\sigma}{1 + \varepsilon}$$

at two points. This provides a stable neck as observed with linear poly-thene and many other plastics. The neck then extends throughout the test-piece, after which the stress will rise steadily up to the point of fracture. This third type of behaviour is illustrated in Fig. 8(a) and (b).

The above discussion gives an essentially valid account of necking instability in polymers, but leaves out two significant factors.

As described in the previous chapter, the yield stress is quite sensitive to the rate of strain. Now clearly, when a neck is formed there is a large increase in the rate of strain at the point where the neck forms. Therefore in practice, if the above criteria are only just met, *i.e.* if σ_0 vs. ε has only a rather flat maximum, the local increase in strain rate to form a neck would raise σ_0 above the maximum for the test-piece as a whole. Thus, in practice, it is a necessary requirement for neck formation that σ_0 should have quite an appreciable maximum. Cellulose nitrate sheet seems to be a case in point here (*see* Fig. 9, ref. 64) where the slight drop in σ_0 at yield is insufficient to support the formation of a stable neck.

The second point not considered above is that of thermal effects. These will be discussed in more detail later, but the viscous and entropic compo-nent of the energy of deformation must lead to appreciable heating of the test-piece. Where this heat is not removed the temperature will rise and

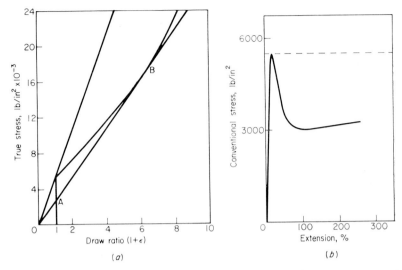

Fig. 8.   The necking of high density polythene. (a) *The complete true stress–strain (draw ratio) curve for high density polythene. The true stress–strain curve has two tangents from l =* 0. (b) *The load extension curve similar to* (a). (*Reproduced from reference* 21 *by permission of the Institute of Physics.*)

yield stress will fall so that any tendency to necking will increase. Since the yield stress increases with the strain rate it is clear that both the heat output and the rate of heating will increase at high strain rates, and for this reason necking is more likely to occur under such conditions. These arguments have been developed by Marshall and Thompson[25] (*see below*) for polythene terephthalate and by Lazurkin[26] for polymethylmethacrylate. In principle, therefore, it is possible for a plastic specimen to change over from a homogeneous to a 'necking' mode of extension with an increase in strain rate. Indeed, even under isothermal conditions, an increase in strain rate leading to an increase in yield stress would tend to favour necking.[12] Examples of this type showing a strain-rate effect have been mentioned by Newman[27] for polycaprolactam and low density polythene and by Muller for PVC[50] but in no case is there a direct presentation of experimental results. Moreover, low density polythene contains a substantial proportion (*e.g.* 40%) of amorphous polymer above its T_g, so that it is perhaps not surprising that the polymer shows analogies with rubber in having a capability for uniform extension with high strains,[29] rather than with a glassy polymer. Thus while there is no doubt that a changeover

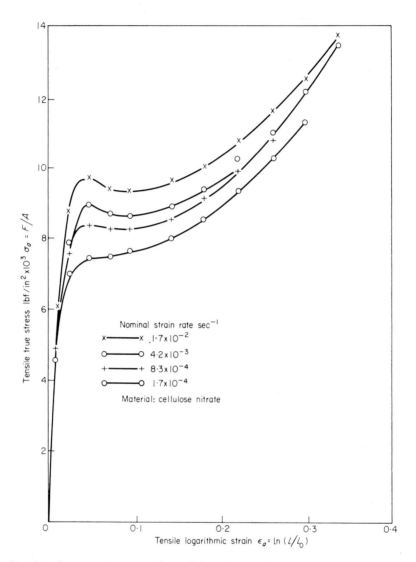

Fig. 9.   Stress–strain curves for cellulose nitrate. Stress–strain curves in simple tension for cellulose nitrate. Higher strain rates lead to a higher yield stress and a greater tendency to plastic instability. (Reproduced from reference 64 by permission of Iliffe Science and Technology Ltd.)

from necking to linear extension at low strain rates is possible, well-documented cases of its occurrence in polymer glasses are actually hard to find.

6.3.2 Plastic instability in different stress fields
As described above, the decline in cross-section during extension (geometrical factor) has a strong influence in favouring plastic instability in tension. In compression, geometrical factors clearly act the other way and tend to stabilise the deformation. However, plastic instability phenomena are by no means confined to tensile tests. Examples of shear bands developed in triaxial stress and other fields have been given in the previous chapter, and the deformed test-piece shown in Fig. 2 is generally of the same type. Shear bands may also be generated by subjecting pre-oriented polymers to uniaxial tension at an angle to the molecular alignments.[30,31]

6.4 THE ADIABATIC HEATING OF POLYMERS SUBJECT TO LARGE DEFORMATIONS

6.4.1 Reversible thermoelastic effect
When a polymer undergoes a large deformation at a high stress the energy applied to the specimen will be taken up in several ways. The two most important of these include the work done against viscous forces and a decrease in entropy due to the orientation of molecular chains. These will be discussed later.

Here we will deal with another, less important but more universal, thermal effect. This is the reversible thermoelastic temperature effect of a Hookean solid, which exhibits a small increase in temperature in compression and a decrease in tension[32] in accordance with conventional thermoelastic relation, namely

$$\frac{\delta T}{\delta \sigma} = \frac{T\alpha}{Jc\rho} \tag{1}$$

where α is the coefficient of linear expansion, J the mechanical equivalent of heat, c the specific heat and ρ the density of the polymer. Thus when a plastic specimen is placed under tension (σ negative) there is first a small cooling effect and later heat is given out as viscoelastic extension (creep) takes place. This was observed in very early work on cellulose ester films by McNally and Shepherd.[33]

Both the viscous heating effect and the reversible thermoelastic heating in compression have been demonstrated experimentally by Binder and Muller.[10] Naturally, the thermoelastic effect is the smaller one but it can be unequivocally demonstrated in the case of polyvinylchloride (PVC) under compression as illustrated in Fig. 10. Here a plug of PVC is subjected to repeated loading and unloading. It will be seen that the steady upward drift of the temperature due to the 'plastic' work done on the material is accompanied by small temperature fluctuations which exactly follow the

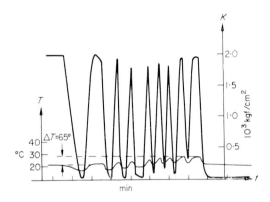

Fig. 10.   *The reversible thermomechanical effect in polyvinylchloride under compression. When the stress is applied the temperature rises and falls when it is removed. Yielding also takes place, leading to a steady irreversible temperature increase. Cylinders 20 × 20 mm. Heavy lines stress, light lines temperature.*
(*Reproduced from reference 10 by permission of Dietrich Steinkopt Verlag.*)

loading sequence, an increase of pressure being associated with a rise in temperature as predicted by eqn. (1). These effects are, of course, on a small scale compared with those which can be caused by large 'plastic' deformation and their omission when calculating the heating during such deformations will not generally cause serious error. They may, however, produce significant effects when cracks and flaws produce high local tensions in an impact test.

6.4.2   Thermal effects in large plastic deformation

The significance of adiabatic heating in the deformation of polymers was recognised at an early date.[34] However, in this early work, mainly carried out with plasticised cellulose esters which were not capable of strains exceeding 0·5, it could be demonstrated that the increase in temperature would not exceed 10°C. Other polymers, of course, are capable of much greater strains and are therefore able to generate much larger quantities of heat. A case of this type was analysed in detail by Marshall and Thompson,[25] in connection with the drawing of polyethylene terephthalate filaments. As these have a high yield stress and a maximum draw ratio of about 4 they were inherently capable of generating a very significant amount of heat. Marshall and Thompson measured and interpolated a

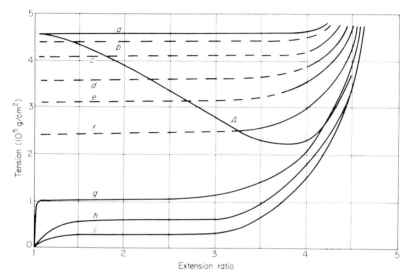

Fig. 11.   The isothermal and adiabatic extension of polyethylene terephthalate. Tension–extension–temperature properties of amorphous polyethylene terephthalate. Initial birefringence 3.1×10^{-3}. (a) 20°C; (b) 30°C; (c) 40°C; (d) 50°C; (e) 60°C; (f) 70°C; (g) 80°C; (h) 100°C; (i) 140°C. A, adiabatic from 20°C. (Reproduced from reference 25 by permission of The Royal Society, London.)

series of force extension curves for this polymer and calculated the adiabatic curve from them, assuming complete conversion of energy to heat. Their results are presented in Fig. 11, where the potential effects due to adiabatic extension are very clearly brought out.

They then analysed the fast necking process in terms of the adiabatic force extension curve. They proposed that the extension of the neck during the drawing of the filament could take place along a constant tension line cutting the adiabatic curve at R_1, R_2, R_3 (Fig. 12) such that the two areas A and B were equal. Extension then occurs at a tension σ_1 below the yield tension σ. For the process to take place in this way it was necessary for

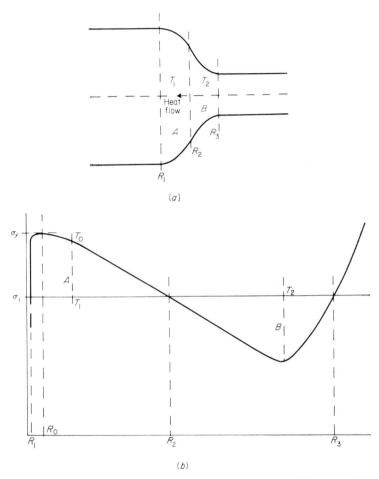

Fig. 12. *System of heat flow during the necking of polyethylene terephthalate.*
(a) *Arrangement of draw ratios, temperatures and heat flow in a neck.* (b) *Adiabatic*
load–extension curve for the neck (a). (*Reproduced from reference* 25 *by permission*
of The Royal Society, London.)

heat to be transferred backwards through the neck, and this in turn
required that the neck depth should be small. They then demonstrated by
semi-quantiative calculations of heat transfer that the calculated neck
depth was in fact close to that observed experimentally. Thus they were
able to offer a rather convincing picture of an adiabatic (or near adiabatic)
necking process.

Recently the role of heating in the necking of polyethylene terephthalate has been confirmed by Kargin and co-workers[34a] in a striking way, and in the course of their research they observed a quite new phenomenon, fundamentally related to the concepts of Marshall and Thompson. By extending a film of this polymer, Kargin found first a normal yield point peak (Fig. 13(a)) followed by a period of steady necking extension. However, as the test-piece extended, oscillation began to appear, and after a time this process became firmly established. This was shown to be a thermal phenomenon. As the test-piece grew longer its ability to store elastic energy increased, so that when yielding at the neck set in it could accelerate with the generation of heat until the larger part of the elastic energy stored in the length of the test-piece had been used up. The neck could then cool down, and no further extension would take place until the stress in the specimen had once more risen to the level required for the cold necking process to start. Thus all the extension took place in short time-intervals following stress peaks as shown in Fig. 13(b) and (c). Kargin also showed, by a process based on the dusting of crystals on to the surface of the film, that the sudden extension at the neck was accompanied by a temperature rise from ambient up to 90°C and even up to 140°C at high deformation rates. When the sample was cooled in a water-bath all the fluctuations disappeared. A very similar series of results, including a marked formation of bands in the drawn filament, has recently been obtained with nylon.[34b]

However, although it is clear that thermal effects can favour neck formation, it is also possible for marked necking to take place under isothermal conditions. This certainly occurs with high density polythene (Fig. 6), but here also there must be a condition of constant load through the test-piece. For this purpose there must also be some balancing process, and it seems most likely that this is promoted by a variation in the strain rate at different points in the neck, and indeed in the whole test-piece.

We will now consider another case in which the adiabatic deformation of a polystyrene-like solid is calculated. The material is assumed to undergo isothermal 'plastic' deformation at a constant yield stress in which all the 'plastic' work is converted to heat.[35] Further, we assume, as can be demonstrated from the results of Binder and Muller,[10,35] that the yield stress varies with temperature in accordance with the equation:

$$\sigma_y = \sigma_{y_0} \frac{(T_s - T)}{(T_s - T_0)}$$

where T_s is the softening temperature (or glass transition on the appropriate time-scale).

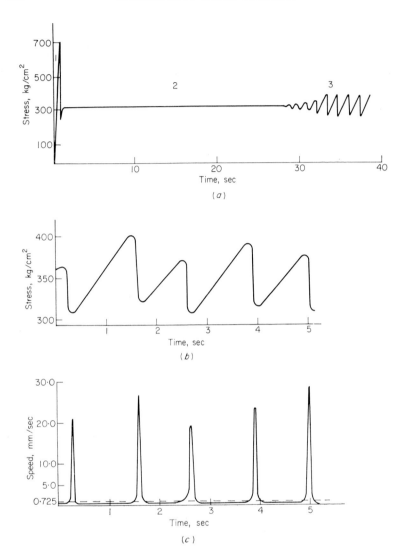

Fig. 13.   *Thermal self-oscillation in the necking of polyethylene terephthalate film.*
(a) *Actual nature of stress development and growth of self-oscillation during
extension of PETP at a constant rate. Variations of* (b) *stress with time and* (c) *accompanying change in true rate of deformation in the region of passage of polymer
into the neck. The broken line shows the imposed 'average' rate of deformation
calculated from the relative speed of clamp movement. (Reproduced from reference
34a by permission of John Wiley and Sons Inc.)*

In this calculation we work in terms of true stress and consider a block of height h_0, which is to be compressed to a height h. We omit corrections due to changes in the initial elastic part of the compression during deformation and heating and also the effects due to thermal expansion.

We consider the block to be of unit cross-sectional area originally and observe that the work done on the test-piece for a reduction in height dh is $-\sigma_y h_0 dh/h$. Thus the temperature rise dT undergone by unit volume of the block is given by

$$dT = \frac{-\sigma_y \, dh}{Jc\rho h}$$

where c is the specific heat, ρ is the density, and J is the mechanical equivalent of heat. This approach of course ignores changes in density. Now introducing eqn. (1)

$$dT = \frac{-\sigma_{y_0}(T_s - T)\, dh}{Jc\rho(T_s - T_0)h}$$

and thus

$$\ln(T_s - T) = \frac{1}{N}\ln h + D \tag{2}$$

where $N = [Jpc(T_s - T_0)]/\sigma_{y_0}$ is a dimensionless material constant, including average values of ρ and c.

It follows that

$$\sigma_y = \sigma_{y_0}\left(\frac{h}{h_0}\right)^{1/N} \tag{3}$$

Now denoting by Q the specific energy generated by the work of compression which is assumed to be all dissipated plastically, we have

$$Q = \int_{h_0}^{h} - \frac{\sigma_y}{J}\, dh \; \text{cals/cm}^2$$

The energy generated per unit volume is

$$\frac{Q}{h_0} = \int_{h_0}^{h} - \frac{\sigma_{y_0}}{hJ}\left(\frac{h}{h_0}\right)^{1/N} dh \; \text{cals/cm}^3$$

and thus

$$\frac{Q}{h_0} = \frac{\sigma_{y_0} N}{J}\left[1 - \left(\frac{h}{h_0}\right)^{1/N}\right] \tag{4}$$

This equation describes the heat generated per unit volume when the height is reduced from h_0 to h.

By a similar argument it may be shown that, in tension, the relations for imposing an engineering strain of e, defined as $h/h_0 - 1$, are

$$\frac{\sigma_y}{\sigma_{y_0}} = \left(\frac{1}{1 + e}\right)^{1/N} \tag{5}$$

and

$$\frac{Q}{h_0} = \frac{\sigma_{y_0} N}{J}\left[1 - \left(\frac{1}{1 + e}\right)^{1/N}\right] \tag{6}$$

In Figs. 14(a) and (b) we have plotted eqns. (3), (4), (5) and (6) using the properties of polystyrene already quoted. It will be seen that the effect of

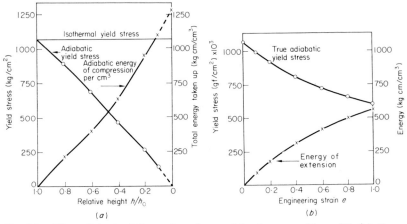

Fig. 14.   *The adiabatic deformation of a model polystyrene-like solid. (a) Compression; (b) tension. (Reproduced from reference 35 by permission of the Institute of Physics.)*

the adiabatic heating on the yield stress at strains of about 50% is very large. This means that large differences would be introduced by using an adiabatic instead of an isothermal model for many deformation processes.

An assumption in the above treatment is that the maximum energy which the polymer can absorb mechanically per unit volume without cooling is given by $c\rho(T_s - T_0)$ (heat units per unit volume), since this amount of energy will cause complete softening of the material. (For thermal effects in fatigue see Section 7.3.1.)

6.4.3   The experimental measurement of temperature changes during deformation

In their extensive study of the large deformations of polymers under compression, Binder and Muller[10] investigated cylindrical test-pieces of polystyrenes and several other plastics and in all cases they obtained curves generally similar to those given in Fig. 3. The form of these curves will be discussed at a later stage. For present purposes, however, it is clear that as the compression continues beyond the yield point a substantial amount of energy is applied to the test-piece. Binder and Muller therefore went on to measure the temperature changes at the centre of the test-piece as a function of specimen size and strain rate. Under favourable conditions these temperature changes were close to those predicted theoretically, as shown in Fig. 15. On discussing their results, Binder and Muller noted that at high strains the temperature increase fell off when compared with that predicted, and they very reasonably ascribed this to a heat loss. For example, if the experiment is run at a high temperature where the yield stress is

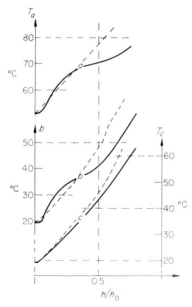

Fig. 15.   Temperature changes during the compression of different plastics. (a) Polystyrene; (b) polyvinylchloride; (c) 6-polyamide. The actual temperature measured at the centre of a cylindrical sample (————) compared with the temperature rise calculated from the work of deformation (– – – – –). (Reproduced from reference 10 by permission of Dietrich Steinkopt Verlag.)

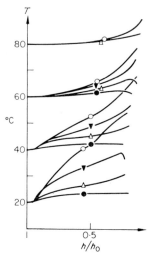

Fig. 16.   *The effect of starting temperature and strain-rate on the heat build-up of polyvinylchloride. The temperature of* 20 × 20-*mm PVC cylinders at different strain rates.* ○ 10 *mm/min;* Δ 0·75 *mm/min;* ▼ 2·5 *mm/min;* ● 0·26 *mm/min. (Reproduced from reference* 10 *by permission of Dietrich Steinkopt Verlag.*)

small, the temperature increases are much reduced. A further case in which the heat generated during the extension of polycarbonate is apparently less than the work input has recently been reported by Muller.[28]

These results demonstrate conclusively the existence of large thermal effects on deformed plastic test-pieces. With slow experiments or small test-pieces it is, however, possible to approach essentially isothermal conditions. Binder and Muller found that with a 20 × 20 mm PVC cylinder the temperature rise was virtually nil at strain rates below 10^{-4} sec.$^{-1}$

The effect of starting temperature and strain-rate on the magnitude of the temperature changes is shown in Fig. 16. When the initial temperature is raised the yield stress falls and the heating of the specimen is reduced. Some heating, of course, always occurs during the yielding of a glassy polymer.

Although the total heat generated generally corresponds with that predicted for the total work, difficulties arise when more detailed questions are asked. Apart from the Joule effect, there are at least three main thermal effects which come into play when a plastic is extended:

(1) Frictional heat due to viscosity. This heat is in no sense recoverable.

(2) Entropic heat, due to configurational changes during the orientation

of polymer chains. This is entirely analogous to the heat released during the stretching of rubber.

(3) Changes due to the storage or release of internal energy.

There are also other, probably minor, energy changes which result from molecular fracture processes leading to the formation of free radicals, and cracking or cavitation processes leading to the formation of new surfaces.

Although it is extremely difficult to separate (1) and (2) above, significant progress has been made with (3) by Stolting and Muller.[36,37] They measured the exact heat of a solution of polystyrene extended just above its glass transition temperature (100°C). Under these conditions the stored entropy generates work which balances the entropic heat taken up so that there is no net thermal effect from this source. However, there are differences of up to 1 cal/g in the internal energy, which was shown to be *reduced* when polystyrene was strained. Thus the positive heat of solution of the deformed polymer was lower than that of the annealed material. These workers showed that it is possible to relate the difference in the heat of a solution

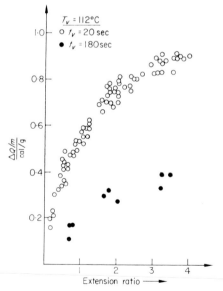

Fig. 17. The effect of pre-straining on the heat of solution of polystyrene. The difference between the heats of solution of polystyrene unstretched and stretched, related to the strain and the rate of strain. t_v refers to the time for extension and T_v the temperature. (ΔQ positive refers to a lower measured heat of solution.) (Reproduced from references 36 and 37 by permission of Dietrich Steinkopt Verlag.)

to the strain and temperature of straining (Fig. 17). It is not, however, known how far this behaviour also occurs with other plastics, but at any rate with polystyrene, the measured internal energy changes were relatively small compared with the other thermal effects observable during yield.

Generally, in studying the yield of polymers, one tries to achieve isothermal conditions by using small test-pieces and low strain-rates. However, when the time scale of the experiment is necessarily short, as in an impact test, or when a glassy polymer shatters, releasing its stored (Hookean) elastic energy by crack extension, all deformations will be adiabatic.[34] Under these conditions it is now clear that very large temperature effects are possible.

Indirect evidence supporting this proposal has come from the electron micrography of fracture surfaces. Long fibre-like structures have been observed on a polyethylene surface by Preuss[38] and more recently on a polystyrene fracture surface as shown in Fig. 20 on page 50. In both cases the formations strongly suggest that melting has taken place, as proposed by Preuss, and this would require a very considerable rise in temperature. Indeed Preuss suggested that in some cases a rise of 300°C occurred.

More direct evidence for such a temperature change has recently been published by Fuller and Fox.[39] They studied the cracking of polymethylmethacrylate by means of high speed infra-red photography. They found that as the crack passed the 'camera' there was first a fall in temperature arising from elastic deformation (eqn. (1)) and then a larger rise in temperature as crazing, associated with large local strains set in. At the maximum the temperature rise was estimated to be as much as 450°C above the starting temperature, i.e. a temperature well above the glass transition temperature as measured at conventional strain rates. However, both this figure and that given by Preuss represent the maximum temperature rises which have been so far suggested. Thermal effects during fracture will be discussed further at the end of this chapter.

6.5   ORIENTATION HARDENING

In Chapter 5 and in the previous section of this chapter it has been shown that under suitable conditions nearly all high polymers can be caused to yield. After yield there is generally some strain softening, which varies in magnitude from one polymer to another. This is observed at strains of 0·05–0·5. However, if deformation continues beyond that range, and if fracture does not intervene there follows almost invariably a rise in true stress. Under tension this rise in true stress may be sufficient at high strains to stabilise the neck (Fig. 8), in a necking mode of extension. Alternatively in the case of the cellulose derivatives, it may set in at strains low enough to prevent a necking mode of extension from taking place. Thus there is a wide range of strain levels in different polymers at which the strain hardening process occurs. Further, again as previously stated, the yield process is generally reversible when the polymer is heated above the glass transition temperature and, as in the case of rubber, the deformation is accompanied by demonstrable birefringence.[13,26,36,40,41,42,43,44,45] Similarly, stretched polymers have been shown to exhibit anisotropy in the dielectric loss factor.[46] As a consequence of all these observations large deformations in glassy plastics have for a long time been regarded as a macromolecular orientation process essentially similar to the extension of a rubber but taking place under conditions of a high internal viscosity, which limits retraction when the stress is removed. Many of the early publications contain discussions on these lines.[3,4,5,9,45,46,47] The occurrence of large extensions leads directly to orientation, and this orientation is reversed whenever the internal viscosity is reduced, e.g. by heating. From this it is a short step to associate the hardening process, which also occurs at large strains, with the orientation which accompanies it.[12] Thus Vincent[7] has described the phenomenon as 'orientation hardening' and this term is used here as an appropriate short description of the process. It is generally found that whenever isothermal stress–strain curves can be properly presented as true stress–strain curves they show a strong upward trend, either from the start (Fig. 18) or at the highest strains (Fig. 3). On the other hand, as shown in the adiabatic curve in Fig. 17, the occurrence of orientation hardening at large strains depends on the efficient removal of heat when the applied stresses are high. When these stresses are low, however, insufficient heat may be generated to have much effect on the temperature of the material (see Fig. 16).

6.5.1 Orientation hardening as a physical process

That orientation during strain is accompanied by hardening is an observation which seems intuitively reasonable, but the mere demonstration of the two features is far from providing a satisfactory theoretical basis for the phenomenon. At the present time a fully satisfactory scientific treatment does not exist. Instead there are a number of scattered observations and suggestions in the literature together with one or two specific proposals applied in a limited field.

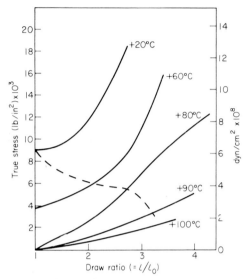

Fig. 18.   Orientation hardening of polyvinylchloride. Isothermal true stress–strain curves of a sample of rigid PVC with an estimated adiabatic curve (broken curve) for 20°C. (Reproduced from reference 7 by permission of The Royal Society, London.)

In the first place the strain at which orientation hardening sets in is markedly dependent on the actual polymer used. This factor has been recognised for some time and formulated in a number of different ways. According to one approach the deformation process may be regarded as approaching an ultimate limit of extension, at which point, in the absence of fracture, the stress would become infinite. This leads to the concept of limited extensibility.[4,34,44] In the fibre field it is found that polymers tend to have a characteristic 'draw ratio' which depends more on the polymer than on the conditions used.[48,49,21] Alternatively it is possible to measure the characteristic strain in a stable necking mode of extension. According to the Considère/Vincent scheme the extension in the neck is determined by the point at which the engineering stress at high extension starts to increase. This can occur only when a substantial amount of orientation hardening has taken place, and consequently the characteristic necking strains are also a measure of the strains at which orientation hardening sets in. Values for necking strains have been reported by Muller[50] as follows:

Necking strains for different polymers[50]
Polyvinylchloride   0·4–1·5

Polycarbonate	2·24
Polyamide	2·8–3·5
Polystyrene (100°C)	3·5
Linear Polyethylene	8–10

Here again the results show that the differences between polymers are highly significant and generally greater than those observed by changing conditions with the same polymer. Thus orientation hardening has to be related to some structural features of the polymer. It also follows that all types of mathematical models of large polymer deformation, in which the ultimate elongation at long times is proportional to stress or to a power of stress greater than say, 0·5, must have a limited range of application to large strains in real polymers below T_g.

Under some conditions the tendency of the polymer to extend to a specific limit is very marked. An example of this type of behaviour was provided by early work with plasticised cellulose nitrate film[4] (Fig. 19). In this case the isothermal extension curves at different loads can all be plotted in an approximately linear form on an empirically derived reciprocal relation, and, although the stresses differ appreciably and the strain

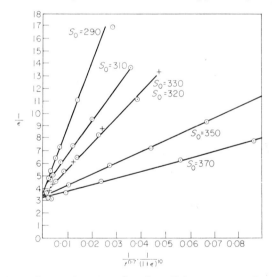

Fig. 19.   Reciprocal extension–time plots for cellulose nitrate under constant load. At infinite time (zero $(1/t)^{0·7}$) all the lines approximate to the same strain. S_0 on the curve indicates the starting load in kgf/cm². The factor $1/(1 + \varepsilon)^{10}$ corrects for the change in stress as extension continues according to a power law. (Reproduced from reference 4 by permission of the Faraday Society.)

rates substantially, each line extrapolated to nearly the same extension at infinite times. Another feature of these linear plots which were based on fitting a power law to relate curves at different stresses, is that the same power law was applicable at different strains. This point has recently been formally reported and confirmed by Ender,[51] using an Eyring model which is, of course, preferable to a power law (see pp. 229, 330). He found that the slopes of the log (rate of strain) stress curves were the same at different extensions for polymethylmethacrylate. In fact, curves essentially the same as Ender's (except for the empirical use of a power law for a stress-rate of strain relation) were used to construct the curves given in Fig. 19 and in references (4) and (34). Thus the two sets of results support each other and indicate that for different stresses it is sometimes possible to separate the effect of the orientation hardening function from that due to viscosity. *i.e.*

$$\text{True rate of strain} = F \text{ (True Stress) } F' \text{ (Strain)}$$

where F' (strain) represents an orientation hardening factor. Further, the existence of this relation argues that orientation hardening is indeed a structural factor and not a viscosity change. However, it is still unclear how far this approach can be extended, *i.e.* whether it applied to other polymers than those studied by the two workers, its accuracy, and the range of strains over which it can represent experimental results. Clearly, even according to the measurements given in Fig. 18, there are experimentally significant small differences in the limiting extrapolated strain at long times. However, the postulation of a limiting strain is a very reasonable approximation in describing constant load experiments with this particular polymer.

6.5.2 Factors affecting orientation hardening

The strains at which orientation hardening sets in differ with different polymers, so that we need to know about the features which control this effect. Once again the amount of available evidence is sparse, though there are a few useful indications of the problems involved. In the first place it can easily be shown that, even the highest strains measured in stress–strain curves (*e.g.* about 10 for high density polythene) do not correspond to the complete unravelling of the polymer molecule. This has been recognised for some time both for rubbers and thermoplastics. For example, Meyer and Van der Wyk[52] proposed a 'felted' structure for an extended rubber molecule in which the orientation took place only between fixed points. Speakman[53] also proposed a limited extension for keratin. More recently the concept of molecular chain entanglements has been developed, especially from studies of melt viscosity[54,55,56,57] and it is reasonable to see these entanglements as providing a unit, smaller than the length of the molecule itself, whose extension would provide large polymer deformations within the range observed. In this case there is an obvious analogy with the theory of rubber elasticity, with the points of entanglement playing the part of cross links in a vulcanised rubber. However, even with rubbers entanglements exist and have been studied by Baldwin et al.[58] who used rubber elasticity measurements, extrapolated to zero chemical cross-linking, to estimate the amount of entanglement. Also, Furakawa et al.[59] and Kotani[60] have measured the maximum elongation of different rubbers

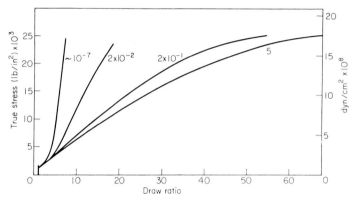

Fig. 20.   The effect of molecular weight on the orientation hardening of polyethylene. True stress–strain curves for four samples of high density polyethylene with different melt flow indices (marked on curves). The low melt indices (high molecular weight) show maximum orientation hardening. (Reproduced from reference 7 by permission of the Institute of Physics.)

and demonstrated its relation to cross links and statistical chain-segment size. Thus the existing theory of rubber elasticity also postulates that a polymer can be extended to a limiting strain depending on its structure.[61]

If the stress–strain curves of polymers below their glass transition temperature are to be interpreted in a similar way then any factor which increases entanglements (such as increasing molecular weight) should increase the effect of orientation hardening at a given strain. At the present time there is relatively little information on this point relating to glassy polymers, but the effect of molecular weight has been conclusively demonstrated in the case of linear, crystalline, polyethylene both by Williamson et al.[62] at ambient temperatures and by Vincent[7] as shown in Fig. 20. A similar situation would be expected to arise in the case of glassy polymers built up by cross-linking reactions, where increased cross-linking should lead to a greater orientation hardening effect. This has been demonstrated in the case of certain epoxy esters by Lohse et al.[63] (Fig. 21). On the other hand the effect of cross linkage in many polymer glasses is not to reinforce them, as would be expected to take place with increased orientation hardening, but to increase brittleness, the reasons for which are not well understood. In fact we still know very little about the effect of cross-links on yield or post-yield behaviour.

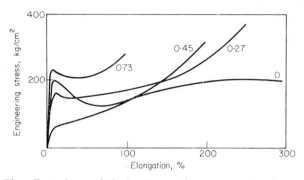

Fig. 21. The effect of cross-link density on the stress–strain characteristics of epoxy resins. The numbers give a measure of cross-link density. It will be seen that as the amount of cross-linkage increases the elongation at which orientation hardening becomes dominant decreases. (Reproduced from reference 63.)

If orientation hardening is actually a phenomenon related to the straightening out of polymer chains between fixed points then certain further analogies with the known behaviour of rubbers should follow. For example, the relation between different types of strain response should be similar for polymer glasses and rubbers. In the case of natural rubber, extended under uniaxial and biaxial tension, it has been shown by Treloar[61] that the true stress–strain curves are close together when plotted in terms of maximum tensile strain, but widely separated when plotted as true axial strain. For a plastic to be compared in the same way a stable mode of tensile extension is necessary and for this reason cellulose nitrate sheet was selected for this work. This sheet was extended in uniaxial tension and in biaxial tension by blowing up under a controlled pressure in a bulge test.[64] The results were plotted as stress–strain curves, in one case against maximum tensile strain and in the other case against axial strain (Fig. 22). In the same figure results are given for rubber plotted in the same way.[65] It is clear that a qualitative analogy exists between the orientation hardening of cellulose

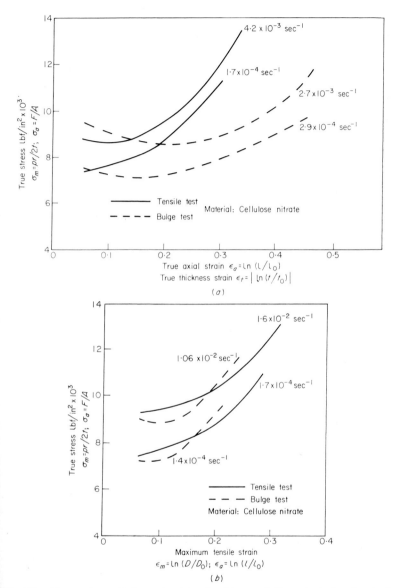

Fig. 22.   Comparison of the extension of rubber and the orientation hardening of cellulose nitrate under two different stress systems–tensile test, uniaxial tension; bulge test, biaxial tension. (a) True stress vs. numerically greatest strain for cellulose nitrate sheet. (b) True stress vs. maximum tensile strain for cellulose nitrate sheet. Cellulose nitrate was used here because of its ability to extend uniformly in tension.

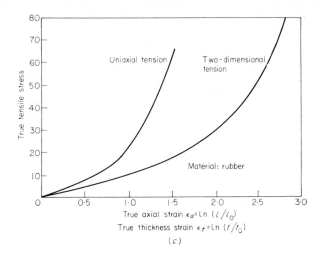

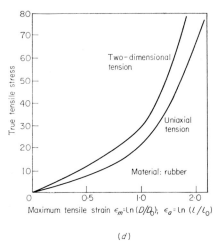

Fig. 22. (c) *True tensile stress* vs. *numerically greatest strain for rubber.* (d) *True tensile stress* vs. *maximum tensile strain for rubber.*[65] (*Reproduced from reference* 64 *by permission of Iliffe Science and Technology Ltd.*)

nitrate and the extension of rubber. Plotted as maximum tensile strain the curves for the two stress systems are close together, plotted as true axial strain they are far apart.

The theory of rubber elasticity has now reached a quantitative stage of development,[61] so that the mechanical properties of a rubber can be directly related to certain molecular quantities. Thus if it is to be applied to a polymer glass, the molecular parameters so obtained must be acceptable. Bueche *et al.*[66] have approached this aspect of the problem by considering the maximum elongation at break for two polymethylmethacrylates and polystyrene. Their maximum elongation (α_c) was estimated by using the theory of failure envelopes[67,68,69] whose applicability had been demonstrated in the rubber field. This provides a value of α_c essentially independent of temperature and which may be regarded as meaningful in the present context. Actually Bueche *et al.* do not state the temperatures at which they work, though these are almost certainly above ambient temperatures and may have been above T_g. Bueche assumed (with certain minor reservations) that

$$\alpha_c = \frac{\text{Maximum length of the polymer chain between entanglements}}{\text{Random statistical length of the chain between entanglements}}$$

and in this way, using literature data for the molecular weight between entanglements of the three polymers, obtained an estimate of the quantity $(\bar{r}^2)^{\frac{1}{2}}/M$ where $(\bar{r}^2)^{\frac{1}{2}}$ is the root-mean-square end-to-end distance of the polymer chain. This value was then compared with results from light-scattering in a theta-solvent. The results showed that values obtained from the tensile tests were low by a factor of about 0·70 compared with the values from light-scattering. However, in the circumstances, the agreement must be regarded as quite good, and indeed within the range of variation of the values for molecular weights between points of entanglement as determined by other different and quite independent methods.[54] Thus Bueche's results also support the concept of entanglement as a determining factor in the stress–strain curves of glassy polymers.

A somewhat similar treatment was applied by Haward and Thackray[70] who constructed a mathematical model from stress–strain curves (*see* below) and used an orientation hardening term based on the theory of rubber elasticity. As a result, using literature values for the size of a statistical link in the polymer chain, the volumes between entanglements could also be checked against literature values (taken from Porter and Johnson[54]) for the polymers as shown in Table 1. Again the results were low and the agreement as to order of magnitude encouraging.

TABLE 1

THE MOLECULAR WEIGHT BETWEEN ENTANGLEMENTS
FROM ESTABLISHED TECHNIQUES AND FROM
STRESS–STRAIN CURVES

Material	Volume between entanglements $(nm)^3$	
	Porter and Johnson[54]	From stress–strain curves[70]
Cellulose nitrate	9·6 (35°C)	4·5 (23°C)
		4·7 (54°C)
Polyvinylchloride	6·2 (30°C)	2·4 (23°C)
(Note 1 nm = 10 Å)		

Finally we may note that if the hardening process is essentially one of chain orientation then it must be strongly affected by a pre-imposed orientation in the polymer. This certainly is the case. Vincent[7] cites the example of rigid PVC sheet in which the length in each direction was increased by a factor of 1·23 by rolling at room temperature. The conventional stress–strain curves were then substantially modified as shown in Fig. 23. However, the true stress–strain curve beyond yield was found to be the same as for the isotropic sample, provided allowance was made for the pre-orientation by multiplying the draw ratio by 1·23. Qualitatively similar results have been obtained by Broutman and Patil.[71] On the same argument it would be expected that the initial extension of a polymer would provide a material in which orientation hardening became effective in

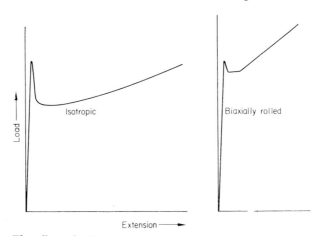

Fig. 23. The effect of rolling on the load–extension curve of PVC. Tensile load–extension curves for rigid PVC; initially isotropic and biaxially rolled. (Reproduced from reference 7 by permission of the Institute of Physics.)

compression only at higher strains than with unstretched material. This effect has been demonstrated with cellulose nitrate by Ito,[72] who produced a material in this way which showed an appreciable yield drop (in compression) and a notably higher compressive strain at a given level of orientation hardening. These curves have changed in the opposite way to those studied by Vincent (Fig. 23).

6.5.3 A model for large polymer deformations

It will be clear from the foregoing discussion that conventional spring and dashpot models in which strain is related to stress or to a power of stress are essentially inapplicable to large strains in polymer glasses. Therefore

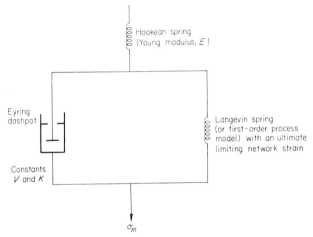

Fig. 24. *A model for large extensions of high polymers below the glass transition temperature. (Reproduced from reference* 70 *by permission of The Royal Society, London.)*

many of the mathematical treatments based on linear viscoelasticity[73] which are sometimes considered as possible starting points for the treatment of large-strain behaviour may be discarded. One simplified model has, however, been put forward which is able to reproduce a number of the features in polymer stress–strain curves. This model is illustrated in Fig. 24. It analyses the stress–strain curve in terms of three processes.

(1) A constant Hookean Viscosity.
(2) A high internal viscosity, which is treated according to the Eyring equation relating shear rate and shear stress.

(3) A limited elastic extensibility for which the conventional Langevin formula used to describe the highly elastic extension of rubbers can be employed. As an alternative a first-order reaction model could be used.

This model leads to the following expressions for a tensile test, using $\sigma_m(1 + \varepsilon)$ as the true stress.

$$\text{Total extensions} = \varepsilon = \frac{\sigma_m(1 + \varepsilon)}{E} + \varepsilon_A$$

where ε_A is the large viscoelastic strain.

Now treating ε_A as a viscous deformation assumed to be large compared with the Hookean deformation, we can write

$$\frac{d \ln (1 + \varepsilon)}{d\tau} = \frac{\tau}{\eta} \tag{7}$$

where η is viscosity and τ the shear stress $= \frac{1}{2}\sigma_m(1 + \varepsilon)$. Then following Eyring we get

$$\frac{d \ln (1 + \varepsilon_A)}{dt} = K \left(\exp \frac{V\sigma_m(1 + \varepsilon_A)}{4kt} - \exp - \frac{V\sigma_m(1 + \varepsilon_A)}{4kt} \right) \tag{8}$$

where V and K are constants of the Eyring equation.

Now according to the model the stress available to shear the dashpot is equal to the applied forces—minus the stress due to the spring. This is then represented by the conventional model for high elastic behaviour at high strains,[61] namely

$$\sigma_m^R = \frac{NkTn^{\frac{1}{2}}}{3} \left\{ \mathscr{L}^{-1} \left(\frac{1 + \varepsilon_A}{n^{\frac{1}{2}}} \right) - \left(\frac{1}{(1 + \varepsilon_A)^{3/2}} \right) \mathscr{L}^{-1} \left[\frac{1}{[n^{\frac{1}{2}}(1 + \varepsilon_A)^{\frac{1}{2}}]} \right] \right\} \tag{9}$$

In this equation $\mathscr{L}^{-1}$ is the inverse Langevin function and n is the number of statistical chain links between points of entanglement. The total equation is reached by subtracting σ_m^R from σ_m in eqn. (8). The whole is then computed as a simultaneous equation with eqn. (7). The resulting curves give a reasonable presentation for the stress–strain curve for plasticised cellulose esters (Fig. 25). In the case of PVC, which shows necking, an idealised stress–strain curve is derived from the model which represents that which would be observed if uniform extension took place. The model shows directly that a polymer having a viscosity like PVC and its characteristic extensibility limits, should exhibit plastic instability of the type associated with necking, and the model makes it possible to relate the ratio

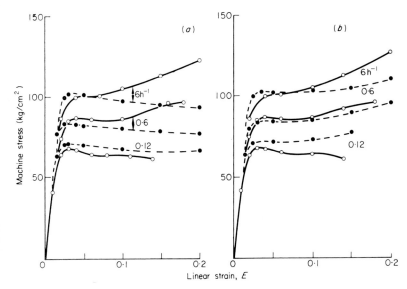

Fig. 25.   *Stress–strain curves for cellulose acetate compared with predictions for the model. Stress–strain curves for cellulose acetate at 23°C ($\circ$) compared with the model ($\bullet$). (a) $(n^{\frac{1}{2}} - 1) = 0\cdot53$, $N = 1\cdot34 \times 10^{20}$ chains/cm². (b) $(n^{\frac{1}{2}} - 1) = 0\cdot30$, $N = 1\cdot85 \times 10^{20}$ chains/cm². For the rigid cellulose ester chain the number of statistical links between effective entanglements has to be quite low (about 2). (Reproduced from reference* 70 by permission of The Royal Society, London.)*

of the minimum engineering stress value (σ_{min}) reached before orientation hardening becomes effective to the maximum value at the yield point (σ_{max}). The model predicts that this ratio, which may be expected to determine the onset of necking is directly controlled by the limiting network strain $(n^{\frac{1}{2}} - 1)$ Fig. 26. The effect of strain rate is here much smaller than the effect of a change in 'n', where n is the number of statistical chain links between points of entanglement. This corresponds with the well-known observations that polymers which show marked necking (like linear polythene) cannot be easily persuaded to go over to a stable mode of elongation by lowering the strain rate.[7] (*See* also Section 6.3.1). On the other hand if some of the extensibility is used up by a pre-orientation process, this is equivalent to reducing n, and the ratio falls (Fig. 23).

It is of course very difficult in tension to measure the real stress–strain curve for a plastic which exhibits a necking mode of deformation, but the theoretical ratio $\sigma_{min}/\sigma_{max}$ is clearly related to the ratio of the 'drawing

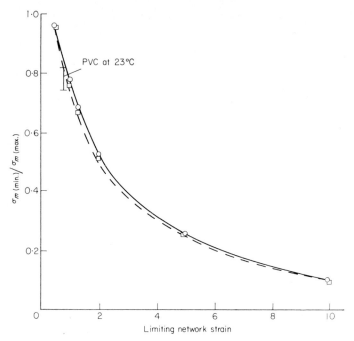

Fig. 26. The relation between limiting network strain and geometric plastic instability in tension. Plastic instability is estimated as an engineering stress ratio ($\sigma_{min}/\sigma_{max}$) and plotted against the limiting network strain ($n^{\frac{1}{2}} - 1$) according to the model in Fig. 24. Viscosity constants as for PVC at 23°C. □ strain rate 171·2 h^{-1}. ○ strain rate 0·856 h^{-1}. (Reproduced from reference 70 by permission of The Royal Society, London.)

stress' (σ_d) for the stable extension of a neck, to the yield stress ($\sigma_y = \sigma_{max}$), *i.e.* σ_d/σ_y. The inverse function of this quantity, *i.e.* σ_d/σ_y has been investigated by Broutmann and Patil[71] for a series of polymers in terms of the thickness reduction in a pre-orientation process. They found that the ratio σ_y/σ_d fell steadily for a series of polymers when the orientation was increased (thickness reduced) as shown in Fig. 27. These observations are in line with the concept of orientation hardening and with the model described above.

However, in spite of fairly good representation of experimental results, the model has two important limitations. In the first place, it does not provide for strain softening and therefore can only be applied in its present form to polymers in which this effect is small, and secondly, it assumes an absolute limit for the extensibility. In practice, this is never quite the case,

and all real stress–strain curves depart from the model's predictions at
the highest strains. It seems likely that the macromolecular network breaks
down as processes such as the slipping of entanglements, chain fracture
and voiding occur. The study of these is important for the future understanding of the still obscure fracture process which takes place in polymers
at intermediate and high deformations.[74,75] It should also be understood

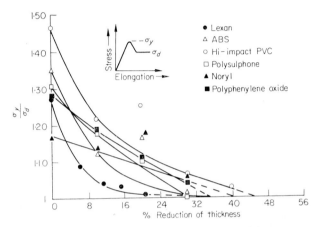

*Fig. 27. The effect of pre-orientation on plastic instability as measured by
σ_y/σ_d. The relation between the ratio of yield stress (σ_y), and drawing stress σ_d, and
the percent reduction in thickness of the tested sheet material by rolling. The ratio
σ_y/σ_d is approximately the reciprocal of the quantity used in Fig. 26. (Reproduced
from reference 71 by permission of the Society of Plastics Engineers Inc.)*

that the model avoids the study of small viscoelastic deformation (creep)
by using an empirical linear modulus and by dealing with deformations
which are much larger than those studied in a typical creep experiment.
Under conditions where small deformations take place before yield the model
could be applied but would not perform any better than other models
directly based on an Eyring viscosity term.

6.6   LARGE DEFORMATION AND FRACTURE

6.6.1   Crack propagation as a deformation process
During the last 15 years a theory of the tearing and fracture of rubbers has
been developed which is based on the concept of viscoelastic extension at a
crack tip.[68,69,76] The success of this theory and the application of similar

concepts in the field of metallurgy[77] has encouraged others to consider a parallel approach to problems of fracture and crack propagation in plastics. As the general problems of fracture are dealt with in detail in Chapter 7, we shall only consider in this chapter how this subject may be related to what is known of deformation processes. We should, however, note that in nearly all cases evidence of large strains is visible in electron micrographs of fracture surfaces of polymers. Further, as will be mentioned later, actual cracking is often preceded by the formation of a craze (*see* Chapter 7) which itself consists of a thin sheet of polymer which has been considerably deformed. These crazes vary in structure from an assembly of holes to that of the polystyrene craze shown in Fig. 28 which may be regarded as an assembly of micro-necks.

An account of the crack propagation process in terms of plastic deformation has been given by Williams and Turner.[78] They treated fracture as an aspect of plastic instability which they defined essentially in the same way as in Section 6.3.1.

By re-calculating the condition for instability in terms of a crack growth

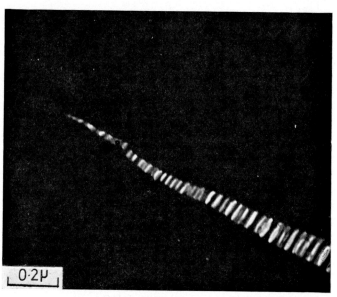

Fig. 28. Micro-necks in a polystyrene craze. The craze is wedge-shaped and may be regarded as a system of micro-necks. When the voids are very small they appear to have a more rounded form. (Reproduced from Beahan, P., Bevis, M. and Hull, D., Phil. Mag., 24, No. 192, p. 1267, by permission of Taylor and Francis Ltd.)

model, and assuming that the stress–strain law could be represented by an equation of the form $\bar{\sigma} = A\bar{\varepsilon}^n$, they showed that the 'fracture toughness' K_c could be given by

$$K_c^2 = E\delta\bar{\sigma}_c Z_c \left(\frac{n}{n+1}\right)$$

where E is Young's Modulus, δ is a natural constant relating to the length (or height) of the plastic element at the crack tip, and the subscript c refers to the critical value at fracture. So that $\bar{\sigma}_c$ is the equivalent stress determined experimentally for fracture conditions and Z_c is the critical value of

$$Z = \frac{\bar{\sigma}}{(d\bar{\sigma}/d\bar{\varepsilon})} = \frac{\bar{\varepsilon}}{\eta}$$

and $\bar{\varepsilon}$ the natural or logarithmic strain at fracture.

Further if δ is approximately constant then a constant relation of K_c^2 to $\bar{\sigma}_c$ would result, as obtained by Irwin.[79] They went on to argue that once a plastically unstable neck or crack had been formed, whose compliance was equal to that of the rest of the test-piece (plus that of the machine where appropriate) then the neck or crack would extend uncontrollably as in a normal fracture situation.

In a later paper Williams and Isherwood[80] have developed these concepts further and combined a work hardening deformation model with a fracture criterion for edge notched specimens, based on a reduction in area ($= R = (A_0 - A)/A_0$ where A is the fracture area and A_0 is the initial area). Their results were applied to metals and to PVC sheet, but with the latter no work hardening term was necessary as they used an engineering stress–strain curve which was found to be nearly horizontal. Thus with PVC a constant engineering yield stress was used and the equation of the type $\bar{\sigma} \propto (\varepsilon)^n$ (which did not fit the results) was avoided. Measurements of E, σ_y and R were then carried out in simple tension and the results applied to single-edge notched sheets. In this way it was possible to predict the fracture stresses of the notched sheets for different temperatures and values of a/w (a = notch depth and w the width of the sheet)—as shown in Figs. 29(a) and (b). These results indicate the way in which measured stress–strain properties can be combined with the theories of fracture mechanics to predict the behaviour of notched sheets of polymer. They do, however, employ an experimentally determined maximum area reduction of stretched polymer which is assumed to be constant under different conditions, including the condition that only one dimension is reduced. Thus the treatment does not set out to provide a fundamental

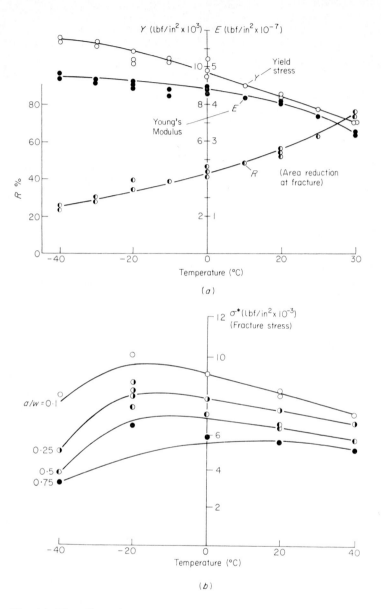

Fig. 29. (a) *The effect of temperature on the tensile properties of PVC sheet.* (b) *The fracture stress of notched PVC sheet as a function of temperature. Curves showing the effect of temperature on fracture stress for 5-in wide × $\frac{1}{16}$-in thick single-edge notched PVC sheet. (a/w = notch depth/width of sheet). Experimental points and theoretical curves derived from tensile measurements (a). (Reproduced from reference 80.)*

answer to the question of why or how the plastic fractures at high strains. Clearly the development of theories of this type is handicapped by the absence of satisfactory general equations describing stress–strain behaviour in plastics at large strains as well as by a very limited understanding of fracture processes under these conditions.

6.6.2   Crazing as a plastic instability phenomenon

As described in the next chapter, in most cases the fracture of polymer glasses is preceded by the formation of a structure known as a craze. Briefly this consists of a very thin sheet of deformed polymer, either consisting of rounded voids or of extended filaments of polymer[81] as shown in Fig. 28. It seems probable that the filament structures visible in this case could be formed by further extension of a craze with rounded voids.[82] Clearly the formation of structures of this type must be a yield process, and evidence to support this concept has been given by several workers.[83,84,85]

It has further been suggested[86] that plastic instability in the sense of a decline in engineering stress as the material is extended, is a requirement for the formation of a craze. This is assumed to provide the essential condition that less energy is required to cause a large strain within a small volume of material than to give a smaller strain to a much larger volume. In the case of polystyrene it was shown that this difference in energy can amount to a factor as great as 2.[86] The importance of plastic instability in fracture processes has also been emphasised by Vincent.[7]

If this hypothesis is correct then the occurrence of crazes should be related to the large strain properties of the polymers, and these as shown in Section 6.5.2 can be significantly modified by pre-orientation of the material. This aspect of the problem has been studied by Rehage and Goldbach[87] who showed that by means of pre-orientation the fall in engineering stress at high elongations could be eliminated with polymethylmethacrylate glass, in a similar way to that observed by Vincent with PVC (Fig. 23). At the same time the tendency of the polymer to give crazes in tension was eliminated. This work was supported by the work of Murphy et al.[85] who showed that oriented regions at the edges of a polystyrene test-piece resisted the propagation of a craze and so made it possible to form stable internal crazes in simple tension.

Thus when subject to a tensile stress high molecular weight glassy plastics can exhibit three main types of response. They can extend uniformly, they can extend in a necking mode and they can craze and break. Three types of tensile stress–strain curves associated with these three types of behaviour are shown in Fig. 30. It will be seen that there are large differences between the amount of energy associated with plastic instability in each case. With polystyrene it is large and with cellulose nitrate it is small, while PVC holds an intermediate position. It is believed that these concepts, which are, however, in an early stage of development and certainly require further evidence to establish them, may offer a useful approach to the problem of crazing.

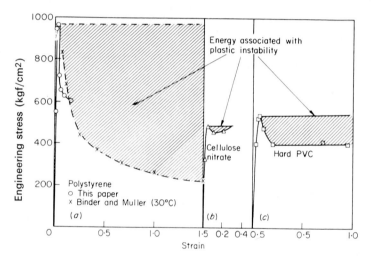

Fig. 30.   *Real and derived stress–strain curves of plastics having a different type of response to stress. Tensile stress–strain curves for different plastics plotted on the same scale. The three plastics show quite different behaviour. (a) Polystyrene exhibits crazing folowed by brittle fracture. (b) Cellulose nitrate extends uniformly. (c) The PVC necks and the measured stress–strain curve are, of course, distorted by this effect. (Reproduced from reference* 21 *by permission of John Wiley and Sons Inc.)*

6.6.3   The growth of voids in a polymer glass

Whether or not the concept of plastic instability is a significant feature for the formation of crazes, it is clear that any craze requires the formation of voids in the polymer at stresses below the bulk-yield stress. This involves the generation of a new surface and there must be enough energy available to do this when the voids are very small.

Thus in order for a void to be formed in an isotropic solid with a yield stress Y two criteria must be met.

(1) The stress must be adequate to provide the surface energy to nucleate the void when it is very small.

(2) The stress must also be large enough for the nucleated centre to grow effectively in the elastic–plastic solid.

However, as shown by Kambour[88] the energy associated with the plastic and elastic deformations to form and break a craze are much larger than the true surface energy. The second of these conditions is therefore likely to be the most significant. It will be dealt with in more detail in Chapter 7. Briefly, there is a problem of how it is possible for voids to grow in a glassy polymer under the influence of hydrostatic tension below the yield stress. One theory put forward by Gent[89] argues that the effect of the hydrostatic tension at the tip of a craze or crack is to increase the free volume of the polymer and so to reduce the glass transition temperature. In this way a viscoelastic deformation can more easily occur. This approach draws support from a large body of theory concerned with the inter-relation of volume and viscosity (Introduction and Ch. 3) and also from the yield stress theories of Robertson[90] and of Ward.[91] The second proposal[92] suggests the voids are able to grow in groups by a process of 'overlapping proliferation' whereby the energy requirement for the formation of a single void is reduced because the zones of plastic deformation of the different voids overlap, and because there is no energy requirement in the volume occupied by another void. This approach is supported by evidence from the electron-micrography of the initiation areas of fracture surfaces,[93,94] one example of which is given in Fig. 31.

6.6.4 The nucleation of voids

If a void, or more particularly a group of voids, is to be formed in a plastic there must be enough energy available for the formation of the new surface as well as to deform the polymer. This requirement has, of course, been known for a long time[4] in connection with fracture processes, and is most important when the hole is small. Thus the hydrostatic tension required to expand a hole of radius r is given by $2S/r$ where S is the surface tension of the liquid or plastic solid. This quantity can be shown to be significant only when the holes concerned are very small ($r = 1$–10 nm) (10–100 Å). The voids observed by Mann[94] have all gone beyond this size but many of those seen by Kambour[88] are indeed of this magnitude as also are the smallest holes at the end of the craze shown in Fig. 28.

On the other hand, there is always a size below which the void cannot be stable in a particular stress field. To reach this size, energy must first be

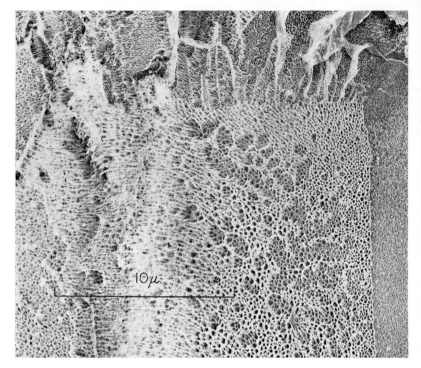

Fig. 31. Voids in the initiation area of the fracture of compression moulded polystyrene. (Reproduced from reference 94 by permission of John Wiley and Sons Inc.)

supplied and the existence of this energy requirement is the factor common to all nucleation phenomena and is believed to be responsible for the 'tensile strength' of liquids. A theoretical treatment of the problem has been given by Irwin[95] and also by Fisher[96] who proposed that

$$p = \left(\frac{16\pi}{3kT} \frac{S^3}{\ln NkT/h} \right)^{\frac{1}{2}}$$

or, more simply, since the absolute value of the constants is inevitably uncertain

$$p \simeq K \left(\frac{S^3}{T} \right)^{\frac{1}{2}}$$

where p is the hydrostatic tension required to form a void, S the surface tension of the liquid and T the absolute temperature.

This equation may be appropriately applied to measurements of the tensile strength of low viscosity liquids. Unfortunately, these measurements are still extremely uncertain so that the values of K obtained vary widely as shown in Table 2. Nevertheless, we can take an average value of $K = 3 \times 10^{14}$ and measured values for the surface tension of polystyrene[97,98] and use them to estimate the cavitation stresses likely to be

TABLE 2

TENSILE STRENGTH OF LIQUIDS

Liquids	Temperature (°C)	Average surface tension (γ) (dyn/cm)	Average tensile nucleation stress (p) (kbar)	K from the equation $p = K \left(\dfrac{S^3}{T}\right)^{\frac{1}{2}}$
Benzene[a]	23	28	30	$1 \cdot 1 \times 10^{14}$
Benzene[b]	0–28	30 (10°C)	130	$4 \cdot 2 \times 10^{14}$
Aniline[b]	-5 ± 5	39·4	270	$5 \cdot 8 \times 10^{14}$
Carbon tetrachloride	-15 ± 30	27	275	$10 \cdot 3 \times 10^{14}$
Ethanol[c]	18·5	22·7	46·5	$2 \cdot 4 \times 10^{14}$
Ethanol[d]	27	22·7	39	$2 \cdot 4 \times 10^{14}$
Ethyl ether[d]	27	17	72	$5 \cdot 6 \times 10^{14}$

[a] Donoghue J. J., Volkath, R. E., and Gerjuoy, E. (1951). *J. Chem. Phys.*, **19**, 55.
[b] Briggs, L. J. (1951). *J. Chem. Phys.*, **19**, 970.
[c] Temperley, H. V. (1946). *Proc. Phys. Soc.*, **58**, 420; (1947) **59**, 199.
[d] Fisher, J. C. (1948). (*Ibid.*)

required in a glassy polymer like polystyrene. These are given and compared with the yield and crazing stress (Fig. 32). Clearly the estimates for nucleation stress may contain very large errors, though we may note that the measurements of Lindsey[97] on polyurethane elastomers do fall within our range of estimates. Nevertheless, even allowing for these errors we can reach the following conclusions:

(a) The nucleation stresses are well below the yield stress or the crazing stress at the temperatures at which the plastic is normally used.
(b) At higher temperatures, however, nucleation stresses do not fall to zero as the glass transition temperature is approached, so that under these conditions, crazing should tend to be suppressed and the test-piece should deform as a whole. This is, of course, observed.
(c) As the temperature is reduced both the yield stress and the crazing stress increase much faster than the nucleation stress. Thus nucleation becomes relatively much easier as the temperature falls.

These conclusions may be related to experiments in a number of ways. For example, it is known[100] that polymethylmethacrylate fracture surfaces show characteristic hyperbolas formed by the creation of fresh nuclei in front of the main crack. The above theory would suggest that the nucleation process would become relatively easier at lower temperatures, and in

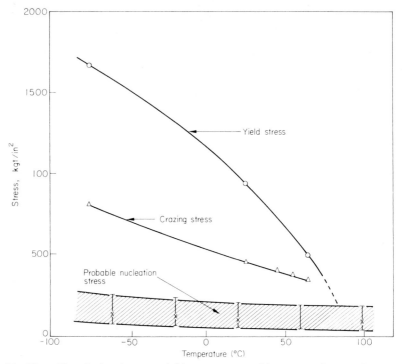

Fig. 32.   The relations between yield stress measured in compression, crazing stress and estimated nucleation stress for polystyrene. Yield stress and crazing stress are measured values and the nucleation stress was estimated as described in Section 6.6.4. This polystyrene showed an estimated ratio of yield stress in compression/ tension of 0·94. (Reproduced from reference 92 by permission of John Wiley and Sons Inc.)

Fig. 33 we show optical micrographs of the surface of Perspex (meth-acrylate) Izod impact test-pieces broken at three temperatures. It will be seen that the number of independent nuclei increases as the temperature falls. A similar but less conclusive observation was made by Beardmore.[101]

It is believed that it is now reasonable to assume that crazing is a process which can occur quite naturally in any orientation hardening material

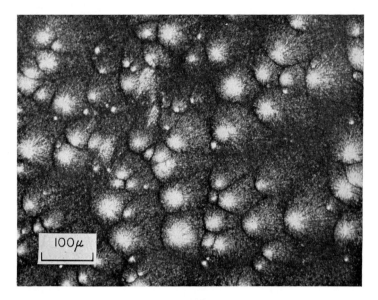

Fig. 33(a)

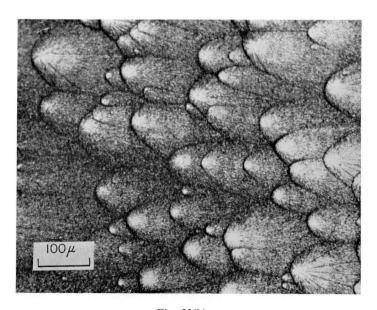

Fig. 33(b)

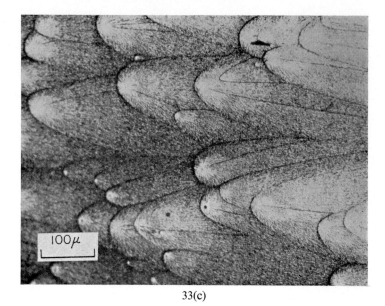

33(c)

Fig. 33.   Parabolas formed in the fracture of polymethylmethacrylate at different temperatures. (a) −65°C; (b) +23°C; (c) +55°C. *Optical micrographs taken from Izod test-pieces. As the temperature decreases the amount of nucleation of new fractures increases. (Reproduced from reference 92 by permission of John Wiley and Sons Inc.)*

which exhibits high plastic instability at moderate strains and in which the yield stresses are much higher than the stresses required for the nucleation of voids. Further it is clear that the formation of a craze is often the first stage of the fracture process. However, the fact that a craze structure is formed does not automatically provide an answer to the problem of the strength of a polymer glass. Obviously, the highest stresses within the craze will be larger than the average stress on the plastic or on the craze. On the other hand, considerable orientation of the polymer has taken place and at high orientations isothermal plastic instability may disappear. On the other hand when the stress is high the tendency to adiabatic instability will increase. The polymer may also become stronger or weaker for other reasons. Thus there arises a new problem relating to the fracture of the craze itself, which should be related to the fracture of polymers at high deformations. This takes the problem out of the province of the study of large deformations and into the field of specific fracture studies. (Chapter 7).

REFERENCES

1. McCormick, H. W., Brower, F. M. and Kim, L. (1959). *J. Pol. Sci.*, **39**, 87.
2. Murphy, B. M., Haward, R. N. and White, E. F. T. (1971). *J. Pol. Sci.*, A-2, **9**, 801.
3. Gurevich, G. and Kobeko, P. (1940). *Rubber Chem. and Tech.*, **13**, 904.
4. Haward, R. N. (1942). *Trans. Farad. Soc.*, **38**, 391.
5. Hoff, E. A. W. (1952). *J. Appl. Chem.*, **2**, 441.
6. Alexander, A. E. and Johnson, P. (1949). *Colloid Science*, Clarendon Press, Oxford, pp. 30, 478, 586, 610.
7. Vincent, P. I. Proc. Conf. Physical Basis of Yield and Fracture, Oxford, Sept. 1966, p. 155 (London: Inst. of Phys & Phy. Soc.).
8. Brown, N. and Ward, I. M. (1968). *J. Pol. Sci.*, A-2, **6**, 607.
9. Lazurkin, Yu. S. and Fogel'son, R. A. (1951). *Zhur. Tech. Phys. U.S.S.R.*, 3, **21**, 267.
10. Binder, G. and Muller, F. H. (1961). *Koll. Zeit.*, **177**, 129.
11. Kirkland, J. T., Duncan, J. L. and Haward, R. N. (1970). *Polymer*, **11**, 562.
12. Haward, R. N. and Thackray, G. (1968). *Proc. Roy. Soc.*, A, **302**, 453.
13. Sternstein, S. S., Ongchin, L. and Silverman, A. (1968). *App. Pol. Symposia*, **7**, 175.
14. Vinogradov, G. V. and Belkin, I. M. (1965). *J. Pol. Sci.*, A, **3**, 917.
15. Leonov, A. I. and Vinogradov, G. V. (March–April 1964). Proc. Acad. Sci., U.S.S.R. *Phys. Chem. Section*, **155**, 270.
16. Holliday, L., Mann. J., Pogany, G. A., Pugh, H. L. D. and Gunn, D. A. (1964). *Nature*, **202**, 381.
17. C. W. Weaver and M. S. Patterson (1969). *J. Pol. Sci.*, A-2, **7**, 387.
18. Ender, D. H. and Andrews, R. D. (1955). *J. Appl. Phys.*, **36**, 3057.
18a. Brady, T. E. and Yeh, G. S. Y. (1971). *J. Appl. Phys.*, **42**, 12, 4622.
19. Ender, D. H. (1970). *J. Macromol. Sci.*, **B4**, (3), 635.
19a. Whitney, W. and Andrews, R. D. (1967). *J. Pol. Sci.*, C, **16**, 2981.
19b. Kramer, E. J. (1970). *J. Appl. Phys.*, **41**, 4327.
20. Robertson, R. E. (1963). *J. App. Pol. Sci.*, **7**, 443.
21. Vincent, P. I. (1960). *Polymer*, **1**, 7.
22. Rehage, G. and Goldbach, G. (1967). *Angew. Makromol. Chem.*, **1**, 125.
23. Biglione, G., Baer, E. and Radcliffe, S. V., *Proc. 2nd Conference on Fracture*, Brighton, April 1969, paper 44/1.
24. Nadai, A. (1950). *Theory of Flow and Fracture of Solids*, McGraw-Hill, New York, p. 71.
25. Marshall, T. and Thompson, A. B. (1954). *Proc. Roy. Soc.*, A, **221**, 541.
26. Lazurkin, Yu. S. (1958). *J. Pol. Sci.*, **30**, 595.
27. Newman, S. (1959). *J. Appl. Pol. Sci.*, **2**, 252.
28. Muller, F. H. (1970). *Pure & App. Chem.*, **23**, 201.
29. Krigbaum, W. R., Roe, R. J. and Smith, K. J. (1964). *Polymer*, **5**, 533.
30. Riches, J. G. and Hargreaves, G. (1968). *J. Pol. Sci.*, **17**, 829.
31. Brown, N. and Ward, I. M. (1968). *Phil. Mag.*, **17**, 961.
32. Joule, J. (1857). *Phil. Mag.*, **14**, 226.
33. McNally, J. G. and Shepherd, S. E. (1931). *J. Phys. Chem.*, **35**, 100.
34. Haward, R. N. (1943). *Trans. Farad. Soc.*, **39**, 267.
34a. Andrianova, G. P., Kechekyan, A. S. and Kargin, V. A. (1971). *J. Pol. Sci.*, A-2, 1919.
34b. Richards, R. C. and Kramer, E. J. (1972). *J. Macromol. Sci.* (*Phys.*), **B6**, (1), 243.
35. Drabble, F., Haward, R. N. and Johnson, W. (1966). *Brit. J. App. Phys.*, **17**, 241.
36. Stolting, J. and Muller, F. H. (1970). *Koll. Zeit.*, **238**, 460.
37. Stolting, J. and Muller, F. H. (1970). *Koll. Zeit.*, **240**, 792.
38. Preuss, H. H. W. (1963). *Plaste u Kautschuk*, **6**, 330.

39. Fuller, K. N. G. and Fox, P. G. (1971). *Nature—Physical Science*, **234**, 13.
40. Bowden, P. B. and Jukes, J. A. (1969). *Nature*, **221**, 462.
41. Muller, F. H. and Binder, G. (1962). *Koll. Zeit.*, **183**, 120.
42. Shishkin, N. I. and Milagin, M. F. (1962). *See* G. M. Bartenev and Y. S. Zuyev. (1968). *The Strength and Fracture of Viscoelastic Material*, Pergamon, Oxford, p. 139.
43. Treloar, L. R. G. (1971). *Plastics and Polymers*, Feb. p. 29.
44. Haward, R. N. (1949). *The Strength of Plastics and Glass*, Clever-Hume Press, London, pp. 80–120.
45. Alfrey, T. Jr. (1948). *The Mechanical Behaviour of High Polymers*, Interscience, New York, pp. 220–8.
46. Muller, F. H. (1961). *Kunstoffe*, **51**, 490.
47. Tuckett, R. F. (1943). *Chem. and Ind.*, **62**, 430.
48. Hansen, D. and Pinnock, J. A. (1965). *J. App. Phys.*, **36**, 332.
49. Hermans, P. H. (1940). *Cellulose Chemie*, **18**, 97.
50. Muller, F. H. (1963). *Material Pruf.*, **5**, 332.
51. Ender, D. H. (1968). *J. Appl. Phys.*, **39**, 4871.
52. Meyer, K. H. and Van der Wijk, A. J. A. (1946). *J. Polym. Res.*, **1**, 49.
53. Speakman, J. B. (1947). *Nature*, **159**, 338.
54. Porter, R. S. and Johnson, J. F. (1966). *Chem. Revs.*, **66**, 1.
55. Bueche, F. (1968). *J. Chem. Phys.*, **48**, 478.
56. Graessley, W. W. (1965). *J. Chem. Phys.*, **43**, 2696.
57. Mills, N. J., Nevin, A. and McAinsh, J. (1970). *J. Macromol. Sci.–Phys.*, **B4**(4), 863.
58. Baldwin, F. P., Borzel, P. and Makowski, H. S. Preprints Div. of Rubber Chem., A.C.S. Meeting, Los Angeles, April 29th–May 2nd, 1969.
59. Furakawa, J., Nishioka, A. and Kotani, T. (1970). *Polymer Letters*, **8**, 25.
60. Kotani, T., Kawashima, M., Suzuki, S. and Nakao, M. (1969). *J. Soc. Rub. Ind. Japan*, **42**, 260.
61. Treloar, L. R. G. (1958). *The Physics of Rubber Elasticity*, 2nd Edn. Oxford Univ. Press.
62. Williamson, G. R., Wright, B. and Haward, R. N. (1964). *J. App. Chem.*, **14**, 131.
63. Lohse, F., Schmid, R., Batzer, H. and Fisch, W. (1969). *Brit. Pol. J.*, **1**, 110.
64. Kirkland, J. T., Duncan, J. L. and Haward, R. N. (1970). *Polymer*, **11**, 562.
65. Treloar, L. R. G. (1944). *Trans. Farad. Soc.*, **40**, 59.
66. Bueche, F., Kimzig, B. J. and Coven, C. J. (1965). *Polymer Letters*, **3**, 399.
67. Bueche, F. and Halpin, J. C. (1964). *J. App. Phys.*, **35**, 36.
69. Halpin, J. C. (1969). *Rubber Chem. and Tech.*, **38**, 1007.
69. Smith, T. L. (1970). *Pure and App. Chem.*, **23**, 235.
70. Haward, R. N. and Thackray, G. (1968). *Proc. Roy. Soc.*, A, **302**, 453.
71. Broutman, L. J. and Patil, R. S. (1971). *Polymer Eng. and Sci.*, **11**, 165.
72. Ito, K. (1971). *Trans. Soc. Rheol.*, **15:3**, 389.
73. For example *see* M. G. Sharma. (1965). *The Testing of Polymers*, ed. J. V. Schmitz, Interscience, New York.
74. Kausch-Blecken von Schmeling, H. H. (1970). *Revs. in Macromol. Chem.*, **5** (2), 97.
75. Zhurkov, S. N., Kuksenko, V. S. and Slutsker, A. I. *Proc. Int. Conf., on Fracture*, Brighton, 1969, paper, 46.
76. Greensmith, H. W., Mullins, L. and Thomas, A. G. (1963). *The Chemistry and Physics of Rubber-like Substances*, ed. L. Bateman, McClaren, London, John Wiley and Sons Inc., New York, p. 246.
77. Kraft, J. M. (1964). *App. Mats. Res.*, **3**, 88.
78. Williams, J. G. and Turner, C. E. *App. Matls., Res.*, July 1964, 144.
79. Irwin, G. R. (1948). 'Fracture Dynamics', *Fracturing of Metals*, p. 152, Am. Soc. Metals, Cleveland.

80. Williams, J. G. and Isherwood, D. P. (1970). *Eng. Fracture Mechanics*, **2**, 19–35.
81. Van der Boogart, A. Proc. Conf. Physical Basis of Yield and Fracture, Oxford, Sept. 1966, p. 167 (London: Inst. of Phys. & Phys. Soc.).
82. Kambour, R. P. (1964). *Polymer*, **5**, 143.
83. Matsuo, M. (1969). *Polym. Eng. and Sci.*, **9**, 206.
84. Sternstein, S. S., Ongchin, L. and Silverman, A. (1968). *App. Polymer Symposia*, **7**, 175.
85. Murphy, B. M., Haward, R. N. and White, E. F. T. *Proc. Int. Conf. Fracture*, Brighton, 1969, paper 45.
86. Haward, R. N., Murphy, B. M. and White, E. F. T. (1971). *J. Pol. Sci.* A-2, **9**, 801.
87. Rehage, G. and Goldbach, G. (1967). *Angew. Macromol. Chem.*, **1**, 125.
88. Kambour, R. P. (1965). *J. Pol. Sci.*, A-1, **3**, 1713.
89. Gent, A. N. (1970). *J. Mater. Sci.*, **5**, 925.
90. Robertson, R. E. (1966). *J. Chem. Phys.*, **44**, 3950.
91. Ward, I. M. (1971). *J. Mater. Sci.*, **6**, 1397.
92. Haward, R. N. (1972). 'Critical stages in the fracture of an organic glass', *in: Amorphous Materials* (eds. R. W. Douglas and B. Ellis), John Wiley, London.
93. Mann, J., Bird, R. J. and Rooney, G. *Polymer* (to be published).
94. Mann, J. (1966). *Chem. and Ind.*, p. 643.
95. Irwin, G. R. (1958). *Handbuch der Physik*, Springer, Berlin, VI, p. 551.
96. Fisher, J. C. (1948). *J. App. Phys.*, **19**, 1062.
97. Lindsey, G. H. (1967). *J. App. Phys.*, **38**, 4843.
98. Gray, V. R. (1955). *Chem. and Ind.*, p. 917.
99. White, E. F. T. and Harford, J. (to be published).
100. Berry J. P. (1964). 'Brittle Behaviour in Polymer Solids.' *in: Fracture Processes in Polymeric Solids*, ed B. Rosen, Interscience, New York, pp. 195–237.
101. Beardmore, P. (1969). *Phil. Mag.*, **19**, 389.

CHAPTER 7

CRACKING AND CRAZING IN POLYMERIC GLASSES

E. H. ANDREWS

7.1 INTRODUCTION

The subject of fracture has obvious practical importance. In any practical or engineering application of polymeric solids, the conditions for fracture inevitably set a limitation both to design and to service conditions. It is therefore necessary to define these 'conditions for fracture' and to define them in such a way as to be directly useful to the engineer. This is the aim of 'fracture mechanics', which can be described as a theory of the fracture of solids viewed as continuous media. Naturally, such a theory is very general and can be applied to glassy polymers as to any other class of coherent solids. It seems appropriate, then, to begin this chapter by considering the fracture mechanics approach to the cracking and crazing of glassy polymers. We shall see that this approach not only provides a theory of use to the engineer, but also affords much insight into the 'mechanisms' of fracture as well as its 'mechanics'.

Fracture mechanics is not the only treatment possible, however. There is also what we might call the microscopical approach, which considers the structure of materials on a very fine scale and the way in which this structure affects (and is affected by) the fracture process. Glassy plastics are, almost by definition, devoid of any clearly defined physical micro-structure except where this has been deliberately introduced by blending or reinforcement with other phases. Single phase glasses are as close an approach to the molecularly homogeneous and isotropic solid as we are likely to obtain. Perfect homogeneity is, however, unlikely and we might expect to find such things as fluctuations in density and local anisotropy on a scale significantly larger than the molecule itself. All real polymeric glasses are also likely to contain significant amounts of impurity, such as dissolved monomer and water, and also structural defects such as dirt inclusions and surface scratches. In those cases where the material is cross-linked, the cross-link density will fluctuate from point to point. Although, therefore, it is not possible to describe the physical microstructure of glasses with the same specificity as in metallic alloys or semi-crystalline polymers, we must not assume the absence of microstructural features of importance to the subject under discussion.

One of the most important, and fascinating, aspects of fracture in glassy polymers is that of crazing or microvoiding, and this is a microscopical feature which *arises* during the fracture process. As we shall see, it affords evidence of 'invisible' microstructural features in the solid, but it is also, in itself, a phenomenon which falls to be considered under the heading of microstructural aspects of fracture. Our second main topic will therefore be the crazing phenomenon viewed as a microscopical process.

Finally, as we reduce the 'scale' of our viewpoint, we come eventually to the molecular aspects of fracture. All fracture eventually involves the breakage of interatomic bonds, whether they be secondary bonds such as operate between the molecules of a thermoplastic, or the primary bonds within the molecules. The kinetic or thermofluctuation theory of fracture in polymers considers fracture as a molecular process analogous to thermal degradation. Whilst this theory is of less direct usefulness from an engineering viewpoint than that of fracture mechanics, it has considerable success in enabling us to picture what is actually happening on a molecular level, and thus in understanding the physics of the process. Needless to say, the kinetic and fracture mechanics approaches are complementary and not contradictory. Important advances in molecular fracture studies have resulted, during the last decade, from the application of electron spin resonance spectrometry to the study of molecular fracture under tensile stress, though most of this work has been carried out on highly crystalline polymers rather than glasses. More recent work on cross-linked glasses, however, will be discussed in detail in the final pages of this chapter.

7.2 FRACTURE MECHANICS

7.2.1 Linear fracture mechanics

Linear fracture mechanics is so called because it is based on the results of linear elasticity theory in which the strains are supposed to be infinitesimal and proportional to stress. It is important to emphasise this, since polymeric materials are frequently (indeed, usually) nonlinear in their stress–strain behaviour and also exhibit finite recoverable strain. Linear theory must therefore be applied with caution to polymeric materials, although polymer glasses well below T_g are often sufficiently 'linear' under low stresses for linear fracture mechanics to be applicable.

Fracture mechanics is concerned with the conditions of stress in a solid necessary to cause propagation of a pre-existing crack. It defines the stress field perturbation produced around a crack in an otherwise uniform stress field and draws certain conclusions about the conditions required to cause the crack to grow. It is clear that the application of fracture mechanics to the fracture of solids either requires the initial presence of a real crack or similar geometrical feature (*e.g.* a surface step) or else involves the assumption that the solid contains 'intrinsic flaws' which can be likened to cracks in their ability to perturb and concentrate the stress field. This is a weakness of the theory, since we are usually interested in the strength of virgin solids. It is not surprising therefore that the major current application of the theory is in predicting lifetimes of components and structures (*e.g.* pressure vessels) in which observable cracks have already developed.

The idea of an 'intrinsic flaw' in an apparently virgin solid is not, however, meaningless. It is often found empirically that a well-defined value can be attributed indirectly to such 'flaws' even though they cannot be identified prior to a fracture test, so that the concept, if not the reality, is empirically valid.

The theory of linear fracture mechanics has been derived elsewhere,[1] and we shall here only outline and discuss its results. Consider a sharp crack in a sheet of uniform thickness subject to a uniform tensile stress σ_0 in the plane of the sheet. At points remote from the crack a state of uniform stress exists, but in the vicinity of the crack a complex stress field will exist. In the simple case illustrated in Fig. 1, the components of stress at a point P will, by dimensional analysis, be given by an expression of the form,

$$\sigma_{ij} = \sigma_0 f\left(\frac{a}{r}\right) g(\theta) \qquad (1)$$

where f, g are functions, $2a$ is the length of the crack and θ, r the coordinates of the point P referred to the crack tip as origin.

Clearly this is a simple case. The applied stress field could be much more complex than a simple tensile stress, and the crack could be oriented at an angle other than $90°$ to the major principal applied stress. Such situations

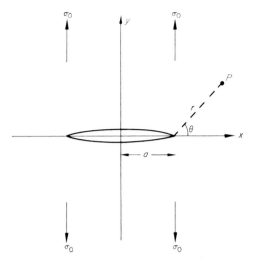

Fig. 1. *Sharp crack in a uniformly stressed, infinite lamina.*

have been considered elsewhere[2,3] and will not be treated here. The simple case chosen is the most useful since fracture in brittle solids under tensile load usually occurs at right angles to the major principal applied stress, *i.e.* the situation covered by eqn. (1).

Linear elasticity theory enables us to evaluate the functions in eqn. (1). They are complicated functions, but can be considerably simplified if we restrict the solution to regions close to the tip of the crack. Equation (1) then takes the form

$$\sigma_{ij} = \sigma_0 \left(\frac{a}{2r}\right)^{\frac{1}{2}} f_{ij}(\theta) - \sigma^* \tag{2}$$

where f_{ij} are known and σ^* is either zero or a small correction factor. Equation (2) is often written,[1]

$$\sigma_{ij} = \frac{K}{(2\pi r)^{\frac{1}{2}}} f_{ij}(\theta) - \sigma^* \tag{3}$$

where K is the 'stress intensity factor', and has the value, for the case illustrated,

$$K_I = \sigma_0(\pi a)^{\frac{1}{2}} \tag{4}$$

The stress intensity factor will vary if the geometrical arrangement varies (*i.e.* if the plane has a finite width D, K_I will become a function of D as well as of a), but once defined, it uniquely governs the stress distribution around the crack. It can then be proposed that the crack will propagate if K_I exceeds some critical value K_{IC}, which will in general be a function only of the material and the conditions of rate and temperature applying to the test in question. In practice it is found that K_{IC} varies also with sheet thickness, over a certain range of thicknesses, because the state of stress near the crack tip varies from plane stress in a very thin plate to plane strain near the centre of a thick plate.

The supposition, borne out in practice, that fracture occurs at a critical stress intensity factor constitutes, of course, a fracture criterion. This criterion avoids the dilemma arising from a 'critical tip stress' criterion for fracture (the dilemma that eqn. (3) predicts infinite stresses at the tip of infinitely sharp cracks) by replacing actual stresses by the stress-field parameter K_I.

7.2.2 Measurements of K_{IC} for glassy polymers

K_{IC} can be measured using a variety of geometrical arrangements of a pre-formed crack in a sheet specimen loaded in tension. One of the most frequently employed is the 'single edge notch' (s.e.n.) specimen which corresponds to Fig. 1 split along the Y-axis to give a crack or notch of length a in a free edge. The formula for K_I is unchanged. Parallel cleavage and tapered cleavage test geometries (Fig. 2) have also been employed,[4] the formulae for K_I being respectively:

Parallel cleavage

$$K_I = \frac{Pa}{h_c H^{3/2}} (3 \cdot 46 + 2 \cdot 38 \, H/a) \tag{5}$$

Tapered cleavage

$$K_I = \frac{2P}{(hh_c)^{\frac{1}{2}}} \left(\frac{3a^2}{H^3} + \frac{1}{H} \right)^{\frac{1}{2}} \tag{6}$$

where P is the applied load, a the crack length, H the width of the cantilever arm and h, h_c are respectively the sheet thickness and reduced thickness (reduced by grooving the specimen to guide the crack in a straight line). In the case of the tapered cleavage specimen, the geometry is arranged so that $(3a^2/H^3 + H^{-1})$ is constant, giving K_I independent of crack length.

The critical value K_{IC} is obtained by using the critical load P_c for crack propagation in eqns. (5) and (6).

Results[4] from all three kinds of specimen are given in Fig. 3 for polymethylmethacrylate at 20°C. The value of K_{IC} is seen to be independent of the specimen geometry (and is thus characteristic of the material rather

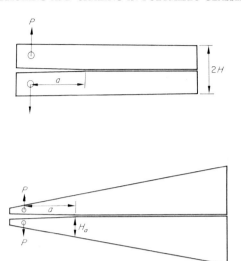

Fig. 2.   Parallel cleavage and tapered cleavage specimens (after Marshall et al.[4]).

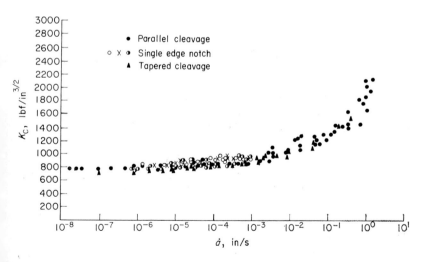

Fig. 3.   Fracture toughness as a function of crack speed in PMMA at 20°C for three different test geometries (after Marshall et al.[4]).

than the specimen), but dependent upon the speed at which the crack grows, especially towards the higher speeds where adiabatic effects may be operative.

Measurements of this kind provide basic data on the fracture resistance of materials where there is already a crack or analogous defect present.

7.2.3 Crack-opening displacement

Linear fracture mechanics assumes the material to be completely elastic, but this is seldom the case in reality. More usually, with metals, glassy plastics and even inorganic glass itself, there is some ductility, even though this may be limited to a very small region at the tip of a propagating crack. If the size of the 'plastic zone' at the tip is very small, and the majority of the specimen remains elastic under test, linear fracture mechanics can still be applied. If, however, the plastic zone grows to such a size that the elastic stress distribution around the crack is significantly modified, this can no longer be done.

A concept which may be used under these circumstances is that of the crack opening displacement (c.o.d.). This quantity, denoted δ, is simply the distance by which the crack faces separate at the tip as a result of plastic deformation. It can be shown theoretically,[49] for an elastic–plastic solid, that

$$\delta = \frac{K_I{}^2}{\sigma_y E} \tag{7}$$

where K_I is the stress intensity factor previously defined, σ_y is the yield stress of the material and E is Young's modulus. The fracture criterion adopted is that fracture occurs at a critical value of δ. If eqn. (7) holds this is no different, of course, from a K_{IC} criterion, since σ_y, E are constants. The c.o.d. criterion is valuable, however, because δ can be measured directly on test specimens, regardless of the truth of eqn. (7) which, in any case, only applies to simple elastic–plastic solids.

No extensive use has so far been made of the c.o.d. concept for plastics, since those materials which form large plastic zones are usually highly nonlinear in bulk. The idea has proved useful in the analysis of craze behaviour, however (see later).

7.2.4 Energy balance approach

The weakness of linear fracture mechanics lies in its restriction to materials which obey infinitesimal strain, linear elasticity theory. Materials not obeying this theory have stress distributions at crack tips which cannot be calculated. A material like rubber, for example, showing finite strains in excess of 100%, makes nonsense of the assumptions of 'classical' elasticity theory.

In the light of this problem, a quite different approach has usually been adopted for polymeric solids.[5] Interestingly enough, it was first proposed by Griffith[6] for fracture in a linear solid, glass, but as we shall see it lends itself to the treatment of materials with very general deformation behaviour.

The energy-balance criterion for fracture states that a crack will propagate if the strain-energy released from the body as a result of propagation equals or exceeds the energy required to cause the crack extension. This 'energy required' is normally equated to the work done in forming the new crack surfaces—the so-called 'surface work'. In Griffith's original theory the surface work was simply the surface free energy of the solid, but we now know that relatively large amounts of plastic or visco-elastic work are also done in the creation of crack surfaces.

The energy requirement also includes terms which are usually ignored, such as the energy radiated from the growing crack in the form of stress-waves or sound.

The energy-balance criterion for slow crack propagation can be expressed mathematically as follows:

$$-\frac{\partial \mathscr{E}}{\partial A} \geq \mathscr{T} \tag{8}$$

where $\mathscr{E}$ is the total elastic stored energy in the body, A the interfacial area of the crack and $\mathscr{T}$ is the surface work. The partial differential denotes that only energy changes arising from increases in A are considered. The symbol $\mathscr{T}$ is used, following Rivlin and Thomas who used 'T' to denote 'tearing energy', but to avoid confusion with the symbol for temperature. The left-hand side of eqn. (8) is sometimes called the 'energy release rate' and denoted G, but this practice can lead to confusion with the symbol for shear modulus.

The first task is to evaluate the left-hand side of eqn. (8) in terms of accessible quantities, such as stress, strain and geometrical factors. This can be done in a very general way without use of classical elasticity theory.

Consider a crack in a semi-infinite sheet of thickness h subject to a system of applied stresses σ_{01}, $\sigma_{02} \cdots$ at infinity. The semi-infinite geometry can be achieved in a number of ways, e.g. an edge crack of length c in a semi-infinite sheet; an infinitely long crack in a sheet of infinite length but finite width l and so on. In each case, however, there is only a single non-infinite 'length' L to be considered.

Choosing some convenient point as origin, any point P in the sheet has co-ordinates X, Y measured parallel to and perpendicular to the crack axis respectively. Then, by dimensional analysis, the stresses at P due to σ_{01} are

$$\sigma_{ij}(P) = \sigma_{01} f_{ij} \left(\frac{X}{L}, \frac{Y}{L} \right) \tag{9}$$

The strains at P will be given by a similar expression and the stored energy density at P, being the integral of stress with respect to strain, will be given by

$$W(P) = W_{01} f \left(\frac{X}{L}, \frac{Y}{L} \right) \tag{10}$$

where f is another function and W_{01} the stored energy density, at points remote from the crack, due to the stress σ_{01}. Any other applied stresses σ_{02}, σ_{03}, etc. will simply add terms of a similar kind to eqns. (9) and (10), providing the superposition of stresses can be applied. It is, therefore, only necessary to consider one of the terms, *i.e.* that arising from the stress σ_{01}, remembering that the effects of σ_{02}, etc. can be superposed at the end of the calculation.

The change in $W(P)$ due to growth of the crack at constant W_{01} (written W_0 for conciseness) is,

$$\frac{\partial W}{\partial c}(P) = W_0 \left(\frac{\partial f}{\partial x} \frac{\partial x}{\partial c} + \frac{\partial f}{\partial y} \frac{\partial y}{\partial c} \right)$$

where $x = X/L$ and $y = Y/L$. Two cases will be considered.

(i) *Infinite crack in finite width sheet; 'pure shear' test piece (Fig. 4(a))*
Here, the non-infinite quantity L is the sheet width, l, which is independent of c. The only locatable point is the crack tip itself, and we therefore choose this to be the origin, noting that the origin will move with the tip. Then

$$\frac{\partial W(P)}{\partial c} = \frac{W_0}{l} \left(\frac{\partial f}{\partial x} \frac{\partial X}{\partial c} + \frac{\partial f}{\partial y} \frac{\partial Y}{\partial c} \right)$$

but because the origin is the tip of the crack, $\partial X/\partial c = -1$ and $\partial Y/\partial c = 0$, so

$$\frac{\partial W(P)}{\partial c} = -\frac{W_0}{l} \left(\frac{\partial f}{\partial x} \right) = -\frac{W_0}{l} g_1(x, y) \tag{11}$$

where g_1 is another function.

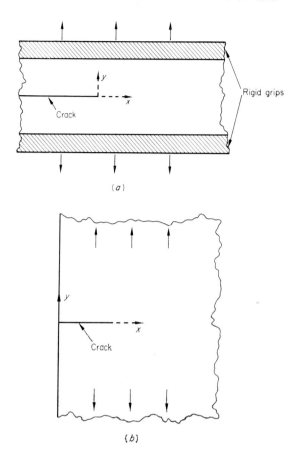

Fig. 4. (a) *'Pure shear' test piece.* (b) *Edge crack in a semi-infinite lamina.*

(ii) *Edge crack in semi-infinite sheet (Fig.* 4(b))
In this case we choose the origin to be the intersection of the crack with the free edge. Then X, Y are independent of c, and the only non-infinite length L is c itself. Then $x = X/c$; $y = Y/c$ and

$$\frac{\partial W(P)}{\partial c} = -\left(\frac{W_0}{c}\right)\left(x\frac{\partial f}{\partial x} + y\frac{\partial f}{\partial y}\right) = -\frac{W_0}{c} g_2(x, y) \qquad (12)$$

where g_2 is another function.
    Clearly eqns. (11) and (12) are of the same form and can be treated simultaneously.

The total energy loss $-\partial \mathscr{E}/\partial c$ is given by summation, over the volume of specimen, of $-\partial W(P)/\partial c$ multiplied by an element of volume δv. Now, for the test piece of Fig. 4(a),

$$\delta v = h\delta X \delta Y = hl^2 \delta x \delta y$$

So that,

$$-\frac{\partial \mathscr{E}}{\partial c} = W_0 lh \sum_P g_1(x, y)\delta x \delta y$$

Or, since $A = 2hc$,

$$-\frac{\partial \mathscr{E}}{\partial A} = \frac{W_0 l}{2} \sum_P g_1(x, y)\delta x \delta y \qquad (13)$$

Similarly for an edge crack (Fig. 4(b))

$$-\frac{\partial \mathscr{E}}{\partial A} = \frac{W_0 c}{2} \sum_P g_2(x, y)\delta x \delta y \qquad (14)$$

The summations in eqns. (13) and (14) are functions only of x, y and providing the summation is always taken over an area or areas bounded by some specified stress or strain contour (e.g. $\sigma/\sigma_0 = 1$), it will be independent of l, c, σ_0, W_0 and other variables. (All these quantities are *invariant* in x, y space in which the summation is taken.)

We therefore obtain,
(i) Pure shear test piece

$$-\frac{\partial \mathscr{E}}{\partial A} = \tfrac{1}{2}kW_0 l \qquad (15)$$

where W_0 is the stored energy density in pure shear (the state of strain at points remote from the crack tip) and the constant k can easily be shown, from eqn. (11), to equal unity.
(ii) Edge crack

$$-\frac{\partial \mathscr{E}}{\partial A} = \tfrac{1}{2}kW_0 c \qquad (16)$$

where W_0 is the stored energy density in simple extension and k has the value 2π for a material which is Hookean in bulk (*i.e.* away from the crack tip).

Finally, therefore, the left-hand side of eqn. (8) is known in terms of the measurable quantities l, c, W_0 and the value of these quantities at the moment of fracture propagation can immediately be used to derive the surface work $\mathscr{T}$ using the equality in eqn. (8) to define the critical condition.

7.2.5   Measurements of surface work

The test-pieces illustrated in Figs. 4(a) and 4(b) have been used (with the relevant dimensions sufficiently large to approximate the semi-infinite conditions treated in the theory), together with other test geometries which allow $-\partial\mathscr{E}/\partial A$ to be explicitly calculated, to determine the actual value of the surface work for glassy plastics. Some of these results are detailed in Table 1. Two things are at once obvious. Firstly, the surface work is usually very much higher than a true surface energy (which would be $\sim 0\cdot 1$ J/m^2) and secondly, the thermoplastics exhibit very much higher $\mathscr{T}$ than the thermosetting epoxy resin.

TABLE 1

SURFACE WORK $\mathscr{T}$ FOR SOME GLASSY POLYMERS

Polymer	$\mathscr{T}$ J/m^2	Remarks	References
PMMA	$1\cdot 2 \cdot 10^2$ to $6\cdot 5 \cdot 10^2$		4, 7–13, 15, 17
Polystyrene	$2\cdot 5 \cdot 10^2$ to 10^3	Most conditions	3, 7, 10, 12, 14, 17, 18
	Up to $3\cdot 4 \cdot 10^3$	Some results	7
Polyester	$1\cdot 2 \cdot 10^4$	One result	10
Epoxy resin	$0\cdot 07$	5% hardener	16
	7	>15% hardener	16

As mentioned earlier, the very high values obtained for $\mathscr{T}$ are attributable to the work done in plastic deformation of the tip material before it fractures to allow crack propagation. This plastically deformed region can be seen under the microscope; it is also sometimes evidenced by interference colours[19] on the fracture surfaces formed because of the presence of a thin layer of highly distorted polymer.

In the thermoplastics this plastic deformation at the tip is accompanied[20] (and, indeed, facilitated) by multiple cavitation or crazing, and the 'plastic zone' which runs ahead of a propagating crack is, in fact, a craze with a void content[21] of 40% to 60%. This explains the low refractive index of the deformed material which is necessary to explain the existence of interference colours. It also explains the curious 'mackerel' patterns sometimes observed on brittle fracture surfaces (Fig. 5) of glassy plastics, notably polystyrene. This is caused by oscillation of the crack front from one side of the pre-formed craze to the other. Cavitation in the plastic zone clearly facilitates its formation since (in thick sheets) it relieves the plane strain condition which inhibits shear yielding and enables the material to draw out into filaments under simple tensile conditions. In

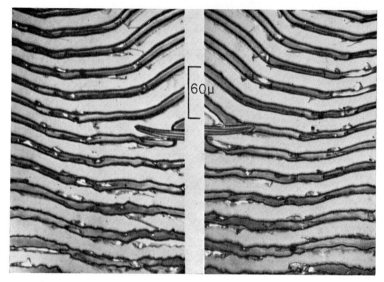

Fig. 5. Optical micrograph of 'mackerel' pattern on matching faces of polystyrene fractured at 20°C. Note that a stripped area on one face corresponds to a band of craze film on the other. (Courtesy J. Murray and D. Hull (1970). J. Poly. Sci., A2, 8, 583.)

materials where cavitation does not occur readily (most metals, thermosetting resins) a plastic zone can still form but its extent is more limited by the elastic constraint of surrounding material.

Kambour[22,23] has analysed the energy contributions to $\mathscr{T}$ arising from different sources as follows. (i) The total surface energy of the holes in the craze (where formed) turns out to contribute only about 1·5% of $\mathscr{T}$. (ii) The plastic work of craze formation is calculated at 16% of $\mathscr{T}$, and (iii) the visco-elastic work of craze breakdown when the crack propagates accounts for the remainder.

There is a strong effect of temperature upon $\mathscr{T}$, which generally increases with decreasing temperature (see Fig. 6) below room temperature. This increase is probably due to the rise in yield stress with falling temperature affecting both the plastic work of craze formation and the visco-elastic work of craze breakdown. The situation is complicated, however, by the ill-defined sharpness of the initial crack. Sternstein and Cessna[24] have shown that cracks introduced into PMMA at lower temperatures are sharper than those formed at higher temperature, giving corresponding reductions in $\mathscr{T}$ measured at a fixed temperature.

It appears that the surface work at any temperature is controlled by the amount of crazed material introduced during the formation (usually at room temperature) of the 'starter crack' whose propagation is to be studied. Under some circumstances a stress-concentrating flaw (a surface step) can be produced in PMMA without significant plastic or craze-zone formation. When fracture occurs from such a feature at 78°K, Beardmore and Johnson[25] showed that the effective value of $\mathscr{T}$ is 0·4 to 0·7 J/m^2,

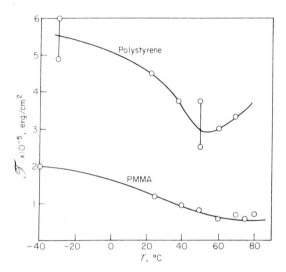

Fig. 6.   Variation of surface work $\mathscr{T}$ with temperature for PMMA and polystyrene (after Broutman and McGarry[10]).

i.e. close to the true surface energy of the solid. The large plastic work contribution at low temperature arising from a plastic or crazed zone produced at room temperature, should not surprise us. Oriented polymeric material (such as exists in this zone) is well known to retain ductility to temperatures far below the ductile-brittle transition temperature of the isotropic form.

The effect of molecular weight upon $\mathscr{T}$ was studied by Berry[26] for PMMA. His results can be summarised by the equation

$$\mathscr{T} = A - \frac{B}{\bar{M}_n} \tag{17}$$

where $\bar{M}_n$ is the number-average molecular weight and A, B are constants of value $A = 155$ J/m^2 and $3·9 \times 10^6$ J/m^2 (mass unit). His actual data are shown in Fig. 7, which also shows that a sample of the same polymer, prepared in a different way, falls well off the curve defined by eqn. (17). The equation (or at least, the value of its constants) is only valid for materials which differ in molecular weight but in no other respect. However limited eqn. (17) may be, it does follow a general relationship which has been found to apply to the molecular weight dependence of tensile strength. It also suggests that $\mathcal{T}$ will fall to zero as $\bar{M}_n$ approaches 25 000, in good agreement with Vincent's data[27] on the tensile strength of PMMA. As $\bar{M}_n$ tends to infinity, $\mathcal{T}$ tends to a limiting value of 155 J/m^2.

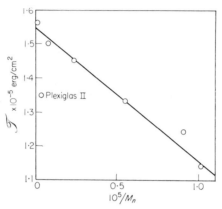

Fig. 7.   *Variation of surface work $\mathcal{T}$ with molecular weight in PMMA (after Berry[26]).*

7.2.6 Fracture stress

Our discussion has so far concerned the energy necessary to propagate a pre-existing crack. How does this knowledge help us to understand the fracture strength of virgin material?

Berry[18] showed that a high surface work value does not necessarily imply a high tensile strength. He found (Fig. 8) that polystyrene, with a higher surface work than PMMA, was in fact weaker than PMMA in a simple tensile test (corresponding in Fig. 8 to zero pre-formed crack length).

Returning to eqn. (16), and allowing W_0 to assume its linear form

$$W_0 = \frac{\sigma^2}{2E}$$

we obtain

$$\mathcal{T} = \frac{\pi c \sigma_c^2}{2E}$$

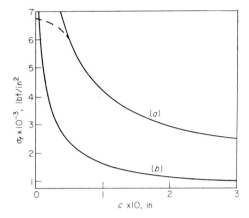

Fig. 8. Variation of tensile fracture stress with edge-crack depth, c, for (a) poly-styrene and (b) PMMA (after Berry[18]).

where σ_c is the critical tensile stress to cause propagation, c is the length of an edge crack and E is Young's modulus. This gives the tensile strength of a material,

$$\sigma_c = \left(\frac{2E\mathscr{T}}{\pi c}\right)^{\frac{1}{2}} \tag{18}$$

where c must now be regarded as an 'intrinsic' surface crack, *i.e.* one present in the virgin material. Let us denote this intrinsic flaw c_0.

Using the values determined earlier for $\mathscr{T}$, and known tensile strengths, values for c_0 can be evaluated from eqn. (18). For tensile fracture of PMMA and PS they turn out to be of the order of 10^{-4} m and 10^{-3} m respectively.

This accounts for the low relative tensile strength of PS, but raises the further difficulty that intrinsic flaws of such a size would be readily visible, whereas they are not. Clearly these 'intrinsic' flaws are themselves produced *during* the tensile test and are, in fact, the crazes which develop at stresses around 50–60% of the fracture stress. The lengths of the crazes do not correspond to the c_0 values quoted; the crazes simply concentrate stress *as if* they were cracks of this length. Another way of putting this would be to say that the crazes could be represented by 'equivalent cracks' of length c_0. Murray and Hull[28] found they could identify c_0 with the region of slow crack growth within the craze prior to catastrophic fracture.

Although this appears to negate the idea of real intrinsic flaws, this is only so for tensile tests to fracture. In certain low-stress fracture tests (creep

fracture or fatigue, for example), intrinsic flaws of much smaller size
($\sim 10^{-5}$ m) are implied and these may well exist in reality.

Further aspects of fracture mechanics will be dealt with later in the
sections on fatigue and environmental cracking and crazing.

7.3   FATIGUE FRACTURE

The wider subject of fatigue in polymers has been reviewed elsewhere[29]
and here we are concerned with the subject as it relates to glassy plastics.
There has not been a large amount of work on this topic, but what has
been done can be divided into two parts. Firstly, glassy plastics can fail
under cyclic loading conditions as a result of 'heat build-up'. As the
specimen is subject to cyclic deformation, mechanical energy is dissipated
visco-elastically (*see* Fig. 9) and reappears as heat. The temperature in the
material rises until the rate of loss of heat by conduction or convection
equals the rate of heat generation. If the temperature so attained is

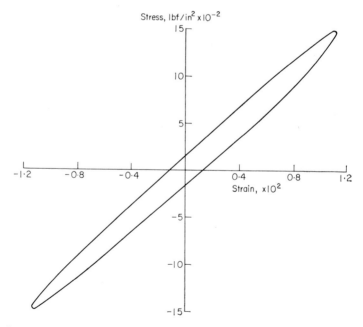

*Fig. 9.   Stress–strain loop for the cyclic deformation in torsion of a PMMA tube
(after Tauchert and Afzal[30]).*

sufficiently high, thermal decomposition, oxidation or other degradative processes set in and so reduce strength that fracture ensues.

Secondly, if the rise at equilibrium is small, the material remains thermally stable and a more normal crack initiation and propagation process occurs, as in metals and other classes of solid. This is 'fatigue' as we usually understand it and can be treated by a modified fracture mechanics. Since fatigue forms a subject in its right, the latter phenomenon is dealt with below rather than as part of the section on 'fracture mechanics'.

7.3.1 Fatigue failure by heat build-up

Theory
A perfectly elastic material will remain at a uniform temperature (equal to that of the environment) throughout a fatigue test, since no energy is dissipated in the specimen. Most real materials, and especially polymers, exhibit mechanical hysteresis even at moderate strains and may be subject to more drastic loss processes such as plasticity at higher deformations. During fatigue, therefore, some of the energy of deformation reappears as heat, and the temperature of the specimen rises as a result. Immediately the specimen temperature exceeds that of the environment, heat flows from the former to the latter. The resulting temperature at any point in the specimen and at any time is thus determined by the balance of these two processes of heat generation and heat loss.

This problem may be treated mathematically. The treatment given below[29] is a simplified theory which provides a good qualitative picture of the phenomenon of 'heat build-up' and the parameters which are important.

Consider an element of material of volume V within a specimen undergoing fatigue. Suppose the frequency of testing is v and the energy dissipated in unit volume is w. Then heat is generated within the element at a rate

$$\frac{\mathrm{d}Q_1}{\mathrm{d}t} = Vvw \tag{19}$$

The outflow of heat is given by the integral, over the surface of the element, of the quantity

$$K\frac{\mathrm{d}T}{\mathrm{d}r}\,\mathrm{d}a \tag{20}$$

where T is the absolute temperature, K is the thermal conductivity, r the vector normal to the surface, and $\mathrm{d}a$ an element of area. In general, of course, dT/dr may be either positive or negative, since our element may have some neighbouring elements colder, and some hotter, than itself. We therefore simplify the problem by choosing our element to enclose the hottest part of the specimen so that dT/dr is negative at all points on its surface, *i.e.* heat flows only out of the element. This choice of element is not really a restriction upon the solution we shall obtain since we are interested ultimately in the maximum temperatures attained in the specimen. If we further choose the shape of our element to correspond to the external shape† of the specimen we may arrange that dT/dr be sensibly constant over the surface of the element so that, from eqn. (20), the outflow of heat occurs at a rate

$$\frac{dQ_2}{dt} = -KA\frac{dT}{dr}\bigg|_{r_0} \tag{21}$$

where A is the surface area of the element and r_0 defines the location of the surface.

The next simplification concerns the temperature gradient $(dT/dr)_{r_0}$. It is reasonable to assume that this gradient, *taken at a fixed point in the specimen*, is linearly related to the excess temperature θ defined as

$$\theta = \bar{T} - T_0 \tag{22}$$

where $\bar{T}$ is the mean temperature within the element and T_0 the temperature of the environment. This assumption is based upon the reliable ground that when the mean temperature of the specimen or its constituent parts rises, the temperature profile (*i.e.* the relative spatial distribution of temperature) is unaltered. We therefore set

$$\left(\frac{dT}{dr}\right)_{r_0} = \frac{\theta}{P} \tag{23}$$

where P is a function of r_0 and is constant at any fixed r_0.

We may now write for the accumulation of heat in the element

$$\frac{dQ}{dt} = \frac{dQ_1}{dt} + \frac{dQ_2}{dt} = Vvw - \frac{KA\theta}{P} \tag{24}$$

---

† Shape alone is not sufficient to determine this matter, since it depends also upon the heat flow boundary conditions at the specimen surface which may differ from point to point. This difficulty is here passed over. The practical effect is that our solution cannot be applied to regions where the boundary conditions are likely to be atypical, *e.g.* where the specimen is in contact with grips.

but

$$\frac{dQ}{dt} = \frac{V\rho C \, d\theta}{dt} \tag{25}$$

where ρ is the density of the material, C its specific heat, and $d\theta/dt$ the rate of increase of temperature in the element. Thus

$$\frac{V\rho C \, d\theta}{dt} = Vvw - \frac{KA\theta}{P}$$

$$\frac{d\theta}{dt} = \frac{vw}{\rho C} - \frac{K\alpha\theta}{P\rho C} \tag{26}$$

where $\alpha = A/V$ and is the surface-to-volume ratio of the element. Because of the choice of element shape to equalise the temperature gradient over its surface, α will also in general be related to the surface-to-volume ratio of the specimen itself.

Equation (26) has the form

$$\frac{d\theta}{dt} = X - Y\theta \tag{27}$$

which has the solution

$$\theta = \frac{X}{Y}[1 - \exp(-Yt)] \tag{28}$$

This solution is shown graphically in Fig. 9. In particular,

$$\left. \begin{aligned} X &= \frac{vw}{\rho C} \\[6pt] Y &= \frac{K\alpha}{P\rho C} \\[6pt] \frac{X}{Y} &= \frac{vwP}{K\alpha} \end{aligned} \right\} \tag{29}$$

Equilibrium temperature

These equations allow us to predict the effect of various parameters. The temperature within the element rises as shown in Fig. 10 to an equilibrium value, at long times, of X/Y, i.e.

$$\theta(\text{equil.}) = \frac{vwP}{K\alpha} \tag{30}$$

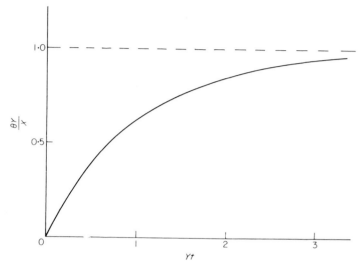

Fig. 10.   *Dependence of excess temperature θ upon time t and the parameters X, Y*
(*after Andrews*[29]).

The ultimate temperature rise is therefore greater (1) at large values of the energy dissipation, (2) at large values of the frequency of testing, (3) at small values of the surface-to-volume ratio, and (4) at small values of the thermal conductivity K. These effects are all intuitively obvious, but eqn. (30) indicates more precisely the nature of these dependencies, *i.e.* it predicts a linear dependence in each case. The effects of frequency may be *more* severe than indicated, however, because w may itself increase with increasing v. This will certainly be the case for truly viscoelastic deformations. We may say therefore that the equilibrium temperature increases at least in proportion to the frequency and possibly more rapidly.

The higher the amplitude of deformation, the higher will w become, and hence the equilibrium temperature will rise. If the stress–strain curve exhibits a definite yield w will increase suddenly beyond some particular deformation range.

The surface-to-volume ratio is, to some extent, under our control, and this quantity should be maximised in designing against 'heat build-up'. Two points should be emphasised, however. The dependence of $θ$ upon $α$ means that the results of a laboratory fatigue test may not be applicable to the behaviour of a component in service if the component differs significantly in either shape or size from the fatigue specimen. Size is as important as shape since, for example, $α$ for cylindrical specimens varies inversely as the radius. Secondly, it is only permissible to relate α for the element considered in the analysis to the surface-to-volume ratio of the whole specimen if the energy dissipation w is the same at all points in the specimen, *i.e.* if the specimen is uniformly stressed. If there are significant stress concentrations in the specimen, the hottest point will not be at its centre, the element considered will not be symmetrically disposed with respect to the exterior of the specimen, and there is no reason to expect α (element) and α (specimen) to correspond. In the case of a notched specimen, for example, α (element) is likely to depend far more strongly on the notch depth and radius than on the shape and size of the entire specimen.

It should be noted, finally, that the low values of K typical in polymers will encourage large temperature rises and the *absolute* value of the temperature attained will increase with the environmental temperature, since $T = \theta + T_0$.

Attainment of equilibrium

The rate at which equilibrium is approached depends only upon the exponential term in eqn. (28), *i.e.* upon the quantity

$$Y = \frac{K\alpha}{P\rho C}$$

If this parameter is large, equilibrium will be approached rapidly and, if it is small, slowly. The predominant effect of material parameters will be that of K, the low values found in polymers delaying the attainment of equilibrium so that the effects of heat build-up may take a considerable time to manifest themselves. Other than this, only the surface-to-volume ratio plays a significant role, a large α reducing the time for equilibrium.

Failure from thermal causes

So far we have only considered the temperature distribution in the specimen, and it has been assumed that the only effect of heat build-up is to raise the mean temperature of the specimen. If this were the case, we should observe only such modification of other fatigue processes (*e.g.* crack initiation and propagation) as might result from elevated temperature. In practice the effects of heat build-up can be very much more severe; this arises from two causes. Firstly, the energy dissipation w may increase rapidly as the temperature rises. This will not occur in pure viscoelastic deformations, since in these cases w will *decrease* with rising temperature, but it is likely to occur if plastic deformation increases markedly as a result, for example, of the yield stress being lowered by rising temperature.

Secondly, whether or not w increases with temperature, a value of T may be reached at which structural changes or thermal decomposition set in. These may lead to embrittlement and failure by catastrophic cracking, or the reverse effect of a catastrophic loss in modulus, or the creation of gas bubbles or voids. Even where such processes do not sever the specimen they cause such loss of mechanical stiffness or strength, or such large permanent deformations, as to constitute real failure.

These thermally induced chemical or structural changes may proceed only slowly at the temperatures attained during fatigue, especially if they obey the familiar rate process law

$$\text{rate of reaction} = A \exp\left(-B/kT\right)$$

where A and B are constants, k is Boltzmann's constant, and T the absolute temperature. This, rather than the relatively slow attainment of equilibrium in low conductivity materials, accounts for the delayed onset of obvious thermal damage in many instances.

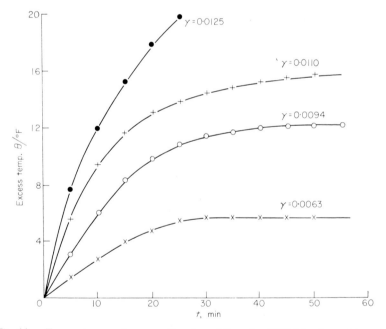

Fig. 11.   Excess temperature as a function of time for PMMA tubes subjected to torsion at various shear strain amplitudes γ and constant frequency of 65/min (after Tauchert and Afzal[30]).

Experimental studies of heat build-up

Tauchert and Afzal[30] have described measurements of temperature rises occurring during torsional testing of poly(methyl methacrylate) tubes. A typical stress–strain hysteresis loop for such a specimen was shown in Fig. 9, the energy dissipated being proportional to the area enclosed by the loop. Their data for temperature rise as a function of time are shown in Figs. 11 and 12 which show also the effects of strain amplitude (Fig. 11) and cycling frequency (Fig. 12). Temperatures were measured only at the surface by an attached thermocouple and therefore were not those obtaining at the hottest (*i.e.* internal) part of the specimen, and this may account for the observation that only 60–70 % of the mechanical energy dissipated

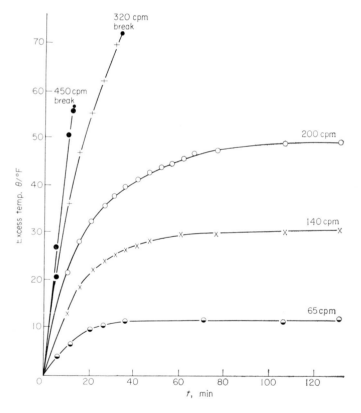

Fig. 12.   As Fig. 11 but at constant strain amplitude $\gamma = 9\cdot4 \times 10^{-3}$ *and various frequencies (after Tauchert and Afzal[30]).*

seemed to reappear as heat. Apart from this, however, the results agree very well with the theory outlined above. When the heat dissipated is low, the curves of Figs. 11 and 12 follow the pattern indicated by eqn. (28) and illustrated in Fig. 10, rising to an equilibrium value which is higher for higher frequencies and higher strain amplitudes (*i.e.* energy dissipation). In quantitative terms agreement with theory is quite good. The rate of attainment of equilibrium is governed by

$$Y = \frac{K\alpha}{P\rho C}$$

a quantity independent of the variables w and v. This means that whatever w and v may be, the time to achieve, say, half the equilibrium temperature rise should be constant. In all tests illustrated in Figs. 11 and 12 this 'half-life' is between 480 and 720 s, from which can be derived the value

$$Y = \frac{K\alpha}{P\rho C} \simeq 0{\cdot}010\text{--}0{\cdot}013 \text{ s}^{-1}$$

Agreement for equilibrium temperature is not quite so good. Equation (30) gives,

$$\theta(\text{equil.}) = \frac{vwP}{K\alpha}$$

and substitution of values for v and w from the data of Tauchert and Afzal gives,

$$\frac{P}{K\alpha} = 8 \pm 2°\text{K s m}^2(\text{MN})^{-1} \tag{31}$$

The variability of this parameter is still within 25% of a mean value, however, so that the theory can be said to broadly reproduce experiment.

When the temperature increase was large, failure occurred before thermal equilibrium was established. According to Tauchert and Afzal the surface temperature of the specimens at failure approached the glass transition temperature of PMMA, suggesting that 'structural' changes (*i.e.* glass to fluid) are here responsible for failure rather than chemical changes. However, failure was still by crack propagation resulting in fracture of the tube perpendicular to its axis.

A further observation of interest is that, although a higher ambient temperature in theory leads to higher specimen temperatures, this effect may be partially cancelled by a softening of the specimen and a consequent reduction of the mechanical hysteresis per cycle at fixed strain amplitude.

An increase in excess specimen temperature with increasing ambient temperature is only predicted by theory if the energy dissipated is constant. In some tests on the PMMA tubes an increase in ambient temperature from 24 to 52°C resulted in a *decrease* in the equilibrium excess temperature θ from 27 to 15°C, giving actual specimen temperatures of 51 and 67°C, respectively. This moderation of heat build-up by softening of the specimen will, of course, also occur as a result of the temperature rise occasioned by cycling, even if the ambient temperature is held constant. It will inevitably affect the overall behaviour, so that any value derived for the quantity

$$\frac{P}{K\alpha}$$

by fitting eqn. (28) to experimental data is an apparent value, and this may account for its variability noted above (*see also* Fig. 16, Chapter 6).

It should be pointed out that softening of the specimen with rising temperature only results in *lower* energy dissipation per cycle if the cycle is between fixed *strain* limits as in the experiments of Tauchert and Afzal. Tests at a fixed stress amplitude would give *greater* dissipation in a softer material, and softening would then result in more rapid failure.

The above analysis takes no account of the changes in energy dissipation with temperature, but it is well known that mechanical damping in polymers is strongly temperature dependent. This question has been discussed by Riddell *et al.*[31] and by Constable *et al.*[32] who obtained a solution for temperature rise in a specimen of simple geometry, taking into account the maximum value of loss modulus likely to be obtained in the course of the experiment. Their solution for PMMA specimens gave excellent qualitative agreement with experiment but quantitative agreement was not good (Fig. 13). Their work does, however, point the way forward for a more precise definition of the conditions for thermal failure of specific materials.

7.3.2   Fatigue crack propagation

Some quite extensive studies have been made of fatigue crack propagation in polymers under isothermal conditions (*i.e.* in the absence of significant heat build-up). Unfortunately, most of this work has been carried out on elastomers and crystalline polymers and cannot concern us in this discussion of polymeric glasses. However, the same general approach described below is valid for most kinds of solid and it is to be hoped that further data will accrue in due course on the particular materials which concern us here.

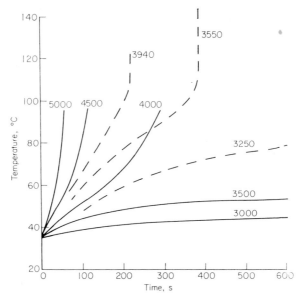

Fig. 13. *Temperature as a function of time in PMMA cycled at 50 Hz. Solid lines give theory, broken lines give experimental results. Numbers give stress amplitude in lbf in^{-2} (after Constable et al.[32]).*

The 'fracture mechanics' approach to fatigue can be summarised by the statement that the propagation of a fatigue crack is governed entirely by the stress–intensity factor at its tip or, alternatively, by the energy $-\partial\mathscr{E}/\partial A$ available for its extension (*see* Section 7.2). This 'philosophical' statement can be reduced to a mathematical form by specifying that the growth per fatigue cycle, dc/dN is a function only of K_I or of $(-\partial\mathscr{E}/\partial A)$.

$$\frac{dc}{dN} = f(K_I)$$

or

$$\frac{dc}{dN} = f\left(-\frac{\partial\mathscr{E}}{\partial A}\right) \tag{32}$$

Provided the specimen has a geometry for which K_I or $-\partial\mathscr{E}/\partial A$ is given explicitly in terms of known parameters, the validity of this idea can be tested. Since fatigue fracture usually occurs in practice from the growth of a fatigue crack from the specimen surface, the edge-crack (or s.e.n.) specimen will be taken as our model.

Experimental verification of eqn. (32) is thus sought by measuring directly the growth per cycle (usually averaged over a number of cycles) as a function of the maximum value of K_I (or $-\partial\mathscr{E}/\partial A$) attained each cycle. Borduas et al.[33] obtained results of the kind shown in Fig. 14 where the rate of growth of a fatigue crack in PMMA was found to depend only on the value of ΔK_I (the stress–intensity factor amplitude). In these tests they varied the applied stress as the crack grew to maintain a constant value of ΔK_I.

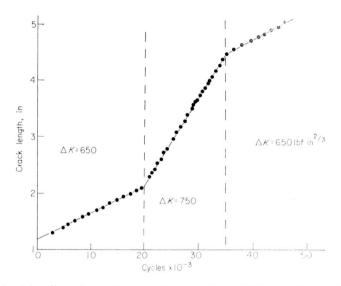

Fig. 14. *The effect of stress intensity factor amplitude (ΔK) on crack growth 'rate' in PMMA (after Borduas et al.[33]).*

Herzberg et al.[34] observed the growth of fatigue cracks in a wide variety of plastics and showed that the logarithm of dc/dN plotted fairly linearly against log ΔK. Their data for polycarbonate and PMMA is shown in Fig. 15. Some of the deviations from linearity may be attributable to the use of the linear fracture mechanics parameter K_I rather than ($\partial\mathscr{E}/\partial A$). There may also be more than one linear region of the curve, with different slopes, as demonstrated by Andrews and Walker[35] for polyethylene, but this question has been discussed elsewhere.[36] The important thing to note is that the relationship of eqn. (32) can be expressed, with reasonable accuracy as a power law. (This has previously been established

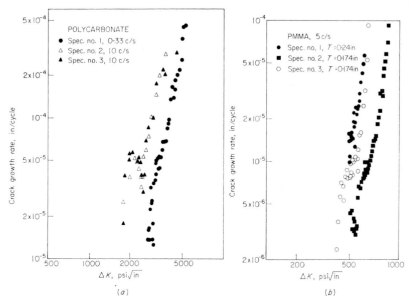

Fig. 15.   *Cyclic crack growth rate as a function of stress intensity factor amplitude in* (a) *polycarbonate and* (b) *PMMA* (*after Herzberg* et al.[34]).

for metals, elastomers and semi-crystalline polymers).[29] Thus, for glassy plastics, we may write,

$$\frac{dc}{dN} = B(\Delta K_I)^n$$

or   (33)

$$\frac{dc}{dN} = B\left(-\frac{\partial \mathscr{E}}{\partial A}\right)^n$$

For conciseness we shall, from now on, examine the latter of these equations, but both are equally amenable to the following treatment.

For the s.e.n. test piece,

$$-\frac{\partial \mathscr{E}}{\partial A} = kcW_0$$

So that

$$\frac{dc}{dN} = B(kcW_0)^n$$ (34)

where W_0 is the stored energy density in simple extension at the maximum of the cycle. (For simplicity we consider a cycle taken between zero stress and some positive tensile stress.) Then,

$$\int_0^{N_f} dN = \frac{1}{Bk^n W_0{}^n} \int_{c_0}^{\infty} \frac{dc}{c^n} \tag{35}$$

where N_f is the number of cycles to failure, c_0 is the length of the crack at zero cycles (the 'intrinsic flaw' size for virgin specimens) and an infinite crack length is taken to indicate fracture. Provided $n \neq 1$,

$$N_f = (Bk^n W_0{}^n c_0{}^{n-1})^{-1} \tag{36}$$

This equation predicts the fatigue lifetime of specimens in terms of known quantities and the value of c_0. Unfortunately, no experimental test of this equation has yet been made for glassy plastics, but excellent agreement is obtained for elastomers[37] and for polyethylene[35] (Fig. 16) using a single well-defined value of c_0 for each material. These values are of the order of 10^{-5} m to $6 \cdot 10^{-5}$ m, sufficiently small to correspond to surface scratches or (in the case of polyethylene) the interspherulite boundaries.

7.4 CRAZING

The importance of crazing in the study of fracture in glassy polymers cannot be overstated. We have already noted that brittle fracture in such

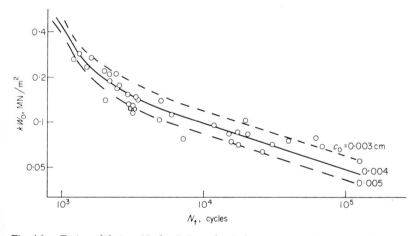

Fig. 16. *Fatigue lifetime N_f for L.D. polyethylene as a function of input energy density W_0. Points are experimental data, lines give theory for a range of values of intrinsic flaw size c_0 (after Andrews and Walker[35]).*

materials as PMMA and PS is preceded by crazing, which determines the all-important parameter c_0 for tensile fracture. We also noticed that a running crack in PMMA is preceded by a zone of crazed material, the crack propagating through the pre-formed craze matter, rather than through bulk polymer. The formation and deformation of the craze thus contribute the major part of the surface work.

Quite apart from their role in brittle fracture, crazes constitute in themselves a form of non-catastrophic failure, giving rise to irrecoverable deformation, visual impairment and enhanced permeability. In the presence of active environments, crazes can develop under very low stresses and initiate catastrophic fracture, and a great deal of research effort has been devoted to this problem in recent years.

In this section we shall consider first the phenomenon of crazing in air ('dry crazing'), then that of environmental crazing and finally some theoretical aspects of the subject.

7.4.1 Crazing of glassy plastics in air
Morphology

The morphology of crazes has been widely discussed in recent years.[22,38] Generally speaking, a craze is a narrow zone of highly deformed and voided polymer, resembling a true crack. Like cracks, crazes in isotropic materials grow at right angles to the major principal tensile stress and only propagate if the stress at their tip exceeds a certain value.

Like cracks, crazes tend to be wedge-shaped, the distance between the craze walls increasing with distance behind the tip, but the wedge angle is only 1° or 2°. At the tip the wedge-shape sometimes gives way to a cusp-like form.

The material constituting the craze (the 'craze matter') contains typically from 40% to 60% of voids,[21] obviously formed to allow an increase in thickness without lateral contraction, the latter being prohibited (in thick sheets at least) by the elastic constraint of the surrounding undeformed polymer. The polymer in the craze is drawn out into a 'lacework' of oriented threads or sheets. (*See* Fig. 17.)

The craze can be described as an open-cell foam with voids of the order of 10–20 nm in diameter and a centre-to-centre separation of 50–100 nm. These figures naturally vary from case to case, but the general nature of the craze appears to be surprisingly similar in all polymers subject to the phenomenon.

Although crazes are usually narrow and crack-like, thick crazes can be obtained, especially in highly ductile materials like polycarbonate.

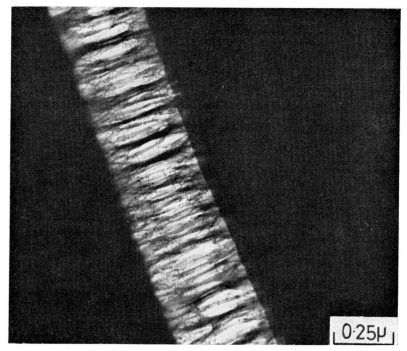

Fig. 17.   *Transmission electron micrograph of a craze in polystyrene (courtesy P. Beahan, M. Bevis and D. Hull, University of Liverpool).*

Indeed, under some conditions in cross-linked glasses (*see* later) the craze-polymer boundary can be made to propagate normal to the craze plane (much as a neck propagates in a shear-yielding specimen) to produce a large volume of homogeneously crazed material.

Working on relatively thick crazes grown so as to completely divide a solid specimen into two parts, Kambour[23] was able to measure the stress–strain and retraction properties of the craze matter itself (Fig. 18).

At the other extreme, it is found that craze thickness in PMMA decreases with decreasing temperature of formation[39] and with increasing strain rate,[25] so that extremely thin crazes can be grown. It appears that thin crazes are more stable than thick ones, so that much longer crazes can grow under tensile load before fracture.

Mechanical considerations

Crazes usually form under tensile stress and grow at right angles to the major principal stress. They do not occur under compressive stress and

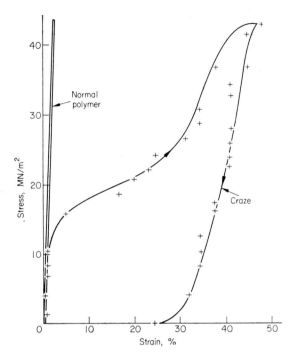

Fig. 18. *Stress–strain loops for normal polycarbonate and a polycarbonate craze (after Kambour*[23]*).*

their development can be inhibited by applying hydrostatic pressure during tensile deformation. There have been reports of crazes forming under shear stress,[40] and in anisotropic materials they do not always grow normal to the major tensile stress,[40] but these results are not typical and will not be considered further here.

At a given straining rate, craze nucleation occurs at a well-defined critical stress (or strain), but this stress is dependent upon time as well as temperature.[41,42] Like most mechanical property parameters, the crazing stress exhibits visco-elastic characteristics, decreasing with increasing temperature and with decreasing strain rate (increasing time).

In isotropic glasses crazes normally nucleate at the specimen surface, but if the surface is oriented (as, *e.g.* in injection moulded specimens), internal nucleation may occur preferentially.[42] Surface nucleation is to be expected in isotropic materials for two reasons. Firstly, the surface is more liable to damage and the creation of stress-concentrating 'intrinsic' flaws.

Secondly, an 'intrinsic' crack of a given length is twice as effective in concentrating stress at the surface than internally. (The stress-intensity factor for a surface crack of length a, is similar to that of an internal crack of length $2a$.) Crazes always nucleate preferentially at points of stress-concentration such as a notch or rough surface.

The conditions for craze nucleation are difficult to study for the very reason that nucleation in virgin specimens occurs at adventitious flaws (including regions of atypical molecular orientation) which, by their very nature, remain uncharacterised. The conditions for propagation of an existing craze, or for propagation of a craze from a 'starter' crack are much more readily defined, and the existence of a critical stress for propagation has been convincingly demonstrated by Sternstein et al.[41] They studied the growth of crazes around a circular hole in a strip of PMMA held under tension, and compared the results with the known stress distribution in the specimen. The results showed that the crazes (a) grow perpendicular to the major principal stress direction and (b) do not grow unless this stress exceeds a certain fixed value. A similar striking illustration of this feature is given by Beardmore and Johnson's three-point bending test.[25]

The stress referred to above (either for initiation or propagation) is, of course, the applied stress. It does not refer to the stress at the tip of the craze or at the stress-raising flaw, under which the polymer is actually transformed into craze matter. This local crazing stress is of greater intrinsic interest, since it is *this* stress which must have a critical value for craze formation. That a well-defined critical applied stress is sometimes found, simply reflects the fact that the stress intensification at flaws or at the tip of growing crazes is usually constant. Exceptions to this do occur, however, as when craze growth arrests spontaneously without changes in the applied stress.

The stress intensification at a craze tip is not as easily established as for a crack, since the craze walls are joined by load-bearing material and are not stress-free. Knight[43] calculated the stress distribution at a craze, making certain assumptions, the most significant of which was the shape assumed by the craze under load. The craze was considered to be parallel sided, with a 'craze opening displacement' of 2ε, except near the tip where its thickness decreased to zero over a length κ. If the uniform applied stress is σ_0, Knight found the peak stress σ_p at the craze tip to be,

$$\sigma_p = \sigma_0 + b\varepsilon/\kappa \tag{37}$$

where $b = 1{\cdot}80\,E(1 - v^2)/\pi$ and v is Poisson's ratio.

This analysis shows that κ, the length of the tapered region governs the peak stress, but that the total craze length does not enter explicitly into the expression. Unfortunately, the parameters ε and κ occurs as independent variables, whereas they must be controlled by σ_0. Knight's analysis does not, therefore, provide an analogous expression to the Inglis formula[44] for the stress intensity at a crack, namely

$$\frac{\sigma_p}{\sigma_0} = 1 + 2 \left(\frac{a}{\rho}\right)^{\frac{1}{2}} \tag{38}$$

where $2a$ is the crack length and ρ its tip radius.

An alternative approach to the explicit calculation of the tip stress distribution has been proposed by Andrews and Bevan.[45] They introduced an hypothetical 'equivalent crack' as a mechanical analogue to the craze. The 'equivalent crack', length l, is that crack which would produce the same stress intensification at its tip as does the craze. The value of l can, in principle, be evaluated by observing the applied stress σ_0 required to just propagate a craze from the tip of a pre-formed 'starter' crack of length c_0, and comparing this with the applied stress σ_1 needed to cause craze propagation in a uniform tensile stress field. Since, for two cracks, the same stress-intensity factor is given by stresses in the ratio of the square root of their lengths,

$$l = c_0 \left(\frac{\sigma_0}{\sigma_1}\right)^2 \tag{39}$$

Andrews and others[45,46] have used this concept mainly to describe environmental crazing phenomena, but its general value lies in the ability to monitor the mechanical behaviour of the craze in fracture mechanics terms. Changes in l also reflect changes in the load-bearing capacity of the craze matter, and this may vary in a single craze, e.g. with the passage of time or as a result of stress cycling. Clearly, if the load-bearing capacity of the craze matter reduces to zero, l is simply the craze length, whilst a maximum load-bearing capacity is reflected in a small constant value of l.

Finally, craze growth from a starter crack can be envisaged as the growth of a plastic zone by analogy with Dugdale's model.[47] This method of representing the mechanics of craze growth has been used by Marshall et al.,[48] again in connection with solvent-induced growth.

Dugdale analysed the stresses in an infinite plate of an elastic–plastic solid containing a central crack of length $2a$ and subject to a uniform tensile stress p. His solution was developed by Burdekin and Stone[49] who derived the following expressions for the length, X, of the plastic zone (in our case, the length of the craze) and the crack-opening displacement δ at the tip of the starter crack;

$$X = a_p - a \tag{40}$$

where a_p is given by,

$$\frac{p}{p_y} = \frac{2}{\pi} \cos^{-1} \left(\frac{a}{a_p} \right)$$

where p_y is the yield stress of the bulk material. Also,

$$\delta = \frac{K^2}{p_y E} \tag{41}$$

where K is the stress intensity factor and E is the Young's modulus for the bulk material.

Equation (40) indicates that a craze growing from a starter crack will increase in length as the applied stress rises and measurements support the form of the equation, at least for solvent-induced crazes. Under constant applied stress, eqn. (40) suggests that a craze of constant length should precede a running crack (ignoring adiabatic effects), and this again accords with experience.

Further mechanical aspects of crazing will be considered in the theoretical Section 7.4.3.

7.4.2 Environmental crazing

Stress crazing in the presence of active environments (notably organic solvents in the case of polymeric glasses) resembles crazing in air in almost every respect except that it occurs at greatly reduced levels of stress. From a practical viewpoint it constitutes a far more serious problem than 'dry' crazing for this very reason. Crazing in air can usually be avoided in engineering applications simply by keeping design stresses sufficiently low. Solvent crazing, however, can occur at stresses two orders of magnitude lower, making it almost impossible to design against its occurrence.

It is not intended here to review the considerable amount of literature on the phenomenology of solvent crazing. We shall concentrate on two or three recent investigations which are reasonably definitive as regards both the mechanics and the mechanisms of environmental stress crazing in glassy plastics.

The physical–chemical factors involved were examined in detail by Bernier and Kambour[50] who studied the critical surface stress (or strain) required to produce crazing in poly-phenylene oxide in a wide variety of solvents. Their most interesting finding was, perhaps, the dependence of

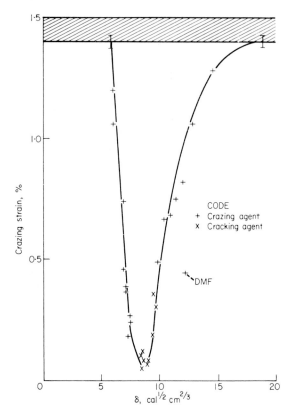

Fig. 19. *Crazing strain of poly-phenylene oxide as a function of solubility*
parameter of immersion fluid (after Bernier and Kambour[50]*).*

craze initiation strain upon the solubility parameter of the solvent (*see*
Fig. 19). This strain was almost uniquely defined (at room temperature) by
the difference $|\delta_s - \delta_p|$ between the solubility parameters of the solvent
and the polymer, passing through a minimum at $|\delta_s - \delta_p| = 0$. This effect
is not limited to PPO and was found also for PMMA, polystyrene and
polycarbonate.

The role of interfacial energy between polymer and solvent was also
investigated, although direct measurement of this quantity is not normally
possible because the liquids concerned spread on the polymer surface.
Bernier and Kambour concluded that the stabilisation of voids by reduction of their surface energy was the reason why solvents induce a transition
from shear yielding to craze formation. The main effect of plasticisation

was concluded to be a sharp reduction of the critical strain as δ(solvent) $\rightarrow$ δ(polymer).

A fracture mechanics approach to the critical condition for craze growth was taken by Andrews and Bevan.[51] Using single-edge notch specimens of PMMA immersed in methylated spirit, they showed that the applied stress needed to propagate a craze from a starter crack was dependent upon the combined length of crack and craze in such a manner as to indicate propagation at a constant stress-intensity factor (or constant $\mathscr{T}$). In this particular case the craze was obviously non load-bearing and behaved mechanically as an extension of the crack. In later work,[45] using a series of aliphatic alcohols, alcohol–water mixtures and CCl_4, they found

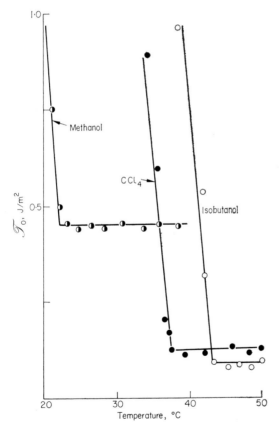

Fig. 20.   Variation of minimum surface work for crazing in PMMA in various solvents, with temperature (after Andrews and Bevan[45]).

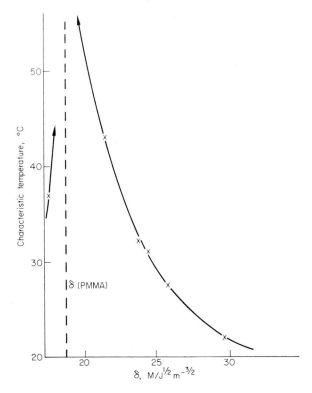

Fig. 21. *Characteristic temperature T_c as a function of solvent solubility parameter, δ (after Andrews and Bevan[45]).*

that the critical applied stress was very variable for some solvents, but that a minimum surface work $\mathscr{T}_0$ could always be defined, corresponding to the work of craze formation at the tip of a crack.

This minimum or threshold surface work displayed a characteristic temperature dependence, as shown in Fig. 20 for several solvents. Below a 'characteristic temperature', T_c, $\mathscr{T}_0$ increased strongly with falling temperature, but above T_c it remained constant at a value denoted $\mathscr{T}^*_0$. Following Bernier and Kambour, Andrews and Bevan plotted the parameters T_c and $\mathscr{T}^*_0$ against the solvent solubility parameter with the results shown in Figs. 21 and 22. They proposed that the characteristic temperature was, in fact, the glass transition temperature of a solvated zone at the crack or craze tip, the solvent being absorbed there rapidly by stress-assisted diffusion. Subsidiary work[52] established that T_g was

indeed reduced by the various solvents used in the order observed for
T_c and by an appropriate magnitude. In fact, T_c was found in all cases to
correspond to the T_g of PMMA containing about 70% of polymer and
30% of solvent. Andrews and Bevan argued that below T_c the surface
work included a term involving the yield stress of the plasticised zone and
is temperature dependent because the yield stress is a function of temperature. Above T_c, only a surface energy term remains (see Section 7.4.3),
since the local yield stress is zero, and $\mathscr{T}^*_0$ therefore reflects the interfacial
energy of the voids. Its variation with δ_s would follow, since both δ_s and
interfacial energy γ are measures of intermolecular forces.

Marshall et al.[48] studied the kinetics of craze propagation. They

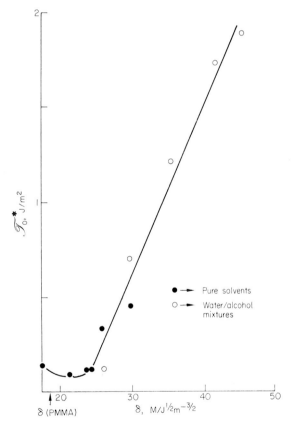

Fig. 22.   Surface work for craze formation (above T_c) as a function of solvent
solubility parameter (after Andrews and Bevan[45]).

measured craze velocities as a function of applied stress, starter crack
length and sheet thickness for PMMA immersed in methanol at 20°C.
Supposing the craze velocity to be controlled by the rate of flow of solvent
through the voids of the craze, they derived the expression, for craze
velocity $\dot{c}$,

$$\dot{c} = \frac{K_0{}^2}{2H\Delta} \left(\frac{l_0\bar{P}}{10p_yE\mu} \right) \tag{42}$$

where K_0 is the initial stress intensity factor (calculated from the starter-
crack length and the applied stress), $\bar{P}$ is the atmospheric pressure, H is

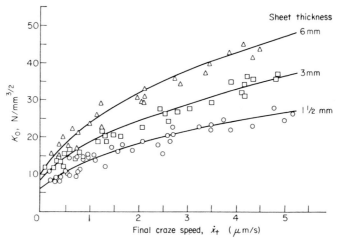

Fig. 23.   Solvent craze velocity, $\dot{x}$, as a function of initial stress intensity factor K_0
in PMMA/methanol at 20°C (after Marshall et al.[48]).

the sheet thickness, μ the solvent viscosity and l_0 and Δ are constants.
Figure 23 shows that eqn. (42) can be fitted closely to the experimental
results by appropriate choice of l_0 and Δ. In particular it accounts for the
dependence of $\dot{c}$ upon K_0 and upon sheet thickness.

Andrews et al.[53] studied the effects of temperature upon $\dot{c}$, the kind of
results obtained being illustrated in Fig. 24 for polycarbonate. The very
strong temperature dependence cannot be accounted for by eqn. (42),
neither p_y, E or μ varying sufficiently rapidly. If p_y were the yield stress of
the solvated zone discussed above, rather than the bulk material, the right
order of temperature dependence might be obtained, but this would give
unacceptable values for l_0 which is approximately the void spacing in the
craze.

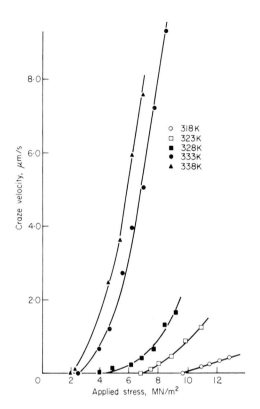

Fig. 24.   *Solvent craze velocity as a function of applied stress for polycarbonate in n-propanol at various temperatures (after Andrews* et al.[53]*).*

The 'equivalent crack' concept was applied to solvent craze growth by Andrews and Levy.[46] They confirmed the finding of Marshall *et al.*[48] that craze growth was affected by the length of the starter crack, even if the latter is removed by planing away the edge of the specimen after the craze has been initiated. This 'c_0 effect' is dramatically illustrated by the values for equivalent crack lengths l, as shown in Fig. 25 for PMMA in ethanol. At a temperature above T_c, l is virtually equal to c_0, but at a temperature only 10 K lower, but below T_c, the equivalent crack length is greatly reduced and its dependence on c_0 is minimised.

It is clear that the mechanics of craze growth are still not fully explained, and that further work is necessary to elucidate some of the interesting effects described above. The methods of study described, however, point

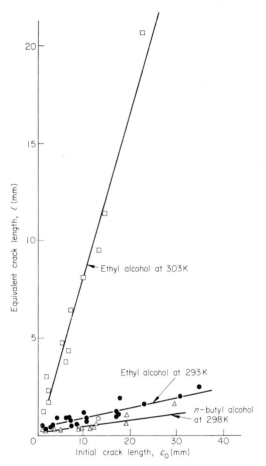

Fig. 25.   *Equivalent crack length as a function of starter crack length for PMMA in two solvents and at two temperatures (after Levy[46]).*

the way forward and we may expect rapid progress towards a detailed understanding of these phenomena.

7.4.3   Theoretical aspects
Some theoretical matters have, of course, already been considered in preceding sections. Our concern here is to examine the attempts which have been made to account theoretically for the basic process of crazing. Why does it occur at all, and what are the conditions required to bring it

about? We shall consider these questions under two headings. Firstly, the stress-field conditions required to cause crazing and secondly, the mechanism of void formation or cavitation.

Stress-field conditions for crazing
Mention has already been made of the existence of a critical tensile stress or strain, normal to the direction of craze growth, below which crazing will not occur. A simple tensile stress, however, can be resolved into shear and hydrostatic components, and Sternstein and Ongchin[54] have attempted to define more closely the role of these two types of stress. Working with PMMA under biaxial tension, they found that the conditions for visible crazing could be defined as follows,

$$\sigma_b = A + B/I_1 \tag{43}$$

where $\sigma_b = (\sigma_1 - \sigma_2)$, *i.e.* the difference in the in-plane principal stresses and represents the shear stress intensity, whilst I_1 is the first stress invariant (*i.e.* the sum of the three principal stresses) representing the dilatational

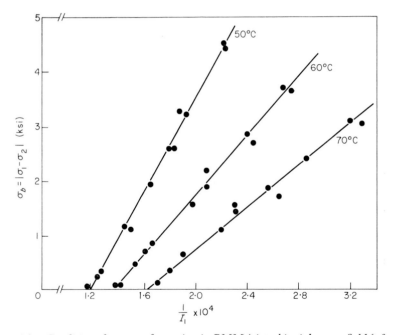

Fig. 26. *Conditions for craze formation in PMMA in a biaxial stress field (after Sternstein and Ongchin[54]).*

component. Their data for three temperatures is shown in Fig. 26, indicating that the constants A, B are functions of temperature. (They will also be dependent on time, environment and the material used.) Figure 26 shows that, for a sufficiently high dilatational stress field, crazing will occur for zero stress bias, but as I_1 decreases, an increasing stress bias is required to produce crazes. Sternstein and Ongchin proposed that the role of the dilatational stress field was to increase molecular mobility by increasing the free volume and thus decreasing steric hindrances to molecular rotation. This idea is supported by the temperature dependence; if the slopes S of the lines in Fig. 26 are plotted as a function of temperature, a reasonable extrapolation gives $S \to 0$ as $T \to T_g$ for PMMA. This means that, notionally, at T_g a zero dilatational stress is required since sufficient free volume exists for free molecular rotation by virtue of temperature alone.

The role of the stress bias is to produce the molecular elongation and orientation which is intrinsic to the crazing process.

Much attention has been paid to crazing as an alternative yield process to 'normal' shear yielding, such as occurs in neck formation or shear bands. Since shear yielding *can* occur in narrow bands, the chief difference between it and crazing is not that the latter is localised (or inhomogeneous) but that it occurs with increase in volume. This emphasises the role of the dilatational stress component in crazing.

Haward et al.[55] have examined the relationship between the yield stress measured in compression and the crazing stress in polystyrene, and Fig. 32 of Chapter 6 shows some data. The crazing stress is about half the yield stress at all temperatures except close to T_g. The similarity between the temperature dependence of the two stresses at lower temperatures can be attributed to the involvement of shear-yielding in the crazing process, and the failure of the crazing stress to collapse to zero at T_g, and to the fact that some stress is required, even in a liquid, to create void interfaces (*see* below).

Under certain circumstances, cross-linked glasses have been observed to exhibit a transition from shear yielding to craze formation with decrease in temperature. Figure 27 shows data obtained by Natarajan and Reed[56] on vulcanised natural rubber, pre-oriented above T_g by 100% to induce low-temperature ductility, and then subjected to tensile deformation below T_g. At temperatures immediately below T_g shear yielding (necking) was observed, the yield-stress rising with falling temperature as commonly observed. At slightly lower temperatures a ductile $\to$ brittle transition ensued, again as expected. As the temperature of test was further reduced, however, a new region of ductility was found, the plastic deformation now taking place by cavitation, beginning as narrow crazes but developing by

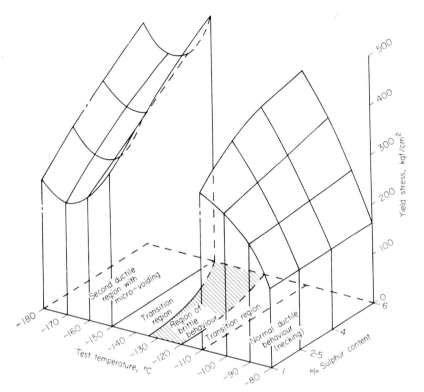

Fig. 27. Yield stress of pre-oriented natural rubber below T_g showing one brittle and two ductile regions (after Natarajan and Reed[56]).

lateral growth of the craze to give homogeneous voiding over a large volume. In this region the yield (crazing) stress passed through a minimum as shown. Unlike crazing in uncrosslinked glasses, void formation here was accompanied by molecular fracture (observed by e.s.r. spectrometry, *see* later).

To summarise, then, it has been shown that specific stress-field criteria for craze formation can be defined which are distinct from the criteria for shear-yielding in requiring a dilatational stress field component. Crazing is not, however, initiated at a unique critical hydrostatic tensile stress, except in the absence of stress bias. If σ_b is non-zero, crazing can occur under reduced hydrostatic tension. The role of the shear components of the stress field is further emphasised by similarity between the time and temperature dependencies of the shear and crazing stresses, suggesting that local shear deformations are involved in the crazing process. The similarities between shear yield stress and crazing stress cannot be pressed too far, however. Both the observations on cross-linked glasses cited above and the low temperature dependence of brittle fracture stress ('brittle' fracture being preceded by craze formation) commonly observed in glassy thermoplastics, indicate that crazing and yield stresses *can* behave in quite different ways.

Mechanism of crazing
The actual sequence of events which give rise to craze formation has been discussed by several authors, both for dry and for solvent-induced crazing. Since crazes develop in localised regions, it is reasonable to suppose that they are initiated at stress-raising flaws, which may be surface cracks or scratches, but may equally well be regions of elastic inhomogeneity within the material. (These can arise, *e.g.* from local fluctuations in molecular orientation.) For convenience we shall consider the stress-raising flaw to be a crack-like entity.

The importance of the stress-raising flaw is not only that it localises craze initiation, but that it modifies the stress-field in its locality. The discussion in the previous section of stress-field concentrations related to the stresses in the bulk of the material (the 'bulk stresses'). Our concern here is with the local stress field at the tip of a stress-raising flaw, which differs in important respects from the bulk stress field. For one thing, the magnitudes of the stresses are greatly enhanced (Gent[57] has estimated that stress magnifications of 10–50 would not be unreasonable for surface flaws). Secondly, a crack in a bulk tensile field produces a local triaxial state of stress which is most marked at a point ahead of its tip about equal to the tip radius. Although the bulk tensile stress, σ_0, has a hydrostatic component $p = \sigma_0/3$, the local hydrostatic component at the point referred to can (because of stress intensification) rise to 5–25 times σ_0. Consider what happens, therefore, at the tip of our stress-raising flaw as bulk tensile stress is progressively increased. Two cases arise.

(i) If the material is completely elastic, the maximum uniaxial stress at the tip and the hydrostatic tension ahead of the tip both increase, the latter always being smaller than the former. If the critical cavitation stress is sufficiently smaller than the uniaxial tensile strength, cavitation will occur at the point of maximum hydrostatic tension ahead of the tip. Otherwise the crack will simply grow by tensile fracture at its tip.

(ii) The perfectly elastic situation is quite unrealistic for most materials, even inorganic glass. A closer approach to reality is the elastic–plastic situation where the material possesses some constant tensile yield stress σ_y.

In case (ii), material at the extreme tip of the crack, where the local uniaxial stress is highest, will deform plastically once σ_y is exceeded, and an expanding plastic zone forms at the tip (Fig. 28(a)). Since the local stresses are highest along the crack axis, the plastic zone will tend to grow

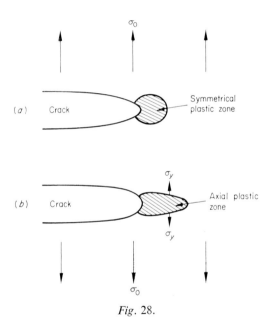

σ_0

(a) Crack Symmetrical plastic zone

σ_y

(b) Crack Axial plastic zone

σ_y

σ_0

Fig. 28.

as a narrow axial region. Unless the crack is in a very thin lamina, however, this tendency is inhibited by the 'elastic constraint' of the surrounding unyielded material which prevents the change of shape implicit in plastic deformation. This has two consequences. Firstly, it raises the local stress necessary for axial propagation of the plastic zone so that the zone finds it easier to spread sideways, forming a more or less symmetrical region. Secondly, in so far as the zone does advance along the axis, it constitutes a layer of compliant material sandwiched between walls of stiff, unyielded material. Under these circumstances the hydrostatic tension in the compliant layer rises to equal the tensile stress in the unyielded material acting normal to the plane of the sandwich (Fig. 28(b)). This stress has a maximum value of σ_y.

If cavitation occurs in the compliant zone under a hydrostatic tension $p < \sigma_y$, the elastic constraint of the unyielded material will be relieved (by fibrillation in the compliant zone) and the conditions for craze formation are satisfied. If the cavitation stress $p > \sigma_y$, an axial extension of the plastic zone is inhibited and symmetrical growth of the zone, leading to homogeneous yield, is to be expected.

This simple picture is complicated by the fact that our materials are not ideally elastic–plastic. For example, if a stress-drop occurs at yield, the plastic zone will tend to localise, giving rise to shear bands rather than homogeneous shear. Strain hardening will also affect the subsequent development of the plastic zone or cavitated zone (craze) as the case may be. It is clear, however, what conditions are necessary for craze formation, namely a cavitation stress $p \leq \sigma_y$.

Conditions for cavitation

The hydrostatic stress required to nucleate a cavity in a polymeric liquid has been estimated by Haward.[58] His predictions are compared with bulk yield and crazing stresses in Fig. 32 of Chapter 6 and are seen to be much lower than either of the last-named stresses, except as $T \to T_g$. This suggests that the hydrostatic stresses for void formation are controlled by the growth rather than the nucleation phase.

From this point, two quite distinct lines of reasoning have been followed by different authors. The basic difference lies between the theory proposed by Gent,[57] in which void formation follows inevitably once certain conditions are established at the crack tip, and the theories of Haward[58] and of Andrews and Bevan,[45] in which the hydrostatic stress for void growth is regarded as the controlling parameter. All authors agree, however, on the fact that a craze is formed by cavitation under hydrostatic tension in the polymer.

Gent[57] considered the situation referred to earlier in which an axial plastic zone is prevented from forming by the elastic constraint of unyielded material. Although a plastic zone does not form, the material in a narrow axial band is raised to the yield stress and, though unable to flow, is nevertheless compliant. The 'sandwich' situation gives rise to enhanced hydrostatic tension in the compliant layer which increases the free volume and, if sufficiently high, leads to a glass $\to$ rubber-like transition. The closer the temperature to T_g, the less free volume will need to be generated. On the other hand, any externally applied hydrostatic pressure P will have to be compensated by the local hydrostatic tension p. Gent thus derived the following criterion for the formation of a narrow band of rubber-like material.

$$\sigma_0 = [\beta(T_g - T) + P]/k \tag{44}$$

where σ_0 is the bulk tensile stress, k the stress intensification at the flaw and β is a coefficient related to the pressure dependence of T_g. If $k\sigma_0$ approaches the tensile yield stress $\sigma_y(\sim E/3)$, thin-band softening would give way to general yield. Expressing this in terms of the external pressure P_t needed to suppress crazing, Gent obtained

$$P_t = \left(\frac{E}{9}\right) - \beta(T_g - T) \tag{45}$$

These equations were found to be in close agreement with experimental data obtained on polystyrene and polycarbonate, using reasonable values for k, E and β.

Solvent-induced crazing was included in Gent's theory by taking into account (i) the reduction of T_g caused by swelling in the tip region and (ii) by calculating the degree of swelling in terms of the dilatational stresses operating there.

In Gent's theory, the hydrostatic tension required to produce cavitation is more than provided by that required to produce thin-band softening (except as T approaches T_g closely), so that voids form spontaneously once the thin softened zone has been produced.

Haward,[58] and Andrews and Bevan[45] have adopted the view that the conditions for cavitation are controlled by the actual hydrostatic stress necessary to enlarge the cavity. In an elastic–plastic solid, a cavity of radius r is in equilibrium with a hydrostatic tension p given by

$$p = \frac{2\sigma_y}{3}\left(\ln\frac{E}{3\sigma_y(1 - v)}\right) + \frac{2\gamma}{r} \tag{46}$$

where v is Poisson's ratio and γ the interfacial tension of the void. The first term in this equation represents the stress necessary to expand the void against the resistance to plastic flow. Approximately,

$$p = \psi\sigma_y + 2\gamma/r \tag{47}$$

where ψ has a value between 2·4 and 3·3 for a wide range of glassy plastics, temperatures and conditions of solvation. Haward has pointed out that, if p in eqn. (47) represents the hydrostatic cavitation stress,

$$p > \sigma_y$$

and the condition $p < \sigma_y$ is not fulfilled. He proposed that voids nucleate in clusters rather than singly, the overlapping of their plastic zones causing an order-of-magnitude reduction (relative to eqn. (47)) in the resistance to plastic enlargement and allowing $p < \sigma_y$. Unfortunately this effect is difficult to quantify.

An alternative solution to the dilemma is to apply the idea (already cited in connection with Sternstein and Ongchin's work, and that of Gent) that the hydrostatic tension increases the free volume of the material in the compliant zone and thus reduces its yield stress. It is not necessary to suppose, with Gent, that σ_y is reduced to zero, but only that is it reduced below the yield stress of the surrounding glassy matrix. (Although the bulk also experiences a hydrostatic stress by virtue of the tensile stress, its magnitude cannot exceed $\frac{1}{3}\sigma_y$, whereas in the compliant zone p can rise to equal σ_y.) Under these circumstances, cavitation can occur according to eqn. (47), σ_y now being the reduced yield stress of the compliant zone.

The dilemma discussed above does not arise in the case of solvent crazing discussed by Andrews and Bevan, since here the stress-dilated tip region is considered to become swollen by the penetration of solvent, reducing T_g locally to the experimentally observed T_c as discussed earlier, and allowing the compliant zone to be identified with the swollen region. Then, naturally, σ_y in equation is lower than σ_y (bulk), and the condition $p < \sigma_y$ (bulk) is easily satisfied.

Andrews and Bevan integrated eqn. (47) with respect to void volume and obtained the following expression for the surface work of craze formation.

$$\mathscr{T} = 2\cdot42 \left(\frac{h\gamma}{\rho}\right) f^{\frac{2}{3}} + \psi\sigma_y h f \qquad (48)$$

where h is the craze thickness, ρ the mean separation of void centres in the craze, and f is the void fraction. All these quantities are ascertainable, and good agreement is obtained between eqn. (48) and the data of Fig. 20 using reasonable values for them and for γ. In particular, the characteristic temperature dependence of $\mathscr{T}_0$ is explained by eqn. (48), the strongly temperature dependent region below T_c being accounted for by the variation of σ_y (swollen) with T, and the temperature independent region for $T > T_c$ arising from the surface energy term, σ_y being zero.

Finally, we may now refer back to the results of Sternstein and Ongchin for the bulk stress field conditions which cause crazing. The importance of the dilatational stress component is self-evident, since this acts directly to promote cavitation. The reason why shear stress assists crazing may now be seen in terms of the effect of the stress-raising flaw on the stress field. A bulk shear stress field may give rise to dilatational stress components in the vicinity of the crack, thus also promoting cavitation.

7.5 MOLECULAR FRACTURE

7.5.1 Kinetic theories of fracture

All fracture events necessarily involve the breakage of interatomic bonds, whether they be primary bonds within the molecules or secondary bonds between them.

According to the kinetic theory of fracture, macroscopic failure is governed by the microscopical process of stress-activated bond-rupture. The theory was first proposed by Taylor[59] in 1947 but has been developed by Stuart and Anderson[60] and by Zhurkov[61] and co-workers. The transitions

$$\text{Bond intact } (A) \rightarrow \text{bond broken } (B)$$

$$\text{Bond broken } (B) \rightarrow \text{bond remade } (A)$$

are seen as thermally activated processes. In accordance with chemical rate theory, the transitions occur at frequencies,

$$v_{AB} = v_0 \exp\left(-U_{AB}/kT\right)$$

$$v_{BA} = v_0 \exp\left(-U_{BA}/kT\right) \tag{49}$$

where v_0 is a constant of value 10^{12} to 10^{13} sec^{-1}, U is the height of the energy barrier (the activation energy) and k is Boltzmann's constant.

Clearly, in the unstrained state $U_{AB} > U_{BA}$, the difference representing the excess energy of broken bonds, *i.e.* a form of surface energy, and as a result the material remains coherent.

The energy barrier can be modified, however, by the application of mechanical stress, *i.e.* by the presence of elastic potential energy. A tensile stress acting upon an atomic bond decreases the thermal energy required to cause rupture, and this can be expressed mathematically as,

$$U^*_{AB} = U_{AB} - \text{f}(\sigma) \tag{50}$$

where U^*_{AB} is the stress-modified energy barrier, f is a function and σ is the stress acting on the bond. The simplest functionality is usually chosen, and accords well with experimental findings, namely

$$U^*_{AB} = U_{AB} - \beta\sigma \tag{51}$$

where β is a constant with the dimensions of volume (the 'activation volume').

As stress increases, it first achieves a threshold value at which U^*_{AB} and U^*_{BA} become equal. This threshold stress (or its equivalent potential energy) represents the condition required to overcome the energy penalty of creating new surfaces, and corresponds closely to the Griffith criterion for fracture.

With further increase of stress, $U^*_{AB} \sim 2U^*_{BA}$, and the probability of the reverse reaction $B \to A$ becomes negligible compared with that of the forward reaction. We thus have

$$v^* \simeq v_0 \exp - [(U_{AB} - \beta\sigma)/kT] \qquad (52)$$

If we stipulate, as a crude fracture criterion, that a given number N of bonds must be broken for the remaining intact bonds to be unable to carry the load, we obtain from eqn. (52), the time to fracture,

$$t_f = \frac{N}{v^*} = \frac{N}{v_0} \exp \left(\frac{U_{AB} - \beta\sigma}{kT} \right)$$

or

$$\ln t_f = C + \left(\frac{U_{AB} - \beta\sigma}{kT} \right) \qquad (53)$$

where C is a constant.

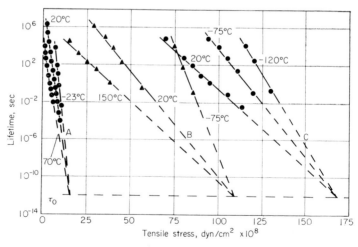

Fig. 29. *Dependence of lifetime upon tensile stress in (a) unoriented PMMA, (b) viscose yarn and (c) nylon 6 yarn (after Zhurkov and Tomashevsky[61]).*

A plot of $\ln t_f$ against σ should therefore be a straight line of negative slope β/kT, a result fully borne out[61] by experiment (Fig. 29). When the quantity U_{AB} is evaluated from such experiments, its magnitude agrees almost precisely with the values obtained for chemical bond rupture in thermal degradation, as seen in the table of Zhurkov and Tomashevsky[61] (Table 2).

TABLE 2

Polymer	U_{AB} (kcal/mol)	U (thermal)
PVC	35	32
Polystyrene	54	55
PMMA	54	52–53
Polypropylene	56	55–58
Teflon	75	76–80
Nylon 6	45	43

7.5.2 Experimental evidence for bond fracture

The analogy between mechanical and thermal degradation suggests strongly that primary, and not only secondary, bonds rupture in the fracture of thermoplastics. In cross-linked networks, of course, primary bond fracture is unavoidable. Regel and co-workers[62] deformed polymer specimens to fracture in the vacuum of a mass-spectrometer with the purpose of directly confirming the incidence of molecular degradation during a tensile test. Figure 30 shows the height of one peak in the mass-spectrum from PMMA plotted against time for a constant strain-rate tensile test. Volatile matter is observed as soon as the specimen is loaded, but its rate of evolution is constant until the point of fracture is approached, when the evolution rate accelerates sharply. The mass/charge ratio distributions in the spectra were very similar for mechanical and for independent thermal degradation tests on the same polymer, for PMMA, polystyrene and polypropylene.

Although these experiments appear to confirm the occurrence of molecular fracture by stress-assisted thermal activation, a word of caution is necessary. The results *may* be explicable in terms of the evolution of low molecular weight species already present in the specimen, retained in spite of pre-evacuation, but released by stress-assisted diffusion (a well-established effect in polymers) into the vacuum of the mass-spectrometer. These volatile species would then be degraded at the ion-source of the spectrometer to give fragments characteristic of thermal degradation. The rapid rise in evolution as fracture is approached could arise from craze formation, enhancing the outward diffusion of pre-existing volatiles.

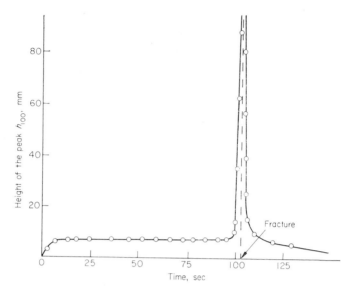

Fig. 30.   *Mass spectrometric intensity at mass number* 100 *as a function of time during the* in situ *tensile deformation of PMMA (after Regel* et al.[62]).

   Such objections cannot, however, be maintained against a more recent and more direct method of investigating molecular fracture events, namely the use of electron spin resonance (e.s.r.).[61,66] E.s.r. spectrometry detects and measures the concentration of free radicals (*i.e.* unpaired electrons) in a specimen. Any process or reaction which produces free radicals may thus be monitored by e.s.r., and primary bond rupture in polymer molecules or networks is just such a process.

   Molecular fracture in polymers can, of course, be brought about in a variety of ways, *e.g.* by high energy irradiation. It can also be caused by mechanical operations such as shearing, mastication, grinding or ball-milling, and the study of the degradation, cross-linking and other processes which result from such treatments forms the well-established subject of mechano-chemistry (recently reviewed by Casale *et al.*[63]). Our interest here, however, is in molecular rupture events as they relate to macroscopic fracture, and we shall therefore be concerned only with e.s.r. spectra produced by the application of tensile load. This is the subject of an excellent review by Kausch.[64]

   Until recently free radical formation under stress had been observed only in highly crystalline, oriented fibres. Kausch gives a table of radical concentrations for various polymers (Table 3).

TABLE 3

Polymer	Temp. °K	Concn./cm³	References
PMMA	243, 293	$<10^{14}$ ⎱ no detectable	68, 61
Polystyrene	243, 293	$<10^{14}$ ⎰ signal	
PET	⎰ 293	$<10^{15}$	68, 61
	⎱ 243	$8\cdot10^{15}$	61, 68
Polyethylene	243	$5\cdot10^{16}$	61
Nylon 6	243, 293	$5\cdot10^{17}$	68, 61, 67
Nylon 66	293	$1\cdot10^{17}$	65
Natural silk	243	$7\cdot10^{17}$	61

Campbell and Peterlin[65] calculated that a concentration of $10^{17}/cm^3$ free radicals implied that only one molecule in 250 underwent fracture.

It appears that thermoplastics only exhibit significant molecular fracture in tension when there are crystallites present to provide molecular 'anchorages', and that the effect is most evident in oriented fibres where a high proportion of inter-crystalline tie molecules is to be expected.

The requirement for molecular anchorage can be fulfilled in polymeric glasses if they are cross-linked. In Fig. 31, e.s.r. data obtained by Reed and Natarajan[56] on cross-linked cis-polyisoprene, tested below T_g, are

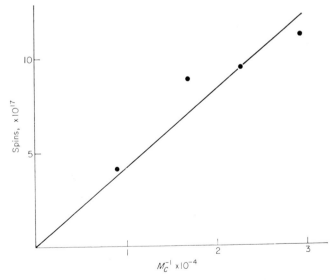

Fig. 31. *Maximum free radical concentration in tensile deformation of* cis-*polyisoprene below* T_g, *as a function of cross-link density.*

plotted in the form of radical concentration against cross-link density (reciprocal inter-cross-link molecular weight). Although the data are not numerous, they are well represented by a straight line through the origin, indicating negligible radical concentration for uncross-linked glasses. This suggests that molecular rupture plays a relatively small part in the macroscopic fracture of thermoplastic glassy polymers, and that the cavitation (crazing) which is a precursor to fracture, occurs by molecular flow and the rupture of secondary bonds rather than primary ones.

In cross-linked glasses the situation is quite different. Here cavitation associated with molecular fracture is readily observed under suitable conditions, *viz.* pre-orientation to induce low temperature flow and a temperature sufficiently far below T_g. Results on cross-linked *cis*-polyisoprene tested below 200°K by Natarajan and Reed[56] were summarised in Fig. 27.

Immediately below T_g the pre-oriented specimens cold draw without cavitation and without free radical formations (at least under the conditions employed). At a lower temperature of about 150°K a ductile-brittle transition occurred, but was followed, below about 130°K by a second ductile region in which the ductility was associated with generalised cavitation and in which copious radical formation was observed. This region is therefore analogous to the room-temperature behaviour of some crystalline fibres, in which e.s.r. signals were found by Zhurkov *et al.*[69] to be associated with the formation of 'micro-voids' of 1 to 100 nm in size.

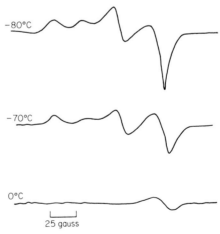

Fig. 32. Decay of e.s.r. signal in deformed cis-*polyisoprene as the temperature is raised from below* T_g *(−73°C) to above* T_g *(after Natarajan and Reed[56]).*

The radicals observed appear often to be secondary radicals associated with resonant structures or formed by reaction with oxygen (peroxyradical). They are stable in the glassy state, but decay rapidly if the speciment is heated above T_g, as illustrated in Fig. 32 for *cis*-polyisoprene. This decay is accompanied by an increase in cross-link density (of between 4 and 13% in polyisoprene) and, often, by the evolution of hydrogen. Hydrogen evolution and cross-linking are undoubtedly direct consequences of radical decay as the molecular chains become mobile around T_g.

7.6 CONCLUSION

The major growth points of the subject of fracture in glassy polymers can be summarised as follows. In fracture mechanics, the emphasis is on applications to engineering design and, as a necessary corollary, upon the closer definition of fracture mechanics parameters for different materials, fracture modes and conditions of fracture. In the study of crazing, rather more attention has properly been paid to elucidating the mechanisms by which crazes grow. Even here, however, mechanics are proving important in defining the stress field conditions for crazing and in codifying the behaviour of crazes themselves. An added bonus is that crazing conditions can now be defined in terms useful to the engineer who wishes to design against this mode of failure or deterioration. Finally, the relatively new study of molecular fracture is both scientifically fascinating and potentially useful in providing insight into the micro-mechanisms and time-dependent aspects of macro-fracture. Attempts to relate molecular fracture to cavitation and continuum parameters like yield and fracture stresses appear promising and will no doubt be vigorously pursued.

REFERENCES

1. Irwin, G. R. (1958). 'Fracture', In *Encyclopaedia of Physics*, vol. 6, Springer-Verlag, Berlin, p. 551.
2. Andrews, E. H. (1968). *Fracture in Polymers*, Oliver & Boyd, London, p. 120.
3. Williams, J. G. and Ewing, P. D. (1972). *Int. J. Fracture Mechanics*, **8**, 447.
4. Marshall, G. P., Culver, L. E. and Williams, J. G. (1969). *Plastics & Polymers*, **37**, 75.
5. Rivlin, R. S. and Thomas, A. G. (1953). *J. Polym. Sci.*, **10**, 291.
6. Griffith, A. A. (1921). *Phil. Trans. Roy. Soc.*, **A221**, 163.
7. Svennson, N. L. (1961). *Proc. Phys. Soc.*, **77**, 876.
8. Benbow, J. J. and Roesler, F. C. (1957). *Proc. Phys. Soc.*, **70B**, 201; and (1961) **78**, 970.
9. Berry, J. P. (1961). *J. Polym. Sci.*, **50**, 107.

10. Broutman, L. J. and McGarry, F. J. (1965). *J. appl. Polym. Sci.*, **9**, 589.
11. Van den Boogaart, A. (1966). In *Physical Basis of Yield and Fracture*, Inst. of Physics, London, p. 167.
12. Berry, J. P. (1963). *J. appl. Phys.*, **34**, 62.
13. Higuchi, M. (1966). *Proc. 1st Int. Conf. Fracture, Sendai*, **2**, 1211.
14. Tattersall, H. G. and Tappin, G. (1966). *J. Mater. Sci.*, **1**, 296.
15. Davidge, R. W. and Tappin, G. (1968). *J. Mater. Sci.*, **3**, 165.
16. Griffith, R. and Holloway, D. G. (1970). *J. Mater. Sci.*, **5**, 302.
17. Williams, J. G., Radon, J. C. and Turner, C. E. (1968). *Polym. Eng. Sci.*, **8**, 130.
18. Berry, J. P. (1961). *J. Polym. Sci.*, **50**, 313.
19. Berry, J. P. (1960). *Nature*, **185**, 91.
20. Kambour, R. P. (1965). *J. Polym. Sci.*, A, **3**, 1713.
21. Kambour, R. P. (1964). *J. Polym. Sci.*, A, **2**, 4159.
22. Kambour, R. P. (1968). *Appl. Polym. Symposia*, **7**, p. 215.
23. Kambour, R. P. (1968). *Polym. Eng. Sci.*, **8**, 281.
24. Cessna, L. C. and Sternstein, S. S. (1965). *J. Polym. Sci.*, B, **3**, 825.
25. Beardmore, P. and Johnson, T. L. (1971). *Phil. Mag.*, **23**, 1119.
26. Berry, J. P. (1964). *J. Polym. Sci.*, A, **2**, 4069.
27. Vincent, P. I. (1960). *Polymer*, **1**, 425.
28. Murray, J. and Hull, D. (1971). *J. Mater. Sci.*, **6**, 1277.
29. Andrews, E. H. (1969). In *Testing of Polymers IV*, ed. W. Brown, Interscience, New York.
30. Tauchert, T. R. and Afzal, S. M. (1967). *J. appl. Phys.*, **38**, 4568.
31. Riddell, M. N., Koo, G. P. and O'Toole, J. L. (1966). *Polym. Eng. Sci.*, **6**, 363.
32. Constable, I., Williams, J. G. and Burns, D. J. (1970). *J. Mech. Eng. Sci.*, **12**, 20.
33. Culver, L. E., Burns, D. J. and Borduas, H. F. (1967). *Proc. 23rd SPE Ann. Technol. Conf.*, Detroit, p. 233.
34. Hertzberg, R. W., Nordberg, H. and Manson, J. A. (1970). *J. Mater. Sci.*, **5**, 521.
35. Andrews, E. H. and Walker, B. J. (1971). *Proc. Roy. Soc.*, A, **325**, 57.
36. Andrews, E. H. (1972). In *MTP Int. Review of Science* (Phys. Chem. Ser. I, vol. 8), Butterworths, London.
37. Greensmith, H. W. (1963). In *Chemistry and Physics of Rubberlike Substances*, ed. L. Bateman, Maclaren, London, p. 291.
38. Kambour, R. P. and Robertson, R. E. (1972). In *Materials Science of Polymers*, ed. A. D. Jenkins, North Holland Co., Amsterdam.
39. Beardmore, P. and Rabinowitz, S. (1971). *J. Mater. Sci.*, **6**, 80.
40. Harris, J. S. and Ward, I. M. (1970). *J. Mater. Sci.*, **5**, 573.
41. Sternstein, S. S., Ongchin, L. and Silverman, A. (1968). *Appl. Polym. Symposia*, No. 7, Interscience, New York, p. 175.
42. Haward, R. N., Murphy, B. M. and White, E. F. (1969). In *Fracture*, Chapman and Hall, London, p. 519.
43. Knight, A. C. (1965). *J. Polym. Sci.*, A3, 1845.
44. Inglis, C. E. (1913). *Trans. Inst. Naval Architects, London*, **60**, 219.
45. Andrews, E. H. and Bevan, L. (1972). *Polymer*, **13**, 337.
46. Levy, G. M. Ph.D. Thesis, 'The stress corrosion failure of glassy polymers' (Univ. of London, 1972).
47. Dugdale, D. S. (1960). *J. Mech. Phys. Solids*, **8**, 100.
48. Marshall, G. P., Culver, L. E. and Williams, J. G. (1970). *Proc. Roy. Soc.*, A, **319**, 165.
49. Burdekin, F. M. and Stone, D. E. W. (1966). *J. Strain Analysis*, **1**, 145.
50. Bernier, G. A. and Kambour, R. P. (1968). *Macromolecules*, **1**, 393.
51. Andrews, E. H. and Bevan, L. (1966). In *Physical Basis of Yield and Fracture*, Institute of Physics, London, p. 209.

52. Andrews, E. H., Levy, G. M. and Willis, J. *Polymer*. (1973). *Mater. Sci.*, in press.
53. Andrews, E. H., Levy, G. M. and Willis, J. *Polymer*. (To be published.)
54. Sternstein, S. S. and Ongchin, L. (1969). *ACS Polymer Reprints*, **10**, 1117.
55. Haward, R. N., Murphy, B. M. and White, E. F. T. (1971). *J. Polym. Sci.*, A2, **9**, 801.
56. Natarajan, R. and Reed, P. E. (1972). *J. Polym. Sci.*, A2, **10**, 585.
57. Gent, A. N. (1970). *J. Mater. Sci.*, **5**, 925.
58. Haward, R. N. Int. Symp. Phys. of Non-cryst. Solids, Sheffield, Sept. 1970 (preprint).
59. Taylor, N. W. (1947). *J. appl. Phys.*, **15**, 943.
60. Stuart, H. A. and Anderson, D. L. (1953). *J. Amer. Ceram. Soc.*, **36**, 416.
61. Zhurkov, S. N. and Tomashevsky, E. E. (1966). In *Physical Basis of Yield and Fracture*, Institute of Physics, London, p. 200.
62. Regel, V. R., Muinov, T. M. and Pozdnyakov, O. F. (1966). In *Physical Basis of Yield and Fracture*, Institute of Physics, London, p. 194.
63. Casale, A., Porter, R. S. and Johnson, J. F. (1971). *Rubber Chem. and Technol.*, **44**, 534.
64. Kausch, H. H. (1970). *Reviews in Macromol. Chem.*, **5**, Pt. 2, 97.
65. Campbell, D. and Peterlin, A. (1968). *Polymer Letters*, **6**, 481.
66. DeVries, K. L., Roylance, D. K. and Williams, M. L. (1969). In *Fracture 1969*, Chapman & Hall, London, p. 551.
67. Becht, J. and Fischer, H. (1969). *Kolloid Z.*, **229**, 167.
68. Becht, J. and Fischer, H. *Kolloid Z.* (To be published.)
69. Zhurkov, S. N., Kuksenko, V. S. and Slutsker, A. I. (1969). In *Fracture 1969*, Chapman & Hall, London, p. 531.

CHAPTER 8

RUBBER REINFORCED THERMOPLASTICS

J. MANN AND G. R. WILLIAMSON

8.1 INTRODUCTION

Thermoplastic polymers may be divided into broad classes depending on type, chemical composition or behaviour. For example they may be classified as crystalline or amorphous polymers, or we may group them according to whether they are tough or brittle materials. The latter classification has great commercial significance since many amorphous or glassy polymers are brittle and consequently have limited application.

At one time it was believed that all glassy polymers and rubbers became brittle below their glass transition temperature T_g. This, of course, has never been universally true and polymers exhibiting tough behaviour below T_g are well known—for example cellulose nitrate, polyvinylacetal, polyvinylchloride, polycarbonate and polypropylene oxide.[1,2] Toughness here implies bulk yielding and large deformation on breakage.

On the other hand, PVC which is classified as a tough polymer, is very notch sensitive—that is to say small surface defects such as scratches or cracks cause the polymer to have a relatively low impact strength at room temperature.

It was suggested as early as 1959[3] that in order to avoid brittleness below T_g, molecular motion should be possible, i.e. relaxation peaks should be present below T_g. This has recently been shown not to be a prerequisite since polyphenylene oxide[1,2] is tough without the peaks, whereas the copolymers of methyl and cyclohexylmethacrylates[1,2] show a pronounced peak and yet are extremely brittle at room temperature.

These fundamental considerations attempt to relate polymeric structure and brittle behaviour and are necessary to increase our understanding of thermoplastic failure. In this chapter, however, we do not wish to consider in detail the ideal tough polymeric structure. Primarily our aim is to consider in detail those polymers of commercial importance falling within the classification glassy/brittle and the conversion to tough materials by the incorporation of a rubber. These include polymers such as polystyrene (PS), styrene acrylonitrile copolymer (SAN) and polyvinylchloride (PVC).

Such materials have many useful properties, *i.e.* they are easy to process and hence fabricate, they possess high tensile strength and good dimensional stability, reasonable to good chemical resistance, good to excellent optical properties and weathering characteristics. They lack toughness which limits their applicational usefulness.

For many years now (and indeed it is perhaps surprising to realise the first patent on the subject was granted over half a century ago[4]) it has been recognised that the incorporation of an elastomeric material into such polymers leads to reinforcement or toughening. This behaviour is not of course confined to the amorphous polymers but also occurs with crystalline structures such as polypropylene. Indeed the success of this apparently simple procedure may be gauged from some of the world production figures for toughened 'glassy/brittle' polymers for 1970.[5]

Polymer	Tonnes $\times$ 10^{-6}
SAN	0·08
Toughened SAN–(ABS)	0·52
PS	1·8
Toughened PS–(TPS)	1·2

In the early years toughening of thermoplastics with rubbers for a large part proceeded on an *ad hoc* trial and error basis. However, with the advent of new techniques for studying polymeric structures such as the torsional pendulum, improvements in optical microscopy and advances in electron microscopy, certain features have emerged which have not only helped our understanding but allowed the development of unified theories and descriptions of the toughening process in polymers. It has for example become apparent that the morphology of the system plays a very important part in the optimisation of the glassy polymer-elastomer structure, and a great deal of our knowledge results from the very large volume of work published on toughened polystyrene (TPS) during the last decade. Sophistication has entered the manufacture of ABS and TPS polymers to the extent that the dispersed phase morphology can be controlled and within limits the characteristics of the dispersed phase itself.

Our aim is to describe the state of knowledge of the toughening of glassy polymers, particularly PS, SAN and PVC, by the incorporation of elastomers. A great industry revolves around the simple fact that most polymer mixtures are molecularly incompatible, and yet it is apparent that the term compatibility in this context is abused. Systems are described as completely compatible and yet they contain a dispersed phase when examined by electron microscopy. We have consequently included a discussion on polymeric compatibility and its consequences. Methods of manufacture are briefly outlined, followed by detailed descriptions of morphology leading to a discussion of the mechanism of toughening by rubbers in glassy polymers.

8.2   RUBBER REINFORCED GLASSY POLYMERS
OF COMMERCIAL IMPORTANCE

Subsequent sections will be devoted mainly to a discussion centred around three polymers developed solely to obtain improved toughness over the 'parent' polymer by rubber reinforcement. A brief description of the polymers is given below.

8.2.1   Based on polystyrene

This polymer has variously been termed impact polystyrene, rubber modified polystyrene, toughened polystyrene and high impact polystyrene (HIPS). Since the term HIPS is applied indiscriminately and embraces medium to super impact grades, we prefer to use the term toughened polystyrene (TPS). Structurally TPS consists of an elastomer (usually an unsaturated rubber such as styrene–butadiene copolymer or polybutadiene) in a matrix or continuous phase of polystyrene. A variety of microstructures is possible. Dispersed phase particle size ranges from 1 to 20 μ, but better products have particles within the range 1 to 5 μ.

8.2.2   Based on styrene acrylonitrile copolymer (SAN)

If the matrix in TPS is replaced by SAN, increased modulus, yield strength, and softening point, together with improved chemical resistance can be obtained in the toughened polymer.[6] This product is a terpolymer of acrylonitrile–butadiene–styrene commonly termed ABS. Structurally the polymer consists of a matrix of SAN containing a dispersed rubber phase which may be one of two types.

(1) A butadiene–acrylonitrile copolymer (nitrile rubber).
(2) A polybutadiene rubber grafted with SAN.

The dispersed phase particle size is considerably smaller than TPS and within the range 0·1 to 0·5 μ.

8.2.3 Based on polyvinylchloride

PVC may be toughened by the addition of elastomers such as nitrile rubbers, or an elastomer contained as a dispersed phase within a toughened polymer such as ABS. Alternatively toughening may be achieved by the addition of non-elastomeric polar polymers such as the acrylic ester polymers, e.g. polymethylmethacrylate or chlorinated linear polyethylene.

We are primarily concerned with toughening by the addition of rubbers; the addition of ABS provides a finely dispersed rubbery phase of grafted cross-linked polybutadiene. On the other hand, the addition of nitrile rubber may give a variety of dispersions from interpenetrating phases to discrete disperse phase particles.

8.3 METHODS OF MANUFACTURE

The manufacture of polymers containing rubber as a reinforcing agent may be carried out by three distinct processes.

8.3.1 Physical blending

This is by far the oldest and simplest method and the blending of rubber with polystyrene was described as early as 1912.[4] The thermoplastic and elastomer are mechanically blended together above the softening point of the thermoplastic on a two-roll mill or in an enclosed mixer such as a Banbury. The degree of dispersion of the rubber depends on the time of mixing, the amount of shear, the temperature and the rheological properties of the system. As Rosen[7] points out, molecular scission and grafting may also occur, and the amount of crosslinking (insoluble gel formation) increases with time of milling.[8] It is almost impossible to exercise independent control of all these variables, and now generally recognised[9] that mechanical blends formed in this way are inferior to products made by other routes. Alternative processes are used in the production of ABS and TPS although mechanical blending is still widely used in the manufacture of impact PVC. In order to improve the dispersion of rubber in the glassy matrix an alternative method is to blend the latices of rubber and polymer produced by emulsion polymerisation. The polymer blend is recovered by spray drying, or filtered and dried. After drying, the crumb is then compounded with other additives in a Banbury or an extruder. This method is used in the production of ABS, but laboratory studies showed[10] that TPS samples produced by latex blending were inferior to those produced by the interpolymerisation process.

8.3.2   Interpolymerisation process

A rubber, usually unsaturated, is dissolved in the monomer of the glassy matrix component and the monomer is polymerised either by added initiators or thermally. Formation of the second (glassy) polymer leads to the separation of a dispersed rubber phase, due to the general incompatibility of two polymers in a common solvent. Agitation of the system, which rapidly becomes highly viscous, is necessary to create and adjust the microstructure of the dispersed phase and maintain temperature control. Polymerisation proceeds in this way until some 15 to 35% of the monomer has been polymerised. This prepolymer is then transferred to subsequent stages adapted to cope with the highly viscous melt which develops as polymerisation proceeds. Polymerisation is carried out to high conversion, and the melt is then usually extruded through a devolatilising extruder to remove unreacted monomer. Alternatively, to aid temperature control the prepolymer can be suspended in water, and polymerisation completed under the usual type of suspension polymerisation conditions.

When the rubber is unsaturated, grafting of the rubber by matrix molecules occurs throughout the process and crosslinking of the rubber may also occur. The formation of the graft molecule plays a very important part in determining the microstructure and subsequent reinforcement of the glassy matrix.

8.3.3   Latex interpolymerisation

This process utilises the latex blending route to ensure good dispersion of the rubbery phase, but also enables chemical grafting of the rubber to occur. This is one of the key features of the interpolymerisation route.

Monomer(s) is added to the rubber latex produced during a normal emulsion polymerisation. Provided excess emulsifier is avoided the monomer migrates to the dispersed phase and swells the rubber particles. The monomer may now be polymerised in the rubber phase when grafting occurs. After polymerisation the rubber latex is treated in the usual way as described under the latex blending procedure. ABS polymers with enhanced impact properties are made by this process.[11]

8.4 INCOMPATIBILITY IN POLYMER MIXTURES

In rubber reinforced systems such as TPS and ABS it has been established beyond doubt that we are dealing with a two phase polymeric system. Indeed as we shall see later the toughening or reinforcing mechanism of glassy polymers such as polystyrene or SAN depends essentially on the presence and morphology of a dispersed phase. It is therefore of some interest to examine the reasons for incompatibility in mixed polymer systems.

On mixing two pure liquids at constant temperature and pressure the changes in free energy (*i.e.* the thermodynamic driving force) is given by $\Delta F = \Delta H - T\Delta S$, where ΔH and ΔS are the change in enthalpy and entropy of the system on mixing at constant absolute temperature T. The physical nature of the resulting mixture depends on the change in ΔF. A decrease in free energy ($-\Delta F$) shows that molecular dispersion is thermodynamically favoured whereas a positive value of ΔF indicates a two phase system will be the stable form. The free energy change is dependent on $T\Delta S$, which is always a positive term in any mixing process, and on ΔH. The enthalpy change may be negative, for example, on mixing polar liquids together, or positive on mixing non-polar components together. Since $-T\Delta S$ is always negative, and large in simple mixing processes, the nature of the final system depends mainly on the sign and value of ΔH. As a consequence many pairs of nonpolar liquids give rise to true single phase solutions and different chemical structures are perfectly compatible.

Similar considerations apply to the mixing of two polymers. However, in this case the value of ΔS may be several orders of magnitude smaller than in the case of simple liquids. Hence the major driving force towards molecular mixing is greatly reduced and is easily offset by a small positive value in ΔH. (Values of ΔH are similar to those obtained in the mixing of liquids of similar chemical composition).

Thus we find that except in systems where ΔH is large and negative (for example where hydrogen bond formation occurs) polymer mixtures generally show incompatibility.

Incompatibility also occurs extensively on mixing two polymer solutions involving a common solvent as shown by Dobry and Boyer-Kawenkoi.[12] Theoretical treatment by Scott[13] using Flory's[14] dilute polymer solution theory showed that this was to be expected, and the solvent merely dilutes the mixture and decreases the heat of interaction between the polymers. Scott also showed that phase separation in such systems would occur at low solids content (unless the molecular weights of the polymers were very low) and very small changes in polymeric chemical structure could lead to incompatibility.

Thus incompatibility has been observed between the following non-polar polymers in a common solvent: poly-o-methyl styrene/poly-p-methyl styrene; polystyrene/poly-p-tert-butyl styrene; polystyrene/polyvinyl toluene.[15] Negative enthalpy changes do not occur. In somewhat more polar systems similar changes have been observed;[16] thus incompatibility occurs between polymethyl methacrylate/polymethyl acrylate; polybutyl methacrylate/polybutyl acrylate; polymethyl methacrylate/polyvinyl acetate. An extremely comprehensive but seemingly little known paper by Bohn[17] gives a detailed account of compatibility in polymeric systems.

Attempts to quantify the problem and enable predictions to be made regarding incompatible systems have been carried out with some success,[16] using the solubility parameter approach of Hildebrand.[18,19] However, as Rosen[20] has pointed out the formation of incompatible polymeric structures will rarely present a problem. Toughening of a glassy polymer by a rubbery component requires not only a two phase structure but a subtle degree of compatibility between the phases. Good adhesion between the dispersed and continuous phase is usually achieved by graft formation between the elastomeric and glassy polymer components, and results in a dramatic improvement in the efficiency of the dispersed phase toughening action.[10,21]

8.5   IDENTIFICATION OF TWO PHASE RUBBER REINFORCED SYSTEMS

As we have shown, the theoretical, and to some extent the practical demonstration of the general phenomena of polymeric incompatibility was established beyond doubt in the late 1940s.[12,13] However, in the general field of toughening of polymers by the incorporation of an elastomer one now receives the impression that there has been some reluctance to accept this as a most probable feature.

Indeed we find that with TPS a two phase system was first suggested some years later by Buchdahl and Nielsen[22,23] who showed the presence of two separate glass transition peaks corresponding to the rubber and polystyrene components, by torsional damping measurements. It is now generally accepted that a low temperature damping peak in a rigid glassy polymer indicates a two phase system.[1] With the development of optical phase contrast microscopy convincing evidence was provided by Claver and Merz,[24] and Traylor,[25] and greater structural detail became available using the electron microscope.[26] The use of analytical methods such as infra-red spectroscopy, chemical separation of polymers and grafted polymers has been described.[27]

Visual observation of toughened polymers is sometimes useful, but must be interpreted carefully. Thus amorphous glassy polymers which lose transparency on blending with other polymers almost certainly consist of two phase structures. The reverse is certainly *not* necessarily true and does not indicate compatibility, since a two phase system with matching refractive indices will appear transparent as, for example, with mixtures of polyacrylates and polymethacrylates.[28] It is unfortunate but true that even today transparent clear blends of polymers are sometimes stated to be compatible, when a little more analysis using the correct technique would demonstrate a two phase structure.

8.6 DISPERSED PHASE MORPHOLOGY

We shall now consider in greater detail the morphology of the reinforcing dispersed phase. When the dispersed phase is produced by simple mixing of the polymeric constituents the structure may range from discrete dispersed particles to two continuous interpenetrating networks. The structure of the dispersed phase formed is dependent on the mixing procedure, and consequently on the degree and duration of shear and the temperature of mixing. Studies of these systems have not been very rewarding in increasing our understanding of rubber reinforcement. Major advances have been made in studies of products from the more reproducible manufacturing processes where the size and shape of the dispersed phase particles are controllable, for example in the latex blending route for ABS or the interpolymerisation process for TPS.

The amount of published information on ABS is somewhat limited, but as a result of a tremendous amount of theoretical and practical work the mechanism of reinforcement in TPS is particularly well developed. Consequently the emphasis in the following review will lie mainly with TPS morphology, although we shall consider ABS and PVC subsequently.

8.6.1 Toughened polystyrene
Phase changes during the interpolymerisation process
The interpolymerisation process may be carried out as a batch or continuous operation, but for simplicity we shall discuss phase changes occurring during batch polymerisation.

The process involves the polymerisation of a styrene solution containing rubber (usually unsaturated, for example styrene–butadiene copolymer or polybutadiene). Polymerisation may be carried out with initiators such as peroxides or azo compounds, or thermally. Whichever route is chosen, the resulting phase changes are the same. Within a short time, during which only 1 to 2% of polystyrene has been formed, the clear single phase rubber–styrene solution becomes hazy. This as we have seen is due to the incompatibility of two polymers, rubber and polystyrene, in the common solvent styrene. In an agitated system a polystyrene–styrene solution separates as tiny droplets in a continuous rubber styrene solution phase. Because of the difference in refractive index between the two phases, light is scattered at the droplet interface, and the system appears turbid. Continued polymerisation of styrene increases the volume of the polystyrene phase and the hazy dispersion rapidly becomes opaque. These phase changes are clearly shown in Figs. 1a and 1b.

As expected similar phase behaviour occurs on polymerisation of other polymer–styrene solutions such as polyethylacrylate, poly-t-butyl styrene.[15] Thus the phase ratio as defined by Molau[15] ($\psi = A/B$ where A = volume of polymeric phase initially dissolved in the monomer and B = volume of the newly formed phase) decreases with continuing polymerisation. A point is reached during the polymerisation when the polystyrene phase can no longer be accommodated as the dispersed phase, and the phenomenon of a phase inversion occurs. Essentially rubber solution droplets now form the disperse phase and the continuous matrix phase consists of a solution of polystyrene dissolved in styrene monomer (Fig. 1c).

The formation of the rubber dispersed phase is called prepolymerisation and on a commercial scale may be continued up to conversions as high as 35%. Substantial conversion of the remaining styrene is carried out at appreciably faster rates of reaction (up to 40% conversion/hour) either as a bulk system (which may contain an inert diluent) or as a suspension process. The use of diluent in a bulk process, or polymerisation by a suspension process are aids in attaining temperature control during the highly exothermic polymerisation occurring in a very viscous system.

During this latter 'finishing' stage little change occurs to the volume of the disperse phase, and styrene is converted to polystyrene both inside and outside the dispersed rubber phase. The unsaturated rubber undergoes grafting reactions with polystyrene, and may also become cross-linked. Keskkula[29] in a recent review over-simplifies the picture by stating that, 'the particle morphologies for both TPS and ABS are firmly established in the polymerisation process so that no alteration of the particle size

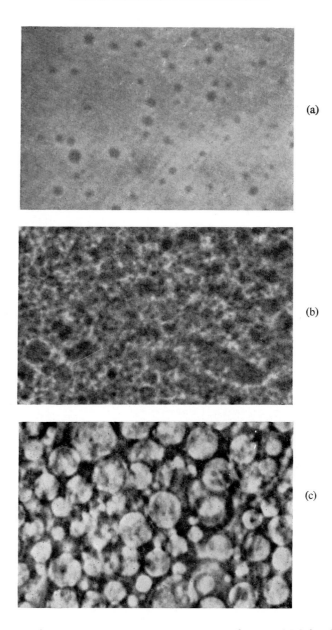

Fig. 1. *Prepolymer structure at various conversions during a TPS batch inter-polymerisation.* (a) 1·4% *conversion;* (b) 6·5% *conversion;* (c) 25% *conversion.*

takes place due to shearing of the melt, *i.e.* compounding, extrusion moulding'. Whilst it is essential that the particle morphology is fixed during polymerisation,[30] this is obtained by cross-linking the rubber. The extent of cross-linking depends on the conditions within the polymerising system and is controllable. However, it is also necessary to attain the right amount of cross-linking for, while the particle morphology may be very well retained by over cross-linking the rubber, other physical properties of the polymer will suffer in consequence.

Phase inversion

Phase inversion, which occurs in the batch bulk interpolymerisation process, represents the most important phase change occurring. The inversion point may be detected by phase contrast microscopy,[15] or by observing changes in apparent viscosity of the system which take place on passing through the inversion point.[31,32] Without inversion the final product is a rubbery opaque solid consisting of 'a continuous phase of rubber with a disperse phase of polystyrene or as a spongy, interwoven network of two continuous phases. . . .'[33] Since cross-linked rubber is now contained in a continuous phase the melt flow properties are very poor and commercially the products are of little interest.[26]

It has been established[34] that agitation of the polymerising system is necessary during the first 40% conversion to obtain good impact properties. Molau and Keskkula[33] believe that agitation does not cause phase inversion but it acts as a catalyst and increases the rate at which inversion takes place. Recent work by Freeguard and Karmarkar[32] has shown that in a constant shear field inversion will not occur unless the shear rate is greater than a defined minimum which depends on the nature of the system.

In general the phenomenon of phase inversion is reversible[33] and the phase inversion point is roughly constant dependent on the characteristics of the system, *i.e.* type and concentration of elastomer, temperature, and emulsifier concentration. There is some evidence which shows that as the emulsifier concentration (in TPS systems this is the rubber polystyrene graft molecule) rises, the inversion point occurs at higher styrene conversions. Similar effects have been observed in non-polymeric emulsion systems such as water–hexane using propionic acid as the emulsifier.[35,36]

Although several theories exist for the phase volume relationship at the inversion point, factors which determine the phase inversion point and phase volumes in polymeric emulsions are not well understood.

Graft formation

Prepolymers are stable polymeric emulsions which may be kept at room temperature in a non-agitated state for weeks without gross phase separation taking place. Model prepolymers of apparently identical composition, prepared by agitating a rubber–styrene–polystyrene system, phase separate into two layers in the absence of agitation in a matter of hours.[15] The stabilising entity is the rubber polystyrene graft molecule which is formed *in situ* during prepolymerisation. It seems likely that graft formation occurs by initiator attack on the elastomer. Such a mechanism is consistent with the fact that the free polystyrene formed has the same molecular weight as the polystyrene chains attached to the elastomer,[37] and that peroxides are effective whilst azo initiators give little or no grafting.[38,39,40] Grafting with a growing styryl radical would be infrequent in view of the probable low transfer constant for rubber.[8]

Molau[41] has recently shown that synthetic two-block butadiene–polystyrene copolymers can act as emulsion stabilisers in the TPS system. The activity of the molecule increases with increasing molecular weight, and the minimum block length for each constituent appears to be around 500 monomer units.

Further grafting, in fact the majority, occurs during the finishing stage of the polymerisation. Since this is normally carried out at appreciably faster reaction rates we may expect the polystyrene grafts to be of lower molecular weight. The graft polymer plays a somewhat different role to the emulsifier formed during prepolymerisation and confers the necessary degree of compatibility, and hence adhesion, between the rubbery dispersed phase and the polystyrene matrix phase to achieve good impact properties in the final polymer.

Composition of the dispersed phase

Toughened polystyrenes consist of a continuous phase composed almost entirely of polystyrene, and a dispersed phase containing virtually all the rubber. We shall see later that there are certain requirements regarding the continuous polystyrene phase. These are relatively straightforward. On the other hand the nature of the dispersed phase is relatively complex, and it is mainly this structure which controls the impact properties of the polymer.

Treatment of a TPS with solvents for polystyrene results in a solution consisting mainly of polystyrene, and a highly swollen gel. The gel is a result of a cross-linked network of grafted rubber, and the cross-links are

believed to result from two growing polystyrene graft molecules terminating by combination.[8] Addition of transfer agents such as α-methyl
styrene or a mercaptan has been claimed[42,43] as a means of regulating the
cross-linking reaction, since grafts are terminated by transfer.

The weight of the dried gel is considerably greater than the amount of
elastomer used and the butadiene content of impact polystyrene gels has
been determined.[44,45] Early reports in the literature[44,46] suggest that the
increase in weight of gel above the elastomer content represents the amount
of chemical grafting occurring. This is not the case. The gel content
determination is usually carried out according to well defined conditions,
and amounts to a time dependent extraction procedure. Thomas[47] (in an
apparently little known paper) showed that by repeated extraction with
toluene the gel content of a TPS was reduced from 12% to 10% wt and by
changing the solvent to dimethyl formamide, to 8%. This gel was produced
from 5% wt of dissolved rubber and Thomas queried whether any grafting
had occurred.

The authors' experience has also shown that indeed the gel content may
be reduced on exhaustive extraction with good solvents (from 17·5 to
11% wt) but a gel weight is obtained which is higher than the original
elastomer content. There seems little doubt that extensive chemical
grafting of polystyrene to the rubber does occur, but the gel also contains
considerable amounts of soluble graft and homopolystyrene.

It has in fact become apparent, particularly with advances in microscopy,
that the dispersed rubber phase particles contain polystyrene occlusions.[47,48] As a consequence the volume of the dispersed phase is many
times greater than the original volume of rubber used. Rubber loadings of
3 to 10% may give rise to a disperse phase volume fraction of 10 to
40%.[49,50] It is clear therefore that the dispersed rubbery particle consists
mainly of polystyrene, and such a composite structure is still capable of
reinforcing the glassy matrix.

The volume fraction of the dispersed phase
In the most general case of a system containing a matrix and a dispersed
phase, the modulus of the system depends on the moduli of the components. Simple calculations show[51] that the volume fraction of the
dispersed phase is of major importance in determining the overall modulus.

As we have seen the dispersed phase particles in TPS produced by the
interpolymerisation process are a mixture of rubber and polystyrene, and
consequently the modulus term required for the dispersed phase will be
a composite value. On the other hand experimental evidence shows that the

volume fraction in an ABS polymer is directly proportional to the rubber content, since little if any occlusion of matrix material occurs.

The determination of volume fraction is usually carried out in polymeric rubber reinforced systems by an examination of a planar cross-section. In this context, since the particles in the dispersed phase are usually within the range 1 to 5 microns, it is essential that the cross-section is

(a) flat, and certainly without deformation exceeding 2 or 3 microns in order to minimise multilayer formation;

(b) a typical, but random, selected area.

Provided these conditions are met and the dispersed phase is clearly displayed, for example by vapour etching a microtomed section and double

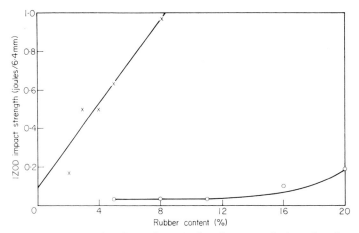

Fig. 2. Impact strength of copolymerised polystyrene (×) and polystyrene reinforced in a latex process (○). (Reproduced by courtesy of Cambridge University Press; Haward, R. N. and Mann, J. (1964). Proc. Roy. Soc., 282A, 120.)

replication with an electron microscope,[26] then a measurement of the area fraction or a fractional linear intercept allows the volume fraction to be determined regardless of particle distribution, shape or size.[52] These measurements are usually made on photographs of the selected area. Alternatively the information may be obtained from microtomed sections of the selected area.

A comparison of TPS produced by mechanical blending of a rubber with polystyrene, and polymers prepared by interpolymerisation shows that at the same rubber loading interpolymers have superior impact properties[10] (Fig. 2). This may be attributed to the following:

(a) An enhanced volume fraction due to polystyrene inclusions within the rubbery dispersed phase. It should be noted, however, that the average rubber particle size in polymers prepared by latex blending (Fig. 2) is much smaller than in those made by interpolymerisation.

(b) The better control of the dispersed phase particle size—for good reinforcement there is an optimum particle size range, and this is better controlled in interpolymerisation than blending.

(c) The formation of the rubber polystyrene graft leads to good adhesion between the dispersed and matrix phases.

Even though the volume fraction may be adequate good adhesion is necessary and there is no evidence for the formation of such a graft during mechanical blending.[8] It is for these reasons that mechanical blending techniques for TPS production were rapidly superseded by interpolymerisation.

Dispersed phase structure

With the improvement and development in electron microscope techniques over the last few years there has been a very considerable effort devoted to the analysis of the rubbery dispersed phase in TPS. Williams and Hudson[53] have described the techniques available for detailed examination of the dispersed phase in TPS. Replication of fracture surfaces obtained above and below the rubber T_g give electron micrographs around and through the rubbery particles. Other techniques involve polishing and etching of the polystyrene matrix (using isopropanol vapour) to reveal the dispersed phase particles. However, smearing occurs and cleaner cut surfaces are obtained by cross-linking the rubber with a cobalt-60 source. Excellent detailed pictures have been obtained[53,54,55,56] using the method described by Kato[57] by staining with OsO_4. Preferential staining of the rubber occurs thus increasing the contrast between the rubber and polystyrene phases, and the rubber is also hardened, enabling undistorted microtomed sections to be obtained. Electron micrographs (Fig. 3) clearly support the earlier observations of Thomas[47] and Spit[48] that the internal structure consists mainly of polystyrene inclusions surrounded by rubber membranes.

Molau and Keskkula's[33] early classification of polystyrene occlusions into two types formed in a batch prepolymerisation is clearly too simple. Type I, occurring after phase inversion, resulted from multiple emulsion formation within the rubber phase at relatively low conversions and viscosities, leading to relatively large round inclusions. Type II, on the other hand, were believed to form much later during the polymerisation and because of the high viscosities involved are small with irregular peripheries. Electron micrographs are available (Fig. 3) showing large irregular shaped polystyrene inclusions, and also small round ones, obviously in conflict with Molau and Keskkula's suggestion.

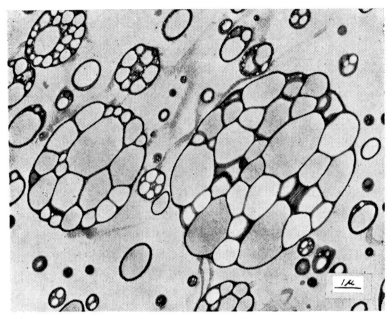

Fig. 3. *Electron micrograph showing the internal structure of a TPS rubbery particle. (Reproduced by courtesy of Division of Rubber Chemistry, American Chemical Society; Wagner, E. R. and Robeson, L. M. (1970). Rubber Chemistry and Technology, 43, 1129.)*

It is now obvious that the morphology of the rubber particle, the size and size distribution, and the structure of the internal polystyrene occlusions is very variable. Commercially, of course, it is highly desirable to define the optimum morphology for TPS. Fletcher et al.[6] stated that the most successful toughened polystyrenes have a narrow range of particle sizes evenly distributed throughout the polystyrene matrix. Lannon[58] has reported that a wide particle size distribution (1 to 20 μ) gives poor rubber utilisation, lowering the tensile yield strength and producing a poor surface finish (gloss) compared to particles within a narrow size distribution such as 1 to 5 μ. The published literature suggests that the optimum morphology may depend on a large number of factors, such as

(a) rubber type,
(b) rubber molecular weight,
(c) concentration of rubber,
(d) type of agitation and shear employed,
(e) reactor geometry,
(f) polymerisation conditions, *i.e.* temperature and initiation,
(g) amount of graft formation,
(h) amount of rubber cross-linking.

With so many variables it seems probable that no single universal optimum morphology will emerge, but rather that an optimum morphology will be related to a specific TPS process.

8.6.2 ABS copolymers

By virtue of the current methods available for its manufacture using emulsion and mass suspension polymerisation, the ABS terpolymer structure shows greater variability than TPS products. Electron micrographs[29] show commercial ABS polymers with a particle size as small as $0.1\ \mu$ and others with particles of $2\ \mu$. Generally speaking the rubber particles are smaller than those in TPS and it is significant that only particles above about $1\ \mu$ diameter contain obvious glassy polymer inclusions and are almost certainly made by mass suspension polymerisation processes.

In the early production days two ABS types were produced

(a) the *B* or blended polymers—latex of nitrile rubber and SAN; and
(b) the *G* or grafted structures—latex of grafted polybutadiene rubber and SAN.

Both types were prepared by the latex blending route and contained a dispersed particle size of 0.1 to 0.5 microns. Polymers based on nitrile rubber achieved good impact due to the partial compatibility of these rubbers with SAN[17] resulting in good adhesion between the matrix and dispersed phase. Some reduction in the softening point of the SAN occurred due to 'plasticisation' by the nitrile rubber, and use of the more compatible nitrile rubbers with a high acrylonitrile content and increased glass transition temperature, led to products failing around 0 to 10°C under high frequency impact conditions.

Incorporation of the incompatible polybutadiene rubber as the dispersed phase effectively eliminated low temperature brittleness problems, at the same time preserving the softening point of the polymer. High impact strength was achieved by chemically grafting the matrix glassy polymer to the rubber backbone. As a result the G or grafted ABS has now largely superseded the B type polymer.

The dispersed phase structure from products produced by the latex blending route consists mainly of solid rubber particles with little or no glassy polymer inclusions. Consequently the volume fraction of the dispersed phase is essentially that of the rubber within the system.

The fine morphology of similar polymers was shown quite clearly in a set of electron micrographs of ABS fractured surfaces by Haward and Mann.[10] Figure 4 shows an electron micrograph of a replicated fracture surface of an ABS at low temperature. The ABS was prepared from a polybutadiene latex and a SAN latex, and consequently contained ungrafted rubber. This material had a low Izod impact strength (0·11 joules/6·4 mm), and the rubber particles are seen to be clustered together giving

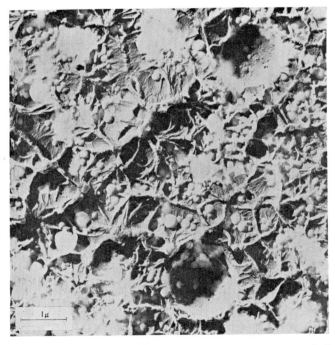

Fig. 4. Replicated fracture surface of an ABS containing ungrafted rubber. (*Reproduced by courtesy of Cambridge University Press; Haward, R. N. and Mann, J.* (1964). Proc. Roy. Soc., **282A**, 120.)

a poor dispersion through the SAN matrix. Removal of the rubber particles from the matrix during the fracture process leaves craters which are fairly rough but devoid of any significant features.

A similar micrograph for an ABS prepared from a polybutadiene grafted with SAN is shown in Fig. 5. Here the craters show where the rubber particles have been situated and small hillocks represent rubber particles still embedded in the SAN matrix. The rubber particles are well dispersed throughout the matrix and show little tendency to cluster.

The base of the craters show very interesting features. Some are covered with convex shaped pimples which are caused by the ductile deformation of the matrix as the rubber particle is pulled away during fracture. This is direct evidence for very strong adhesion between the dispersed and matrix phases.

The strong bonding occurs *via* the formation of a graft copolymer. This was clearly demonstrated by comparing electron micrographs of dried

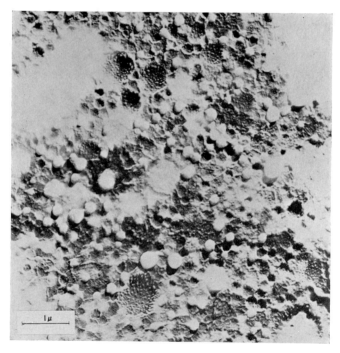

Fig. 5.   Replicated fracture surface of an ABS containing grafted rubber. (Reproduced by courtesy of Elsevier Publishing Company; Composite Materials, *ed. by L. Holliday, Ch. 6, 1966.)*

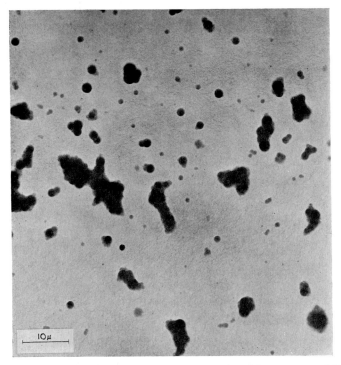

Fig. 6. An ungrafted polybutadiene latex. (Reproduced by courtesy of Elsevier Publishing Company; Composite Materials, ed. by L. Holliday, Ch. 6, 1966.)

ungrafted and grafted rubber latices. Particles of ungrafted latex are irregular in shape and form agglomerates as shown in Fig. 6. Each particle of the grafted latex remains distinct, and the rubber particles (white in Fig. 7) are not spherical but are covered with hemispherical bumps (like a raspberry surface). These bumps are styrene–acrylonitrile copolymer grafted to the rubber particle which is consequently covered with a shell of SAN giving good adhesion to the matrix.

Similar conclusions have more recently been reached[59] from a study of the SAN–nitrile rubber system in which chemical grafted chains are attached to the surface of the rubber.

8.6.3 Polyvinylchloride

While possessing many desirable properties, such as high rigidity and high tensile properties, good weatherability and chemical resistance, rigid PVC although regarded as a tough material at room temperature[1] is a very

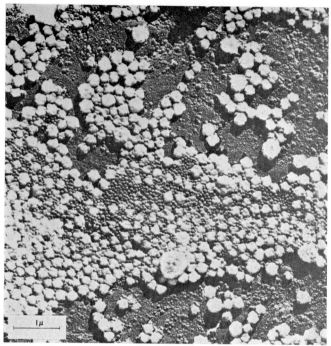

*Fig. 7. A polybutadiene latex grafted with styrene acrylonitrile copolymer. (Reproduced by courtesy of Cambridge University Press; Haward, R. N. and Mann, J. (1964). Proc. Roy. Soc., **282A,** 120.)*

notch sensitive material.[60] The material fails in a brittle fashion at low temperatures. This behaviour of course limited the use of PVC in certain applications subject to impact. Early work overcame the rigid character of PVC by the introduction of plasticisers (low molecular weight materials such as esters, with low volatility) which produced pliable, flexible products. However, addition of up to about 20 phr of plasticiser actually reduced the impact strength. Boyer[1] states that the addition of 10 phr dioctyl phthalate, for example, reduces the impact strength from 1·0 J to 0·1 J. It is also well known that the β relaxation peak simultaneously disappears.

Plasticisers tend to migrate to the surface resulting in undesirable effects. Early work on the incorporation of elastomers into PVC was not primarily aimed at the reinforcement or toughening of PVC, but essentially aimed at finding higher molecular weight plasticisers free from migratory tendencies.

Toughening with acrylonitrile–butadiene rubbers

The acrylonitrile–butadiene or nitrile rubber was found to exert a plasticising effect on the PVC[61] similar to low molecular weight plasticisers, *i.e.* the softening point was reduced and flexibility of the PVC was increased. The effect of the nitrile rubber on the impact strength of PVC was very similar to a simple plasticiser[60] as shown in Fig. 8; to achieve significant toughening a considerable amount of rubber must be used. Boyer[1] in considering

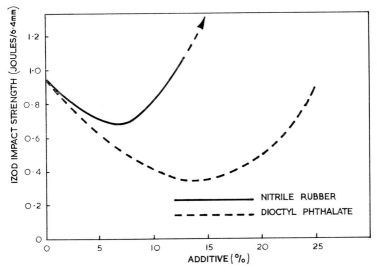

Fig. 8. *Variation in impact strength with concentration of additive in PVC.* (*Reproduced by courtesy of Engineering, Chemical and Marine Press Ltd; Davenport, N. E. et al. (1959). British Plastics,* **32**(12), 549.)

the effect of a simple plasticiser on PVC impact strength used the data of Bohn[62] and obtained a crude correlation between the height of the β relaxation peak and the amount of plasticiser added. It is tempting to suggest that the addition of nitrile rubber in relatively small amounts also interferes with the β relaxation process in PVC, causing a drop in impact strength.

Following along similar lines a great deal of work has been carried out examining the effects of incorporating various uncross-linked rubbers into PVC. The nitrile rubbers (NBR) appear to be the most effective, and this is almost certainly related to the polar nature of the rubber and PVC. Much work has been carried out in examining the effect of composition of the rubber on its compatibility with PVC (for example see references 63, 64, 65). Generally speaking an increase in the polar acrylonitrile constituent leads to an improved plasticising action of the rubber.[66]

The nitrile rubber–PVC system has been examined by several workers in attempts to define the mutual compatibility of these polymers. Nielsen,[67] Takayanagi[68] and Bohn[17] conclude that the system shows a considerable degree of compatibility—indeed Bohn[17] lists PVC–NBR as one of the thirteen pairs of known compatible polymers. Nevertheless, it is obvious from many of the publications that there is an optimum composition and the compatibility of the system must be controlled in order to gain maximum reinforcement and an overall balance of properties. When the acrylonitrile content of the nitrile rubber is too high PVC–NBR films are brittle.[63] On the other hand when the acrylonitrile content is low, compatibility is poor and films produced have poor tensile properties. Similarly it has been shown that for a given rubber concentration the Izod impact strength passes through a maximum with increasing ACN content.[69] It is interesting to note that recent work[69] has shown by torsional damping that NBR and PVC are molecularly compatible (i.e. only one loss peak is observed), and compatibility increases with the acrylonitrile content.

Nitrile rubber is still used for producing impact PVC by mechanical blending, and the morphology which results depends on the time and temperature of blending, the degree of shear imparted and the composition of the rubber. It is unfortunate, as a result, that so little work has been published of a definitive nature regarding the morphology of the system. Rovatti and Bobalek[70] have shown that the optimum tensile properties are obtained when the degree of mixing establishes a structure resembling a fibrous interweaving of continuous domains of PVC and rubber. Kühne,[71] on the other hand, claims that the best impact improvement is obtained not with the linear NBR but with heavily branched and partly cross-linked rubbers with an optimum particle size of 0·1 to 0·3 μ.

Toughening with polybutadiene rubbers
Again little published work is available but studies using the electron microscope on blends of polybutadiene and PVC, and ABS–PVC showed that the impact strength was improved with an optimum dispersed rubbery particle size of 0·8 to 1·0 μ.[72] ABS is used extensively in the reinforcement of PVC and early patents date from 1957.[73] Originally the ABS used was prepared by latex blending of nitrile rubber with SAN, and mixing of this ABS type with PVC may well have yielded a terpolymer compatible system (PVC–NBR and NBR–SAN are pairs of compatible polymers[17]).

Most of the ABS used today is of the grafted type, and the structure is more readily defined since the morphology of the dispersed cross-linked rubber phase from the ABS is known, controllable and shear insensitive. Remarkable improvements in toughening of PVC with ABS are reported —e.g. a 5% wt addition of ABS raises the Izod impact strength from 0·5 to 8·3 J/6·4 mm, and within certain blends it is possible to retain transparency.[74]

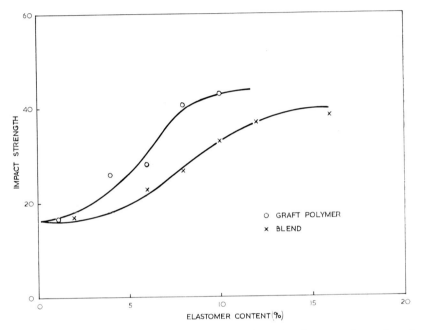

Fig. 9. Relationship between impact strength of PVC and type and quantity of elastomer. (Reproduced by courtesy of Plastics Engineers Inc.; Kühne, G. F. (1971). SPE Technical Papers, 17, 491.)

Kühne[71] has described further improvements in the reinforcement of PVC. Using a commercial process vinyl chloride was grafted on to poly-butadiene by adding the elastomer latex to a vinyl chloride polymerisation reaction near the gel point (70 to 80% conversion). The grafted rubber when incorporated into a rigid PVC polymer gave enhanced impact reinforcement when compared with the addition of non-grafted rubbers. The improvement is particularly significant at relatively low rubber loadings as shown in Fig. 9.

Chlorinated polyethylene in PVC

Effective reinforcement of PVC can be obtained by incorporating a chlorinated polyethylene (CPE). The best effects are obtained using a CPE with a low crystallinity (5%) and a high content of randomly distributed chlorine groups. Adjustment of the chlorine content allows some control of the compatibility of CPE with the PVC, and the best results are obtained where compatibility is limited.[75] Mixing and dispersion were also found to be very important; with optimum compositions a thirty-five fold increase in Izod impact strength was obtained with the addition of 12·5 phr CPE.

The published literature shows that except where the dispersed phase morphology is predetermined and retained by the use of a cross-linked rubber, such as reinforcement with ABS, the morphology of toughened PVC may be very variable. Indeed it appears that the manufacture of the polymer, mainly by blending, depends on a trial and error basis, with time, temperature and shear as some of the variables. Repeatedly throughout the literature a requirement for limited compatibility is stated in rather vague terms. It is obvious from some of the data that excellent improvements in impact properties of PVC can be achieved. One wonders whether even better results could be obtained if the toughening of PVC became more of a science rather than an art.

8.7   OPTICAL PROPERTIES

Glassy polymers such as polystyrene, polyvinylchloride and SAN have good optical properties, being clear and transparent, which is important for certain applications. Two phase polymeric systems are generally opaque, or at best translucent, and this change occurs during the toughening of PS, PVC and SAN with rubber. The opacity is due to the scattering of light at the interface of two phases (*i.e.* the matrix and dispersed phase rubbery particles possessing different refractive indices).

In principle there are two ways of overcoming the development of opacity.

(i) to match the refractive indices by appropriate copolymerisation of one or both phases;
(ii) to reduce the dispersed phase particle size.

8.7.1   Matching of the refractive index

Matching of the refractive index is the subject of several patents which describe, for example, reduction of the matrix refractive index in TPS by copolymerisation with methylmethacrylate,[76] or increasing the refractive index of the rubber by copolymerisation with aromatic monomers.[77] This method has been used commercially[78,79] with some success to produce a clear toughened polymer based on methylmethacrylate. However, matching of the refractive index at any particular temperature to gain transparency may be transient due to the high sensitivity of the refractive index to temperature.

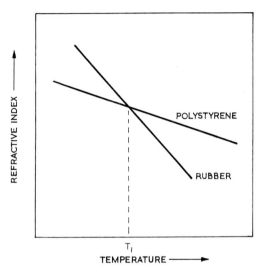

Fig. 10. *Effect of temperature on refractive index of rubber and polystyrene.*

Thus, as shown in Fig. 10, a perfect match of refractive indices may be achieved at temperature T_1 but they then drift apart at other temperatures, leading to opacity.

8.7.2 Reduction in particle size
By reducing the dispersed phase particle size so that it becomes small compared to the wavelength of visible light (*i.e.* <0·1 μ) the amount of scattering may be reduced significantly. This has been achieved commercially in ABS,[80,81] and the thermoplastic rubbers recently developed are often transparent because of the small domain size.[82]

A recent paper[83] has described some interesting results demonstrating both principles. Table 1 shows data for toughened PVC in which the refractive index match between the two phases was obtained by the

TABLE 1

EFFECT OF ACRYLIC MODIFIERS ON IMPACT PVC

Particle size dispersed phase, Angstrom	n_D match between phases	Clarity of impact PVC	
		(%) transmission	(%) haze
1600	Poor	65	23
1000	Poor	70	14
1600	Good	85	4
1000	Good	84	3·5

addition of an acrylic modifier. When the refractive index match is poor then the effect of particle size is important. With a system in which refractive index differences are small then as expected the dispersed phase particle size is relatively unimportant. However, to obtain a good refractive index match by addition of additives is difficult because the additive may be soluble in the PVC or rubber phase, and the solubility will be temperature dependent. As we have seen, a change in temperature results in the system becoming unmatched in refractive index and the PVC may develop either a blue or yellow haze. The yellow haze may be eliminated completely by the addition of a low molecular weight additive of low refractive index soluble in PVC.

8.8 MECHANICAL PROPERTIES

Modification of a polymeric glass (Young's modulus typically 3×10^3 MN/m^2 and Poisson's ratio 0·35) by the incorporation of a rubber (Young's modulus typically 20 MN/m^2 and Poisson's ratio 0·5) leads to a reduction in modulus and an increase in work to fracture. Although rubber modified polymers are used in practice because of their increased impact strengths, fundamental studies of the mechanisms responsible for these property changes have been carried out mostly with the slow speed tensile mode of strain. The emphasis which we shall devote to this type of deformation is a simple reflection of this fact. It is not our intention to give a balanced review of the mechanical properties of rubber modified glassy polymers in end use applications.

8.8.1 Tensile properties

Figure 11 illustrates the general form of the slow-speed tensile stress–strain curve of a brittle glassy polymer and a rubber modified polymer

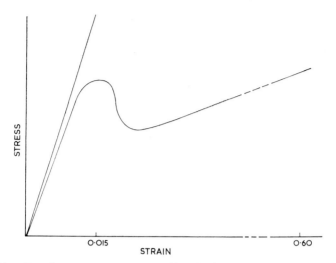

Fig. 11.   *Tensile stress–strain curves of brittle glassy polymer and corresponding rubber modified polymer.*

derived from it. The glassy polymer exhibits a nearly linear stress–strain curve up to fracture which occurs at a low elongation, typically 0·5–5%. The rubber modified polymer shows a remarkably different stress–strain curve when it is remembered that the glassy polymer forms the continuous phase. The stress–strain curve can be divided into four parts:

  (a) an initial linear portion with a slope lower than that of the glassy polymer;
  (b) a yield point which occurs approximately at the same elongation as the fracture of the glassy polymer but at a lower stress;
  (c) a reduction in stress after the yield point;
  (d) a further linear portion during which extensive elongation occurs and the material shows apparent work-hardening;
  (e) fracture at an elongation which is typically of the order of 30–100%.

The lower modulus of the rubber modified polymer is readily understood in terms of its structure, namely a dispersion of flexible rubber in a rigid matrix. The yield point and the extensive deformation which ensues are more remarkable. Two basically different types of deformation can occur. These are:

  (a) a yield process which involves a reduction in cross-sectional area, which is manifested as the formation and subsequent growth of a neck;

(b) a yield process which involves extensive deformation with little or no reduction in cross-sectional area, *i.e.* a deformation in which the polymer dilates.

It is unfortunate that many published papers, especially those relating to structural studies, do not specify which type of deformation is involved. Indeed it seems likely that the existence of these two basically different types of deformation is not generally recognised. Both types of deformation can occur with polystyrene (TPS systems) and styrene–acrylonitrile (ABS systems) matrices. The structural factors which determine the type of elongation are not at all well understood. The authors' experience of TPS and ABS systems suggests that rubber content is an important factor. Both systems exhibit deformation with dilation at lower rubber contents and deformation with necking at higher rubber contents.

Deformation with necking
Deformation with necking, *i.e.* deformation at effectively constant volume, involving extensive cold drawing, is very common with ABS systems. As with ductile non-glassy polymers, *e.g.* high-density polyethylene, the cold drawing process leads to a permanent molecular orientation. This is illustrated in Fig. 12 which shows an X-ray diagram of the cold drawn,

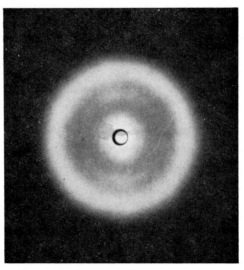

Fig. 12.   *X-ray diagram showing orientation in necked region of an ABS polymer.* (*Reproduced by courtesy of Society of Chemical Industry, London; Fletcher, K., Haward, R. N. and Mann, J.* (1965, 6 Nov.). Chemistry and Industry, p. 1854.)

necked portion of a compression moulded ABS polymer after removal of the tensile load. The molecular orientation in the matrix is readily apparent.

There are surprisingly few reported studies on this type of deformation, especially in view of the remarkable change which occurs in the mechanical properties of the matrix material. How can the incorporation of rubber spheres in a brittle matrix polymer enable the composite to deform by *bulk plastic flow*? The observation of shear band deformation in a rubber modified epoxy resin[84] and polyphenylene oxide,[85] and the reference to similar observations on an ABS polymer[86] may provide clues to the mechanisms involved. The early paper by Newman and Strella,[87] however, appears to be the only study specifically devoted to this problem. Careful reading of this paper suggests that their 50:50 mixture of styrene–acrylonitrile copolymer and rubber graft deformed by necking. These authors suggest that the most probable cause of bulk plastic deformation is local increases in free volume within the matrix (equivalent to a lowering in T_g of the matrix) brought about by hydrostatic tensile stresses. They consider that localised hydrostatic tension exists in the matrix phase near the rubber particles because

(a) the rubber phase shrinks more than the matrix phase when the temperature during the moulding process falls below the glass transition temperature of the matrix;
(b) hydrostatic tension arises during straining because of the difference in Poisson's ratio between the two phases;
(c) the rubber phase is well bonded to the matrix phase and voids cannot form between the two phases at low strains.

The validity of this explanation must remain in doubt until the phenomenon has been studied more carefully in terms of the structural changes that occur and in terms of a more careful definition of the nature of the deformation, *e.g.* the extent to which volume changes occur.

Deformation with dilation—qualitative description
In general TPS systems deform to 30–100% strain with a negligible reduction in cross-sectional area. The implication is that a cavitation process is involved and that density is lowered. This was first recognised by Merz *et al.*,[88] who demonstrated the reduction in density and drew attention to the fact that a stress-whitening occurred, which was consistent with light-scattering to be expected from a cavitation process. These authors suggested that the cavitation process consists of the formation of microcracks and that elongation and energy absorption proceed *via* the

widening of cracks and the buckling of the polystyrene spanning the cracks.

The stress-whitening first occurs just before the yield point, and intensifies as the strain is increased. Bucknall and Smith[89] made the first correct diagnosis of the deformation mechanism involved by carrying out a careful microscopic study on thin films of TPS in uniaxial tensile strain. Under polarised light they observed a series of parallel bright bands about 50 microns long at right angles to the direction of the applied stress. This study showed conclusively that these bands were crazes, *i.e.* regions of localised plastic deformation in the matrix containing voids. Crazes in glassy polymers form before fracture and are extensively discussed in Chapter 7. They contain 40–60% by volume of voids and the plastically deformed material in them has undergone a similar elongation.[90]

This key feature of the mechanism of deformation with dilation has since been amply demonstrated by elegant electron microscope techniques,[91,92,93,94,95] an example of which is shown in Fig. 13. The first crazes are formed immediately prior to the yield point and beyond this point the number of crazes increases progressively, with more of the matrix being involved until fracture occurs by the generation of a crack which propagates across the specimen.

The function of the rubber particles in increasing the energy to fracture can be understood in terms of this craze formation. In a brittle glassy polymer such as polystyrene a tensile stress induces craze formation at a limited number of sites where there are local stress concentrations. As the stress level increases crazes grow in size in a direction perpendicular to the applied stress. Eventually the stress reaches a magnitude sufficient to generate a crack in a craze and this then propagates to give catastrophic failure. In a similar polymer containing a large number of rubber particles of low modulus, stress is concentrated at the equators of the rubber particles by a factor of about two.[96] These stress concentrations lead to the generation of crazes which do not continue to grow in size but terminate at another rubber particle or by mutual interference. Crazes are then generated at other sites in the material and the process continues until fracture eventually intervenes.

It is apparent, however, that it is not a sufficient condition for toughening that rubber particles act as stress-raisers. If this were the case replacing the rubber particles by voids would lead to a similar toughening. However, polystyrenes containing say 20–40% by volume of voids do not show a large elongation to fracture. The further necessary condition for toughening is that rubber particles should not act as stress-raisers for the fracture process. Electron micrographs show how this condition is met. During the craze formation rubber particles extend in the direction of the applied stress, but do not contract laterally (see large particle in Fig. 13), since there is good interfacial adhesion between the rubber and the matrix. The rubber particles, therefore, bear part of the load, are under hydrostatic tension, and prevent the stress-level building up to the fracture stress within adjacent crazes.

The mechanism of tensile elongation may be summarised as follows:

(a) Before the yield point the stress is largely borne by the matrix and stress concentrations exist at the equators of rubber particles.

(b) Crazes are initiated near the yield point at points of maximum stress. The crazes grow until terminated and new crazes form. Hydrostatic tensile forces build up on the rubber and energy is consumed in the plastic deformation of the matrix involved in craze formation.

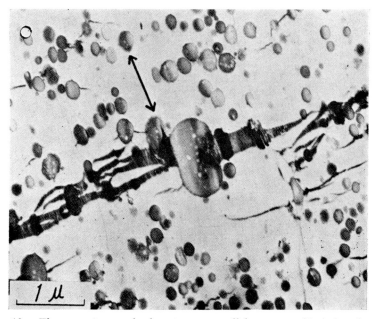

Fig. 13. Electron micrograph of section cut parallel to stress-whitened surface of an ABS polymer. Dark portions represent rubber particles and crazes. Arrow indicates direction of applied tensile stress. (Reproduced by courtesy of Polymer and Engineering Science; Matsuo, M. (1969). Polymer and Engineering Science, **9***, 206.)*

(c) The applied force is distributed between the resin and rubber which is in a state of triaxial tension. This causes fracture of crazes to be delayed in favour of new craze initiation elsewhere.

The picture of craze growth presented above is modified in polymers where rubber particles are sufficiently close together that their stress concentration fields overlap. As can be seen in Fig. 13 this leads to craze generation at points other than the equators of rubber particles and crazes are not strictly located in planes at right angles to the applied stress.

Deformation with dilation—quantitative studies
    (*a*) *Modulus*
As stated in Section 8.6.1 the modulus of a composite is determined by the moduli of the matrix phase and dispersed phase and the volume fraction of the latter. In the case of TPS systems the dispersed phase is in itself a composite, namely a spherical particle with a continuous rubber phase containing a dispersion of polystyrene. The relevant parameters which determine the modulus of the overall composite are the total volume of the primary dispersed phase (rubber plus polystyrene inclusions) and the modulus of the composite dispersion. Both these parameters are greater than the corresponding values for the rubber phase alone.

Wagner and Robeson[54] have demonstrated the effect of the volume fraction enhancement which results from the polystyrene sub-inclusions by studying TPS systems which are identical in all respects apart from volume fraction. Their data are shown in Table 2.

The theoretical calculation of moduli for rubber modified glassy polymers is a matter of some difficulty since they are viscoelastic systems and moduli are time dependent. No theoretical treatment of time dependent

TABLE 2
EFFECTS OF DISPERSED PHASE VOLUME
FOR TPS SYSTEMS CONTAINING 6% RUBBER

Dispersed phase volume (%)	Tensile modulus $MN/m^2 \times 10^{-2}$
6	28
12	24
22	19
30	10
78	5·5

tensile moduli has been made. It is unfortunate that most of the experimental information relates to time dependent moduli,[6,51,97] whereas the theoretical calculations of moduli relate to purely elastic moduli.[98,99]

In only one case has it been possible to make a meaningful comparison of theory and experiment. Broutman and Panizza[98] have presented an analysis based on a simplified model of an axisymmetric system of equal sized rubber spheres dispersed regularly in a rigid matrix. By assuming reasonable values for modulus and Poisson's ratio of the rubber phase they obtained excellent agreement with experimental data on a rubber modified epoxy system.[100]

Hashin[99] has demonstrated that there is little hope of calculating moduli rigorously other than the bulk modulus of a composite in which there are interacting inclusions. For tensile and shear moduli only upper and lower bounds can be calculated. The problem lies in the fact that results obtained by specifying minimum strain energy in terms of the admissible stress field are different from those obtained using the admissible strain field.

The distance apart of the upper and lower bounds increases with the ratio of the moduli of the two phases of the composite. Mann and Holliday[101] have presented a comparison of experimental tensile moduli of ABS systems, where volume fraction is not much greater than the rubber phase volume, with the upper and lower bounds calculated from Hashin's theory. The bounds are so far apart that the theory is unhelpful.

Bucknall and Hall[102] have used the Hashin theory to calculate shear moduli for TPS systems where the rigid polystyrene sub-inclusions in the rubber give a much larger volume fraction enhancement than in emulsion produced ABS systems. Both the calculated upper and lower bounds demonstrate that the modulus of the overall composite is progressively lowered as polystyrene is transferred from the matrix to the rubber phase.

The modulus of these composite rubber particles must play an important part in determining the properties of the overall composite. There is no really satisfactory way of determining this modulus, however, either theoretically or experimentally. The best experimental method is to isolate the rubber particles by dissolving the polymer and separating the insoluble cross-linked rubber particles (gel) from the dissolved matrix.[103] After drying this gel can be moulded into strips and its mechanical properties determined. Unfortunately the rubber particles isolated in this way contain a smaller amount of polystyrene inclusions than does the original composite, since part of the polystyrene inclusions is dissolved. Bucknall[104] quotes an example of TPS in which the original rubber particles contained

72% by volume of polystyrene, whilst the particles contained 62% after isolation.

(b) Stress concentration by rubber particles

Crazing in rubber modified glassy polymers is initiated in the matrix by the stress concentrations which develop at the surface of the rubber particles. Wang *et al.*[105,106] have studied craze initiation under uniaxial tension in model systems of polystyrene containing both steel (rigid) and rubber (soft) balls of macroscopic dimensions in an attempt to establish the criteria which control craze initiation. This in turn, of course, is related to the initiation of yield.

With the steel balls the crazes initiated from the interface at locations remote from the equator, as would be expected from theory. With the rubber balls the crazes initiated at the equators of the balls. By studying crazing between two balls with varying distances between them and applying Goodier's[96] solution for the stress field around spherical inclusions, they arrived at the criteria for crazing consistent with the experimental observations. Three craze initiation criteria were used, *i.e.* the principal stress,[89] principal strain[107] and strain-energy criteria.[108,109] They concluded that only the principal strain criterion satisfied their observations on the two systems.

Broutman and Panizza[98] have extended their theoretical calculations to the crazing of rubber modified glassy polymers. Using a critical stress criterion for craze initiation, they conclude that the first few volume per cent of rubber lead to a decrease in the critical stress of about 50%, and thereafter the decrease with increasing rubber volume is much less pronounced. It must be remarked again, however, that the study of craze initiation is complicated by the fact that we are dealing with viscoelastic materials and the phenomenon is therefore time dependent. The theoretical calculation does not take this time dependence into account.

(c) Post-yield behaviour

Quantitative information on the energy absorbing mechanisms in the deformation of rubber modified glassy polymers can be obtained from tensile tests at constant strain rate. Figure 14 reproduces results of Bucknall[104] obtained with a commercial grade of TPS. The stress–strain curves were obtained by removing and reapplying the stress at intervals, thus giving a picture of the change in mechanical properties resulting from craze formation. Figure 14 shows that as deformation proceeds there are increases in stored elastic energy in the loaded specimen, in mechanical

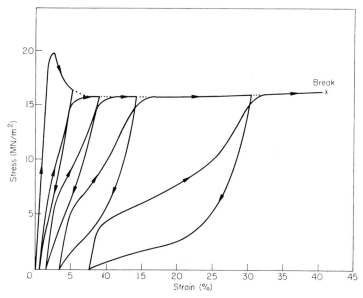

Fig. 14.   *Tension test on TPS polymer with intermittent recycling. Dotted line shows curve obtained with no recycling.* (*Reproduced by courtesy of the American Society for Testing and Materials; Bucknall, C. B.* (1969). Journal of Materials, **4**, 214.)

hysteresis and in irrecoverable strain. The results can be understood in terms of the fact that the elastic moduli of craze material are some twenty times lower than the moduli of the corresponding uncrazed polymer and the fact that deformation of craze material involves considerable hysteresis.[90]

By measuring areas under the curves in Fig. 14 it is possible to obtain measures of the amounts of work involved in different types of processes. The results of such an analysis are shown in Fig. 15. All the work terms increase as the deformation increases with the exception of the stored elastic energy in the uncrazed matrix. This is, of course, a reflection of the increasing total amount of craze material as deformation increases. A notable feature of this analysis is the relatively small proportion of the total energy which exists as stored elastic energy and is therefore available for fracture.

A more elegant method of carrying out quantitative measurements has been introduced by Bucknall and Clayton,[86] namely the measurement of dimension and volume changes during creep under a constant uniaxial

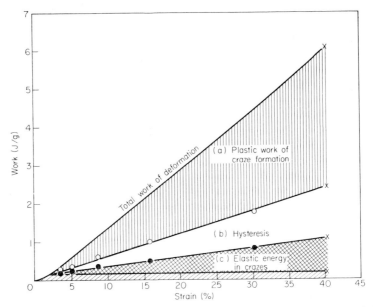

Fig. 15.   *Analysis of work done in a tension test on TPS using data in Fig.* 14. *The hatched area at the bottom of the graph corresponds to elastic energy in the uncrazed material.* (*Reproduced by courtesy of the American Society for Testing and Materials; Bucknall, C. B.* (1969). Journal of Materials, **4**, 214.)

tensile load. Results have so far been presented on only one polymer, Monsanto HT-91, a commercial TPS grade.

Curves of volumetric strain *versus* time show three stages:

(a) an instantaneous increase due to the normal response of the polystyrene matrix to tension;

(b) a slow but accelerating increase with time due to craze formation, and finally;

(c) a rapid increase which occurs at a constant high rate and is also due to craze formation.

The specimens were unloaded at a longitudinal strain of 5 % and this strain can be divided into three parts: instantaneous elastic strain 1·1 %, shear-yielding and time-dependent elastic strain 0·1 % and crazing 3·8 %. The figure of 0·1 % for shear-yielding and time dependent elastic deformation was estimated from the lateral dimensions of the specimen which exhibited a small decrease with time. Bucknall and Clayton state that measurements on ABS polymers show that shear deformation plays an important part in deformation along with crazing, though the results on which the statement is based have not yet been reported.

The fact that under constant tensile load volumetric strain rate increases with strain until a limiting rate is reached is related to the fact that under constant strain rate there is a fall in stress beyond the yield point. The volumetric creep data show that this drop in stress must be due to the fact that a lower stress is required to maintain the same rate of crazing once yield has initiated. Not all TPS polymers show this drop in stress after yield, however (*e.g.* the commercial grade of BASF Polystyrol 475K), and the factors controlling the magnitude of the drop are not at all clear.

The stage of constant high rate of volumetric strain found in this work implies that in a conventional constant strain rate test, the material (HT-91) would extend at constant stress following the post yield drop, *i.e.* the material would show no work-hardening. Most TPS polymers, however, do show work-hardening to varying degrees. Bucknall[110] attributes this to the fact that the amount of polymer available for craze formation decreases as extension increases and hence a higher stress is required to maintain a constant rate of crazing. Whilst this idea seems eminently reasonable, TPS polymers show widely varying degrees of work-hardening and it seems likely that other factors are involved as well.

The initiation and growth of crazes are activated processes which depend upon load, time and temperature. Bucknall and Clayton have analysed their creep results in terms of the Eyring rate equation (*see* p. 232).[111,112] They find that both the rate constant for the craze initiation process and the rate constant for the craze propagation process exhibit an Eyring type dependence on stress, with the same apparent activation volume of 5000 Å^3.

8.8.2 Dynamic mechanical properties

Measurements of dynamic mechanical properties have long been a popular method for studying rubber modified glassy polymers. Such polymers show two prominent loss peaks, one at low temperatures which is due to the glass transition of the rubber (*e.g.* $-80°C$ for polybutadiene) and one at high temperatures which is due to the glass transition of the matrix (*e.g.* $+100°C$ for polystyrene). Interest in such measurements was originally based on two ideas. Firstly, that the loss peaks demonstrated unambiguously the existence of two phases, and secondly, that there might be a relation between the size of the low temperature loss peak and impact strength.[113,114]

Karas and Warburton[113] found a linear relationship between Izod

impact strength and size of the loss peak in a series of TPS polymers, and
Turley[9] showed that TPS polymers made by interpolymerisation have
higher impact strengths and mechanical loss peaks than similar polymers
made by mechanically blending rubber with polystyrene. Keskkula et al.[115]
showed later, however, that impact strength and size of the loss peak do
not correlate in general. Only in specific groupings of polymers which are
closely related can a correlation be established.

The reason for the general lack of correlation lies not only in the
tenuous connection between small strain and large strain properties
(especially failure properties) but also in the variable dispersed phase
structure of rubber modified polymers and variations in the matrix
composition, e.g. molecular weight.

Some of the structural factors affecting the loss peak and the associated
change in shear modulus have been demonstrated both experimentally
and theoretically. Wagner and Robeson[54] have shown that the size of the
loss peak in TPS systems of constant rubber content increases as volume
fraction increases. This can be readily understood in a qualitative way

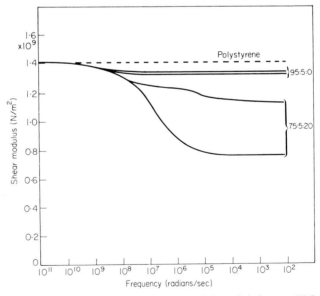

Fig. 16.   Upper and lower bounds on storage modulus G′(ω) for two TPS polymers,
both containing 5% by volume of SBR. The labels on the curves specify the volumetric ratio of matrix polystyrene:SBR:polystyrene sub-inclusions in the TPS.
(Reproduced by courtesy of Chapman and Hall, London; Bucknall, C. B. and
Hall, M. M. (1971). J. Mat. Sci., 6, 95.)

since the volume of dispersed phase (rubber plus polystyrene sub-inclusions) undergoing modulus relaxation increases with increasing volume fraction.

Kraus et al.[116] have investigated the dynamic mechanical properties of dispersions of polystyrene in styrene–butadiene rubber. This is the type of system which forms the dispersed phase in TPS polymers. They report that the loss peak is not broadened or shifted in temperature and although it is reduced in height, the reduction is not in proportion to the rubber content. This finding is in accord with the results on TPS systems reported above.

Bucknall and Hall[102] have carried out a theoretical study of TPS systems using Hashin's theory[99] with the modification that the viscoelastic nature of the system was taken into account. Although Hashin's theory allows only upper and lower bounds of properties to be calculated, the results of the analysis clearly confirm the experimental findings reported above. This is shown in Fig. 16 where the calculations of shear modulus are shown rather than the loss tangent. Whether we take the upper bound result or the lower bound result, the relaxed modulus of the system (SBR in the rubbery state) is lower for the polymer with the higher volume fraction, i.e. rubber containing sub-inclusions of polystyrene.

In summary it may be stated that measurements of dynamic mechanical properties provide important information on the dispersed phase of rubber modified glassy polymers.

8.8.3 Impact properties

The impact strengths of rubber modified glassy polymers can be understood in terms of crazing and the effect of speed of deformation on the mechanical properties of the dispersed rubbery phase.[110] The general form of impact strength versus temperature is shown in Fig. 17. The curve shows that there are three regions of fracture behaviour and the form of the curves can be understood in terms of measurements of force–time curves during an impact test.

In the region of low impact strength at low temperatures the force builds up rapidly (10^{-3} sec) and then decays even more rapidly (10^{-5} sec) to zero. In this temperature range the rubber is below its T_g and is in the glassy state. It is unable to relax during the test and cannot act as a stress concentrator for crazing. Accordingly the specimen fractures in a manner characteristic of a brittle glassy polymer and there is no stress whitening.

In the intermediate temperature region which starts at a temperature near the glass transition point of the rubber, the impact strength increases as temperature increases. In this region the rubber is able to relax and act

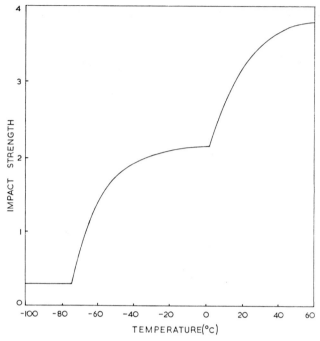

Fig. 17.   Generalised relationship of impact strength and temperature for rubber modified polymers.

as a stress concentrator during the comparatively slow build up of the stress. In an Izod test this is reflected in an area of stress whitening around the base of the notch where crack initiation takes place. The load then decays very rapidly to zero as the crack initiated at the notch propagates rapidly across the specimen. The fracture surface shows no signs of stress whitening and it is clear that the speed of crack propagation is too fast for the rubber to relax and act as a stress concentrator. The fracture is typically brittle in nature.

In the third high temperature region which usually starts around 0°C, impact strength continues to increase with temperature. This region can be understood in terms of the activated nature of crazing which is both time and temperature dependent. Force–time curves show a relatively slow build up to a maximum followed by a relatively slow decrease to zero and stress whitening occurs over the whole fracture surface. It is evident that the rubber can relax and act as a stress concentrator both during the crack initiation and the crack propagation stages.

The general picture of the behaviour of rubber modified glassy polymers does not seem to be applicable to PVC toughened by the incorporation of the toughening agent used in ABS polymers,[104] namely cross-linked polybutadiene particles grafted with styrene–acrylonitrile copolymer. This type of PVC is brittle below about $-30°C$, in spite of the fact that the rubber particles are able to initiate crazes in styrene–acrylonitrile copolymer at temperatures as low as $-75°C$. The reason for this behaviour is not clear, but it emphasises the need to consider factors other than the rubber in discussing properties of toughened glassy polymers, *e.g.* the inherent properties of the matrix material and the interfacial adhesion between the rubber and the matrix.

Schmitt[49] has emphasised the latter aspect and suggested that it plays a very important role in impact resistance. He studied thin mouldings of polystyrene reinforced with a styrene–butadiene rubber by microscopy after subjecting them to a miniature drop-dart impact test. He found that in the stress-whitened areas rubber particles had partially separated from the matrix and that multitudes of crazes/microcracks had formed at these regions of phase separation. Schmitt demonstrated that interfacial failure also occurred in tensile tests and argued that the phase separation plays an important role in the mechanism of rubber reinforcement. Whilst there is no doubt about the reliability of the experimental observations, there is no quantitative evidence which would allow an estimate of the importance of interfacial adhesion to be made.

Schmitt attributes the interfacial failure to the hydrostatic tensile stress which builds up within the rubber during cooling of a moulding, due to the differential contractions of the rubber and matrix. In a later paper[117] he claimed to have demonstrated experimentally that the existence of this triaxial tension in the rubber is essential for impact improvement. His experiments are open to alternative interpretation, however, and the present authors do not believe that the necessity of triaxial tension on the rubber has been demonstrated.

8.8.4 Structure–property relationships

The relationship between structure and properties of rubber modified glassy polymers is a complex problem because of the number of structural variables involved (*see* Section 8.6.1). Nevertheless these polymers present a unique opportunity for such studies, since their structures can be characterised unambiguously and can be varied in a systematic way. In addition, as we have already seen, many of their properties are amenable to theoretical treatment. Although they have received less attention than crystalline polymers, they present a more tractable opportunity for the polymer scientist to reach a fundamental understanding of structure–property relationships. The work carried out so far has done little more than provide indications and the whole field is open to systematic attack.

The structural variables which determine properties are listed in Table 3.

Of the ten structural variables listed only the last presents difficulties in complete characterisation and understanding of its effects, especially

TABLE 3
VARIABLES OF RUBBER MODIFIED GLASSY POLYMERS
WHICH AFFECT PROPERTIES

Phenomenological variables		Structural variables involved
Matrix properties	(1)	Chemical structure
	(2)	Average molecular weight
	(3)	Molecular weight distribution
Dispersed phase properties	(4)	Chemical structure of rubber
	(5)	Volume of rubber
	(6)	Volume fraction of dispersed phase
	(7)	Average particle size
	(8)	Particle size distribution
	(9)	Degree of cross-linking of rubber
	(10)	Degree and structure of rubber matrix grafting
Interfacial adhesion	(10)	Degree and structure of rubber matrix grafting

in its relation to interfacial adhesion. In the case of many properties, however, the interfacial adhesion is so high that it can be assumed to be ideally perfect. The one remaining point of doubt in this area which requires resolution is the observation of interfacial failure by Schmitt[49,117] and his suggestion that it plays an important role at higher elongations and in failure. The degree and structure of the rubber matrix grafting which controls interfacial adhesion is also the most difficult parameter to vary independently of other parameters, e.g. degree of cross-linking of rubber. Nevertheless, it can be varied in polymers made by the latex route,[118] e.g. ABS polymers, though methods of measuring interfacial adhesion quantitatively have not been developed.

Haward and Mann[10] have quoted extreme examples of the effect of structure on properties (see Fig. 2). They compare the impact strengths of a series of TPS polymers prepared by interpolymerisation in such a way as to optimise impact properties with the impact strengths of a series of polymers prepared by blending a grafted polybutadiene latex with a polystyrene latex. The level of variation obtained can be judged by the fact that at 8% wt rubber the interpolymerised polymer had an Izod impact strength some 15 times greater than of the latex blended polymer.

We will now review the scattered literature on property–structure relationships in terms of the structural variables 1–9 listed in Table 3.

(i) Chemical structure of matrix

Perhaps the most interesting example of the effect of chemical structure of the matrix on properties lies in the comparison of ABS polymers (styrene acrylonitrile copolymer–polybutadiene) with TPS polymers (polystyrene–polybutadiene). Fletcher et al.[6] have shown that the effect of introducing increasing amounts of acrylonitrile into styrene–polybutadiene interpolymers is to give a modest increase in impact strength and a larger increase in yield stress. At 18% wt. acrylonitrile the ABS interpolymer had an impact strength 1·2 times that of the corresponding TPS interpolymer and a yield stress higher by a factor of 1·5. Although the authors do not present evidence that other structural variables were constant, these findings are presumably related to the fact that styrene–acrylonitrile copolymers are tougher and have higher fracture stresses than polystyrenes.

Inherent differences in matrix properties may well be the reason for the reported differences between ABS and TPS polymers in creep[86] referred to in Section 8.8.1.

(ii) Average molecular weight

Grmela et al.[119] have studied the effects of average molecular weight of the polystyrene on the properties of TPS polymers prepared by mechanically blending styrene–butadiene rubber with polystyrene. For injection moulded specimens tensile strength increased with molecular weight up to an M_v of 300 000 and levelled off at higher molecular weights. The notched impact strength increased to an M_v of 200 000 and then reached a plateau, whereas the unnotched impact strength continued to increase in a linear fashion. These increases in ultimate properties are to be expected in terms of our understanding of the fracture of glassy polymers where a strong dependence of fracture properties on molecular weight has been established (see pp. 341, 407).[120,121] In the present case, however, it is likely that a second effect of molecular weight is superimposed. The mechanical property results relate to injection moulded specimens and it is likely therefore that strain and orientation in the mouldings increased with increasing molecular weight. It is well known that this orientation leads to higher tensile properties in the direction of flow and lower tensile properties in the perpendicular directions.[122,123,124]

Wagner and Robeson[54] have made a limited study of the effect of molecular weight distribution on properties of TPS polymers. They state that good commercial TPS polymers have matrix molecular weights characterised by $M_w \sim 250\,000$ and $M_n \sim 70\,000$. They found that addition of increasing amounts of low molecular weight polystyrene of $M_w \sim 30\,000$ led to a rapid reduction in elongation at break and in impact strength, whereas blending in polystyrene of M_w 240 000 and 305 000 led to much smaller changes in these properties. They conclude that the presence of a substantial low molecular weight tail of matrix polystyrene is harmful.

(iii) Chemical structure of rubber

Perhaps the most important single effect of the chemical structure of the rubber is its influence on low-temperature impact properties. As stated in Section 8.8.3 a high-impact strength can only be obtained at a temperature well above the glass-transition temperature of the rubber. Simmons[125] has compared the temperature dependence of impact strength for two TPS polymers based on styrene–butadiene rubber (T_g at low rates of deformation $\sim -40°C$) and one based on a polybutadiene (T_g at low rates of deformation $\sim -80°C$). Whilst the two polymers had the same impact strengths at $+20°C$, the impact strength of the styrene–butadiene rubber based polymer fell rapidly below $0°C$, whereas the polybutadiene based polymer had a constant impact strength from $0°C$ down to $-60°C$.

(iv) Volume of rubber

The volume of rubber, as distinct from the volume fraction of dispersed phase, is one of the primary variables controlling properties. It is the main variable used by manufacturers to obtain products with different levels of impact strength in both ABS and TPS polymers. The effects of increasing rubber volume are well established[6,10] and include decrease in modulus and yield strength, and increase in impact strength and elongation to fracture.

(v) Volume fraction of dispersed phase

Various aspects of the influence of volume fraction on properties have been discussed in earlier sections. Most of the observations in the literature are of doubtful significance in a quantitative sense, however, since they relate to systems in which variables other than volume fraction are changing. Perhaps the best study which has been carried out is that by Wagner and Robeson[54] on TPS polymers. A number of the results of these authors have already been discussed. Some of their remaining observations are reproduced in Table 4 where it can be seen that both impact strength and elongation at break pass through maxima with increasing volume fraction. These relationships are realistic for TPS systems produced by the interpolymerisation route, since factors such as rubber

TABLE 4

EFFECTS OF DISPERSED PHASE VOLUME ON PROPERTIES
OF TPS POLYMERS AT A RUBBER CONCENTRATION OF 6% WT

Phase volume (%)	Pendulum impact strength (joules/m^3 × 10^{-5})	Elongation at break (%)
6	4	3
12	19	20
22	116	45
30	56	34
78	13	8

cross-linking and matrix molecular weight were kept constant by using the same time–temperature cycles during polymerisation. However, other variables change together with volume fraction due to the nature of preparative process. Dispersed phase particle size increases with increasing volume fraction as does degree of grafting. The maxima observed for impact strength and elongation at break are probably due to the opposing effects of increasing volume fraction and increasing modulus of the rubber phase (partly due to polystyrene inclusions and partly to increasing grafting). It is also possible that the very large particles in the polymers of highest volume fraction may contribute to the decreasing impact strength.

(vi) Particle size and (vii) Particle size distribution

Systematic study of these two variables has not yet been carried out, although there are a number of references to suspected effects.

Starting from the crazing mechanism of deformation, it has been argued that at a given volume fraction, the energy to fracture will increase as particle size becomes smaller, since the number of craze initiation sites increases.[20] In the same paper it is also argued that there will be a minimum size of particle which can be effective in initiating crazing. Rosen suggests that this may be about 100 Å. Similar suggestions have been made by Bender[31] and Willersim[126] and Keskkula has touched on the subject in a review article.[29]

Definitive statements cannot be made on the subject at this time, though it has been reported that in a rubber modified epoxy resin large particles initiate crazes, whereas small particles tend to generate shear bands.[127]

(viii) Degree of cross-linking of rubber

The degree of cross-linking of the rubber phase affects the properties of the dispersed phase and thereby influences the properties of the composite polymer. The effect of cross-linking can be isolated from the effects of other variables in TPS polymers by cross-linking further a polymer containing a lightly cross-linked rubber.[54] Sulphur was added to the TPS polymer and further cross-linking effected by heating the compounded mixture. Starting with a polymer with a degree of cross-linking characterised by a swell index of 12 in toluene, tensile modulus increased and impact strength and elongation at break decreased as the swell index was reduced. The glass-transition temperature of the rubber increased from $-87°C$ (swell index 12) to $+10°C$ (swell index 5). According to Schmitt[117] cross-linking is also important in providing a rubber particle capable of supporting triaxial tension.

In summary it may be stated that the broad effects of most structural variables have been established. Much remains to be done, however, in obtaining a quantitative understanding and unravelling details. It is perhaps unfortunate that many excellent studies of mechanical properties are carried out on commercial polymers that have not been adequately characterised structurally or even in terms of composition. Thus most commercial TPS polymers contain a lubricant or flow promoter in addition to polystyrene and rubber. In addition commercial polymers are the result of searches for a compromise between different properties, e.g. gloss of fabricated product, impact strength, melt flow and set-up time in a moulding process. As a result commercial polymers cover only a restricted range of structural variables. The problem of structure–property relationships is a rewarding field which should yield to a combined approach by polymerisation chemists and physicists. The investigations of Wagner and Robeson[54] and Keskkula et al.[115] form good examples of this approach in which specially prepared laboratory polymers are used to tackle this type of problem.

REFERENCES

1. Boyer, R. F. (1968). *Polymer Engineering and Science*, **8**, 161.
2. Heijboer, J. (1969). *British Polymer J.*, **1**, 3.
3. Bohn, L. and Oberst, H. (1959). *Acustica*, **9**, 431.
4. British Patent 16, 278; (1913). *Chemical Abstracts*, **7**, 279.
5. Schaab, H. (1971). *Kunstoffe*, **61**(9), 717.
6. Fletcher, K., Haward, R. N. and Mann, J. (6 November, 1965). *Chemistry and Industry*, p. 1854.
7. Rosen, S. L. (1970). *J. Elastoplastics*, **2**, 195.
8. Angiers, D. J. and Fettes, E. M. (1965). *Rubber Chemistry and Technology*, **38**, 1164.
9. Turley, S. G. (1963). *J. Polymer Sci.*, **C1**, 101.
10. Haward, R. N. and Mann, J. (1964). *Proc. Roy. Soc.*, **282A**, 120.
11. Basdekis, C. H. (1964). *ABS Plastics*, Reinhold Publishing Corp., New York, p. 71.
12. Dobry, A. and Boyer-Kawenkoi, F. (1947). *J. Polymer Sci.*, **2**, 90.
13. Scott, R. L. (1949). *J. Chem. Phys.*, **17**, 279.
14. Flory, P. J. (1944). *J. Chem. Phys.*, **12**, 425.
15. Molau, G. E. (1965). *J. Polymer Sci.*, **A3**, 1267.
16. Schwarts, A. G. (1956). *Kolloid Zhur.*, **18**, 753.
17. Bohn, L. (1968). *Rubber Chemistry and Technology*, **41**, 495.
18. Hildebrand, J. H. and Scott, R. L. (1955). *Solubility of Non Electrolytes*, Reinhold Publishing Corp., New York.
19. Gee, G. (1943). *Inst. Rubber Ind. Trans.*, **18**, 206.
20. Rosen, S. L. (1967). *Polymer Engineering and Science*, **7**, 115.
21. Bevilacqua, E. M. (1957). *J. Polymer Sci.*, **24**, 292.
22. Buchdahl, R. and Nielsen, L. E. (1950). *J. App. Phys.*, **21**, 482.
23. Buchdahl, R. and Nielsen, L. E. (1955). *J. Polymer Sci.*, **15**, 1.
24. Claver, G. C., Jr. and Merz, E. H. (1956). *Official Digest, Federation Paint Varnish Prod. Clubs.*, **28**, 858.
25. Traylor, P. A. (1961). *Anal. Chem.*, **33**, 1629.
26. Keskkula, H. and Traylor, P. A. (1967). *J. App. Polymer Sci.*, **11**, 2361.
27. Gesner, B. D. (1968). *Applied Polymer Symposia*, No. 7, 53.
28. Hughes, L. J. and Brown, G. L. (1961). *J. App. Polymer Sci.*, **5**, 580.
29. Keskkula, H. (1970). *Applied Polymer Symposia*, No. 15, 51.
30. British Patent 1,105,634.
31. Bender, B. W. (1965). *J. App. Polymer Sci.*, **9**, 2887.
32. Freeguard, G. F. and Karmarkar, M. (1971). *J. App. Polymer Sci.*, **15**, 1657.
33. Molau, G. E. and Keskkula, H. (1966). *J. Polymer Sci.*, **A4**, 1595.
34. US Patent 2,694,692.
35. Sherman, P. (1955). *Research (London)*, **8**, 396.
36. Luhning, R. W. and Sawistowski, H. (1971). *Proceedings of the International Solvent Extraction Conference*, Soc. Chem. Ind., **2**, 873.
37. Mori, Y., Minoura, Y. and Imoto, M. (1957). *Makromol. Chem.*, **25**, 1.
38. Merrett, F. M. (1954). *Trans. Faraday Soc.*, **50**, 759.
39. Mori, Y., Minoura, Y. and Imoto, M. (1957). *Makromol. Chem.*, **24**, 205.
40. Smets, G., Roovers, J. and van Humbeck, W. (1961). *J. App. Polymer Sci.*, **5**, 149.
41. Molau, G. E. (1970). *Kolloid Zeitschrift und Zeit*, Band 238, 493.
42. US Patent 2,646,418.
43. US Patent 2,886,553.
44. Crompton, T. R. and Reid, V. W. (1963). *J. Polymer Sci.*, **A1**, 347.
45. Keskkula, H. and Turley, S. G. (1969). *Polymer Letters*, **7**, 697.

46. Blanchette, J. A. and Nielsen, L. E. (1956). *J. Polymer Sci.*, **20**, 317.
47. Thomas C. M. (1963). *British Plastics*, **36**, 645.
48. Spit, B. J. (1963). *Polymer*, **4**, 109.
49. Schmitt, J. A. (1968). *J. App. Polymer Sci.*, **12**, 533.
50. Walker, D. A. (1968/69). *Modern Plastics Encyclopaedia*, **45**, 334.
51. Holliday, L. (1966). *Composite Materials*, Elsevier, Amsterdam, p. 15.
52. Underwood, E. E. (1962). *Am. Soc. Metals Eng. Quart.*, **1**, 70; (1962). **1**, 162.
53. Williams, R. J. and Hudson, R. W. A. (1969). *Rubber Chemistry and Technology*, **42**, 641.
54. Wagner, E. R. and Robeson, L. M. (1970). *Rubber Chemistry and Technology*, **43**, 1129.
55. Moore, J. D. (1971). *Polymer*, **12**, 478.
56. Seward, R. J. (1970). *J. App. Polymer Sci.*, **14**, 852.
57. Kato, K. (1965). *J. Electron Microscopy*, **14**, 220; (1967). *Polymer Engineering and Science*, **7**, 38.
58. Lannon, D. A. (1966). *Encyclopaedia of Science and Technology, Plastics Resins and Fibres*, **7**, 612.
59. Bergen, R. L. (1968). *Applied Polymer Symposia*, No. 7, 41.
60. Davenport, N. E., Hubbard, L. W. and Pettit, N. R. (1959). *British Plastics*, **32**(12), 549.
61. Young, D. W., Newberg, R. G. and Howlett, R. M. (1947). *Ind. Eng. Chem.*, **39**, 446.
62. Bohn, L. (1963). *Kunstoffe*, **53**, 826.
63. Reznikova, R. A., Zalonchkovskii, A. D. and Voyutskii, S. S. (1953). *Kolloid Zhur.*, **15**, 108.
64. Sharp, T. J. and Ross, J. A. (1961). *Trans. Inst. Rubber Ind.*, **37**, 157.
65. Byl'ev, V. A. and Voskresenskii, V. A. (1962). *Izv. Vysshikh Uchebn. Zavedenii, Khim. i Khim. Tekhnol.*, **5**, 474.
66. Rozhkov, Yu. P. and Frost, A. M. (1965). *Lakokrasochnye Materialy i ikh Primenenie*, **4**, 19.
67. Nielsen, L. E. (1953). *J. Am. Chem. Soc.*, **75**, 1435.
68. Takayanagi, M. (1963). *Mem. Faculty Eng. Kyushu Univ.*, **23**(1), 11.
69. Zelinger, J., Sununkova, E. and Heidingsfeld, V. (1966). *Sb. VSCHT Prague*, **9**, 73.
70. Rovatti, W. and Bobalek, E. G. (1963). *J. App. Polymer Sci.*, **7**, 2292.
71. Kühne, G. F. (1971). *SPE Technical Papers*, **17**, 491.
72. Kakutani Tsutomu, Kasuya Tanekau, Innami Hidetoshi and Ozi Toshitake (1966). *Kobunshi Kagaku*, **23**, 700.
73. US Patent 2,802,809.
74. Potthoff, H. (1966). *Kunstoffe*, **56**(10), 703.
75. Blanchard, R. R. and Burnett, C. N. (1968). *SPE Journal*, **24**(1), 74.
76. British Patent 863,279.
77. Belgian Patent 638,546.
78. Anon. (1965). *Modern Plastics*, **42**(9), 43.
79. Landers, L. A. and Meisenhelder, W. C. (1964). *SPE Journal*, **20**, 621.
80. Anon. (1965). *Chemical Eng.*, **72**, No. 17 (30 Aug.), 43.
81. Anon. (1965). *Chemical and Eng. News*, **43** (16 Aug.), 45.
82. Meier, D. J. (1969). *J. Polymer Sci.*, **C26**, 81.
83. Ryan, C. F. (1970). *Applied Polymer Symposia*, No. 15, 165.
84. McGarry, F. J. (1970). *Proc. Roy. Soc.*, **319A**, 59.
85. Bucknall, C. B., Drinkwater, I. C. and Keast, W. *Polymer*, in press.
86. Bucknall, C. B. and Clayton, D. (1972). *J. Mat. Sci.*, **7**, 209.
87. Newman, S. and Strella, S. (1965). *J. App. Polymer Sci.*, **9**, 2297.

88. Merz, E. H., Claver, G. E. and Baer, M. (1956). *J. Polymer Sci.*, **22**, 325.
89. Bucknall, C. B. and Smith, R. R. (1956). *Polymer*, **6**, 437.
90. Kambour, R. P. (1968). *Applied Polymer Symposia*, No. 7, 215.
91. Matsuo, M. (1966). *Polymer*, **7**, 421.
92. Kato, K. (1967). *Kolloid Zeitschrift und Zeit, Polymere*, **220**, 24.
93. Kato, K. (1966). *Polymer Letters*, **4**, 35.
94. Matsuo, M. (1969). *Polymer Engineering and Science*, **9**, 206.
95. Kambour, R. P. and Russell, R. R. (1971). *Polymer*, **12**, 237.
96. Goodier, J. N. (1933). *J. App. Mech.*, **55**, 39.
97. Schmitt, J. A. and Keskkula, H. (1960). *J. App. Polymer Sci.*, **3**, 132.
98. Broutman, L. J. and Panizza, G. (1971). *Intern. J. Polymeric Mat.*, **1**, 95.
99. Hashin, Z. (1962). *J. App. Mech.*, **29**, 143.
100. McGarry, F. J. and Sultan, J. N. (1969). *Research Report R* 69-8, Dept. of Civil Engineering, MIT, Cambridge, Mass.
101. Holliday, L. and Mann, J. (1966). *Advances in Materials*, Pergamon Press, London, p. 95.
102. Bucknall, C. B. and Hall, M. M. (1971). *J. Mat. Sci.*, **6**, 95.
103. Gesner, B. D. (1967). *J. App. Polymer Sci.*, **11**, 2499.
104. Bucknall, C. B. (1969). *J. Mat., JMSLA*, **4**, 214.
105. Wang, T. T., Matsuo, M. and Kwei, T. K. (1971). *ACS Polymer Preprints*, **12**, 671.
106. Wang, T. T., Matsuo, M. and Kwei, T. K. (1971). *J. App. Phys.*, **42**, 4188.
107. Maxwell, B. and Rahm, L. F. (1948). *Ind. Eng. Chem.*, **41**, 1988.
108. Spurr, O. K. and Niegish, W. D. (1962). *J. App. Polymer Sci.*, **6**, 585.
109. Gesner, B. D. (1969). *Encyclopaedia of Polymer Science and Technology*, **10**, 694.
110. Bucknall, C. B. (1967). *British Plastics*, **40**(12), 84.
111. Kauzmann, W. (1941). *Trans. Am. Inst. Min. Met. Eng.*, **143**, 57.
112. Haward, R. N. and Thackray, G. (1968). *Proc. Roy. Soc.*, **302A**, 453.
113. Karas, G. C. and Warburton, B. (1962). *Plast. Inst. Trans. J.*, **30**, 198.
114. Staverman, A. J. and Heijboer, J. (1960). *Kunstoffe*, **50**, 23.
115. Keskkula, H., Turley, S. G. and Boyer, R. F. (1971). *J. App. Polymer Sci.*, **15**, 351.
116. Kraus, G., Rollmann, K. W. and Gruver, J. T. (1970). *Macromolecules*, **3**, 92.
117. Schmitt, J. A. (1970). *J. Polymer Sci.*, **C30**, 437.
118. Mann, J., Bird, R. J. and Rooney, G. (1966). *Makromol. Chem.*, **90**, 207.
119. Grmela, V., Petru, B. and Sarka, P. (1971). *Mechanics of Polymers*, **3**, 545.
120. Benbow, J. J. (1961). *Proc. Phys. Soc. Lond.*, **78**, 970.
121. Rudd, J. F. (1963). *J. Polymer Sci.*, **B1**, 1.
122. *Composite Materials* (1966). Ed. L. Holliday, Elsevier, Amsterdam, p. 246.
123. Keskkula, H. and Norton, J. W. (1959). *J. App. Polymer Sci.*, **2**, 289.
124. Evans, L. J., Bucknall, C. B. and Hall, M. M. (1971). *Plastics and Polymers*, April, 118.
125. Simmons, P. (1967). *Rubber and Plastics Age*, **48**, 442.
126. Willersim, H. (1967). *Makromol. Chem.*, **101**, 306.
127. McGarry, F. J. and Oien, H. M., quoted by Bucknall and Clayton in reference 86.

CHAPTER 9

THE DIFFUSION AND SORPTION OF GASES AND VAPOURS IN GLASSY POLYMERS

H. B. HOPFENBERG AND V. STANNETT

9.1 INTRODUCTION

The systematic study of small molecule transport in polymers has received increasing attention since the classic paper by Graham in 1866 presented the qualitative features of fixed gas diffusion in polymer membranes.[1] Most of the published research, until about 1950, focused on diffusion of small molecules in rubbery polymers. In this regard, a rather consistent transport mechanism involving solution of penetrant in the polymer followed by diffusion through the membrane characterised virtually all of the many polymer-penetrant systems studied. Small deviations from this diffusion model were encountered for rubbery systems complicated by crystalline regions susceptible to reordering by an interacting or plasticising vapour or liquid penetrant. The more recent study of transport of penetrants in organic glasses revealed that transport in the glassy state is characterised more accurately by anomalous or complicated behaviour than it is by a simple, unifying mathematical or conceptual model. These complications include dual sorption modes for even the most noble of gases in organic glasses, time dependent boundary conditions for vapour transport, diffusion coefficients characterised by an apparent time dependence, polymer relaxations providing the rate determining transport step (rather than diffusion), polymer fracture and microfracture (crazing) accompanying transport, and a significant change in the transport mechanism as the glass transition temperature is traversed. These non-ideal or anomalous behavioural features will be treated explicitly and in detail for it is these independent, seemingly unrelated observations that describe the diffusion and sorption of gases and vapours in glassy polymers.

9.2 IDEAL AND NON-IDEAL SORPTION AND DIFFUSION OF FIXED GASES

9.2.1 Ideal diffusion and sorption of fixed gases

Diffusion is the net transport of matter in a system by means of random molecular motion. This results in the removal of chemical potential differences in a system and eventually produces a uniform state of equilibrium if the boundary conditions are not held constant for a permeation experiment.

Frequently the rate of diffusion is proportional to the concentration gradient although the proportionality constant known as the diffusion coefficient may be a function of the diffusant concentration in the polymer:

$$J = -D(c) \frac{\partial c}{\partial x} \tag{1}$$

This is Flick's first law of diffusion and is found experimentally to represent diffusion in many systems. For gases above their critical temperature (fixed gases) the diffusion coefficient is not a function of concentration. Fick's second law may be derived from Fick's first law:

$$\frac{dc}{dt} = \frac{\partial}{\partial x} \left(D(c) \frac{\partial c}{\partial x} \right) \tag{2}$$

Diffusion which follows Fick's first and second laws is termed Fickian diffusion.

When the boundary conditions are fixed such that a steady-state diffusion flux is maintained, eqn. (1) can be used to calculate the steady state permeability, defined as the flux per unit pressure gradient across a polymer membrane; assuming Henry's law to describe the gas–membrane equilibrium. Henry's law simply states that the concentration of penetrant in the polymer, C, is directly proportional to the gas pressure, p, on the polymer:

$$C = kp \tag{3}$$

The relationship between permeability, diffusivity, and gas solubility becomes:

$$\bar{P} = Dk \tag{4}$$

where $\bar{P}$ is the steady state permeability, $\dfrac{\text{cc (s.t.p.) cm}}{\text{sec cm}^2 \text{ atm}}$

D is the concentration independent diffusion coefficient of the fixed gas in the polymer, $\dfrac{cm^2}{sec}$

C is the concentration of fixed gas in the polymer, $\dfrac{cc\ (s.t.p.)}{cc\ polymer}$

k is the Bunsen solubility coefficient, $\dfrac{cc\ (s.t.p.)}{cc\ atm}$

p is the fixed gas pressure on the polymer.

   For the frequently observed ideal behaviour noted in organic rubbers, the diffusion coefficient varies with temperature by an Arrhenius relationship:

$$D = D_0 \exp\left(-E_D/RT\right) \tag{5}$$

where D_0 is the pre-exponential factor, E_D is the activation energy for diffusion, R is the gas constant, and T the absolute temperature. The normal range of values for E_D is 5–10 kcal/g mol.
   The solubility coefficient, k, varies with temperature according to the thermodynamic relationship:

$$k = k_0 \exp\left(-\Delta H_s/RT\right) \tag{6}$$

where ΔH_s is the enthalpy change upon solution of the gas in the polymer.
   Strictly idealised behaviour results not only from Fickian diffusion but additionally from a Henry's law description of solution and invariant activation energies and enthalpies of solution. This simplified behaviour is usually observed in rubbery polymers but frequently, below T_g, even for fixed gases, a more complicated equilibrium relationship is observed between the polymer and the gas phase; enthalpies of solution as well as activation energies for diffusion are significantly different below T_g than those observed above T_g. This effect is treated in detail in Section 9.3 of this chapter.

9.2.2   Non-ideal sorption and diffusion of fixed gases
Non-ideal sorption
The magnitude of the negative enthalpies of sorption reported by Meares [2,3,4] for neon, nitrogen, oxygen and argon in glassy polyvinylacetate and by Barrer [5] for organic vapours in ethyl cellulose were inconsistent with the sorption theories of rubbery systems and led Barrer [5] to suggest a

two-mode, concurrent sorption mechanism for glassy polymers, namely ordinary dissolution and 'hole' filling.

Michaels et al.[6,7] also reported that the sorption of helium, nitrogen, oxygen, argon and methane in glassy, amorphous and glassy, crystalline polyethylene terephthalate for pressures up to 1·0 atmosphere obeyed Henry's law, but carbon dioxide at 25°C and 40°C and ethane at 25°C

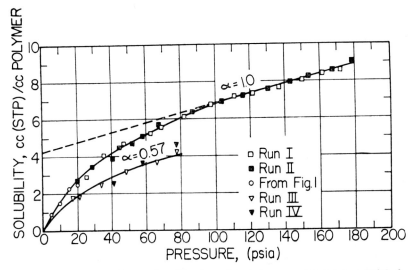

Fig. 1.   Sorption isotherms for CO_2 in poly(ethyleneterephthalate) at 25°C for amorphous fractions, α, of 1·0 and 0·57.[7] The intercept is C'_H (eqn. (17)). (Reproduced with permission of the American Institute of Plastics.)

in the same pressure range deviated from Henry's law. The sorption isotherms, measured over a large pressure range, for CO_2 in poly(ethylene-terephthalate) are shown in Fig. 1. The carbon dioxide isotherms prompted Michaels et al.[6] to propose a two-mode sorption model of ordinary dissolution and adsorption in microvoids ('holes') for gas sorption in glassy amorphous polymers. It was assumed that the total concentration of the sorbate in the polymer, C, consisted of two thermodynamically distinct molecular populations; molecules 'adsorbed' in the 'holes', C_H, and molecules dissolved in the amorphous polymer matrix as shown in eqn. (7):

$$C = C_H + C_D \qquad (7)$$

The concentration C_H was represented by a Langmuir isotherm, eqn. (8):

$$C_H = \frac{C'_H bp}{1 + bp} \tag{8}$$

where C'_H = hole saturation constant $\dfrac{\text{cc (s.t.p.)}}{\text{cc polymer}}$

b = hole affinity constant (atm^{-1})
p = equilibrium pressure (atm).

and the concentration C_D by Henry's law, eqn. (9),

$$C_D = k^*_D p \tag{9}$$

where k^*_D = Henry's law constant for dissolution in the amorphous matrix

$$\frac{\text{cc (s.t.p.)}}{\text{cc polymer atm}}$$

The substitution of eqns. (8) and (9) into (7) yields the 'dual mode sorption model':

$$C = \frac{C'_H bp}{1 + bp} + k^*_D p \tag{10}$$

This model gave an excellent fit of the carbon dioxide–glassy, amorphous poly(ethyleneterephthalate) data,[6] and the isotherm is represented by eqn. (11):

$$C = \frac{2 \cdot 33\, p}{1 + 0 \cdot 44\, p} + 0 \cdot 38\, p \tag{11}$$

It is instructive to examine the two limiting cases of this model. At low pressures where $bp \ll 1$, eqn. (10) reduces to:

$$C = C'_H bp + k^*_D p \tag{12}$$

which can also be written as

$$C = (C'_H b + k^*_D)p \tag{13}$$

Equation (13) is of Henry's law form:

$$C = Kp \tag{14}$$

where K is redefined by

$$K = C'_H b + k^*_D \tag{15}$$

For many glassy polymer systems $C'_H b$ is significantly larger than k^*_D therefore reducing eqn. (15) to:

$$K = C'_H b \qquad (16)$$

which indicates that at low pressures the 'hole' filling process dominates.[4,8] At high pressures $bp \gg 1$ which reduces eqn. (10) to:

$$C = C'_H + k^*_D p \qquad (17)$$

which can also be written in Henry's law form:

$$C = \left(\frac{C'_H}{p} + k^*_D \right) p \qquad (18)$$

that is

$$C = K'p \qquad (19)$$

by defining K' as

$$K' = \frac{C'_H}{p} + k^*_D \qquad (20)$$

But in this case for high pressures K' is not a constant; it is a function of the gas pressure. At sufficiently high pressures the term C'_H/p becomes negligible compared to k^*_D, therefore indicating that the 'holes' have become saturated and that ordinary dissolution dominates. Later investigations by Vieth et al.[8] on glassy polystyrene have indicated that the gas molecules sorb in the holes only as monolayers.

The form of eqn. (17) indicates that a quantitative separation of the sorption contributions is possible at high pressures, if the model adequately describes the data, because the isotherm is linear of slope k^*_D and intercept C'_H. After k^*_D has been determined from the slope of the best straight lines through the high pressure data, the 'hole' contribution, C_H, for each pressure can be determined by subtracting $k^*_D p$ from C.

$$C_H = C - C_D \qquad (21)$$

$$C_H = C - k^*_D p \qquad (21a)$$

The expression for C_H in eqn. (8) can be rearranged to the form

$$\frac{p}{C_H} = \frac{1}{C'_H b} + \frac{p}{C'_H} \qquad (22)$$

Then the Langmuir plot, p/C_H versus p, should yield a straight line of slope $1/C'_H$ and intercept at ($p = 0$) of $1/C'_H b$. This procedure, as in most procedures involving curve fitting of the data, is of a trial and error nature

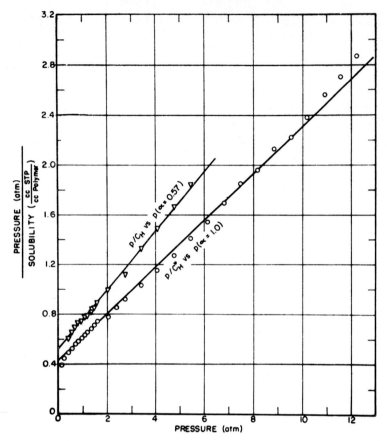

Fig. 2. Langmuir plots for CO_2 sorption by 'hole filling' in glassy poly(ethyleneterephthalate).[7] (Reproduced with permission of the American Institute of Physics.)

and it is continued until the best (least mean-squares) fit of the data on
the Langmuir plot is achieved. This procedure is illustrated in Fig. 2.

Effect of crystallinity on sorption
The effects of the degree of crystallinity on the permeability of semi-
crystalline polymers was first discussed in 1958 by Stannett and his
colleagues.[9]
   Michaels and Parker[10] and Michaels and Bixler[11] have extended this
study to the effect of crystallinity on the sorption of several gases in rubbery,
crystalline polyethylene, and found that the solubility constants for a

particular gas were proportional to the amorphous volume fraction, α, that is:

$$k = \alpha k^* \qquad (23)$$

where k^* is the solubility constant of a hypothetical completely amorphous polyethylene and k is the solubility constant of partially crystalline polyethylene. This relationship suggested that the gases sorb entirely in the amorphous phase of rubbery crystalline polymers and that the quantity sorbed was directly proportional to α.

The relationship in eqn. (23) was used by Michaels, Vieth and Barrie[6] in studying the effect of crystallinity on the sorption of several gases in glassy crystalline poly(ethyleneterephthalate). Unlike the rubbery crystalline polyethylene, it was found that the gas solubility, with the exception of helium, is not directly proportional to the amorphous volume fraction. The decrease in solubility accompanying crystallisation, $(C^* - C)/C^*$ (C^* is the amorphous polymer solubility and C is the crystalline polymer solubility), was smaller than the corresponding reduction in amorphous volume fraction, $1 - \alpha$; and this solubility decrease on crystallisation tended to become less with increasing Lennard–Jones force constants, $\varepsilon/\bar{k}$, of the sorbed gas.

This result can be satisfactorily accounted for in terms of the 'hole' model of the glassy amorphous phase. Upon annealing the polymer it is more probable that the denser regions crystallise first, tending to remove more of the amorphous phase used for gas dissolution, therefore leaving the residual amorphous phase with a higher concentration of 'holes' than in the previously amorphous polymer. This means that crystallisation in glassy polymers tends to increase the relative contribution of 'hole' filling as indicated by the C'_H/α values; by definition the 'hole' saturation-limit per unit volume amorphous phase. Also such an increase in concentration of 'holes' with increasing crystallisation accounts for the decreased reductions in solubility with increasing $\varepsilon/\bar{k}$ of the gas, a measure of the tendency of the gas to condense.[6]

Michaels et al.[6] generalised their original dual sorption model, eqn. (10), to include the effects of crystallinity on the solubility of the 'dissolved' species as shown in eqn. (24)

$$C = \frac{C'_H b p}{1 + bp} + \alpha k^*_D p \qquad (24)$$

The fit of eqn. (24) to their sorption data for carbon dioxide–poly(ethylene-terephthalate) ($\alpha = 0.57$) at 25°C yielded

$$C = \frac{1\cdot69p}{1 + 0\cdot45p} + (0\cdot57)(0\cdot38)p \qquad (25)$$

In comparing this with eqn. (11) it was noted that with crystallisation C'_H was decreased from 5·3 cc s.t.p./cc polymer to 4·20 cc s.t.p./cc polymer although b was essentially unaffected, therefore indicating that a dual sorption model fitted to the sorption data of a particular gas-polymer system of one α could not be used to predict the gas solubility at another degree of crystallinity.

Enthalpies of gas sorption in glassy polymers
The exothermic heats of sorption of gases and vapours in glassy polymers reported by several investigators[2−7] had in part prompted the introduction of the dual mode sorption mechanism. Michaels *et al.*[6] used this dual sorption mechanism to derive relationships which may be used to determine the heats associated with dissolution, ΔH_D, and 'hole' filling, ΔH_H.

The low pressure limiting case of the model was the starting point since in this region both processes are competing.

$$C = (C'_H b + k^*_D)p \qquad (26)$$

A Henry's law constant is defined as:

$$K = C'_H b + k^*_D \qquad (27)$$

The natural log of eqn. (27) is differentiated with respect to the reciprocal temperature to yield

$$\frac{\partial \ln K}{\partial(1/T)} = \frac{\partial \ln (C'_H b + k^*_D)}{\partial(1/T)} \qquad (28)$$

From a thermodynamic rearrangement eqn. (28) becomes:

$$\frac{\ln (C'_H b + k^*_D)}{(1/T)} = \frac{-\Delta H_s}{R} \qquad (29)$$

Equation (29) is the expression for the over-all heat of sorption in glassy amorphous polymers.

If $bC'_H \ll k^*_D$ (dissolution dominates) eqn. (29) becomes:

$$\frac{\partial \ln K}{\partial(1/T)} = \frac{\partial \ln k^*_D}{\partial(1/T)} = \frac{-\Delta H_D}{R} \qquad (30)$$

and if $bC'_H \gg k^*_D$ ('hole' filling dominates) eqn. (29) then reduces to

$$\frac{\partial \ln K}{\partial (1/T)} = \frac{\partial \ln (bC'_H)}{\partial (1/T)} = \frac{-\Delta H_H}{R} \tag{31}$$

It is the magnitude of the ΔH_H term that is believed to account for the high exothermic heats of sorption.

Gas diffusion in glassy polymers
Michaels et al.[7] presented a diffusion model based on the dual mode sorption mechanism in their investigations on poly(ethyleneterephthalate), but this model was later shown to be a limiting case of a model proposed by Vieth and Sladek.[12] The diffusion constants measured by Michaels et al.[7] were determined by low pressure time-lag and sorption techniques, and therefore the low pressure limiting case, eqn. (13), was justified to represent C.

The diffusion model[7] assumed that the driving force for the diffusion in glassy polymers is the concentration gradient of the 'dissolved' species, C_D, and the 'holes' offered no resistance to diffusion.

A material balance on a volume element of the film yields, if D is assumed to be constant,

$$D\frac{\partial^2 C_D}{\partial x^2} = \frac{\partial (C_D + C_H)}{\partial t} \tag{32}$$

where

$$C_D = k^*_D p \tag{33}$$

$$C_H = C'_H bp \tag{34}$$

which relates C_H in terms of C_D by

$$C_H = \left(\frac{C'_H b}{k^*_D}\right) C_D \tag{35}$$

The substitution of eqn. (35) into (32) yields

$$D\frac{\partial^2 C_D}{\partial x^2} = \frac{\partial C_D}{\partial t}\frac{1 + C'_H b}{k^*_D} \tag{36}$$

and with rearrangement becomes

$$\frac{D}{(1 + C'_H b/k^*_D)}\frac{\partial^2 C_D}{\partial x^2} = \frac{\partial C_D}{\partial t} \tag{37}$$

If an apparent diffusion constant is defined as

$$D_A = \frac{D}{(1 + C'_H b/k^*_D)} \qquad (38)$$

then eqn. (37) assumes the form of Fick's equation where D_A is the experimentally determined diffusion constant.

Equation (38) is important because it predicts that the actual diffusion constant, D, will be larger than the one measured. The same equation also predicts that the actual and apparent diffusion constants will be identical in the rubbery state where the 'holes' disappear, therefore suggesting that the Fickian equation for rubbery systems may be viewed as a special form of this more general equation.

Another important consequence of eqn. (38) involves the magnitudes of the calculated energies of activation for diffusion. The differentiation of the natural log of eqn. (38) with respect to reciprocal temperature provides:

$$\frac{\partial \ln D}{\partial (1/T)} = \frac{\partial \ln D_A}{\partial (1/T)} + \frac{\partial \ln (C'_H b + k^*_D)}{\partial (1/T)} - \frac{\partial \ln k^*_D}{\partial (1/T)} \qquad (39)$$

Referring to eqns. (29) and (30), eqn. (39) is equal to

$$E_D = E_{D_A} + (\Delta H_D - \Delta H_s) \qquad (40)$$

Equation (40) predicts that the actual activation energy for diffusion will be larger than the observed activation energy, E_{D_A}, because ΔH_s is large and negative, e.g. 2–10 kcal/g mol, therefore making $\Delta H_D - \Delta H_s$ positive. This suggests that the activation energy in the rubbery polymer may not exceed the actual activation energy in the glassy polymer by an amount as large as has been reported.[2,6,7]

The Vieth and Sladek diffusion model for glassy polymers[12] was developed in conjunction with their new transient experimental technique of measuring D by high pressure decay. The model was based on three assumptions: C_D and C_H are in equilibrium; the gas sorbed in the 'holes' is immobilised; and D is constant.

The mathematical derivation parallels that of Michaels et al.[7] with one exception; a more general expression for C_H is used:

$$C_H = \frac{C'_H bp}{1 + bp} \qquad (41)$$

which is related to C_D by

$$C_H = \frac{(C'_H b/k^*_D)C_D}{1 + (b/k^*_D)C_D} \tag{42}$$

The substitution of eqn. (42) into (32) yields

$$D\frac{\partial^2 C_D}{\partial x^2} = \frac{\partial C_D}{\partial t}\left(1 + \frac{C'_H b/k^*_D}{[1 + (b/k_D)C_D]^2}\right) \tag{43}$$

with the boundary conditions

$$C_D = 0 \quad \text{at } t = 0, \qquad 0 \le x \le L \tag{44}$$

$$\frac{\partial C_D}{\partial x} = 0 \quad \text{at } t \ge 0, \qquad x = 0 \tag{45}$$

$$C_D = k^*_D p \quad \text{at } t > 0, \qquad x = L \tag{46}$$

where, in the pressure decay technique

$$p = p_0 - \frac{RT}{22\ 400\ Z}\int_0^L (C_D + C_H)\,\mathrm{d}x \tag{47}$$

with $p = p_0$ at $t = 0$; $2(Z + L)$ is the inside diameter of the high pressure cell, $2L$ is the polymer film thickness and Z is the distance from the film surface to the cell wall.

This model is a nonlinear second-order partial differential equation with one time-dependent boundary condition and therefore no analytical solution exists. Vieth and Sladek, however, obtained a numerical solution of the equation by using a finite difference approximation.[12]

The numerical solutions of eqn. (43) have been determined for several sets of parameters—b, C'_H, k^*_D, L/a—and then correlated in terms of two variables φ and θ' as a φ versus θ,[12] plot where

$$\varphi = \frac{p_0 - p}{p_0 - p_f} \quad \text{with } p_f \text{ being the final equilibrium pressure} \tag{48}$$

$$\theta' = \frac{Dt}{L^2}\left(1 + \frac{C'_H b/k^*_D}{(1 + bp)^2}\right)^{-1} \tag{49}$$

The value of D is determined by plotting the pressure decay data as φ versus $(t/L^2)^{\frac{1}{2}}$ and scaling it to fit the curve φ versus $(\theta')^{\frac{1}{2}}$. The value of D is then related to the scale factor by:

$$D = (1/\text{scale factor})^2 \tag{50}$$

The foregoing analysis has assumed that:[12,13,14]

(a) there is always an equilibrium between gas molecules in the two different molecular populations;
(b) only the 'dissolved' population is free to diffuse whereas the penetrant molecules 'adsorbed' into the 'holes' are immobilised;
(c) the diffusion coefficient, D, of the dissolved molecules is constant.

These assumptions seem to be borne out by all current experimental evidence; however, it is very difficult to explore the limits of their validity except through extensive investigations using a variety of experimental techniques some of which require very precise measurements and analysis. Paul[13] and Petropoulos[14] have suggested experiments and have made theoretical analyses of them which would shed light on the observed dual sorption mode and test the limits of the above assumptions. However, no experiments along these lines have been reported to date for glassy polymers.

Paul[13] proposed that the diffusion time lag which may be obtained from a transient permeation experiment would be a sensitive method of examining the effect of the proposed adsorption accompanying diffusion. He developed an asymptotic solution to eqn. (43) for the time lag experiment. This solution requires that assumptions (b) and (c) are valid but does not require (a) provided steady-state has indeed been reached in the experiment. This result predicts that the proposed immobilisation does not affect the steady-state permeability but causes a very significant increase in the diffusion time lag θ beyond that which would occur in the absence of this adsorption, i.e. $l^2/6D$. The result for the time lag, θ, may be expressed in the following mathematical form:[13]

$$\theta = \frac{l^2}{6D} [1 + Kf(y)] \tag{51}$$

where

$K = C'_H b / k_D$
$y = b p_2$
$p_2 = $ upstream gas pressure
$f(y)$ is a tabulated function (13) with the limits

$$f(0) = 1$$
$$f(\infty) = 0$$

Kemp and Paul[15,16] have tested the quantitative predictive power of eqn. (51) by performing time lag measurements on a system which has a sorption isotherm of the form given by eqn. (10). This system was not a glassy polymer but a rubbery polymer which had dispersed in it molecular sieves as a discrete phase. The continuous rubber phase sorbs gas according to Henry's law while the discrete sieve phase adsorbs gas according to a Langmuir isotherm and may be presumed to immobilise those molecules adsorbed. Consequently this system fulfils conditions (b) and (c) above. Experimental results for this model system revealed that the time lag was greatly increased by the existence of the adsorption process and that the time lag decreased as the upstream gas pressure was increased. These responses were quantitatively described by the previous theoretical results given by Paul[13] using only parameters defined by independent experiments.

Petropoulos[14] has considered other theoretical approaches designed to relax all three assumptions stated above and has indicated how various experimental data might be analysed to test more rigorously the dual sorption model. A point of significant interest in the Petropoulos development is the relaxation of the assumption that the population following the Langmuir isotherm is immobilised. He defines a thermodynamic diffusion coefficient for each population so that Fick's law may now be written as

$$ J = -\frac{1}{RT}(D_{T_D}C_D + D_{T_H}C_H)\frac{\partial \mu}{\partial x} \tag{52} $$

where:

μ = chemical potential of the penetrant

D_{T_D} = thermodynamic diffusion coefficient for the dissolved species (a constant)

D_{T_H} = thermodynamic diffusion coefficient for the adsorbed species.

In eqn. (52) the driving force for diffusion mass transfer is taken to be the gradient of chemical potential. Neither D_{T_D} or D_{T_H} is known *a priori*; however, each may be determined from experiments provided adequate data are available. This model predicts that if the adsorbed species is not totally immobilised, *i.e.* $D_{T_H} \neq 0$, then the steady-state permeability coefficient will not be a constant and will depend on the upstream gas pressure. If immobilisation is complete, then the permeability will *not* depend on upstream gas pressure[13] unless the diffusion coefficient for the dissolved or mobile species happens to be concentration dependent. If a variable permeability were observed, it may be difficult to delineate experimentally which of these two factors is the root cause. If assumptions (b) and (c) are met, then the model developed by Petropoulos predicts the same results for the time lag indicated by Paul.

The ideas embodied in eqn. (52) are not perfectly general since they imply that transport of the two populations occurs in parallel. In other words, this model considers that a molecule which is adsorbed into a 'hole' at the upstream face of the membrane may be transported through the entire membrane without ever leaving this population. This assumes that the 'holes' are continuous regions which traverse the entire thickness of the membrane. If on the other hand the 'holes' are discrete domains which do not connect one with the other, then eqn. (52) is inapplicable. In the model system of Paul and Kemp the synthetic 'holes' or sorption sites created by dispersing molecular sieves in a rubbery matrix were of this latter type. One might envision for this case a diffusion coefficient for the gas in these dispersed domains not equal to zero, and there is clearly a diffusion coefficient for the matrix phase. Fick's law for such a disperse system cannot be written as shown in eqn. (52) since the two diffusion processes do not occur in parallel. Instead a single *effective* diffusion coefficient for the composite must be used which is a function of the properties of both phases. Kemp[15] has elaborated on this formulation. From this discussion, it is clear that many questions remain regarding the observations originally reported by Michaels, Vieth *et al.*[6,7,8,10,11,12] on the peculiar transport behaviour in glassy polymers. It is very likely that significant strides in understanding the structure and nature of the polymeric glassy state may be derived from future investigations of gaseous transport in such materials.

9.3   THE EFFECT OF THE GLASS TRANSITION ON GAS AND VAPOUR DIFFUSION IN POLYMERS

Meares,[2] in 1954, studied the effect of the glass transition temperature, T_g, on the diffusion of gases in poly(vinylacetate). Meares presented data which could not be explained adequately at that time by extending the diffusion theories for rubbery polymers and, therefore, his pioneering work led to a variety of experimental and theoretical studies considering the change in mechanism for small molecule diffusion in the glassy versus the rubbery state. Specifically, a change in slope was observed at the glass transition temperature for the Arrhenius plot of the diffusion coefficient suggesting discretely different activation energies in the rubbery versus the glassy state. The activation energy in the rubbery state was higher than the activation energy calculated from the Arrhenius plot of the glassy data.

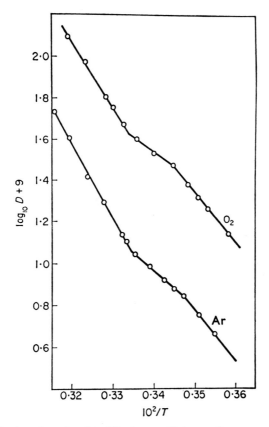

Fig. 3. *Arrhenius plots for the diffusion coefficients of oxygen and argon in poly(vinylacetate) in a temperature region encompassing the glass transition temperature.*[2] (*Reproduced with permission of the Mack Printing Company.*)

Meares[2] suggested that a change in the segmental mobility of the polymer chains upon traversing T_g was reflected by the measured sorption and diffusion properties. This supposition was verified by Meares[2,3] for the diffusion of helium, neon, argon, oxygen, hydrogen, krypton, and methane in high molecular weight polyvinylacetate. The Arrhenius plot of the diffusion data for O_2 and Ar, shown in Fig. 3, afforded three distinct straight lines of differing slopes. This indicated different activation energies in the three temperature regions. The upper transition temperature of 26°C in the Arrhenius plot corresponded with the normally observed glass transition temperature for which values between 25° and 31°C have been reported. The unexpected break in the Arrhenius plot at the lower transition temperature was found to decrease slightly on increasing the size of the diffusing gas molecule. Meares suggested that at the upper transition temperature, T_g, in the Arrhenius plot the polymer microstructure changes from a liquid-like phase to an amorphous solid or glass-like phase, but this transition leaves some liquid-like regions dispersed throughout the continuous solid-like phase. These liquid-like regions are centered on the polymer chain ends and possess some freedom of rotation or torsional oscillation at a frequency comparable with or greater than the jump frequency of the diffusing gas molecules. As the temperature is lowered the dimensions of these liquid-like regions are decreased until a critical size is reached below which rotation is no longer possible. It is this essentially complete cessation of segmental rotation that characterises the lower transition temperature.[2,3]

Meares[2,3] proposed the following idealised concept of the gaseous sorption and diffusion process in polymers at temperatures above and below T_g, based on the relative activation energies for diffusion and heats of solution for polyvinylacetate in the two temperature regimes and the zone of activation theory. At temperatures above T_g gas molecules which dissolve in the polymer must create their own 'holes' by separating the interchain polymer contacts. The penetrant then diffuses through the polymer matrix along cylindrical voids created by the synchronised rotation of polymer segments about the –C–C– bonds. Below T_g the polymer consists of regions of densely packed and arranged chains which have limited freedom for rotation, separated by less dense regions of disordered chains that form the 'holes' into which the gas sorbs. The gas molecules diffuse between these 'holes' by the slight compressing of localised chains in the dense regions enabling the gas molecules to pass through. This compression in the glassy state does not create the long cavities common to the rubbery state, indicating that the zone of chain activation is much larger in the rubbery state. This zone of activation was found to be essentially independent of the size of the penetrating molecule.[2]

The sorption and diffusion data of Meares[2,3] for polyvinylacetate can adequately be explained in the light of the mechanisms presented. The sorption of gases above T_g indicates that the heat of solution must include, along with the heat of interaction between the diffusant and polymer, the energy for separating the polymer chains which is endothermic, therefore accounting for the endothermic and slightly exothermic heats of solution. The exothermic heats of solution below T_g can be explained by the inclusion of the exothermic heat of adsorption for the 'hole filling' in the heat of solution. The diffusion process above T_g requires a larger zone of chain activation than below T_g which is consistent with the higher energy of activation reported above T_g.

Michaels et al.[6,7] studied the sorption and diffusion of He, O_2, N_2, Ar, CO_2, and CH_4 in glassy and rubbery polyethylene terephthalate. Basically, Michaels et al. found the effects of glass transition on diffusion to be similar to those observed by Meares for polyvinylacetate. The amorphous glass transition was found to occur at 67°C while T_g for the crystalline films studied occurred about 82°C. This was attributed to the crosslinking effect of crystallites, which lower chain mobility. In the glassy state, the activation energies of diffusion were virtually equal for both the amorphous and crystalline films. This suggests, that below T_g, the concept of chain immobilisation by crystallites is insignificant since the rigidity of the polymer backbone far outweighs the restrictions on mobility caused by the crystallites, although the magnitude of the diffusion constant is reduced by their presence.

Michaels also found that E_D was greater in the rubbery polymer than it was below T_g, again supporting Meares' idea of a larger zone of activation, due to increased segmental mobility above T_g. These effects were also noted and reported by Ryskin.[17]

Kumins et al. in 1961 discussed their experiments involving water vapour diffusion through vinyl chloride–vinyl acetate copolymers.[18] The water vapour did exhibit an effect on E_D at the transition temperature of both the plasticised and unplasticised films. The effect of the plasticiser on T_g is noted by Kumins and it is pointed out that T_g for the plasticised film is lower than for the unplasticised copolymer.

A more recent article by Barrer et al.[19] also compared plasticised and unplasticised polymers. A change in slope of the Arrhenius plot was observed for the diffusion of neon and hydrogen in unplasticised and plasticised poly(vinylchloride), at the respective glass transition temperatures.

Kumins and Roteman in 1961 published data on diffusion of a series of gases and vapours through poly(vinylchloride)–poly(vinylacetate) copolymer films.[20] The effect of penetrant diameter on the nature of the discontinuity of the Arrhenius plots at T_g was studied. He, H_2, Ne, NH_4, O_2, CO, CO_2, Kr, and water vapour were studied; none of the penetrants except CO_2 and H_2O showed the change in slope of the Arrhenius plots at T_g. This work was rather provocative in that it suggested a critical size of a zone of activation; penetrant molecules much smaller than this zone would obey similar mechanisms in the rubber and the glass.

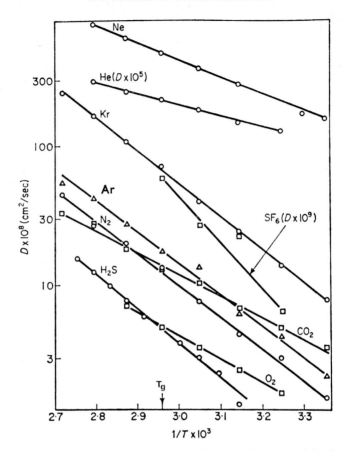

Fig. 4.   Arrhenius plots for the diffusion coefficients of a series of fixed gases in poly(ethylmethacrylate) in a temperature region encompassing the glass transition temperature.[21] *(Reproduced with the permission of John Wiley and Sons Inc.)*

After confirming the mechanistic change at T_g described by Meares in poly(vinylacetate), Stannett and Williams[21] extended the work on the effect of penetrant size on the various mechanisms of transport above and below T_g to the study of diffusion in poly(ethylmethacrylate) membranes. Their data are presented in Fig. 4. The diffusivities of He, Ne, Ar, O_2, N_2, Kr, CO_2, H_2S, and H_2O were measured above and below T_g. Only the Arrhenius plots for water vapour exhibited a change in slope at T_g. It was suggested that poly(ethylmethacrylate) was a sufficiently stiff polymer that segmental motion in the rubbery state was little different from that encountered in the glass. The mechanistic change observed for water diffusion was attributed to plasticisation effects accruing from water–polymer interactions. Stannett and Williams suggested that some polymers would show a transition effect with only large penetrants (*e.g.* CO_2 in poly(vinylchloride), some with no fixed gas penetrants (*e.g.* poly(ethylmethacrylate), and some with all penetrants (*e.g.* poly(vinylacetate)).

Stannett and Williams collaborated with Tikhomirov and Hopfenberg[22] to determine if diffusion in unplasticised poly(vinylchloride) homopolymer would exhibit transitional behaviour that was dependent upon penetrant size. There was no evidence of a discrete change in activation energy at T_g for He, Ne, N_2, CO_2, O_2, CH_4 and H_2O although clear slope changes were apparent on the Arrhenius plots for the diffusion coefficients of Ar and Kr.

Burgess, Hopfenberg, and Stannett[23] studied gas diffusion in poly(methylacrylate) which is a structural isomer of poly(vinylacetate). Explicit comparisons between the behaviour of these polymeric isomers were drawn. The permeability, diffusivity, and solubility of He, Ne, Ar, and Kr were determined in a temperature range encompassing T_g. Activation energies for diffusion were higher above T_g than below T_g for all four gases in both polymers. The data of Fig. 5 indicate that the enthalpy of solution was positive for all gases above T_g but exothermic for all gases in glassy poly(methylacrylate) suggesting a hole filling contribution to gas sorption. For all gases studied, the T_g, the enthalpy of mixing, as well as the E_D were all larger for poly(vinylacetate) than for poly(methylacrylate). These differences were attributed to the stronger dipole–dipole interactions possible in poly(vinylacetate) where the dipolar carbonyl group is separated from the chain backbone by an incremental atomic spacing.

9.4 RELAXATION CONTROLLED TRANSPORT AND RELATED CRAZING OF POLYMERIC GLASSES BY VAPOURS

9.4.1 Introduction

Below the glass transition temperature, a second limiting transport process is frequently observed during the penetration of polymers by organic vapours. The presentation to this point has dealt exclusively with diffusion controlled transport of small molecules in polymers. The second limiting transport mechanism which is mechanistically and phenomenologically quite different than Fickian diffusion has received increasing attention since 1965.

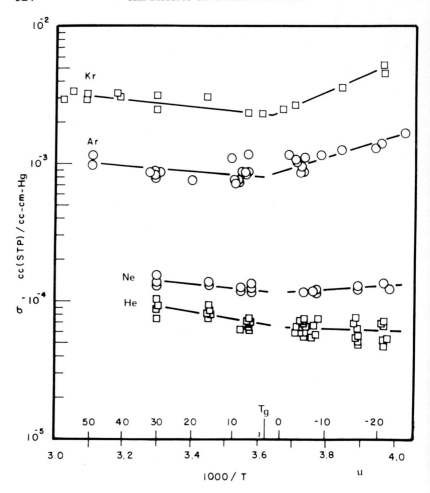

Fig. 5.   The temperature dependence of the solubility coefficients of a series of Noble Gases in poly(methylacrylate) in a temperature region encompassing the glass transition temperature.[23] *(Reproduced with the permission of Marcel Dekker Inc.)*

Alfrey[24] defined normal Fickian sorption into a polymer membrane as Case I transport. Fickian sorption is characterised by a linear relationship between initial weight gain of the sample undergoing organic vapour sorption and the square root of time. In addition, a smooth and continuous concentration profile exists through the film. These observations are consistent with Fickian transport if the typical boundary conditions used for a sorption experiment are employed; *e.g.*

$$C(x, 0) = 0 \tag{53}$$

$$C(0, t) = C(L, t) = C_0 \tag{54}$$

where C is the penetrant concentration, C_0 the equilibrium penetrant concentration, t and x the independent variables time and distance, and L the film thickness.

For the second limiting transport process, the weight gain of a polymer membrane immersed in vapour obeying the boundary conditions of eqns. (53) and (54) is linear in time until equilibrium is established. There is a discrete discontinuity between the near uniform, equilibrium, penetrant concentration in the outer swollen layers and the virtually unpenetrated central core. Alfrey termed this limiting behaviour as Case II transport. There is now quite clear evidence that the rate determining step of Case II transport is osmotically induced polymeric relaxations at the boundary between the unpenetrated central core and the swollen, rubbery outer shell.[25,26,27,28] The superposition of relaxation controlled transport and Fickian diffusion in the same experimental time scale, leads to apparent time dependent anomalies.

The transport features observed for normal hydrocarbons in polystyrene are qualitatively quite similar to those observed in other, rather diverse, polymer-penetrant systems.[25,26] The similarities in qualitative behaviour suggest that the diverse behavioural features noted in glassy polymers such as polystyrene probably occur for most amorphous systems if a sufficient range of temperature and activity (traversing the glass transition range) is encompassed by experimental conditions. The patterns of behaviour are quite diverse and complicated. The relationship between the various transport features are more easily assimilated, however, by examining the various regions of the temperature-activity plane presented in Fig. 6.

The following features are readily apparent:

(1) Time dependent anomalies and Case II sorption including solvent crazing are confined to relatively high penetrant activities and temperatures in the vicinity of and below the effective T_g of the system. The effective T_g of the system is represented by the dashed line extending through the anomalous diffusion region.

(2) The region of Case II sorption (relaxation-controlled transport) is separated from the Fickian diffusion region by a region where both mechanisms are operative giving rise to diffusional anomalies.

THE PHYSICS OF GLASSY POLYMERS

(3) The activation energy characterising Case II sorption decreases as
penetrant activity is reduced.
(4) Concentration-independent diffusion is only apparent at very low
temperatures and/or activities.
(5) Concentration-dependent diffusion occurs above the glass temperature with the more highly sorbed organic penetrants or at high
activities.

It should now be readily apparent that diverse transport behaviour
occurs for a specific polymer-penetrant pair if the investigator is willing to
extend his analysis to a broad range of temperature and penetrant activity.
One must specify a limited temperature-activity regime when referring to
the likelihood of observing a given transport feature. All of the limiting
and intermediate transport features can most likely be observed experimentally if a sufficiently broad temperature-activity plane is explored.

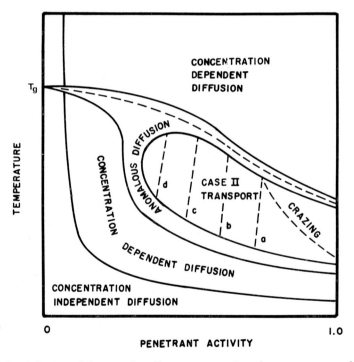

Fig. 6. *Behavioural features for alkane transport in polystyrene presented on a
temperature-penetrant activity plane.*[28] *(Reproduced with the permission of John
Wiley and Sons Inc.)*

For some systems, insufficient penetrant levels may be achieved at equilibrium to generate an osmotic stress large enough to bias relaxations controlling Case II transport and/or solvent crazing. For these special systems, the crazing region and possibly the Case II transport regime would disappear from the temperature-activity plane.

9.4.2   Relaxation controlled transport and solvent crazing

Relaxation controlled transport

In the introduction, it was emphasised that the mode of transport depended markedly on temperature, solvent activity, and other system parameters such as thermal history, orientation, and molecular weight. Below the glass transition temperature the transport process often becomes 'anomalous'. Frequently the diffusivity not only depends upon concentration, but upon time and position as well and is characterised by the following features:

(1) At temperatures well below T_g, a linear relationship exists between the initial weight gain of a polymeric film undergoing sorption and time. (In contrast, Fickian sorption leads to a linear relationship between the initial weight gain and the square root of time.)

(2) A sharp boundary separates an inner glassy core of essentially zero penetrant concentration from an outer swollen, rubbery shell of uniform concentration (not a sufficient criterion for non-Fickian diffusion since sharp advancing boundaries have been observed for Fickian diffusion with a strongly concentration-dependent diffusivity).

(3) The boundary advances at a constant velocity.

This model, which Alfrey developed for a simple limiting case for anomalous diffusion, fits several of the anomalous features of the transport process below T_g observed by King and others. King[29] reported a linear relationship between the initial weight gain and time in his study of the sorption of alcohol vapours in wool and keratin. His explanation for the linear advance was a concentration-dependent diffusion coefficient which led to a build-up of a steep front which then moved through the medium. Other authors have reported anomalous behaviour in their studies of organic vapour transport in glassy polymeric systems, but have offered no simple explanation for the behaviour. Crank[30] did develop a model to describe the behaviour with a time-dependent diffusion coefficient and/or a nonconstant boundary condition, $C_0(t)$; but in each case he had to include several additional parameters to describe the behaviour satisfactorily.

   It is now generally agreed that Case II transport is a relaxation controlled transport process and, therefore, the parameters affecting relaxation such as polymer orientation, molecular weight, molecular weight distribution, temperature, penetrant activity, and penetrant physicochemical properties are important parameters which affect the transport of organic molecules in glassy polymers. The effects of temperature, penetrant activity and penetrant structure on the sorption kinetics and equilibria of hydrocarbons

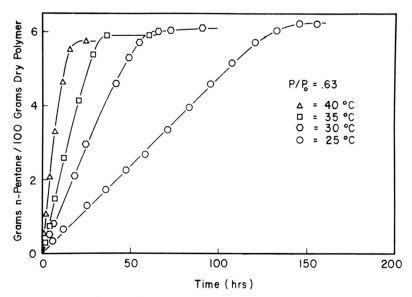

Fig. 7.   Sorption kinetics for n-pentane at an activity of 0·63 *in biaxially oriented polystyrene.*[27] (*Reproduced with permission of the Society of Plastics Engineers Inc.*)

in biaxially oriented and cast-annealed polystyrene have been presented by Hopfenberg, Holley and Stannett.[27,31] The limiting kinetics characteristic of relaxation-controlled sorption are shown in Fig. 7. The Arrhenius plots of these sorption kinetics are presented in Fig. 8. The activation energy calculation from Fig. 8 is 28 kcal/g mol; the activation energies increased monotonically with penetrant activity to a value of 60 kcal/g mol for sorption in liquid *n*-pentane.

   The effects of polymer molecular weight, molecular weight distribution, and orientation on the rate of relaxation-controlled sorption of *n*-pentane by glassy polystyrene were studied by Bray[32] and Baird *et al.*[33] The

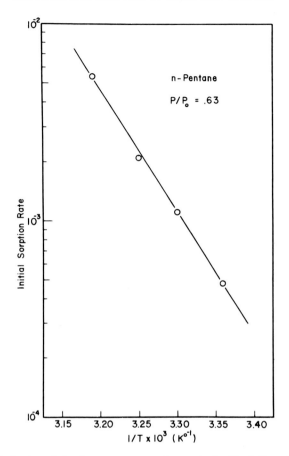

Fig. 8.   Arrhenius plot of n-pentane sorption rate in biaxially oriented poly-styrene.[27] (Reproduced with permission of the Society of Plastics Engineers Inc.)

sorption of *n*-pentane follows Case II kinetics but for films which sorb slowly the sorption rate increases at relatively long times until sorption is sharply terminated. This effect is apparent in the plots of Fig. 9.

The systematic variation in the accelerated weight gain with initial sorption rate in presented in Fig. 10. This reproducibly observed phenomenon was explained by extending Peterlin's model[34] for the concentration profile which develops during Case II sorption. Peterlin suggests that a Fickian diffusion front precedes the advancing convection front manifest by the boundaries between the swollen shell and the partially penetrated core. His suggested concentration profile is presented in Fig. 11. For relaxation controlled sorption processes which are slow (owing to low temperature, low penetrant activity, or low degrees of orientation) a more fully developed Fickian front can develop. Relaxation processes taking place in this more plasticised environment are more rapid and therefore the sorption appears to accelerate at long times when the rate determining relaxations are taking place in the presence of elevated penetrant concentrations.

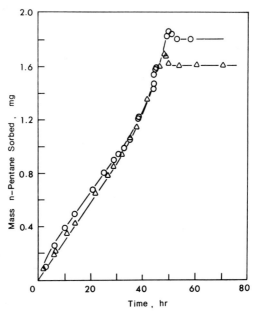

Fig. 9. Sorption kinetics for n-pentane at an activity of 0·89 *in polystyrene.*[33]
$\bigcirc = $ *Film mass* 16·78 *mg* $M_w(M_w/M_n)$: 225 000 (1·96)
$\Delta = $ *Film mass* 15·6 *mg* $M_w(M_w/M_n)$: 447 000 (2·85)
(*Reproduced with permission of the Society of Plastics Engineers Inc.*)

Overshoot of the equilibrium *n*-pentane content occurs in sorption experiments in which accelerated sorption is pronounced. The overshoot increase may be explained by the development of dispersed microvoids within the unrelaxed film core which 'heal' after equilibrium is attained.

The sorption rate is independent of polymer molecular weight and molecular weight distribution *per se* over a broad range of these parameters. Essentially identical vapour sorption kinetics were observed for well

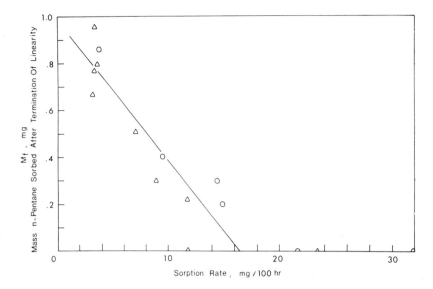

Fig. 10. *The relationship between long time deviations from ideal Case II transport and the initial Case II transport rate.* [33] (*Reproduced with permission of the Society of Plastics Engineers Inc.*)

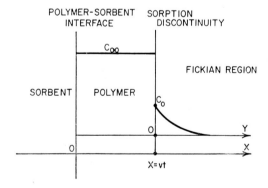

Fig. 11. *Idealised concentration profile proposed by Peterlin for Case II sorption into an infinite sheet with a Fickian Diffusion front preceding the advancing boundary between swollen, relaxed polymer and the essentially dry inner region.* [34] (*Reproduced with permission of Huthig and Wepf Verlag.*)

annealed polystyrene films of different molecular weights and distributions. The sorption rate increased monotonically with orientation (characterised by birefringence). Apparently the orientation stresses couple with the swelling stresses to increase the sorption rate. For vapour sorption by uniaxially oriented films and for liquid sorption by partially annealed films, high molecular weight film (1 880 000) exhibits greater sorption rates than low molecular weight film (*ca.* 200 000). These differences in rate are not due to molecular weight differences *per se*, but are a consequence of the dissimilar response of free volume and strain development for films of different molecular weight prepared with a given time–temperature–strain history.

Crazing

Crazing of carefully annealed polystyrene films occurs during desorption of *n*-pentane from partially saturated films. The depth of craze penetration reflects the point of advance of the discontinuous Case II sorption boundary. The stresses exerted on the polymer may be a combination of external applied stress, osmotic swelling stresses, or internal residual preorientation stresses.

   Environmental stress cracking may be defined as cracking or crazing of a polymer specimen under stress (external and/or internal) in the presence of a second component without which the polymer would not fail under the given stress.[35,36] Solvent and environmental stress cracking are differentiated by their modes of initiation. Initiation of solvent stress crazing involves a liquid which is at least a partial solvent at elevated temperatures and is absorbed, perhaps with mild swelling, at ordinary temperatures. Crazing will occur when the combined internal and external stresses exerted on the polymer lead to an inhomogeneous deformation with the formation of voids. (*See* Chapters 6 and 7.)

   Thus crazing may be induced under a variety of test conditions. Kambour[37] has observed crazing preceding fracture in eight glassy polymers in air. Most studies on environmental stress cracking have used a glassy polymer subjected to an external stress while in the presence of an organic penetrant. Rudd[38] examined polystyrene in butanol under a tensile stress of 1000 psi. Bernier and Kambour[39] studied stress crazing and cracking of poly(phenyleneoxide) bars under strains from 0·1% to 1·5% exposed to environments of twenty-eight different organic vapours. They also studied crazing of equilibrated films. As described previously, Michaels, Bixler, and Hopfenberg[40] have observed solvent crazing where the swelling stresses were of such a magnitude that crazing resulted without application of an external stress. Mercury cast annealed polystyrene films supposedly free of internal stress were also shown to craze in organic liquids.[40]

The nature of the craze

As described in previous chapters Kambour and others have investigated the nature or morphology of microformations in polymers and have distinguished between what they term crazes compared with larger scale cracks. Like normal cracks, crazes reflect light and are planar. In contrast to earlier concepts, however, crazes are understood today not to be true cracks but rather thin platelike regions containing polymer material which is interconnected with the normal polymer surrounding the craze.[41] No holes or discontinuities of an optical size are observed in the craze.

Craze formation takes place by a plastic deformation in the stress direction.[42] The degree of deformation residing in any craze depends on its history. Freshly formed but unstressed crazes have been observed to undergo a 60% plastic elongation.[43] The elongation process appears to occur without macroscopic reduction in cross section. This results in creation of a substantial void content. Kambour[44] concludes that the void content of the craze is large but relatively invariant from one polymer to another and independent of the crazing environment.

Dry crazes have been known to sustain surprisingly high stresses for long times. The strength of the craze is relatively low when the crazing agent is present, but upon drying, the craze strength can increase markedly and in the case of polycarbonate, at least, can sometimes exceed the normal yield stress of the polymer.[45]

X-ray scattering and electron microscopy studies of craze material have confirmed that the void content appears to consist of an open-celled foam, the holes and polymer elements of which appear to be approximately 200 Å in diameter for poly(phenyleneoxide) crazes grown in ethanol. Michaels *et al.*[40] observed a hole size of about 3 microns (3000 Å) in diameter in polystyrene crazed in *n*-heptane in the absence of isothermal stress. The holes in the craze are interconnected by evidence of the ease of exchange of liquids in the craze.[41] Internal specific surface area of a freshly formed craze has been roughly calculated to be 100–200 m^2/cm^3 of craze as determined by X-ray scattering.[45]

Kambour has observed two kinds of craze structure:[46] an unfibrillated kind in the peripheral region and an oriented fibrillar kind constituting the interior portions of the craze. He suggests that craze development might sometimes take place in two steps: first a nucleation and growth of spheroidal voids followed by an elongation of elements in the stress direction which begins to occur only when the crazing region is somewhat removed from the craze-polymer interface. He also shows a craze which split during formation where the irregular tearing process resembles 'that kind easily observed on the macroscopic scale with soft tissue paper'. Kambour suggests that substantial amounts of plastic deformation occur locally during the final act of craze breakdown, a conclusion also supported by Berry.[47]

Theories on environmental craze formation
A good deal is now known about the role of organic agents in the enhancement of environmental stress cracking and crazing. There exists a number of theories which attempt to rationalise the crazing phenomenon in light of processes known or suspected to take place in a stressed glassy polymer in contact with a liquid.

Nielsen[48] discussed the concept of stress crazing in view of his 'domain' theory. A 'domain' consists of imperfections or inhomogeneities in a polymer sample which are revealed by crazing. Robertson[49] has suggested that glassy polymers consist of randomly oriented regions inside of which an imperfect alignment of chains exists; that the average length of such a 'domain' is of the order of 100 Å; and that the elemental step in craze growth may be the opening up of a void in a 'domain' (*see* pp. 15–25).

The role of an organic crazing agent is further complicated by the differential expansion of the sample due to swelling. Rosen[50] explains that in order to reach swelling or solubility equilibrium, an organic glass must frequently undergo a large expansion to accommodate the vapour or liquid. Since this pronounced swelling is at first restrained by the glassy film, the rate of solvent sorbed is often largely controlled by the stress relaxation of this macromolecular medium rather than being controlled by simple diffusion. As the film begins to absorb vapour or liquid at its surface, the initial resistance to the localised osmotic swelling creates severe compressions acting along the planes of the surface. This initial swelling occurs perpendicular to the surface with an increase in the film thickness. This condition is obtained even at the expense of introducing long range macromolecular orientation near the surfaces during this, partly irrecoverable, tensile strain.

Thus the vapour or liquid sorption must initially be retarded in awaiting these viscous adjustments. As the film absorbs more vapour, it undergoes a belated, osmotically forced area extension which aggravates the biaxial tensions acting in the plane of the film at the central core. This internal tension can be severe enough to cause internal fracture or crazing. During this abrupt area expansion, the film absorbs solvent at a very high rate and a tensile, strain-enhanced diffusion takes place. After the glass reaches swelling equilibrium, an abrupt removal of vapour or liquid from the atmosphere initiates an over-rapid desorption of solvent from the film. This initial vapour desorption creates a severe tension at the film surfaces. Even biaxial, tensile stress crazing can result at the surface from this severe condition.[50]

One theory that attempts to rationalise solvent crazing holds that the organic agent acts as a plasticiser.[39] Originally it was suspected that solvent crazing occurred when the combination of stress and plasticiser lowered the polymer T_g to ambient temperature. Because of our present knowledge of the structure and mechanical properties of crazes and because of current concepts about flow in the glassy state under stress, a modern casting of this hypothesis would be that limited plasticisation lowers T_g to a degree, and application of sufficient stress promotes a liquid-like flow of the glass in the stress direction (see Ch. 5). Lowering T_g depends directly on plasticiser concentration. Bernier and Kambour[39] attempted to measure the lowered T_g of a poly(phenyleneoxide) film containing several organic agents and compare this with the critical strain necessary to induce crazing. Solvents with a high equilibrium volume solubility acted as cracking agents rather than crazing agents. They concluded that most small organic molecules act as plasticisers in reducing resistance to craze formation in poly(phenyleneoxide).

In the same articles, Kambour and Bernier found that even liquids of negligible solubility in the polymer increased the crazing tendency. They suggested that these liquids act by reducing the surface energy of the holes in the craze, making the craze formation easier. This theory was first made by analogy with certain effects in inorganic systems and now exists in the

TABLE 1

THE EFFECT OF n-PENTANE ACTIVITY ON THE MODE OF TRANSPORT AND THE MAGNITUDE OF THE ACTIVATION ENERGY ASSOCIATED WITH THE RATE DETERMINING PROCESS IN BIAXIALLY ORIENTED POLYSTYRENE

Activity of n-pentane P/P_0	Form of kinetics	E_{act} (kcal/g mol)
1·0	Case II: relaxation controlled sorption accompanied by crazing	57
0·63	Case II: relaxation controlled sorption only	28
Approaching zero	Fickian diffusion	5·6

form stated by Bernier and Kambour. Hopfenberg *et al.*[31,32] hold that solvent crazing and some forms of environmental stress cracking are a simple extension of relaxation controlled, or Case II, transport. If the summation of stresses generated at the boundary between swollen and unswollen polymer reaches a sufficient level, over and above the stresses associated with the rate-determining relaxations controlling sorption, then crazing accompanies the Case II sorption process. (*See* Table 1.)

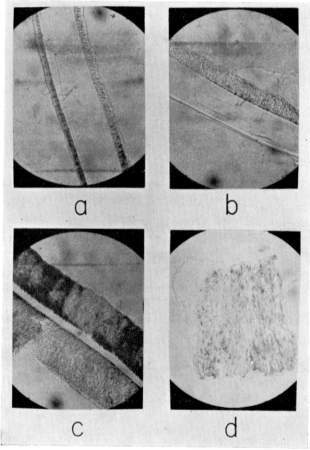

Fig. 12. *Photomicrographs* (× 170) *of crazed cross-sections of biaxially oriented film which has been immersed in* n-*heptane for various times and temperatures.*[40] (*a*) *treated on both sides at* 35°C *for* 20 *min ;* (*b*) *treated one side at* 40°C *for* 15 *min ;* (*c*) *treated both sides at* 35°C *for* 92 *min;* (*d*) *treated on both sides at* 40°C *for* 25 *min.* (*Reproduced with permission of John Wiley and Sons Inc.*)

They noted a sharp boundary between the crazed outer surfaces and the unaffected central core advancing with a constant velocity through a film. Photomicrographs of cross-sections of crazed samples are presented in Fig. 12. A study of the temperature dependence of this process revealed an apparent activation energy of approximately 60 kcal/g mol, which is in the range of activation energies for stress relaxation of polystyrene and well above that for a normal diffusion process. More importantly, this activation energy is sufficiently high to be consistent with primary bond breakage and therefore with free-radical formation at the advancing penetrant front, although no significant evidence for such a process has been published. It was concluded that the rate-controlling step of this transport process is the osmotically induced relaxation of the polymer at the boundary between the crazed outer layers and the unaffected central core. Diffusion to the boundary is rapid and does not affect the observed transport kinetics. If the stresses exerted are large enough to bias a relaxation but not polymer failure then transport of penetrant is limited by polymeric relaxations and the sample remains craze-free.

In summary, it should be re-emphasised that because of the complex nature of stress crazing, drastic changes in behaviour may be observed depending upon subtle changes in (a) test conditions, *e.g.* rate of strain, type of strain, temperature, activity of liquids, and vapours present, and physicochemical properties of penetrants; (b) sample history, *e.g.* pre-orientation, annealing procedures; and (c) secondary structural variables, *e.g.* molecular weight, molecular weight distribution, branching, cross-linking, and crystallinity.[31,32,33]

9.5   SOME EFFECTS OF CRYSTALLINITY AND ORIENTATION ON THE TRANSPORT OF GASES AND VAPOURS IN GLASSY POLYMERS

9.5.1   Effect of crystallinity

Some effects of the degree of crystallinity on the sorption of gases in glassy polymers have been discussed in Section 9.2.2. It was found that, whereas for rubbery unoriented polyethylene the solubilities were directly proportional to the amorphous content, this relationship was not followed in glassy semicrystalline polyethylene terephthalate.[6] These discrepancies were satisfactorily explained by the dual theory of sorption, *i.e.* in holes and in molecular solution.

In more recent years it has been found that even in some samples of polyethylene and in polypropylene the simple proportionality between solubility and amorphous content did not hold. This was particularly true for oriented samples. Lasoski and Cobbs[51] on the other hand did find a simple linear relationship to hold for water sorption in unoriented polyethylene terephthalate and Nylon 6–10 films.

The effect of the degree of crystallinity on the diffusion of gases and vapours has been discussed in terms of the tortuosity or structural factor arising from the increased diffusive path length around the impermeable crystallites. A second factor has also been introduced, the chain immobilisation factor, to account for the restrictions on chain mobility due to the cross-linking effect of the crystallites. Thus

$$D = D^*\tau^{-1}\beta^{-1} \tag{55}$$

where τ is the tortuosity factor and β the chain immobilisation factor; D^* is the diffusion constant for the completely amorphous polymer.

These concepts were mainly applied to rubbery semicrystalline polyethylene and polypropylene. Michaels et al.[7] however, also examined glassy poly(ethyleneterephthalate) in the completely amorphous and semicrystalline forms. The tortuosity factor was found to be similar for many different gases, including helium, showing the absence of a chain immobilisation factor. Such a factor obviously loses its significance in the glassy state.

With an amorphous fraction of 0·58 the tortuosity factor was found to be 1·78 ± 0·41% within 95% confidence limits for helium, oxygen, argon, carbon dioxide, nitrogen and methane gases. These results are in agreement with those found for water vapour by Lasoski and Cobb in that the diffusivity was directly proportional to the amorphous content, i.e. $\tau \propto \alpha^{-1}$.

In contrast, with various polyethylenes τ was found to be equal to α^{-n} with n varying between 1·25 and 1·88. The data for helium agreed well with that reported previously by Jeschke and Stuart[52] and showed some evidence of diffusion through defects in the structure.

Lasoski and Cobbs[51] examined the water vapour sorption and permeability of glassy, unoriented poly(ethyleneterephthalate) and of Nylon 6–10. They found the solubilities for both systems were directly proportional to the amorphous content and the permeabilities were proportional to the square of the amorphous content. This implies, as mentioned earlier, that the tortuousity factors for water vapour were equal to the reciprocal of the amorphous content. Polyethylene showed no such simple relationship which is consistent with the results obtained with gas permeation.

9.5.2 The effect of orientation

Introduction

Orientation effects on transport properties in polymeric materials have been known for a considerable time. Perhaps textile chemists and colourists were the first to recognise that dye diffusion was substantially altered by the degree of orientation of the synthetic fibre being dyed. In the early days of synthetic fibres, when draw ratio and extrusion conditions were not held rigorously constant, dyed fabrics were often streaked as a result of the non-uniformity in draw ratio during fibre spinning. An even more quantitative observation made by the earlier dye chemists was the lack of dyeability of certain fibres that had been cold drawn to impart higher tensile strength by orientating the chains in the amorphous regions. They noted that dyeing times or dye concentrations had to be increased in order to obtain the same shade as obtained with the unorientated fibre; both are consistent with a lower rate of diffusion in the highly drawn fibre.

These earlier observations have in recent years been examined more carefully by several authors. For instance, Davis and Taylor[53] found that diffusion constants decreased considerably and the activation energies for diffusion increased greatly with increasing draw ratio for the sorption of dyes in Nylon 6–6. Takagi and Hittori[54] in experiments with Nylon 6 fibres, found there was an increase in the values of the diffusion constants followed by a considerable decrease, with increasing draw ratios; a corresponding decrease and increase in the activation energy was observed. In a subsequent paper, Takagi[55] described work with dye diffusion parallel and perpendicular to the fibre axis. It was shown that in the experiments perpendicular to the axis results similar to those observed earlier were found. In the parallel direction, however, the diffusion constants decreased, and the activation energies increased steadily with increasing draw ratio.

Although dye diffusion in microcrystalline polymers is drastically altered by uniaxial orientation owing to the large molecules involved, studies of simple molecules have also shown marked reductions in transport properties accompanying the drawing process. Bixler and Michaels,[56] for example, in their study using small organic molecules found a substantial decrease in the permeation rate at higher draw ratios (500 %) in the case of stretched polyolefins. Later, Michaels et al.[57] found similar trends with this system using atmospheric gases.

More recently Peterlin and his colleagues[58,59,60,61] found dramatic reductions in both the solubility and diffusivity of water and small organic molecules consequent to deep drawing of polyethylene. This was attributed to the change in morphology from the spherulitic to the fibrillar structures.[60]

Gases and water vapour

Studies on the effect of orientation on the transport of gases in glassy polymers are rare and, in general, the effects *per se* are small, as shown by the results of Morgan,[62] for example with oriented and unoriented polystyrene films. Two studies, however, show that large effects can be produced when submicroscopic voids and cracks are opened by the straining procedure. Vieth *et al.*[63] studied the effect of drawing amorphous poly(ethyleneterephthalate) films at 80°C (close to the glass temperature) on both the helium and oxygen permeabilities. During the drawing process the crystallinity increased from zero to a maximum of 30% at 300% elongation. The effect of the drawing was quite different with helium compared with oxygen. The helium permeability decreased steadily with drawing but with an overall reduction of less than one half. The corresponding activation energies also decreased by a similar factor. Since it is known[64] that gas solubilities in the polymer are hardly affected by the orientation itself, the small reductions can be explained mainly by the effects of the increased crystallinity. Thus the amorphous fraction decreases from 1·0 to 0·7 and the permeability should decrease by $(0·7)^2$ or 0·49 which is of the order of change actually found. The small reductions in activation energy probably indicate an increase in diffusion through imperfections as discussed earlier.[7,52]

The behaviour of oxygen is quite different and plots of the changes in the permeability and the corresponding activation energies are shown in Figs. 13 and 14. It can be seen that at moderate elongations large increases in permeability result, there is then a sharp decrease on further stretching until finally no further changes take place. The final permeabilities are, however, much higher than the initial value for the unstretched film. The corresponding activation energies show a marked decrease followed by a small increase and then a further increase. Within the experimental error, however, the activation energies can probably be said to remain constant after the initial large decrease.

The authors propose that two avenues for increased diffusion in drawn poly(ethyleneterephthalate) are developed, both of which are related to the crystalline phase: (1) an increase in microvoids and (2) channels or cracks which extend throughout the film. Although the permeation of oxygen in stretched poly(ethyleneterephthalate) is predominately through defects in the crystalline phase, helium permeation of this material was not as low as expected. In this system the permeation of helium is not thought to be strongly affected by voids and/or channels due to its small size and ability to diffuse easily through non-voided material.

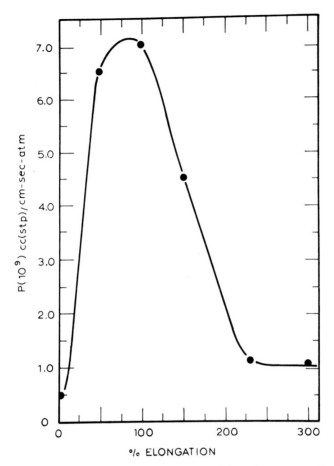

Fig. 13. *The effect of elongation on the permeability of oxygen in glassy poly-(ethyleneterephthalate).*[63] (*Reproduced with permission of the American Institute of Physics.*)

Rosen[65] carried out rather different experiments with glassy polystyrene films. By increasing the gas pressure on unsupported films in a permeability cell he was able to study the effect of biaxial strain. Whereas the permeability constants for the supported films did not change with pressure the unsupported films showed a considerable increase coupled with a decrease in the selectivity towards helium and nitrogen mixtures. The results were interpreted in terms of the development of invisible microcracks in the film. Interestingly the cracks healed on removing the pressure. Biaxially

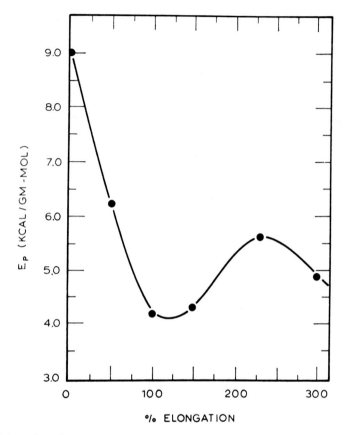

Fig. 14. *The effect of elongation on the activation energy for permeation of oxygen through poly(ethyleneterephthalate).*[63] (*Reproduced with permission of the American Institute of Physics.*)

oriented films showed slight haze development (annealed films did not) although both showed the same increase in permeability with pressure. Poly(methylmethacrylate) films showed similar effects but not poly-(ethyleneterephthalate) at the pressures used. Smaller but similar effects were found by McAfee[66] with pyrex inorganic glasses.

Lasoski and Cobbs[51] extended their work on the water vapour permeability of poly(ethyleneterephthalate) films to uniaxially and biaxially oriented samples. The crystallinity increased somewhat during the stretching process. It was found that at the same density the water vapour permeability was decreased similarly by either uniaxial or biaxial orientation. The effects were not large, however, with a maximum reduction of only about fifty per cent.

Organic vapours and liquids
The effects of orientation on the transport of organic vapours and liquids in glassy polymers have been investigated extensively compared with corresponding gas and water vapour studies. The reasons are that the effects are much greater and that the sorption is often accompanied by anomalies such as polymer relaxation, cracking, crazing, and other important and interesting phenomena.

Historically some of the earliest work appears to have been carried out by Hartley and his colleagues.[67-9] They pointed out that the diffusion of vapours into a two dimensionally restricted piece of polymer will result in the polymer molecules being oriented and extended in the direction of the diffusion. A number of ingenious optical experiments were devised to illustrate these effects. Hartley[69] also studied directly the effect of orientation on the rate of penetration of solvents by stretching cellulose acetate films and following the sorption optically. The oriented samples were penetrated up to 24 times faster than the unoriented films. Hartley suggested that the higher sorption rate was due at least partly to the greater transverse oscillation of the polymer chains contributing to the sorption process. Russell[70] studied the effect of orientation on the crazing of poly-(methylmethacrylate) sheets. Again rates of absorption were found to be many times greater in the oriented material. He showed that applying solvent to a sample under stress caused instantaneous crazing, for example. Since this early work there have been many more investigations, all indicating the increased rate of sorption into oriented glassy polymers. Some of these investigations will now be reviewed in chronological order.

Crank and Robinson[71] used the interferometric technique developed earlier by Robinson[72] to continue the studies of Hartley on the influence of concentration and orientation of solvent transport into cellulose acetate films. It was shown that the calculated diffusion coefficients were considerably less in the direction of stretch. Such effects are found also in the diffusion of dyestuffs into oriented fibres.[55]

Drechsel *et al.*[73] found that cellulose nitrate films cast on glass were anisotropic, compared with similar films cast on mercury, as evidenced from optical birefringence measurements. The rate of vapour uptake was much greater in the oriented films but decreased on successive sorption–desorption cycles. Optical anisotropy studies showed that the orientation of the polymer molecules normal to the film surface increased during the successive cycles presumably causing the decreased rates. Park[74] studied the sorption and desorption of methylene chloride into cellulose acetate and polystyrene films. Orientation was found to give small but significant increases in the rates of sorption. A theoretical analysis of these and other effects was presented by Crank.[30] Bagley and Long[75] found a two-stage sorption and desorption process for organic vapours in cellulose acetate. Again an increase in diffusivity with orientation was reported together with a decrease in diffusion rates due to molecular orientation being induced in the direction of diffusion. This latter effect was also shown with polystyrene films by Long and Kokes.[76] An interesting discussion of the role of severe compressive and tensile stresses generated in glassy films by the sorption and swelling process has been presented by Rosen.[77] It was shown that both acceleration and retardation of vapour transport can result from these effects.

Alfrey et al. in their classic paper of 1966 first pointed out the extreme non-Fickian behaviour of the sorption of many solvents in glassy polymers.[78] The significance of the dependence of the rate of the advancing front on time was first pointed out and the term Case II sorption was defined. The effect of the stresses induced by the swelling process was treated both experimentally and theoretically.

The authors and their colleagues also examined the effects of molecular weight and orientation on the sorption and desorption of alkanes into polystyrene films.[31,32,33]

They did not observe an effect of molecular weight per se or sorption kinetics; however, for samples that were incompletely annealed, films with higher molecular weight sorbed more rapidly. Completely annealed samples showed no effect of molecular weight. Presumably, for a given set of incomplete annealing conditions, the higher molecular weight samples are more internally strained giving rise to larger coupled stresses during relaxation controlled sorption.

The magnitude of the penetrant activity not only affects the rate of sorption but the relative contributions of Fickian diffusion and relaxation controlled transport. The penetrant activity, therefore, biases the effect of orientation on these processes. At low activities Fickian diffusion predominates and the effect of orientation on the Fickian diffusion rate is small. Conversely, at high activities where the transport is controlled by polymeric relaxations, the relaxation rate is a strong function of orientation which in turn strongly affects the rate of sorption.

More explicitly, the sorption rate increased monotonically with uniaxial

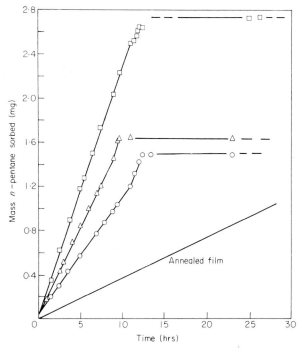

Fig. 15.   *Sorption of* n-*pentane in uniaxially oriented polystyrene films of molecular weight:* $M_w(M_w/M_n)$: 1 880 000 (1·65). [33]

	Optical	
Symbol	*Birefringence*	*Film mass, mg*
○	$-2·04 \times 10^{-3}$	13·10
Δ	$-2·54 \times 10^{-3}$	14·73
□	$-19·08 \times 10^{-3}$	22·37

(Reproduced with permission of the Society of Plastics Engineers Inc.)

orientation as determined by birefringence measurements as illustrated, for example, in Fig. 15. These results which are completely consistent with the observations of the many diverse, albeit related, systems studied suggest that the orientation stresses couple with the osmotically induced stresses (swelling stresses) to bias more rapid rate-determining relaxations in the oriented polymers.

ACKNOWLEDGEMENTS

The contributions of our colleagues: Mr R. L. Stallings, Mr C. J. Smith, Mr C. H. M. Jacques, M. J. West, and Mr L. D. Lineback, are sincerely appreciated. We would also like to thank Professor D. R. Paul for his helpful review of this chapter.

REFERENCES

1. Graham, T. (1866). *Phil. Mag.*, **32**, 401.
2. Meares, P. (1954). *J. Am. Chem. Soc.*, **76**, 3415–22.
3. Meares, P. (1957). *Trans. Faraday Soc.*, **53**, 101–6.
4. Meares, P. (1958). *Trans. Faraday Soc.*, **54**, 40–6.
5. Barrer, R., Barrie, J. and Slater, J. (1957). *J. Polymer Sci.*, **23**, 315.
6. Michaels, A., Vieth, W. and Barrie, J. (1963). *J. Appl. Phys.*, **34**(1), 1.
7. Michaels, A., Vieth, W. and Barrie, J. (1963). *J. Appl. Phys.*, **34**(1), 13.
8. Vieth, W., Tam, P. and Michaels, A. (1966). *J. Colloid and Interface Sci.*, **22**, 360–70.
9. Myers, A. W., Rogers, C. E., Stannett, V. and Szwarc, M. (1958). *Tappi*, **41**, 716.
10. Michaels, A. and Parker, R. (1959). *J. Polymer Sci.*, **41**, 54–71.
11. Michaels, A. and Bixler, H. (1961). *J. Polymer Sci.*, **50**, 413–39.
12. Vieth, W. and Sladek, K. (1965). *J. Colloid Sci.*, **20**, 1014–33.
13. Paul, D. R. (1969). *J. Polymer Sci.*, A2, **7**, 1811–8.
14. Petropoulos, J. (1970). *J. Polymer Sci.*, A2, **8**, 1797–801.
15. Kemp, D. R. (1972). Ph.D. Dissertation, University of Texas at Austin.
16. Paul, D. R. and Kemp, D. R. (1972). *ACS Polymer Preprints*, **13** (No. 2) in press.
17. Ryskin, G. Y. (1954). *Zhur. Tekh. Fiz*, **24**, 197
18. Kumins, C. A., Rolle, C. J. and Roteman, J. (1957). *J. Phys. Chem.*, **61**, 1290.
19. Barrer, R. M., Mallinder, R. and Wong, P. S. L. (1967). *Polymer*, **8**, 321.
20. Kumins, C. A. and Roteman, J. (1961). *J. Polymer Sci.*, **55**, 683.
21. Stannett, V. and Williams, J. L. (1965). *J. Polymer Sci.*, **C10**, 45.
22. Tikhomirov, B. P., Hopfenberg, H. B., Stannett, V. T. and Williams, J. L. (1968). *Macromol. Chemie.*, **118**, 177.
23. Burgess, W. H., Hopfenberg, H. B. and Stannett, V. T. (1971). *J. Macromol. Sci.*, **B5**, 23.
24. Alfrey, T. (1965). *Chem. and Eng. News*, **43**, 64.
25. Kwei, T. K. and Zupko, H. M. (1969). *J. Polymer Sci.*, A2, **7**, 867.
26. Frisch, H. L., Wang, T. T. and Kwei, T. K. (1969). *J. Polymer Sci.*, A2, **7**, 879.
27. Hopfenberg, H. B., Holley, R. H. and Stannett, V. T. (1969). *Polymer Eng. and Sci.*, **9**, 242.
28. Hopfenberg, H. B. and Frisch, H. L. (1969). *J. Polymer Sci.*, **B7**, 405.
29. King, G. (1945). *Trans. Faraday Soc.*, **41**, 325.
30. Crank, J. (1953). *J. Polymer Sci.*, **11**, 151.
31. Hopfenberg, H. B., Holley, R. H. and Stannett, V. T. (1970). *Polymer Eng. and Sci.*, **10**, 376.
32. Bray, J. and Hopfenberg, H. B. (1969). *J. Polymer Sci.*, **B7**, 679.
33. Baird, B. R., Hopfenberg, H. B. and Stannett, V. T. (1971). *Polymer Eng. and Sci.*, **11**, 274.
34. Peterlin, A. (1969). *Makromol. Chemie*, **124**, 136.
35. Kambour, R. P. (1968). *Applied Polymer Symposia*, **7**, 215.
36. Holley, R. H. (1969). Ph.D. Thesis, N.C. State University.
37. Kambour, R. P. (1966). *J. Polymer Sci.*, A2, **4**(1), 17.
38. Rudd, J. F. (1963). *J. Polymer Sci.*, **B1**, 1.
39. Bernier, G. A. and Kambour, R. P. (1968). *Macromolecules*, **1**, 393.
40. Michaels, A. S., Bixler, H. J. and Hopfenberg, H. B. (1968). *J. Appl. Poly. Sci.*, **12**, 991.

41. Kambour, R. P. (1968). *Polymer Eng. and Sci.*, **8**, 281.
42. Kambour, R. P. (1969). *J. Polymer Sci.*, A2, **7**, 1393.
43. Kambour, R. P. (1964). *Polymer*, **5**, 107.
44. Kambour, R. P. (1964). *J. Polymer Sci.*, A2, 4159.
45. Kambour, R. P. (1968). *Applied Polymer Symposia*, **7**, 215.
46. Kambour, R. P. (1963). *J. Polymer Sci.*, A2, **7**, 1393.
47. Berry, J. P. (1961). *J. Polymer Sci.*, **50**, 107, 313.
48. Nielsen, L. E. (1959). *J. Polymer Sci.*, **1**, 27.
49. Robertson, R. E. (1965). *J. Phys. Chem.*, **69**, 1575.
50. Rosen, B. J. (1961). *J. Polymer Sci.*, **49**, 177.
51. Lasoski, S. W. and Cobbs, W. H. (1959). *J. Polymer Sci.*, **36**, 21.
52. Jeschke, D. and Stuart, H. (1961). *Z. Naturforsch.*, **16**, 37.
53. Davies, G. and Taylor, H. (1965). *Text. Res. J.*, **35**, 405.
54. Takagi, Y. and Hittori, H. (1965). *J. Appl. Polymer Sci.*, **9**, 2167.
55. Takagi. Y. (1965). *J. Appl. Polymer Sci.*, **9**, 3887.
56. Bixler, H. and Michaels, A. S. (1964). Paper presented at 53rd Natl. Meeting AIChE, Pittsburg, Pa.
57. Michaels, A. S., Vieth, W. R. and Bixler, H. (1964). *J. Appl. Polymer Sci.*, **8**, 2735.
58. Peterlin, A. and Olf, H. G. (1966). *J. Polymer Sci.*, A2, **4**, 587.
59. Peterlin, A., Williams, J. L. and Stannett, V. (1967). *J. Polymer Sci.*, A2, **5**, 957.
60. Williams, J. L. and Peterlin, A. (1971). *J. Polymer Sci.*, A2, **9**, 1483.
61. Willams, J. L. and Peterlin, A. (1970). *Die Makromol. Chemie*, **135**, 41.
62. Morgan, P. W. (1943). *Ind. Eng. Chem.*, **44**, 2296.
63. Vieth, W. R., Matulevicius, E. S. and Mitchell, S. R. (1967). *Koll. Z.*, **220**, 49.
64. Vieth. W. R., Acalay, H. and Frabetti, A. (1964). *J. Appl. Poly. Sci.*, **8**, 2125.
65. Rosen, B. (1960). *J. Polymer Sci.*, **47**, 19.
66. McAfee, K. B. (1958). *J. Chem. Phys.*, **28**, 218, 226.
67. Hartley, G. S. (1946). *Trans. Faraday Soc.*, **42B**, 6.
68. Robinson, C. (1946). *Trans. Faraday Soc.*, **42B**, 12.
69. Hartley, G. S. (1949). *Trans. Faraday Soc.*, **45**, 820.
70. Russell, E. W. (1950). *Nature*, **165**, 91.
71. Crank, J. and Robinson, C. (1950). *Proc. Roy. Soc.*, **A204**, 549.
72. Robinson, C. (1950). *Proc. Roy. Soc.*, **A204**, 339.
73. Drechsel, P., Hoard, J. L. and Long, F. A. (1953). *J. Polymer Sci.*, **10**, 241.
74. Park, G. S. (1953). *J. Polymer Sci.*, **11**, 97.
75. Bagley, E. and Long, F. A. (1955). *J. Am. Chem. Soc.*, **77**, 2172.
76. Long, F. A. and Kokes, R. J. (1953). *J. Am. Chem. Soc.*, **75**, 2232.
77. Rosen, B. (1961). *J. Polymer Sci.*, **49**, 177.
78. Alfrey, T., Gurnee, E. F. and Lloyd, W. G. (1966). *J. Polymer Sci.*, **C12**, 249.

CHAPTER 10

THE MORPHOLOGY OF REGULAR BLOCK COPOLYMERS

M. J. FOLKES AND A. KELLER

10.1 INTRODUCTION

10.1.1 General

It is general knowledge that polymeric materials exhibit a wide range of properties. Thus they can display the properties of a viscous liquid or that of a glass according to temperature (and at a given temperature, according to the time scale of the test). In between these two extremes lies perhaps the most typical macromolecular property of all: the rubbery behaviour characterised by low modulus but very high, recoverable extensibility. These are all properties characteristic of amorphous polymers. To these can be added properties associated with crystalline materials in cases where the polymer is intrinsically capable of crystallising and is given a chance to do so.

Often a particular combination of such properties is desirable. As different polymers exhibit a particular behaviour at different temperatures the possibility arises of obtaining the desired effect by mixing appropriately chosen polymers. However, it is intrinsic to polymeric systems that they are mutually incompatible and thus will defeat attempts at intimate mixing; in fact the different constituents will segregate. Nevertheless, limited mixing can be assured if a whole chain molecule of one species is linked chemically to another. Composite chains of this kind are termed block co-polymers. It will be apparent that combinations achievable in this way are unlimited. In the simplest case, a block copolymer may consist of only two components of two different species (two-block copolymers). Nevertheless, blocks of the same two species can repeat along a given chain forming more complex sequences, and, further, more than two kinds of units can serve as blocks. Except for a few isolated instances of higher block numbers, in practice, the three-block system is usually not exceeded in the controlled building of such composite chains, that is in cases where all composite chains have the same block sequence. Higher block sequences are common in 'random block copolymers' where blocks of the different constituents follow each other in random sequence and consequently also the different chains will have different compositions as determined by random statistics. It will be stated at the onset that such random block copolymers are outside the scope of the present survey: the systems to be reviewed here will contain uniform block sequences throughout, where the composition of the molecules is limited to a very few blocks. (For the method of synthesis of such materials *see* Finaz *et al.*[1]; Morton and Fetters.[2])

The following three examples will illustrate some typical systems under consideration

$$\left[CH_2\!\!-\!\!CH\!\!- \right]_m - \left[CH_2\!\!-\!\!CH = CH\!\!-\!\!CH_2 \right]_n$$

polystyrene (S)   polybutadiene (B)

Schematically

S   B

Similarly   S–B–S   and   B–S–B

S   B   S   B   S   B

Of these and similar other systems more will be said later.

The notation shown in Table 1 is used in this review for the particular copolymer systems under discussion.

TABLE 1

Polystyrene–polybutadiene–polystyrene	S–B–S
Polystyrene–polybutadiene	S–B
Polybutadiene–polystyrene–polybutadiene	B–S–B
Polystyrene–polyisoprene–polystyrene	S–I–S
Polystyrene–polyoxyethylene	S–OE
Polyoxypropylene–polyoxyethylene	OP–OE
Polystyrene–polyvinyl 1-2 pyridine	S–V2P
Polystyrene–polyvinyl 1-4 pyridine	S–V4P
Polyvinyl 1-2 pyridine–polyvinyl 1-4 pyridine	V2P–V4P

10.1.2   Microphase separation

The incompatibility of most polymers pertains not only to macroscopic mixtures but also to the individual blocks of the copolymers. As here the components are chemically linked, phase segregation can only occur on a microscale, which for the usual systems studied is typically in the order of a hundred or a few hundred angstroms. As will be reviewed in some detail the segregated microphases can be of three kinds: they can be spheres, cylinders or lamellae (*e.g.* Sadron[3]).

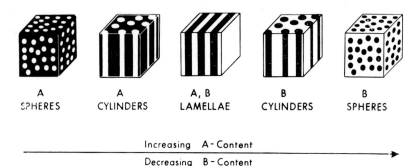

A	A	A, B	B	B
SPHERES	CYLINDERS	LAMELLAE	CYLINDERS	SPHERES

Increasing   A - Content

Decreasing   B - Content

Fig. 1.   *Schematic representation of the dependence of block copolymer morphology on the volume fraction of the blocks. A and B denote the two chemical species forming the molecule without reference to a particular system (B should not be identified with polybutadiene in the present figure and whenever A–B combinations feature in the text).*[66]

The way in which a sample containing such a micro two-phase structure combines the properties of the individual constituents can be illustrated for the case of the polystyrene–polybutadiene systems introduced above. At room temperature the S phase is a glass while the B phase is a rubber. If for example the S phase is the dispersed phase in a B matrix (*see* Fig. 1) the sample will behave as a rubber reinforced by a finely divided glassy constituent. In this respect the sample will be like a typical composite. There is, nevertheless, an additional feature which makes such a block copolymer unique amongst composites. This is the molecular connection between the phases which not only ensures perfect adhesion between the different phases, a usual problem with composites, but that *each* long chain molecule in one phase is molecularly connected with the second phase. In the above case of a glassy S phase dispersed in a rubbery B phase this means that the glassy particles act as cross-links for the rubbery matrix material. Cross-linking is an important requirement for elastomers in order to prevent creep and thus enable elastic deformations to be maintained over long times. In most rubbers this is achieved by chemical cross-linking (vulcanisation). However, such chemical cross-linking is irreversible and sets the sample in a permanent shape. This is not the case for cross-links provided by the glassy particles. If heated beyond the glass-transition temperature the dispersed particles, even if they persist (*see* later), become rubbery or liquid themselves and they cease to prevent flow of the material. Thus the sample can be moulded in new shapes. On cooling, the original behaviour characteristic of a cross-linked elastomer is regained. Thus in final analysis we have a mouldable rubber. For this reason the systems under review are often referred to as thermoelastomers.

The above example should be sufficient to illustrate the great intrinsic potential of these systems in the quest for new materials with specific properties and of the role played by the microphases. It is the shape, size and arrangement of these microphases and the origin of these composite structures which will be the subject of the present review.

At this point the subject matter will be circumscribed further. The segregated microphases are often not randomly arranged but tend to form regular patterns. In fact in case of sufficient molecular uniformity the particles of the dispersed phase give rise to a fully periodic structure, a kind of macro-lattice, where the repeating elements are not atoms or molecules but the submicroscopic particles. Thus spheres give rise to cubic lattices while cylinders arrange themselves in a two dimensional hexagonal lattice. When the structure is lamellar the tendency is to form a regularly repeating lamellar sequence. (It is to be noted that crystallinity is not, or need not be, involved; the lattice can be formed by a periodic arrangement of amorphous microphases.) The present review will be confined to block copolymers exhibiting such a regular arrangement of the microphases.

10.2   TECHNIQUES USED FOR THE STUDY OF THE MORPHOLOGY OF BLOCK COPOLYMERS

The nature of the structures involved clearly points to the most profitable methods for their study. As already stated the structural elements are of the order of several hundred angstroms. The study of structures on this scale obviously calls for electron microscopy. On the other hand the structures are arranged periodically which calls for a diffraction method, and this in view of the scale of the periodicity is X-ray scattering at low angles. In fact, here we have a situation unique in structure studies where direct imaging of the structures and the analysis of the diffraction effects they give rise to are closely combined. This combination will be the central theme around which the present survey will be built.

In ultimate generality the full information on the structural features in question can only come from direct viewing, which in the present case is by electron microscopy. On the other hand, information provided by low angle X-ray scattering is always an average property from which singular features cannot be readily extracted. Nevertheless, diffraction information by its averaging nature can be more representative of the sample as a whole. A practical difference between the two techniques is that direct viewing by electron microscopy requires special sample preparation with all this entails, while scattering techniques can be applied to samples as they are. In the present case this means, amongst others, that liquid or swollen systems cannot be studied by electron microscopy, at least not without some circumvention of the problem, while they can by low angle X-ray scattering. This particular point, more than any other, determined the historical sequence of the development of the subject: namely that the first examinations were confined essentially to low angle X-ray scattering by which method the salient characteristics of the systems were established. Confirmation by electron microscopy together with much new information followed subsequently.

10.2.1   Low angle X-ray scattering (see also Section 2.5)

The application of low angle X-ray scattering for the study of regular microstructures originates from the Strasbourg school and stems from two preceding developments in the same Institute. One of these is the organic synthesis leading to the block copolymers such as produce phase separation on the scale and with the regularity in question.[1] The other is the extensive work on soap gels. It was recognised that amongst other more complicated possibilities, the soap molecules take up lamellar, cylindrical and spherical states of aggregation which themselves give rise to a mesomorphic structure, by forming regular, one, two or three dimensionally periodic sequences.[4, 5] These very same forms and their modes of arrangement were subsequently recognised in the block copolymers presently under review. The conclusions in the soap work were reached by low angle X-ray scattering. Consequently, when the block copolymers came into the forefront little more was required than to apply the X-ray analytical procedure already adopted in the study of soaps.

The principal X-ray scattering phenomenon is the existence of one or several sharply defined reflexions at low angles. This means that there is an underlying periodic structure which is on an appropriately large scale (typically in the range of several hundred angstroms) to produce the scattering effects at the small angles in question. The spacings then follow from Bragg's law. In the works on soaps, and with the exceptions of some quite recent developments, in all subsequent studies on block copolymers this periodicity was randomly oriented on the scale of the X-ray beam used, giving rise to Debye–Scherrer rings (or their smeared out equivalents obtained with the most frequently used slit collimated beams). In order to extract further information the following two features were utilised: (a) the ratio of the spacings manifest in a given system, (b) the relative intensities of the reflexions. Both procedures have been developed by Luzatti et al.[4] and Husson et al.[5] in connection with the soaps.

(a) When proceeding to increasing diffraction angles the spacings of consecutive orders were found to form certain systematic sequences. These are:

$$1:\tfrac{1}{2}:\tfrac{1}{3}:\tfrac{1}{4}$$

Such a sequence is consistent with a regularly periodic arrangement of parallel lamellae of infinite lateral extension.

$$1:1/(3)^{\frac{1}{2}}:1/(4)^{\frac{1}{2}}:1/(7)^{\frac{1}{2}}$$

This sequence of spacing ratios is consistent with a regular hexagonal arrangement of cylinders of infinite length.

$$1:(3)^{\frac{1}{2}}/(4)^{\frac{1}{2}}:(3)^{\frac{1}{2}}/(8)^{\frac{1}{2}}:(3)^{\frac{1}{2}}/(11)^{\frac{1}{2}}$$

This sequence corresponds to the ratios of consecutive (111, 200, 220, 311) spacings in a face centred cubic lattice and is therefore consistent with the existence of spheres packed in this manner. We add for completeness the spacing ratios.

$$1:1/(2)^{\frac{1}{2}}:1/(3)^{\frac{1}{2}}:1/(4)^{\frac{1}{2}}$$

for simple cubic and

$$1:(2)^{\frac{1}{2}}/(4)^{\frac{1}{2}}:(2)^{\frac{1}{2}}/(6)^{\frac{1}{2}}:(2)^{\frac{1}{2}}/(8)^{\frac{1}{2}}$$

for body centred cubic lattices which in themselves do not feature in Luzatti et al.[4] but will nevertheless be referred to later.

(b) The above spacings only define the overall periodicity and do not give information on how the periodicity is subdivided into its individual constituents. Thus in the case of platelets it does not say how thick is the platelet and the intervening space separately (or how thick is each of the two alternating platelets if the structure is regarded morphologically as composed of two sets of platelets). Similarly, in the case of cylindrical and spherical structures, the Bragg spacings themselves do not tell us anything about the diameter of the individual cylinders or spheres. In principle this information is obtainable from the relative intensities of the reflexions by the following considerations: The scattered intensity is the squared product of the lattice and structure factors. If the lattice extension is sufficient the lattice factor actually samples the structure factor at the reciprocal lattice points. Thus if at the appropriate reciprocal lattice point the structure factor is small or zero, the corresponding reflexion is weak or absent; conversely if the structure factor is large the reflexion will be strong.

The structure factor involved is the repeating unit, *i.e.* the unit cell. In the simple case that the cell is primitive this will comprise only one scattering unit. To take a concrete case, in a hexagonal arrangement of cylinders the relevant unit is a single cylinder. The structure factor, *i.e.* the transform of a single cylinder is familiar: it is a first order Bessel function with periodic maxima and minima in reciprocal space, the positions of which are determined by the cylinder diameter. Thus the absence or pronounced weakening of a particular order gives direct information about the cylinder diameter practically by inspection. A more accurate procedure is to match all the observed intensities with the structure factor which is calculated for different cylinder diameters. The same principles apply to platelet and spherical morphologies, in the latter case if the structure is primitive. (For other than simple cubic structures the contribution of all spheres contained by the unit cell need to be considered in the appropriate phase relation.)

The platelet, cylinder or sphere sizes can also be arrived at by calculation from the spacing value alone if the composition of the system (block ratios, solvent content if any) is known and the macroscopic values for the respective specific volumes are assumed to hold also for the finely dispersed states in question. This is the most frequently adopted method in the literature. The formulae giving the required quantities for platelets, cylinders and spheres are contained in Luzzati *et al.*[4] as being related to soaps. They are applied first to the copolymer problem by Skoulios and Finaz.[6] In addition to giving the dimensions of the domains they also express the mean cross-sectional area available for a molecule in the dispersed phase at the phase boundary. Of course such calculations do not represent independent determinations such as provided by the analysis of the intensities.

Everything said so far has referred to random diffraction patterns (rings). Under special circumstances orientated patterns can also arise. The orientation in the crystal domains can arise by deliberate deformation or by the method of sample preparation leading to preferential textures (*e.g.* Charrier and Ranchoux[7]). The extreme limit of a preferred texture is the true single crystal. Indeed under certain conditions such single crystals constituted by the ordered arrangement of segregated microphases could be obtained.[8] Here, the low angle pattern consists of individual spot-like reflexions forming a reciprocal net. Owing to the flatness of the sphere of reflexion in the low angle region, in such cases considerable portions of a given reciprocal lattice net plane are directly mapped. Common to all diffraction studies, as the randomness of the diffraction pattern decreases its informative value is correspondingly enhanced. In the extreme case of an appropriately orientated single crystal, the lattice can be directly displayed by the diffraction pattern in its most informative projection from which the corresponding structure unit (*e.g.* cylinders in the case of a hexagonal lattice) can be immediately inferred.

10.2.2 Electron microscopy
In order to benefit from the intrinsic potential of electron microscopy, the limitations imposed by special sample requirements have to be overcome. For the present application to copolymers these are of two kinds. The first is that in order to directly view one phase in a matrix composed of the other, sufficient contrast between the two phases needs creating. This was achieved by a technique due to Kato[9] in which the sample is stained in osmium tetroxide vapour. Since osmium reacts with the double bond of polybutadiene, but not polystyrene, only the rubbery phase becomes stained, appearing black when viewed by transmission.

The second requirement is that the sample is sufficiently thin for the structure to be observed under transmission microscopy. (Replication techniques cannot usually be used.) For electron microscopic purposes the sample thickness must be of the order of 10^2–10^3 Å. Samples of this type can in general be obtained by one of the following methods: (i) Solvent casting from a solution of the copolymer to yield a film of the required thickness. (ii) Sectioning, using ultramicrotomy, from either solvent cast films that are too thick for transmission microscopy *or* from the massive material as obtained, *e.g.* by moulding or extrusion. It is clearly essential that the material to be sectioned is inherently rigid. This implies that material containing a diluent cannot be studied as such, unless the diluent can be hardened.

Solvent casting has, in general, been the most popular method of thin-film preparation. Irrespective of whether the film is prepared directly or by sectioning, it has been found that the resulting morphology is strongly influenced by the method of film preparation. Thus the degree of perfection of the microphase ordering in the matrix phase can depend on the solvent used and on its rate of evaporation—*see* for example Lewis and Price,[10,11] Matsuo,[12] Douy and Gallot.[13] Matsuo has found that solvents which are preferential to the dispersed phase tend to lead to irregular structures although evidence to the contrary has been reported by Douy and Gallot.[14] Sample annealing after preparation can lead to improved long-range ordering of the microphases.

Directly preparing a film for electron microscopy limits observations to one projection through the film only.[10,11,15,16,17] Conclusions drawn from a single observation can sometimes be ambiguous unless statistically some other projection of the morphology arises in the same film, or projected areas of the dispersed phase are calculated and compared with the known sample stoichiometry.[18]

It is therefore preferable, where possible, to take bidirectional sections from either thick solvent-cast films or moulded material. Sectioning of copolymer samples is not straightforward due to the rubbery consistency of the matrix at ambient temperatures. The usual technique of ultramicrotomy cannot be employed unless the sample rigidity is increased. This can be carried out either by hardening the matrix material, *e.g.* by prolonged exposure to osmium tetroxide—due to Kato[9]—or by sample cooling.[19,20] In the latter case, cooling to liquid air temperatures is necessary, not only to achieve the required rigidity but to minimise disruption of the sample morphology during sectioning.

All of this discussion presupposes that the original material is free of diluent. However, it is known that the presence of a preferential solvent can induce morphological changes in the dispersed phase. This can be of considerable value in achieving structures which cannot readily be obtained by other means. Sectioning of such material can now be achieved by using a swelling agent which is polymerisable. Here the diluent is introduced into the copolymer to achieve a desired morphology. The diluent is then polymerised, which preserves the structure and then enables ultramicrotomy to be carried out as described earlier.[34]

The definiteness of the results obtained using sectioning techniques depends on the range of the local ordering of the microphases. Thus, if the samples to be sectioned are 'polycrystalline' then, unless a direction or surface of the sample exists which is sufficiently unique to act as a reference, sectioning will be a random process, However, if a series of random sections are taken, they will sample on purely statistical grounds a range of projections of the fundamental structure which can lead to definite conclusions.[21,22]

In the case of solvent-cast films, the film surface may serve as a reference plane so that two sections, one parallel and one perpendicular to the film plane, are sufficient to establish the structure. This assumes either that this structure exists in the same orientation with respect to the film surface throughout the whole film or that the two sections are cut across the same aggregate if the film is polycrystalline.[12,23,19]

For sections cut from moulded samples the reference direction can in some cases be related to the fabrication conditions, e.g. in compression moulded samples to the direction of the flow lines. In the special case of extruded SBS material mentioned in Section 10.2.1, where the macro-lattice extends over macroscopic sample dimensions in a well-defined relation to the extrusion direction, the microphase structure can be studied along any preselected viewing direction by appropriately choosing the plane of sectioning.

10.2.3 Other techniques

Besides the two principal techniques some others have also been employed, rather in a subsidiary role from the point of view of this review. Such are (i) polarising microscopy, (ii) light scattering (iii) infra-red spectroscopy (iv) differential calorimetry (v) mechanical tests.

(i) Polarising microscopy has been used in two contexts (a) for direct observation of images between crossed polaroids (b) for measurement of birefringence. (a) Microscopically distinguishable textures are usually seen in block copolymer systems when they contain large amounts of liquid.[6,24] The textures are similar to those displayed by mesomorphic systems, such as liquid crystals. They can be symptomatic of particular states of microphases and of their aggregation and thus are of diagnostic value. (b) Birefringence should clearly provide a measure of molecular orientation. This has been usefully applied only in such special instances when the sample as a whole contained a uniformly oriented macrolattice, in which case the observed optical anisotropy could be attributed to form birefringence at the exclusion of molecular orientation.[53] Birefringence measurements were also used in the study of deformation behaviour.[25]

(ii) Light scattering has been applied to the study of inhomogeneities in block copolymer structures rather in an analogous manner as done for spherulitic crystalline polymers. It is particularly suited to provide information on microscopic domain structures as opposed to the microphases themselves.[26,27]

(iii) Infra-red spectroscopy has been used analytically to distinguish random copolymers from block copolymers.[16] Further, infra-red dichroism provides a measurement of molecular orientation in a manner analogous to birefringence except that it also gives information about the individual components. Again this could be utilised in case of textures which are uniform over macroscopic samples areas.[28]

(iv) Differential calorimetry has been used to supplement the X-ray studies in detecting phase transitions in the exploration of the phase diagram.[29]

(v) Measurement of mechanical modulus and loss factors are of course amongst the principal objectives in the characterisation of mechanical behaviour which is a subject of its own. Here they are invoked only in the limited context that they serve to detect transitions in the microphases as a function of temperature. As these transitions were found to be at temperatures which correspond closely to those of the pure homopolymers they can serve to identify phase segregation.[16]

10.3   VARIABLES CONTROLLING THE MORPHOLOGY

10.3.1   Chemical variables

These include (i) the chemical nature of the blocks, (ii) the type of block structure, (iii) the block length ratios, (iv) the length of the individual blocks.

(i) *Chemical nature of the blocks.* The importance of this factor is self evident as it defines the chemical identity of the materials. While in principle any polymerisable material can be used in practically any combination, the ones usually studied consits of two chemical species (*A* and *B*) where the most widely used ones contain polystyrene and polybutadiene in various combinations (*see* Section 10.1.1).

(ii) *Type of block structure.* This relates to the issue of whether the chains consist of two or three blocks, *i.e.* whether they are *AB* or *ABA* or alternatively *BAB* types. As will be apparent from this survey there are no differences in principle between two and three blocks, or for that matter higher block numbers in those few instances for which such information is available, as far as the main morphological features are concerned.

(iii) *Ratio of block lengths.* In the first instance this determines which is the dispersed and which is the matrix phase. As to be expected, the component which is present in larger overall proportions (expressed by the block ratio) will always be the matrix phase. As will be quoted individually later it has emerged gradually that for the most disparate compositions the dispersed phase is in the form of spheres; for more closely similar but still unequal proportions it is in the form of cylinders. In both cases the matrix becomes the dispersed phase as the ratios are reversed. In the case of comparable compositions the structure is lamellar when there is no distinction between matrix and dispersed phases. The full sequence is shown schematically by Fig. 1.

(iv) *The length of the blocks for a given block length ratio.* This variable of course defines the molecular weight of the full copolymer molecule. This is the factor which determines the scale of the microphase structure.

10.3.2 Physical variables
These include issues such as: (i) Crystallinity (ii) Presence of diluents.

(i) *Crystallinity.* If the copolymer components are intrinsically incapable of crystallising then the full system will always remain amorphous. If at least one component is crystallisable then it will depend on whether we are above or below the melting point of the component in question. If we are sufficiently below, crystallisation will take place. In keeping with the aim of this volume we shall be mostly concerned with amorphous materials. Occasional statements on crystallinity will nevertheless be made and a short section will be devoted to crystallinity at the end of the chapter.

(ii) *Presence of diluents.* A considerable amount of work on these co-polymer systems involves additional low molecular weight liquids which mix preferentially with one of the segregated phases. According to the emphasis of the study such systems can be considered as association colloids or swollen elastomers as will be apparent in the course of this survey.

10.4 STUDIES WITH SPECIFIC SYSTEMS

The description of particular systems will be divided into two categories: (1) those which consider the block-copolymer in combination with a solvent and (2) those which consider the pure block copolymer on its own. It is not implied that this division is categoric, as the solvent-free system features in works under (1) and swelling agents are sometimes introduced in (2). The justification of this division is that the literature is essentially subdivided by these two lines of approach, with only limited cross referencing. It is one of the purposes of this review to bring these separate lines of work under a common survey.

560 THE PHYSICS OF GLASSY POLYMERS

10.4.1 Systems with liquid

The first studies following the line of the preceding works on soaps were on the two and three-block copolymers of polystyrene (S) and polyoxyethylene (OE) using liquids which were preferential solvents for one of these components. Certain analogies with soaps were immediately obvious: thus in aqueous medium they froth on agitation; in the presence of two immiscible liquids they emulsify.[6]

The systems were investigated in preferential solvents, both for S and OE. The gel systems displayed birefringence somewhat analogous to those in liquid crystals. Thus they showed spherulitic patterns or regions of more or less uniformly birefringent grains of differing coarseness. Each of these appearances corresponds to a particular domain type which could be characterised more explicitly by low angle X-ray scattering.

Sharp low angle X-ray reflexions were observed in the case of preferential solvents for both the S and OE components. By using the method of interpretation adopted for soaps, in the case of a preferential solvent for S,

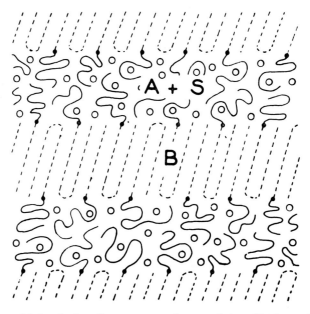

Fig. 2. Model for the lamellar structure of two and three-block copolymers of polystyrene and polyoxyethylene with a solvent for the polysytrene phase illustrating the molecular connection between the two phases. For purposes of the present figure, A *denotes the polystyrene,* B *the polyoxyethylene and* S *the solvent.*[6]

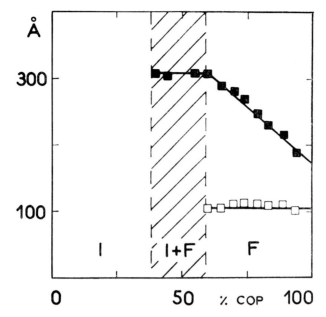

Fig. 3.   *Parameters of the layer structure in the system depicted in Fig. 2 as a function of copolymer concentration in butylphthalate as a solvent. Full squares refer to the lamellar periodicity, empty squares to the thickness of the polyoxyethylene layer. I and F refer to concentrations of isotropic solution and layer structures respectively.*[6]

lamellar structures could be identified for sufficient copolymer concentration. Below this concentration the system is an isotropic solution. As OE is a crystallisable polymer the wide angle X-ray region is also of interest. In fact discrete reflexions were observed in the angular range corresponding to OE spacings and diffuse halos corresponding to that of S. It follows that OE is present in a crystalline form and further, as the layer periodicity is much smaller than the chain length, the OE chain must be folded (Fig. 2) (*see* also Section 10.8). The thickness of the OE layer was determined by calculation from the known compositional parameters of the system. The results are shown in Fig. 3. As to be expected the OE layer is constant while the S layer, which exhibits the swelling, decreases with decreasing dilution. This pattern of behaviour is characteristic of systems containing preferential solvents.

When a preferential solvent for OE was applied, cylindrical structures became apparent by the X-ray evidence at low angles with the cylinders

Fig. 4. Model for the cylindrical structure of two and three-block copolymers of polystyrene and polyoxyethylene containing solvent for polyoxyethylene. Notation identical to that in Fig. 2.[6]

forming the insoluble phase (Fig. 4). In the same way as in the preceding paragraph the cylinder diameters could be determined and were found to be independent of solvent concentration while the distance between cylinder centres decreased with decreasing solvent concentration. At the lowest solvent concentration layer structures also appeared and became representative for the whole sample in the case of the pure polymer.

The work just quoted has set the pattern for a number of subsequent studies from the same school. The next system to be examined comprised copolymers of OP and OE (*see* Table 1) in simple triblock systems and in more complex star shape arrangements such as

$$
\begin{array}{ccc}
\text{B—A} & & \text{A—B} \\
\diagdown & & \diagup \\
& \text{NCH}_2\text{—CH}_2\text{—N} & \\
\diagup & & \diagdown \\
\text{B—A} & & \text{A—B}
\end{array}
$$

(A stands for OP and B for OE).[24] Here OE is crystallisable. The same sequence as in the S–OE system was observed, namely lamellae and cylinders. In the case of the lamellar structure the situation where both layers were amorphous could be realised in addition to the case where OE was crystalline. The major additional feature, however, was the detection of spherical structures in a face centred cubic arrangement by the X-ray evidence described in Section 10.2.1 in certain composition ranges. As to be expected the spherical system was isotropic when viewed under the polarising microscope.

A quite recent work on S–OE and S–B copolymers[29] explored the phase diagram more completely by varying both solvent concentration and temperature. This work is confined to lamellar structures. The OE component can be both crystalline or amorphous and the study in question established the transition between them as a function of temperature and solvent concentration. In addition to low angle X-ray scattering, differential thermal calorimetry has also been employed.

Another class of system studied under analogous conditions included the two-block copolymers S–V2P, S–V4P and finally V2P–V4P (notation in Table 1).[67,30,31] Again, preferential solvents were found for each of the blocks in all of these systems and the low angle X-ray reflexions were recorded as a function of solvent concentration. The S–V2P system was obtained in the form of platelets and cylinders by the method already described. The S–V4P system appeared as cylinders and spheres. The latter was inferred from the $1:(2)^{\frac{1}{2}}:(3)^{\frac{1}{2}}$ ratio of reciprocal spacings which could be compatible with a simple or body centred cubic lattice. (According to the authors, due to absence of higher orders, distinction between these two could not be made.†) The V2P–V4P system was obtained in the form of lamellar and cylindrical structures.

Of the large amount of information contained in these papers there are some notable additions to what has already been found previously. Thus we note that even if the full sequence of phases is not yet established in a single material (in a given material there are only two structural types detected so far, cylinders and lamellae, or spheres and cylinders) the results as they gradually emerge point to the sphere–cylinder–lamella sequence as the concentrations of the polymer components become more commensurate. The addition of solvents has the effect of shifting this ratio qualitatively in the direction which corresponds to a larger concentration of the component which contains it. The authors account for this behaviour qualitatively in terms of the area available for the molecules at the interface. This area can be calculated from the known data on composition and

† For the possibility of the body centred lattice to hold, absences of the (100) and (111) reflexions due to effect of structure factor would need invoking (reviewers' comments).

geometry. The argument is based on the fact that for flat surfaces the packing requirements are the same along both sides of the interface, while for curved surfaces there is a crowding at the boundary inside the dispersed phase; hence the surface becomes increasingly curved when the composition of the molecular components becomes greatly dissimilar. The role of the swelling agent in the matrix is then to enhance this dissimilarity, hence to shift the structures in the direction lamella → cylinder → sphere.

Quite recently a further interesting study has been carried out on the S–V2P system.[65] It was used to examine whether block copolymer/solvent systems are capable of solubilising homopolymers as soap–water systems do in cases of low molecular weight compounds. The S–V2P system was obtained in the form where the S component formed cylinders in a swollen V2P matrix with sharply monodisperse polystyrene *homo*polymers of varying molecular weights present. It was found that the homopolymer solubilised, *i.e.* it became occluded in the S cylinders appropriately increasing thereby the cylinder diameter. However, this occlusion occurred only as long as the molecular weight of the homopolymers did not exceed that of the insoluble S block in the copolymer (this was 9500 in the work under discussion) and only up to a homopolymer concentration which was comparable to that of the S block present in the form of block-copolymer.

An important new feature which arose amongst others from the works on the V2P and V4P systems is the method for preserving the appropriate microphase structure as liquid-free, hard samples. By using a polymerisable monomeric material as a preferential solvent it was found that subsequent polymerisation had left the microphase structure unaltered.

The intrinsic potential of using polymerisable monomer as swelling agent in aid of electronmicroscopy has been utilised for preparing sections for electron microscopy by Douy and Gallot,[13,14,34] in the manner indicated in Section 10.2.2. These authors combined low angle X-ray scattering with electron microscopy. The morphology was first established by X-ray scattering in the manner of the preceding papers. The systems in question were S–B and B–S–B (*see* Section 10.1). The solvent was usually methylmethacrylate (MMA) or styrene and was used in a concentration of 10–40%. It could be established by X-rays that for 30% and 71% S concentration in the block-copolymer the domain structure was cylindrical, while between 35 and 60% it was lamellar, to quote figures for the two-block system. The two cylindrical structures are not equivalent. In the case of 30% S, the cylinders consist of the S phase and the matrix of B while for 71% S, the B phase forms the cylinders and the S phase is the matrix.

The latter is referred to as inverse hexagonal structure. The distinction between the two kinds of hexagonal structures, however, cannot be definitively established from X-ray spacings alone; this was only possible by the subsequent electron microscopy.

In the course of a detailed examination on the S–B and B–S–B systems the effect of MMA content on the lattice period and the dimensions of the dispersed phases (lamellar thickness, cylinder radius) were determined. The effect is always such that increasing MMA content increases the area available for a given molecule at the phase boundary. Usually this involves a decrease in the overall lattice period, while the size of the dispersed domain decreases or increases, according to whether the swelling agent enters the matrix or dispersed phase respectively. Following these determinations the effect of the hardening of the MMA was examined. It was found that it decreased the overall periodicity and the dimension of the phase containing the polymerised material. These changes on polymerisation of the MMA phase, however, were small.

The hardened samples were subjected to ultra-thin sectioning. The B phase was stained with Os and the sections were examined by electron microscopy. Figures 5, 6, 7 show three pictures quoted in support of the

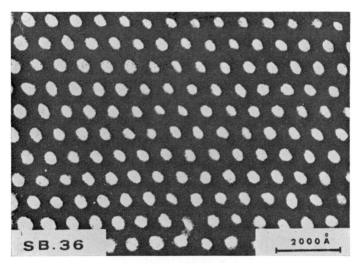

Fig. 5.   Electron micrograph of an S–B copolymer containing 28·3% *S component. Here, as in all subsequent electron micrographs, the white regions correspond to the S phase while the black regions correspond to the osmium stained rubbery matrix.*[34]

*Fig. 6. Electron micrograph of an S–B copolymer containing 61% S component
(plus 32% added polymerised styrene. Compare with Fig. 8).*[34]

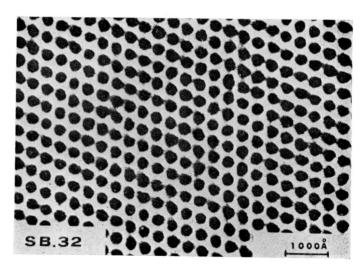

*Fig. 7. Electron micrograph of an S–B copolymer containing 69·5% S component
showing 'inverse' hexagonal structure.*[34]

hexagonal, lamellar and inverse hexagonal structures for the two-block copolymer. These are obviously selections from a larger number of micrographs, as the exact sectioning direction with respect to the morphological features could not be guaranteed. Thus cylinders will appear as circles only if cut exactly perpendicular to their axes, otherwise they will be streaks. In the case of lamellae, the lamellar spacings will depend on the cutting angle but should be a minimum for sections perpendicular to the lamellae. It is not quite clear whether the specimen plane provided some kind of reference or not, or whether the most informative sections were obtained through purely statistical sampling for the conclusions quoted to be reached. Whichever the case, visual evidence for the structures derived from X-ray diffraction was obtained. In fact the existence of matrix-cylinder reversal between Figs. 5 and 7 could be readily verified only in this way. The dimensions actually observed were found in reasonable agreement with those derived from X-ray data.

When the solvent content was increased beyond 45% the regularity of the mesomorphic structure disappeared. The way this happens structurally was followed by electron microscopy. In the case of lamellae the parallelism of the lamellae was first impaired, later for higher solvent content completely removed (Fig. 8). With further increase in solvent concentration the

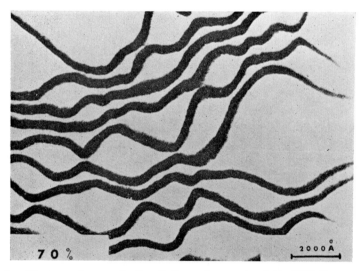

Fig. 8. Electron micrograph of an S–B copolymer containing 61% S component plus 70% added polymerised styrene, showing break-up of the lamellar structure in Fig. 6.[34]

lamellae themselves broke up into cylinders and gradually the whole dispersed phase disappeared.

10.4.2 The pure copolymers

From the point of application this is clearly the most important group of investigations. The individual works can be classified in terms of techniques and sample types. The chief techniques are again electron microscopy and low angle X-ray scattering although in this category the former prevails. Nevertheless, in the most informative works the two are used in conjunction. Sample types are essentially of two kinds: solvent cast and melt fabricated. While solvent casting was often performed to serve the requirements of electron microscopy (thin films) it has a justification in its own right as it features in some applications. It is to be recalled, however, that this preparation method introduces two further variables: the nature of the solvent and rate of its evaporation.

Amongst the first examinations of relevance for this review is that by Hendus et al.[16] Their material was an S–B–S polymer where block ratios and molecular lengths were varied systematically. The film samples were cast from solution or pressed from the melt. The films were examined microscopically either as obtained or in the form of sections cut from the films originally too thick for direct transmission work. For sectioning, the samples were hardened by osmium treatment first. The regularity of the phase separation was not yet as clear as in later works: meandering mottled structures and in some instances localised parallel striations were seen. Certain generalities nevertheless have emerged. Thus the block component which was in smaller proportion was always the dispersed phase while the other was the matrix. The molecular length for the same block ratio determined the scale of the structure. When three different molecular lengths (all with the same block ratio) were mixed, all three could be detected in different sample portions indicating local fractionation by molecular weight. The regularity underlying these structures was borne out by the discrete low angle X-ray reflexions they gave rise to (Fig. 9) with spacing of reasonable, even if not exact agreement with electron microscopy.

Observations of essentially similar kind were made by Bradford and Vanzo[32] on S–B films. Here the sections were cut systematically normal to the film plane. A pattern of stripes was observed indicating lamellar morphology. Further, a square root dependence between domain size and molecular weight was observed.

One of the first works to show a really high degree of long-range regularity was that by Fischer,[15] observed in solvent-cast films of an S–B–S polymer by direct transmission. He interpreted the hexagonal array he saw in terms of hexagonal packing of spherical domains. According to a later suggestion by La Flair,[17] these images should be re-interpreted as short cylinders orientated perpendicularly to the film plane.

Slightly later works attempted to overcome this ambiguity which was due to observing structures in one projection only. Most notable amongst these are the extensive investigations by Matsuo;[12] Matsuo et al.[23] on a variety of solvent-cast S–B, B–S–B, S–B–S and in one case S–B–S–B films.

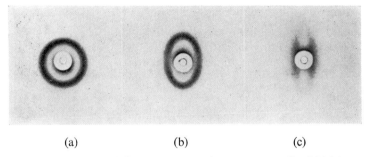

(a)   (b)   (c)

Fig. 9.   Low angle X-ray diffraction patterns from an S–B–S film (39% S content) (a) as obtained from solution, (b) stretched till necking and unloaded, (c) stretched again up to 100% elongation.[16] Stretch direction horizontal.

After hardening with osmium treatment, sections were cut along pre-selected directions, notably parallel and perpendicular to the film surface. The film surface appeared to have imposed an orientation on the under-lying textures which allowed a distinction between spherical, cylindrical and lamellar morphologies. An impressive identification of lamellae is shown in Fig. 10.

In the course of these works, amongst others, S–B–S films with S composition varying from 80% to 40% were examined as cast from toluene, which is a solvent for both phases, followed by two-way sectioning. A progressive change from spherical to cylindrical and finally to lamellar structures was observed as the S concentration decreased. Other studies on S–B, B–S–B and S–B–S–B films were confined to 60% S composition and revealed cylindrical structures of the B phase in a S matrix with the cylinders parallel to the film surface. All this indicates that it is the overall block ratio and the way the blocks are joined which determines the morphology.

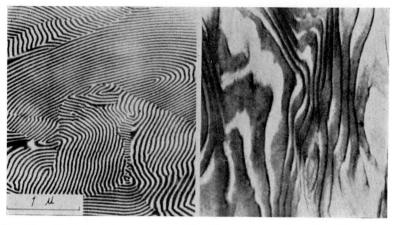

Fig. 10. *Electron micrograph of ultra-thin sections of an S–B–S copolymer containing* 40% *S component, cast from cyclohexane solution. Sections cut normal* (*left*) *and parallel* (*right*) *to the film surface showing lamellar morphology.*[12]

S circles in a B matrix arranged in a regular hexagonal pattern were also observed by Lewis and Price[10,11] in ultra-thin solvent-cast films of S–B–S copolymer of 25% S composition. Regular structures were only obtained when the evaporation rate was slow; for fast evaporation rates the structures were confused. Even when the pattern was regular this arrangement was confined to domains of a few micron diameter (*see* Fig. 11: which was taken from another work). When thick films or moulded samples of the same material were examined by low angle X-ray scattering up to five discrete reflexions were obtained. Application of the analytical method in Section 10.2.1 utilising the ratios of the spacings decided in favour of hexagonally arranged cylindrical structures. Further, the radii of the cylinders could be estimated from the angular position of intensity minima (Section 10.2.1) in reasonable agreement with direct observations on films which were thin enough for electron microscopy. This suggests that the massive sample and the thin films used for X-ray and electron microscope studies respectively had the same morphology. More recently the electron micrographs of the thin films themselves were evaluated more critically by calculating the fraction of the S phase for the alternative cases that the circles seen correspond to spheres and cylinders. The figure for the cylindrical structure agreed with the known block composition.[18]

The same X-ray analytical method was also used in a study on an S–B–S copolymer with 36% S content by McIntyre and Campos-Lopez.[33]

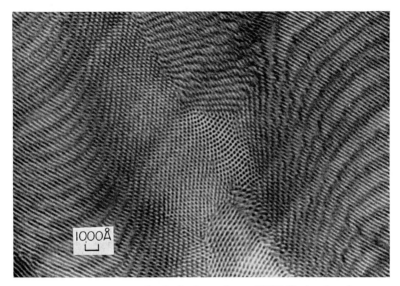

Fig. 11.   *Electron micrograph of a B–S copolymer (68 % S) showing the presence of 'grain' boundaries. Ultra-thin section.*[19]

They infer spherical domains giving rise to a face centred orthorhombic lattice. The validity of their analysis, however, has been questioned.[35]

Perhaps the most comprehensive work in the whole field is by Kämpf *et al.*;[19] Krömer *et al.*;[36] Hoffmann *et. al*;[37] Kämpf *et al.*;[21] Hoffmann *et al.*[38] Most of their experimental work is concerned with B–S two-block copolymers of varying block ratios and molecular weights. The morphologies were established on sections of solvent-cast films obtained by cutting at low temperatures.

The electron micrographs revealed long-range order, which in the case of annealed specimens could extend over sizeable areas. These areas appeared as grains of 'crystallinity' (Fig. 11) sometimes extending over exceptionally large areas revealing surprising uniformity (Fig. 12). By covering a wide range of block ratios the following structure sequence was established: 0–25 % S, S spheres in a B matrix; 15–40 % S, S cylinders in a B matrix; 40–60 % S, lamellar structures; 60–85 % S, B cylinders in an S matrix (Fig. 12) and 85–100 % S, only B spheres in an S matrix. In the 25–10 % range for either component cylinders and spheres can both be present (Fig. 13). However, the justification for assigning the two images to the coexistence of two different structures has been questioned by La Flair.[17]

Fig. 12.   *Electron micrograph of a B–S copolymer* (68% *S*) *showing long range order. Ultra-thin section.*[19]

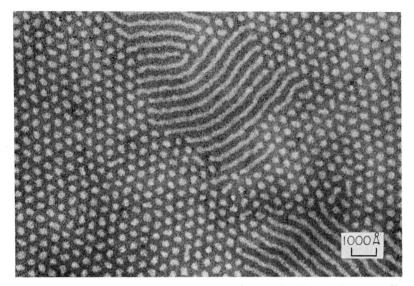

Fig. 13. *Electron micrograph of a B–S copolymer* (17% *S*). *Thin cast film, showing spheres and rods in coexistence.*[19]

The authors are aware of error sources inherent in interpreting only projected views as seen in the electron micrographs and invoke also other methods to support their conclusions. Thus the establishment of the cylindrical nature of the units seen as circles in a sample such as underlying Fig. 12 was achieved by combination of the electron microscope, light optical and X-ray scattering methods referred to above. Figure 14 is a light optical diffraction pattern obtained from an electron micrograph. Low angle electron diffraction patterns on the actual samples were also obtained. These were similar to Fig. 14 but not quite as well-defined. (*See also* Dlugosz *et al.*[20]) The comparison in the table below from Kämpf *et al.*[21] is a demonstration of the soundness of the assignment.

Method	D_C	A_C
Electron microscopy statistical sampling	190 Å	325 Å
Electron microscopy light optical diffraction on micrograph	a	312 Å
Electron low angle diffraction on sample	a	332 Å
X-ray low angle diffraction	180 Å	336 Å

a No statement possible.

D_C and A_C are cylinder diameters and separations respectively. (The cylinders are of the B phase.)

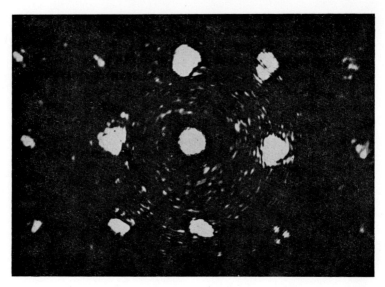

Fig. 14.   *Light optical diffraction from an electron micrograph similar to Fig.* 12.[19]

A variety of further features such as domain boundaries with gradual and abrupt transitions, lattice defects, less regular, wriggly line structures in very thin, cast films are also described in these papers. Short of illustrating each photograph separately it is not possible to continue discussing them here. All this experimental work by Kämpf *et al.*[19] has been the foundation of a theory to be referred to in Section 10.5, where some further results from these works will be invoked.

It is to be noted that in spite of the long-range order such as shown by Fig. 12 the samples in all the above works are 'polycrystalline' in the sense of the present meaning of crystallinity, where the lattice is formed by an ordered arrangement of amorphous microphases. It is the subject of the next development which has led to actual macroscopic single crystals formed by these microphases.

This latest development (for summarising article *see* Keller *et al.*[39]) is essentially centred on one S–B–S copolymer with 25 % S content (Kraton 102), although there are indications that its implications are general. It began with a low angle X-ray examination of some extruded plugs.[8] Here, the low angle X-ray diffraction gave isolated reflexions, in fact patterns, such as characterise single crystals. Figure 15(*a*) was obtained with the beam parallel and Fig. 15(*b*) perpendicular to the extrusion direction. The implications are self evident: we have a regular hexagonal array of cylinders where the reciprocal lattice is seen with the cylinders end-on in Fig. 15(*a*). The fact that the reflexions are confined to one layer line in Fig. 15(*b*) means that the cylinders are very long compared to their diameter. The demonstration of the cylindrical morphology is therefore conclusive. The hexagonal lattice periodicity is 300 Å, the cylinder diameter, as assessed both from the block composition and independently from the intensity of the reflexions, is 150 Å. Thus the closest cylinder separation distance is also 150 Å. It is implicit in patterns

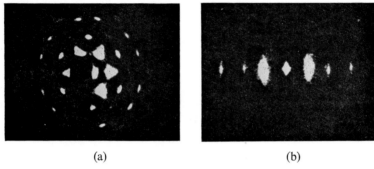

(a)   (b)

Fig. 15. Low angle X-ray diffraction patterns from a 'single crystal' sample of extruded and annealed S–B–S copolymer (Kraton 102) (a) beam parallel to the extrusion direction (plug axis), (b) beam perpendicular to the plug axis, which is vertical (based on Keller[8]; present combination Keller et al.[39]).

such as those shown in Fig. 15 that the lattice comprises macroscopic sample portions. This is usually the outer annulus of the cylindrical plug. Extrusion conditions giving rise to such structures have been established recently.[40] Essentially it relies on solidification during flow. By means of this recognition, 'single crystals' of predesigned shapes and sizes can now be fabricated.

In possession of macroscopic single crystal samples, electron microscopy can now be carried out in a systematic manner through sectioning along preselected directions. Sections were cut parallel and perpendicular to the hexagonal axis (extrusion direction) on specimens cooled by liquid air.[20] The end-on and side-on view of the cylinders and the lattice they give rise to could thus be directly verified in reasonable quantitative agreement with the diffraction patterns (Figs. 16, 17, 18). The fact that the circles in Fig. 16 are due to cylinders is now immediately apparent from the longitudinal sections seen in Fig. 18. This can be verified even on one and the same perpendicular section: a small tilt in the microscopic stage is sufficient to show the cylinders in the off-edge-on view giving rise to streaks (Fig. 17). The cylinders are very long, but terminating cylinders giving rise to image features reminiscent of dislocations can be seen in places (Fig. 18).

The stripes in Fig. 18 are only clearly visible at certain positions of the sample when rotated around the striation direction. These positions

Fig. 16. *Ultra-microtome section cut perpendicular to the extrusion direction of a 'single crystal' sample of extruded and annealed S–B–S copolymer (Kraton* 102).[20]

reoccur on rotations through 60°. This is what is expected when viewing a hexagonally periodic arrangement of cylinders in a sample sufficiently thick to comprise at least a full repeat period.

The single-crystal samples provide an opportunity to perform various macroscopic measurements as a function of cylinder orientation. Such measurements are: infra-red dichroism,[28] birefringence, mechanical anisotropy,[53] deformation[12,41] and swelling behaviour.[39,68] More of these will be said later. At this point only a comment on the swelling behaviour will be added as this item will not feature again: limited swelling in a liquid which swells the B matrix only results in an increased lateral separation of the cylinders. The corresponding lattice changes, as

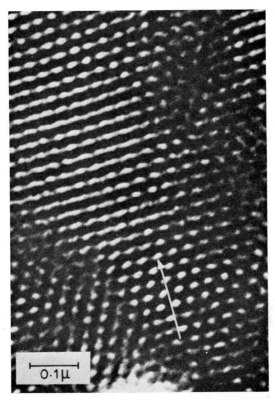

Fig. 17. *Portion of same area as Fig.* 16 (*identifiable by white hole at bottom centre*) *but tilted through* 12° *around the arrow direction.*[20]

assessed by X-rays, could be quantitatively correlated with the lateral dimensions of the sample. More pronounced swelling, however, can also disrupt the cylinders.[68]

Attempts are being made to obtain single-crystal samples of other polymers with different morphologies. Single-crystal diffraction patterns have already been obtained from S–I–S polymers (Kraton 107). Here the S

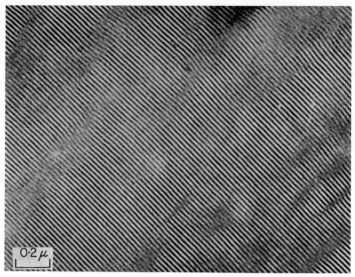

Fig. 18.   *Ultra-microtome section cut parallel to the extrusion direction of a 'single crystal' sample of extruded and annealed Kraton 102 showing striated structure.*[20]

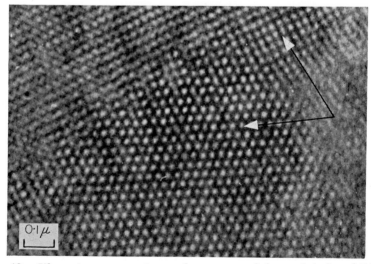

Fig. 19.   *Ultra-microtome section cut from an annealed extruded plug of S.I.S. copolymer (Kraton 107). The arrows indicate regions showing hexagonal and square arrays of white dots (S regions). (Pedemonte, private communication; see also ref. 22.)*

ratio is 12%, hence spherical structures would be expected. The diffraction evidence is not yet fully evaluated, and at present coexistence of spheres with cylinders remains a possibility.[41,42] Cold-cut sections of such S–I–S polymers revealed a domain structure showing streaks and circles in different sample areas where the circles can form hexagonal *and* square lattices (Fig. 19). Pedemonte[22] interprets these images as different views of a body centred cubic lattice of spheres. Currently a uniformly oriented lamellar structure has been achieved in an S–B–S copolymer containing 48% polystyrene.[69]

A further example of microphase orientation over macroscopic sample areas has come to our notice recently. A high degree of overall alignment of the microphases was obtained by shear, such that for appropriately large molecular weights light optical diffraction as from a grating was obtained. The responsible periodicity is of the order of 4000 Å. The nature of the underlying units has not yet been determined.[43]

10.5 THEORIES OF THE MORPHOLOGY OF BLOCK COPOLYMERS

10.5.1 Objectives

Thus far the discussion has been concerned mainly with experimental structural studies of the geometry of the dispersed phase in block co-polymers. The associated theoretical problem of predicting domain shapes and sizes in terms of molecular parameters is comparatively difficult, but considerable progress has also been made in this field.

All theories are based on equilibrium considerations. In general terms the theories fall into three categories, each of which can be further subdivided in terms of the individual models adopted.

(a) Determination of domain size only
This approach seeks to predict the equilibrium dimensions of an assumed domain geometry (usually spherical). Such has been the approach of Bianchi *et al.*[44] and Leary and Williams.[45] Both have applied statistical thermodynamics to a spherical domain system for three-block copolymers. In the former case a sharp boundary between the two phases is assumed, whereas the latter workers allow for the possibility of an interface. This is a region of incomplete phase segregation whose dimensions can also be calculated by minimising the total free energy.

(b) *Determination of domain size and type*

A more ambitious target is the evaluation of the equilibrium domain *type* and its dimensions as a function of block lengths and ratio. La Flair[17] has extended the treatment of Leary and Williams[45] to ordered arrays of spheres, cylinders and lamellae. He evaluates not only the domain dimensions but also the size of the interfacial layer and their dependence on temperature. Meier,[46] Krömer *et al.*[36] and Inoue *et al.*[47] report comprehensive thermodynamic theories of phase segregation taking into account an interfacial layer. They all conclude that for two and three-block copolymers, morphological changes should occur at certain ratios of block lengths. The influence of a preferential swelling agent on domain geometry can also be taken into account.

(c) *Determination of general conditions of phase segregation*

Theories falling within this category are concerned with the general conditions leading to a demixing of a multi-phase system, irrespective of domain geometry and size. For example, Krause,[48,49] has studied the importance of the number of blocks present and concludes that at equal composition and molecular weight, microphase separation becomes progressively more difficult as the number of blocks increases. The model used by Krause assumes no intermixed region, *i.e.* an abrupt phase boundary.

Particularly in the case of (b) the scope of the present theories is limited by the mathematical complexities involved. Even so a number of important results follow, some of which can be explicitly compared with experiment. When direct comparisons can be made this will be stressed separately later.

10.5.2   Principles of calculation

Irrespective of other differences, certain basic principles are common to all methods. As with all problems involving the equilibrium between phases the most favourable configuration corresponds to that which minimises the total free energy. Mixing of phases will occur when the free energy change is positive, while the critical condition of demixing occurs when the free energy change is zero. The whole problem of microphase segregation involves an evaluation of the change in the contributions to the free energy ($dG = dH - TdS$) when a certain dispersed phase is formed from some reference state, which usually corresponds to perfect mixing of the phases.

Thus in principle the problem is solved if changes in the enthalpy (dH) and entropy (dS) can be calculated. Here the problem can be divided into two categories:

(i) An accurate evaluation of domain dimensions and geometry requiring a full and comprehensive calculation of dH and dS.

(ii) An evaluation of the *relative* free energies of a number of alternative domain configurations, which circumscribes some of the inherent mathematical complexities involved in calculating the configurational entropy of a multiphase system. Although less comprehensive than (i) this approach can be successfully used to predict the overall pattern of morphological changes as a function of molecular parameters.

In general terms the differences in the various theories of microphase segregation are mainly due to the particular way the differences in the enthalpy and entropy changes have been calculated.

Let us now consider a number of specific examples which fall within the various methods of approach.

Evaluation of domain dimensions only
Here we will consider the theories of Bianchi *et al.*[44] and Leary and Williams.[45] The former consider a three-block copolymer S–B–S in which the polybutadiene represents the main component. It is furthermore assumed that the glassy S phase exists in the form of spheres whose equilibrium radius at a given temperature is to be calculated. The change in free energy from a state of complete phase miscibility is calculated from the corresponding change in dH and dS described above. Thus:

(i) As the number of S domains decrease and their size increases the total surface energy of interaction between the S and B regions decreases producing a reduction in the internal energy, which depends on the interfacial energy. Hence the internal energy favours a demixing of the system.

(ii) As the domain size increases the number of B chain placements on the surface of the S domain decreases leading to a reduction in the configurational entropy of the copolymer molecules. Hence demixing of the system is opposed by the entropic term.

The critical domain size is thus determined by a balance between these two factors, which in turn will depend on temperature and the interfacial energy. It is shown that the change in Helmholtz free energy (ΔF) is given by:

$$\Delta F = C(\langle i \rangle^{-\frac{1}{3}} - 1) + RT \log \langle i \rangle$$

where $\langle i \rangle$ is the average number of S blocks per domain, which will determine its size. C is a constant dependent on the interfacial energy, while R and T are the gas constant and temperature respectively. The equilibrium value of $\langle i \rangle$ is then derived from this equation using $(\partial \Delta F / \partial \langle i \rangle)_T = 0$, giving:

$$\langle i \rangle_{\text{equilibrium}} = \frac{\text{Constant}}{T^3}$$

that is to say the size of the spherical island is predicted to decrease rapidly with increasing temperature on the basis of this model.

The large reduction in the configurational entropy due to a demixing of the phases can be reduced somewhat by allowing limited mixing to occur at the phase boundaries. Such is the method of approach of Leary and Williams.[45] The model (A–B–A) consists of spherical domains of radius R surrounded by an intermixed zone, thickness ΔR possessing the same composition as the material as a whole. In this case they evaluate the enthalpy of demixing using solution theory and divide the entropy contribution to the free energy into three parts:

(i) Entropy arising from confining the A–B junctions to lie in the ΔR region.
(ii) That arising from confining the A segments to be within the domains.
(iii) That due to the restriction that the B segments lie outside the domains. This is evaluated by replacing the spherical by a lamellar system for the purpose of simplifying the mathematics.

The equilibrium domain dimensions are found by adjusting R and ΔR to minimise the free energy of phase separation. The deepest minimum is used to give the value of ΔR. These calculations have been carried out for an S–B–S copolymer of molecular weight 14 000–70 000–14 000. It is found that $R = 90$ Å and $\Delta R = 40$ Å at a temperature of 100°C. The value of R is clearly in the usual range for such a copolymer, while such a large interfacial region is truly surprising. The implications of this will be discussed later.

Determination of morphological type and dimensions

Within this section we will consider a representative selection of statistical thermodynamic theories of domain morphology (size and shape) in block copolymers, from which predictions can be made of the equilibrium domain shapes (spheres, cylinders or lamellae) given the ratio of block molecular weights, size of blocks, presence of solvents, etc.

To maintain some continuity with the preceding section let us first consider the extension of the theory of Leary and Williams[45] described above, by La Flair[17] to all domain morphologies. He considered regular arrays of lamellae, hexagonally packed rods and close packed hexagonal arrangement of spheres. For these he used two additional relationships:

(i) The exact expression for the fraction of material in the interface region was calculated as a function of ΔR for each morphology.

(ii) The separation of the domains was calculated as a function of the domain size with additional knowledge of the sample stoichiometry.

The predicted morphology and domain dimensions were obtained by computer searching for the minimum free energy.

The results predict an increase in domain size with increasing molecular weight and for rods and lamellae ΔR is also found to increase. For the particular case of rods it is found that all dimensions are little affected by temperature over the range calculated (25–100°C). However, lamellar morphology is predicted to occur under all conditions. La Flair points out that it is probably in the evaluation of the entropy, due to the restriction that the B segments lie outside the domain, that this problem arises. Here a simplified lamellar model was used for all geometries and hence unduly biased the domain morphology in favour of a lamellar structure.

An evaluation of this entropy contribution for geometries other than lamellar is difficult without resource to more sophisticated mathematical techniques. Such is the approach that Meier[46] has adopted. His theory is restricted to two-block copolymers but points out that A–B–A can be treated within the framework of his theory without substantially altering any of his conclusions. This approach is different from those described so far in at least the following two respects:

(i) Particular attention is given to the uniform filling of space by the chain segments to achieve a uniform density.

(ii) An accurate evaluation of the configurational entropy constraints imposed by the particular domain morphology.

To make an analytical approach possible he further assumes that random-flight statistics is applicable, enabling the general diffusion equation to be applied. This is first used to calculate the probability distribution of chains within a domain as a function of its size. The stable domain size is that corresponding to a uniform probability distribution, *i.e.* uniform density. He finds that:

for spheres
$$\text{Radius } R = 1 \cdot 33 \alpha \bar{K} M^{\frac{1}{2}}$$

for cylinders
$$\text{Radius } R = 1 \cdot 00 \alpha \bar{K} M^{\frac{1}{2}}$$

for lamella
$$\text{Thickness } T = 1 \cdot 40 \alpha \bar{K} M^{\frac{1}{2}}$$

where

$\bar{K}$ = constant relating unperturbed r.m.s. end-to-end chain dimensions to molecular weight

M = molecular weight of chains in dispersed phase

α = chain expansion parameter = ratio of perturbed to unperturbed r.m.s. end-to-end chain dimensions.

Thus in order to achieve a uniform density of chain segments within a domain it is necessary for the chains to have end-to-end separations which are different from those of a random coil.

A similar evaluation can also be carried out for the chains in the matrix phase except that the constraints on the placement of matrix chains is not uniform due to the presence of the surrounding domains. The density of chain segments at any point in the matrix is thus the sum of the chain densities arising from all domains surrounding that point. In principle, therefore, the problem is solved if a domain separation can be found which leads to a matrix possessing a uniform density. It is found that this condition leads to the following results relating the chain expansion parameters in the A and B phases:

for spheres
$$\alpha_B \simeq \alpha_A$$

for cylinders
$$\alpha_B \simeq \alpha_A \left(\frac{M_B}{M_A} \right)^{1/6}$$

for lamellae
$$\alpha_B \simeq \alpha_A \left(\frac{M_B}{M_A} \right)^{1/2}$$

The evaluation of α_A (and hence α_B) in order to predict domain dimensions is carried out by minimising the free energy, consisting of the following contributions:

(i) Elastic energy due to the deformation of the A and B random coils.
(ii) Surface free energy due to the interface between A and B segments.
(iii) Constraint free energy due to the fact that A and B segments are confined to restricted volumes.

All other contributions are neglected since they are independent of the morphology. The relative free energies for each domain shape can then be calculated and used to predict stable domain morphologies. It is found that morphological changes occur at certain ratios of block lengths:

Sphere–cylinder when $M_B/M_A \sim 4 \equiv 33\%$ weight fraction of A for three-block. Cylinder–lamellae when $M_B/M_A \sim 3 \cdot 3 \equiv 37 \cdot 5\%$ weight fraction of A for three-block.

The trend of domain stability with molecular weight ratio (and hence volume fraction of phases) is predicted to be spherical–cylindrical–lamellae, in good agreement with that observed experimentally and discussed in the earlier sections of the review.

The effect of adding a preferential solvent to one of the phases is to change the chain expansion parameter for that phase. This, in turn, influences the relative free energies for the three domain morphologies and for a given block molecular weight ratio can result in a morphological change on swelling.

The pattern of results predicted by Meier is also shown by the work of Krömer et al.[36] and Inoue et al.[47] In the case of the former, however, the starting point for their theory rests on the experimental observations that a plot of log D versus log M (where D is the domain size and M the molecular weight of the domain forming block) gives a linear relationship for all morphologies—see Fig. 20. Hence:

$$D = kM^a$$

and a falls between 0·55 and 0·6, i.e. close to that predicted by Meier.

Similar considerations to those of Meier are discussed by Krömer et al.,[36] i.e. the importance of uniform space filling and the contribution to the free energy due to a deformation of the random coils are emphasised. We outline below the stepwise sequence of their approach.

As in the above theories the first problem is to evaluate the change in the Gibb's free energy on forming a two-phase structure. Krömer et al.[36] consider that the internal energy change arises from the formation of

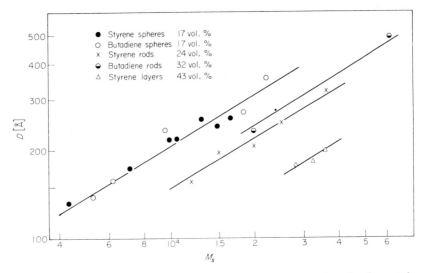

Fig. 20.   *Experimental dependence of domain size* (**D**) *on block molecular weight* (**M_S**) *of S sequence (plotted on a log–log scale) for a variety of B–S copolymer compositions.*[36]

interfaces between the two blocks when microphase ordering occurs. The change in the entropy term is considered to be due primarily to a deformation of the initial random coils (constituting the corresponding homopolymers) on forming a two-phase structure. Other contributions to the entropy change are not considered since these are expected to be independent of morphology.

The dependence of the domain size on the molecular weight described above corresponds closely to the molecular weight dependence of the random coil size as obtained from independent measurements (*e.g.* Flory[50]). This suggests that any deformation of the coils necessary when microphase segregation occurs will be small.

They show that the Gibb's free energy can be expressed in the following form:

$$\Delta G = \frac{C}{D} + \frac{3}{2} NkT \, s(\overline{p^2} - 1) + b(\overline{q^2} - 1) + \Delta G_M$$

where:

$C = f(\Delta W)$, and ΔW is the interfacial energy per unit area
$N =$ number of molecules cm^{-3}
$k =$ Boltzmann's constant

T = temperature

s, b = number of sequences in copolymer molecules, e.g. for three blocks S–B–S, $s = 2, b = 1$

p, q = ratio of end-to-end distance in deformed coil to distance in random coil for S and B phases

and

ΔG_M = change in free energy from other sources but independent of morphology.

As in Meier's calculation it is further assumed that the density of both the matrix and dispersed phase is uniform. This leads to simple relationships between domain sizes and separation in terms of the random coil sizes. Coil overlap occurs until a uniform density is achieved taking into account contributions to the segment density from all close neighbours. This yields the following results:

for spheres
$$D_s = 1 \cdot 8 \, p_s h_0 = P_s h_0 \qquad (D_s = \text{sphere diameter})$$
for cylinders
$$D_c = 1 \cdot 5 \, p_c h_0 = P_c h_0 \qquad (D_c = \text{cylinder diameter})$$
for lamellae
$$D_l = 1 \cdot 2 \, p_1 h_0 = P_1 h_0 \qquad (D_l = \text{lamellar thickness})$$

and h_0 is the random coil size.

Using these relations together with the equation above for ΔG enables the free energy to be plotted as a function of D. This shows a sharp minimum and is little affected by the internal energy term. Thus the inclusion of deformational entropy, only, in the free energy expression still leads satisfactorily to an equilibrium dimension, with values for p and q only slightly different from unity.

Alternatively these equations may be used with experimental values of D to yield values for P. Krömer et al.[36] also show how to estimate this by simple geometric considerations of the overlapping of the coils arising from nearest neighbour domains. The experimental and calculated P values are compared in Fig. 21. The agreement is very good and lends strong support to both Krömer's and Meier's contention that the size and ordering of aggregates is determined by the coil dimensions of the sequences and the condition of uniform space filling.

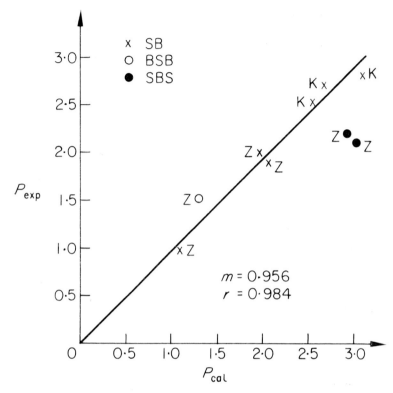

Fig. 21.   *Correlation between the experimental and calculated* P *values (see* text*) for spherical* (K) *and cylindrical* (Z) *domains of a range of S–B, S–B–S and B–S–B copolymers.*[36]

10.6   IMPLICATIONS OF THEORIES AND COMPARISON WITH EXPERIMENT

Certain predictions resulting from the above theories can be directly compared with experimental observation. Such a comparison necessarily implies that equilibrium prevails in the structures observed.

10.6.1   Influence of block molecular weight ratio

It has been shown above that an exact evaluation of domain dimensions and spacing is difficult due to problems arising in the calculation of the free energy change. However, certain definite predictions have been made concerning the pattern of morphological type with change of block molecular weight ratio. Thus the theories of Meier,[46] Krömer et al.[36] Inoue et al.[47] all suggest that the dominant factor influencing domain geometry is the volume fraction of the two phases and its effect is remarkably systematic. Thus they support the sequence, spheres–cylinders–lamellae as the proportion of the dispersed phase increases. Corroborative experimental evidence has been described in the sections concerned with individual experimental works (Section 10.4.2).

10.6.2 Effect of block molecular weights

For a given ratio of block sizes it is found that the block molecular weights primarily influence the scale of the microphase ordering i.e. domain dimensions and separation. This qualitative trend has been confirmed experimentally by Hendus et al.[16] and Bradford and Vanzo.[32] Some later observations of Krömer et al.[36] have enabled domain dimensions and molecular weight to be related quantitatively, as referred to in Section 10.5.2. In fact this has been used as the basis of a theory as discussed earlier. Their findings show remarkable agreement with the independent theoretical work of Meier[46] illustrating that the theoretical models adopted appear to be highly realistic even within the approximations made.

10.6.3 Molecular orientation in the phases

The theories chosen also predict that as a consequence of the uniform filling of space by the A and B segments the end-to-end chain separations are only slightly different from those corresponding to the random coil, hence molecular alignment such as present can only be slight. Depending on the magnitude of the effect, the molecular orientation may be detectable if the dispersed phase has a uniform orientation over macroscopic sample areas. Sufficiently uniform orientation was obtained in solvent cast films of S-I polymers by Inoue et al.[47] for the polarised infra-red technique to be applied. The morphology was lamellar. Some chain orientation normal to the lamellar planes in the I phase was observed.

The macroscopic single crystal textures are obviously even more appropriate for such tests. In the case of the S–B–S single crystals consisting of S cylinders (see Section 10.4.2) no infra-red dichroism could be detected in either phase.[28] To quote the limits stated in that work, orientation—if present—must be less than due to 7% uniaxial strain in a bulk sample.

From the theories of Meier[46] and from that of Krömer et al.[36] distortion of the random chain as far as it occurs is expected to be larger for lamellae which is at least consistent with the difference between the above two experiments. Significant chain alignment nevertheless features in ideas expressed in other works even for cylindrical structures[65] which will need evaluating in the light of the foregoing experimental results.

10.6.4 Interfacial region

The diffuseness of the region forming the interface between the domain and its surroundings features in many of the theories of phase segregation, including those discussed above. Experimental evidence that indeed such regions exist, with dimensions (representing a significant proportion of the total domain dimension) as predicted by theory, is very scarce. Direct inspection of electron micrographs certainly does not indicate any detectable interfacial zone which differs from the pure phases.

Le Grand[51] has measured the absolute value of the small angle X-ray intensity for block copolymers of polystyrene with polyisoprene and polybutadiene. From measurements of the scattering intensity $I(\theta)$ as a function of θ a plot was made of $I(\theta)^3$ against θ^3. According to Porod[52] this should be a constant if a sharp interface exists between domain and matrix. It is found that Porod's law is not satisfied, suggesting that the boundary region is not sharp, although no limits were specified. The small angle X-ray scattering curve shown by Le Grand, however, reveals only a single maximum. This is unusual since most scattering curves show a large first-order peak together with a number of weaker higher orders.

Shen and Kaelble[54] also invoke a three-phase model to interpret their stress-relaxation data. The third phase—an intimate mixture of the A and B phases—may well be the interfacial layer.

Clearly the presence or absence of such a layer in block copolymers is of central importance and requires further definitive work.

10.6.5 Effect of temperature on domain size

Here we will be concerned with the effect of temperature on the equilibrium domain dimensions in those copolymers for which regular domain ordering is observed.

Grosius et al.[55] report measurements of the structural parameters, up to a temperature of 100°C, for a selection of S–VP copolymers. All three morphologies were studied and low angle X-ray diffraction results showed that the lattice spacing for spheres and cylinders and the thickness of lamellae were practically constant over the range of temperatures considered.

Experiments on S–B–S single crystal samples[39] showed no departure from single crystal diffraction patterns such as in Fig. 15(a) even up to

210°C, neither were significant variations in spacings observed. A slight irreversible decrease in spacing nevertheless did occur which is likely to be due to cross-linking reactions on heating.[16]

10.7 MECHANICAL PROPERTIES AND DEFORMATIONS

Many of the studies concerning the mechanical properties of block copolymers are phenomenological, that is, they are directed towards improving or optimising a certain property from a purely practical point of view (*e.g.* Morton *et al.*[56]). In general terms, for example, it has been found that although these materials can be deformed to high elongations, they exhibit considerable hysteresis, the tensile modulus being reduced after an initial elongation (*e.g.* Beecher *et al.*[57]). It has been found that subsequent annealing, at temperatures exceeding the glass transition of the glassy phase, recovers the original tensile modulus of the material. In qualitative terms these effects have been attributed to the following sequence of morphological changes.

The initial elongation of the sample occurs predominantly in the rubbery phase and is reversible. Larger deformations cause a disruption of the glassy domains to occur in which the chain ends are pulled out of individual domains. This results in an overall reduction in the tensile modulus of the material. Annealing enables the domains to reform again thus recovering the original modulus.

Further studies have been carried out investigating the effect of block molecular weight and ratios on the mechanical properties. Results are numerous, but in general terms the predominant factor influencing the mechanical properties is the volume fraction of the phases. An increase in the proportion of the glassy phase manifests itself as a progressive increase in the tensile modulus, beginning with essentially unvulcanised rubber and extending through the range of copolymers showing high extensibility and recovery to finally give a material possessing properties close to those of the high-impact polystyrenes.

This review is concerned with the morphology of block copolymers and thus only those studies where mechanical properties provide additional support for a particular structure will be discussed here.

The 'single-crystal' S–B–S samples, referred to earlier, provide a unique opportunity for such an investigation. Folkes and Keller[53] have studied the low-strain (reversible) mechanical behaviour of such samples, the results of which will now be briefly summarised.

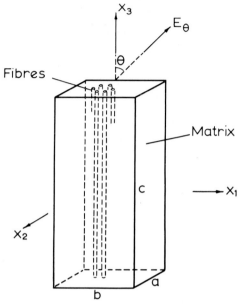

Fig. 22. *Definition of axes used in describing the mechanical anisotropy in transversely isotropic fibre reinforced materials.*[58]

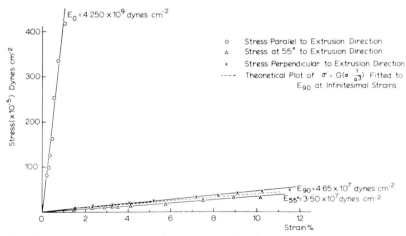

Fig. 23. *Stress–strain curves for some samples of a macroscopic 'single-crystal' of an S–B–S copolymer (Kraton 102). For notation* see *text (for definition of* α *see original reference).*[53]

These 'single-crystal' samples (Section 10.4.2) consist of an hexagonal lattice of polystyrene cylinders whose axes are parallel to the original direction of extrusion—*see* Fig. 22.

The mechanical anisotropy is expected to be exceptionally large when we consider the samples as consisting of parallel glass fibres embedded in a rubbery matrix, whose modulus is lower than that of the fibres by several orders of magnitude. Clearly one expects the material to be very much stiffer in the fibre direction.

This behaviour was examined by cutting test samples from the extruded plug with their long dimension making different angles θ with respect to the plug axis. The stress–strain curves and corresponding Young's modulus E_θ were determined as a function of θ. Figure 23 shows stress–strain curves for some of the most important angles θ while in Fig. 24 the corresponding E_θ values are given. The very significantly larger stiffness along the cylinder direction ($\theta = 0°$) as compared with that for larger θ values is immediately

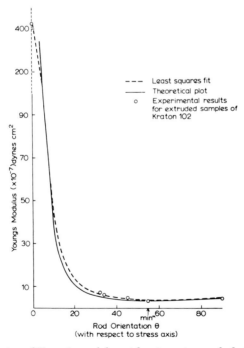

Fig. 24. *Variation of Young's modulus with orientation angle θ, for some samples of a macroscopic 'single-crystal' of an S–B–S copolymer (Kraton 102). (Keller et al.[39] based on Folkes and Keller.[53])*

obvious. Thus these 'single-crystal' samples behave as a glass and as a
rubber in two mutually perpendicular directions respectively. Even the
slight minimum in E_θ at 55° is a predictable consequence of the constraint
imposed by the cylinders on the matrix.

There is complete quantitative consistency between the variation of E_θ
with θ from symmetry considerations for a transversely isotropic uniaxial
system. (Dashed line, Fig. 24.) Further, even the simplest composite model
closely matches the experiment except for the smallest θ values. (Solid
line, Fig. 24.) A complete match—in fact following the dashed line—can
be obtained from a model with the aid of more sophisticated composite

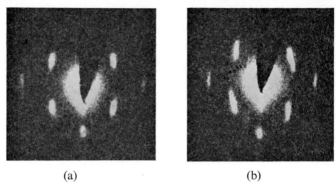

(a)   (b)

*Fig. 25.   Low angle X-ray diffraction patterns from uniaxially stretched 'single-
crystal' samples of extruded S–B–S copolymer (Kraton 102). Axis of elongation
is perpendicular to the extrusion direction and horizontal in the diagram. Strain
(a) 15%, (b) 30%.*[42]

theories (in fact these systems are ideal for testing such theories) provided
a Poisson's ratio of 0·38 is taken for the matrix. This last point in itself
has significant implications as regards the nature of the matrix material.[58]

Recently, further work has been conducted in which low angle X-ray
diffraction patterns have been recorded parallel to the cylinder direction
while a sample has been uniaxially extended perpendicularly.[41] It is
found that the diffraction pattern becomes distorted on sample stretching
but retains its single-crystal nature for strains less than about 30%—*see*
Fig. 25. Thus for this situation the deforming element is the hexagonal
lattice of cylinders. For strains less than 10% there is a complete correspondence between changes in the lattice spacing and macroscopic sample
dimensions. For higher strains, the hexagonal diffraction pattern disappears
and is replaced by rings. Observations on stretched polycrystalline films

have been reported by Hendus *et al.*[16] and Brown *et al.*[59] In the former case the measurements were extended into the high strain (100%) region. The undeformed low angle pattern consisted of rings, as expected from a polycrystalline film, which became ellipses on uniaxially stretching the sample (Fig. 9).

The 'single-crystal' samples were prepared using a special extrusion process. In the case of a more general sample obtained by the same melt processing, the structural and consequent mechanical anisotropy is less pronounced but can be more complex.[7,8,11] The deformation behaviour and mechanical properties of such samples is expected to be less clear cut, interpretable only in the knowledge of the behaviour of the 'single crystal' and in the knowledge of the textures these single crystals give rise to.

10.8   CRYSTALLINITY

In most of the preceding survey the component blocks were irregular stereochemically, hence intrinsically incapable of forming crystals. Consequently the segregated phases were amorphous. If one of the components is capable of crystallising a new variable is introduced. This is the case with copolymers containing polyethylene oxide sequences. Crystallinity in such blocks has already featured in some of the earlier works mentioned in this survey (Fig. 2) where the system contained solvent.

When a melt of such a material (S–OE) crystallises the resultant texture will depend on whether the crystallisable (OE) or the intrinsically amorphous (S) phase forms the matrix. In the former case spherulitic texture develops which is the result of the crystallisation of the OE phase. When the S phase is the matrix the OE blocks crystallise within the dispersed phase which they form without visible rearrangement of the dispersed phase–matrix structure.[60,61]

The next question is to envisage the crystal itself in molecular connection with the amorphous blocks. The basic phenomenon is most clearly apparent in solution-grown single crystals of S–OE two-block copolymers.[62,63] The crystals are the usual lamellae which display the symmetry of the polyethylene oxide lattice (Fig. 26). In molecular terms the OE component forms the crystal lattice and is in a folded configuration while the S component is ejected from the crystal and covers the crystal surface in the form of amorphous material (Fig. 27). There are strong indications that the same situation holds on crystallisation from the melt. At least in the case of spherulitic developments the morphology has been examined

Fig. 26.   Solution-grown single crystal of a polystyrene–polyoxyethylene two-block copolymer (66% S).[63]

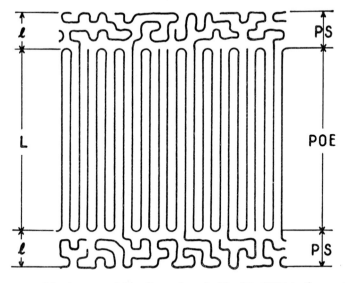

Fig. 27.   Model of a crystal lamella such as in Fig. 26. POE is the crystalline polyoxyethylene core and PS is the amorphous polystyrene surface layer.[62]

directly. The usual fibrous-lamellar morphology is observed but it appears that these textural entities are encrusted with a covering layer which according to all indications is the amorphous polystyrene in accordance with the scheme in Fig. 27.[64]

REFERENCES

1. Finaz, G., Rempp, P. and Parrod, J. (1962). *Bul. Soc. Chim. France*, 262.
2. Morton, M. and Fetters, L. J. (1967). *Macromolecular Reviews*, **2**, 71.
3. Sadron, C. (1966). *Chim. Ind., Genie, Chim.*, **96**(1), 507.
4. Luzzati, V., Mustacchi, H., Skoulios, A. and Husson, F. (1960). *Acta Cryst.*, **13**, 660.
5. Husson, F., Mustacchi, H. and Luzzati, V. (1960). *Acta Cryst.*, **13**, 668.
6. Skoulios, A. and Finaz, G. (1962). *J. Chim. Phys.*, **59**, 473.
7. Charrier, J. H. and Ranchoux, R. J. P. (1971). *Polymer Eng. and Sci.*, **11**, 381.
8. Keller, A., Pedemonte, E. and Willmouth, F. M. (1970). *Nature*, **225**, 538 and *Kolloid Z.u.Z. Polymere*, **238**, 385.
9. Kato, K. (1966). *J. Polym. Sci.*, **B4**, 35.
10. Lewis, P. R. and Price, C. (1969). *Nature*, **223**, 494.
11. Lewis, P. R. and Price, C. (1971). *Polymer*, **12**, 258.
12. Matsuo, M. (1968). *Japan Plastics*, **2**, 6.
13. Douy, A. and Gallot, B. (1972). *C.R. Acad. Sci.*, **274**, 498.
14. Douy, A. and Gallot, B. (1972). *Makromol. Chem.*, **156**, 81.
15. Fischer, E. (1968). *J. Macromol. Sci. Chem.*, **A2**, 1285.
16. Hendus, H., Illers, K. and Ropte, E. (1967). *Kolloid Z.u.Z. Polymere*, **216–7**, 110.
17. La Flair, R. T. (1971). IUPAC Symposium, Boston, published as supplement to *Pure and Applied Chemistry*, **8**, 195.
18. Lewis, P. R. and Price, C. (1972). *Polymer*, **13**, 20.
19. Kämpf, G., Hoffmann, M. and Krömer, H. (1970). *Ber. Bunsenges. physik. Chem.*, **74**, 851.
20. Dlugosz, J., Keller, A. and Pedemonte, E. (1970). *Kolloid Z.u.Z., Polymere*, **242**, 1125.
21. Kämpf, G., Krömer, H. and Hoffmann, M. (1972). *J. Macromol. Sci.* B6(1), 167.
22. Pedemonte, E., Turturro, A., Bianchi, U. and Devetta, P. (1972). *Chimica e Industria*, **54**, 689.
23. Matsuo, M., Sagae, S. and Asai, H. (1969). *Polymer*, **10**, 79.
24. Tsouladze, G. and Skoulios, A. (1962). *J. Chim. Phys.*, **59**, 626.
25. Wilkes, G. L. and Stein, R. S. (1969). *J. Polym. Sci.*, A-2, **7**, 1525.
26. Stein, R. S. and Wilkes, G. L. (1969). *J. Polym. Sci.*, A-2, **7**, 1695.
27. Stein, R. S. (1971). *J. Polymer Sci.*, **B9**, 747.
28. Folkes, M. J., Keller, A. and Scalisi, F. P. (1971). *Polymer*, **12**, 793.
29. Gervais, M., Douy, A. and Gallot, B. (1971). *Molecular Crystals and Liquid Crystals*, **13**, 289.
30. Grosius, P., Gallot, Y. and Skoulios, A. (1970a). *Makromol. Chem.*, **128**, 35.
31. Grosius, P., Gallot, Y. and Skoulios, A. (1970b). *Makromol. Chem.*, **128**, 191.
32. Bradford, E. B. and Vanzo, E. (1968). *J. Polymer Sci.*, Part A-1, **6**, 1661.
33. McIntyre, D. and Campos-Lopez, E. (1970). *Macromolecules*, **3**, 321.
34. Douy, A. and Gallot, B. (1971a). *Molecular Crystals and Liquid Crystals*, **14**, 191.
35. Skoulios, A. (1971). *Macromolecules*, **4**, 268.

598   THE PHYSICS OF GLASSY POLYMERS

36. Krömer, H., Hoffmann, M. and Kämpf, G. (1970). *Ber. Bunsenges, physik. Chem.*, **74**, 859.
37. Hoffmann, M., Pampus, G. and Marwede, G. (1969). *Kautschuk und Gummi Kunststoffe*, **22**, 691.
38. Hoffmann, M., Kampf, G., Kromer, H. and Pampus, G. (1971). *Multicomponent Polymer Systems*, Advances in Chemistry Series, No. 99, p. 351.
39. Keller, A., Olugosz, J., Folkes, M. J., Pedemonte, E., Scalisi, F. P. and Willmonth, F. M. (1971). *J. de Phys.*, **32**, C5a, 295.
40. Folkes, M. J., Keller, A. and Scalisi, F. P. (1973). To be published.
41. Keller, A. and Odell, J. A. (1973). *Kolloid Z.u.Z. Polymere*, in press.
42. Odell, J. A. (1971). M.Sc. Thesis, University of Bristol.
43. Le Meur, Terrisse, J., Schwab, C. (1971). *J. de Phys.*, **32**, C5a, 301.
44. Bianchi, U., Pedemonte, E. and Turturro, A. (1970). *Polymer*, **11**, 268.
45. Leary, D. F. and Williams, M. C. (1970). *J. Polym. Sci.*, **B8**, 335.
46. Meier, D. J. (1969). *J. Polym. Sci.*, **C26**, 81; (1970). *Polymer Preprints*, **11**, 400.
47. Inoue, T., Soen, T., Hashimoto, T. and Kawai, H. (1970). *Block Polymers*, ed. S. L. Aggarwal, Plenum Press, New York-London, p. 53.
48. Krause, S. (1969). *J. Polym. Sci.*, Part A-2, **7**, 249.
49. Krause, S. (1970). *Macromolecules*, **3**, 84.
50. Flory, P. J. (1953). *Principles of Polymer Chemistry*, Cornell University Press, Ithaca, New York, p. 554.
51. Le Grand, D. G. (1970). *J. Polymer Sci.*, **B8**, 195.
52. Porod, G. (1951). *Kolloid Z.*, **124**, 83.
53. Folkes, M. J. and Keller, A. (1971). *Polymer*, **12**, 222.
54. Shen, M. and Kaelble, D. (1970). *Polymer Letters*, **8**, 149.
55. Grosius, P., Gallot, Y. and Skoulios, A. (1970c). *C.R. Acad. Sci.*, **270**, 1381.
56. Morton, M., McGrath, J. E. and Juliano, P. C. (1969). 'Symposium on Block Copolymers', *J. Polym. Sci.*, **C26**, 99.
57. Beecher, J. F., Marker, L., Bradford, R. D. and Aggarwal, S. L. (1969). *J. Polym. Sci.*, **C26**, 117.
58. Arridge, R. G. C. and Folkes, M. J. (1972). *J. Phys. (D)*, **5**, 344.
59. Brown, D. S., Fulcher, K. U. and Wetton, R. E. (1970). *Polymer Letters*, **8**, 659.
60. Lotz, B. (1968). Doctor's Thesis, University of Strasbourg.
61. Lotz, B. and Kovacs, A. (1969). *Polymer Preprints*, **10**, 820.
62. Lotz, B. and Kovacs, A. (1966). *Kolloid Z.u.Z. Polymere*, **209**, 97.
63. Lotz, B., Kovacs, A., Bassett, G. A. and Keller, A. (1966). *Kolloid Z.u.Z. Polymere*, **209**, 115.
64. Crystal, R. G., Erhardt, P. F. and O'Malley, J. J. (1970). *Block Polymers*, ed. S. L. Aggarwal, Plenum Press, New York–London, p. 179.
65. Skoulios, A., Helffer, P., Gallot, Y. and Selb, J. (1971). *Makromol. Chem.*, **148**, 305.
66. Molau, G. E. (1970). *Block Polymers*, ed. S. L. Aggarwal, Plenum Press, New York–London, p. 102.
67. Grosius, P., Gallot, Y. and Skoulios, A. (1969). *Macromol. Chem.*, **127**, 94.
68. Folkes, M. J. (1971). Ph.D. Thesis, University of Bristol.
69. Dlugosz, J., Folkes, M. J. and Keller, A. (1973). *J. Polym. Sci.*, in press.

APPENDIX I

GLASS TRANSITION TEMPERATURES AND EXPANSION COEFFICIENTS FOR THE GLASS AND RUBBER STATES OF SOME TYPICAL POLYMERIC GLASSES

Name	Repeat unit	$T_g(K)$	$\left(\dfrac{dV}{dT}\right)_g \times 10^4$	$\left(\dfrac{dV}{dT}\right)_r \times 10^4$	Ref.
Poly(styrene)	$-CH_2-CH-$ (phenyl)	373	2·50	5·50	1
Poly(α-methyl styrene)	$-CH_2-C-$, CH_3, (phenyl)	453	2·40	5·40	2
Poly(methyl methacrylate)	$-CH_2-C-$, CH_3, $COO\,CH_3$	387	1·65	4·38	3
Poly(ethyl methacrylate)	$-CH_2-C-$, CH_3, $COOCH_2CH_3$	337	2·75, 3·42	5·40	4,5
Poly(sec-butyl methacrylate)	$-CH_2-C-$, CH_3, $COO\,CH<\!\!{}^{CH_2CH_3}_{CH_3}$	330	3·50, 4·08	5·55, 6·60	4,6
Poly(iso-butyl methacrylate)	$-CH_2-C-$, CH_3, $COOCH_2-CH<\!\!{}^{CH_3}_{CH_3}$	327	2·60, 4·02	5·85, 6·00	4,6
Poly(t-butyl methacrylate)	$-CH_2-C-$, CH_3, $COO\,C<\!\!{}^{CH_3}_{CH_3}{}^{CH_3}$	355, 380	2·80, 3·00	6·30, 7·20	4,6

Polymer	Structure				
Poly(2-hydroxy ethylmethacrylate)	CH_3 $-CH_2-C-$ $COO\ CH_2\ CH_2\ OH$	328, 359	1·02, 2·76	2·60, 3·78	4,6
Poly(vinyl chloride)	$-CH_2-CH-$ Cl	355	1·88	4·2	7,8
Poly(4-methyl pentene-1)	$-CH_2-CH-$ CH_2 CH CH_3 CH_3	302	3·83	7·61	9
Poly(3-methyl but-1-ene)	$-CH_2-CH-$ CH CH_3 CH_3	<323			
Poly(ethylene terephthalate)	$-O-CH_2-CH_2-O-C$ (O) (O) $C-$	337	1·44, 1·80	4·34, 4·50	10,11
Poly(2,6-dimethyl-1,4-phenylene oxide)	CH_3 ... CH_3 $O-$	480	2·04	5·13	11
Poly(acrylonitrile)	$-CH_2-CH-$ CN	373	1·8	3·3	12
Poly(2,2-bis(4-phenyl) propane carbonate)	CH_3 $-C-$ (O) $-O-C-O-$ (O) CH_3	422			13

Much of this data has been taken from the recent publication by Sharma, Mandlekern and Stehling[11]; reference (13) has extensive tables of glass transition temperatures and is a valuable reference source.

REFERENCES

1. Fox, T. G. and Flory, P. J. (1950). *J. Appl. Phys.,* **21,** 581.
2. Cowie, J. M. G. and Toporowski, P. M. (1969). *J. Macromol. Sci.,* **B3,** 81.
3. Beevers, R. B. and White, E. F. T. (1960). *Trans. Farad. Soc.,* **56,** 744.
4. Haldon, R. A. and Simha, R. (1968). *J. Appl. Phys.,* **39,** 1890.
5. Wittman, J. C. and Kovacs, A. J. (1969). *J. Poly. Sci.,* **C, 16,** 4443.
6. Krause, S., Gormley, J. G., Roman, N., Shetter, J. A. and Watanabe, J. (1965). *J. Poly. Sci.,* **A, 3,** 3573.
7. Hellwege, K. H., Knappe, W. and Lehmann, P. (1962). *Kolloid Z.,* **183,** 110.
8. Pezzin, G., Omacini, A. and Zilio-Grandi, F. (1968). *Chimica Industria,* **50,** 309.
9. Griffiths, J. H. and Ranby, B. (1960). *J. Poly. Sci.,* **44,** 369.
10. Hellweige, K. H., Henning, J. and Knappe, W. (1962). *Kolloid Z.,* **186,** 29.
11. Sharma, S. C., Mandlekern, L. and Stehling, F. C. (1972). *J. Poly. Sci.,* **B, 10,** 345.
12. Beevers, R. B. (1964). *J. Poly. Sci.,* **A, 2,** 5257.
13. Lee, W. A. (1965). *R.A.E. Technical Rept.,* 65151.

APPENDIX II
CONVERSION FACTORS FOR SI UNITS

Use	SI	CGS	Imperial
Length	1 metre (m)	100 cm	3·281 ft = 39·37 in
	1 millimetre (mm)	0·1 cm	0·039 37 in
	1 micrometre (μm)	10^{-4} cm = 1 micron	$3·937 \times 10^{-5}$ in
	1 nanometre (nm)	10 Å	0·039 37 μin
Time	1 second (s)	1 second	1 second
Mass	1 kilogramme (kg)	1 000 g	2·205 lb
Temperature difference[a]	1 kelvin (K)	1°C	1·8°F
Area	1 m²	10^4 cm²	10·764 ft² = 1 550·0 in²
Volume	1 m³	10^6 cm³	35·31 ft³ = $6·102 \times 10^4$ in³
Frequency	1 hertz (Hz)	1 c/s	1 cps
Density	1 megagramme/m³ (Mg/m³)	1 g/cm³	62·43 lb/ft³ = 0·036 13 lb/in³
	1 kilogramme/m³ (kg/m³)	0·001 g/cm³	0·062 43 lb/ft³
Velocity	1 m/s	100 cm/s	3·281 ft/s = 39·37 in/s
Force	1 newton (N)	0·102 kgf = 10^5 dynes	0·224 8 lbf
Surface tension	1 mN/m	1 dyne/cm	
Pressure[b]	1 MN/m²	10·20 kgf/cm² = 10^7 dynes/cm²	145·0 lb/in²
Modulus	1 mN/m²	$7·5 \times 10^{-6}$ mm Hg	
Stress	1 kN/m²	10·20 gf/cm² = 10^4 dynes/cm²	0·145 0 lb/in²
Strength	1 N/m²	$7·5 \times 10^{-3}$ mm Hg	
Energy (electrical, mechanical or heat)	1 joule (J)[c]	$1·019\ 7 \times 10^4$ gf cm = 0·239 cal	0·738 ft lbf = $9·48 \times 10^{-4}$ Btu
	1 MJ	0·278 kWh = 239 kcal	948 Btu
Viscosity (dynamic)	1 N s/m²	10 poise	

[a] If y is the actual temperature in K, then the temperature in °C is $y - 273·15$ and in °F is $1·8\,y - 459·4$.
[b] Atmospheric pressures may be expressed in bars. The system is then no longer coherent. 1 bar (b) = 10^5 N/m² = 1000 mb = 14·504 lb/in².
[c] Also 1 joule = 10^7 ergs.

INDEX

605

Toughened polyvinylchloride, 457
acrylonitrile–butadiene toughening,
475–476
chlorinated polyethylene
toughening, 478
impact strength, 475, 477
morphology, 473–478
opacity, 479, 480
polybutadiene rubber toughening,
476–477
Transition processes
amorphous between liquid
structures, 162
beta-process, 98, 99, 100, 197, 198,
200, 201, 203, 207, 208, 213,
214, 215
first-order, 65, 66, 67, 162
glassy solidification, in, 65–85,
162–168
equilibrium curve below glass
temperature, 80–84
experimental results, 74–80
freeze-in temperature, 66, 68, 70, 82
vitrification process, 66, 72
interactions between amorphous
and crystallite regions, 162
polyacrylonitrile, 167
polystyrene, 163, 164, 165, 166
pre-melting phenomena, 162
second-order, 65, 66, 67, 71, 78, 80
electrical properties, and,
195–196
mechanical properties, and,
188–195
physical properties, and, 184–188
third-order, 65
Transmission electron micrograph,
425
Tresca yield criterion, 322
modified, 325, 326
True strain, 281
True stress, 280, 341, 365

Ultramicrotomy, 555, 556
Uniaxial compression, 237, 287,
288–289, 294, 296, 299, 300, 301
Uniaxial tension, 236

Van der Waals' volume, 27, 31, 35
Vapour diffusion
crazing, and, 532–537
glass transition temperature, and,
518–523
relaxation controlled transport,
523–537
Vapour sorption kinetics, 528, 529, 530
Viscosity
free volume in polymers, and, 36–38
structure of liquids, and, 33–36
Vitrification process, 66, 72
Voids
growth, 384–385
initiation area of fracture, in, 386
nucleation, 385–390
Voigt's elastic model, 44, 171
Volume
dilatometry, 184, 185
entanglements, between, 373, 374
hysteresis, 58
Volume–retardation curves, atactic
polystyrene, 86, 87
Volume–temperature relations
amorphous polymer, 155, 156
atactic polystyrene, 81, 82, 83, 164
crystalline substances, 6
crystallisable polymer, 155, 156
glasses, 5, 6, 55, 56, 57, 91, 92
polymers, 6, 7, 92
polymethyl methacrylate, 184
polyvinylacetate, 156, 157
polyvinylchloride, 201, 202
von Mises yield criterion, 322–323
modified, 325, 326

Williams, Landel, Ferry ('WLF')
equation, 31, 36–37, 175, 176,
179, 183, 190, 333
Wunderlich helix model of rotation,
199

X-rays
atomic scattering factor, 114–115
Compton scattering, 115–116, 145,
146